Viable Self-Sufficiency
The Ultimate Guide to Living off the Land

Published by Home Farmer,
an imprint of The Good Life Press Ltd., 2016

This book contains some material that first appeared in
Country Smallholding magazine and Home Farmer magazine.

ISBN 978-1-9048-7192-7

A catalogue record for this book is available from the
British Library.

Published by
Home Farmer
PO Box 536
Preston
PR2 9ZY

www.homefarmer.co.uk

Visit Tim and Dot Tyne at
www.viableselfsufficiency.co.uk

All photographs by Tim, Dot, Iestyn, Llinos and Rhian Tyne unless credited otherwise.
Cover painting by Jenny Beck www.jenny-beck.co.uk
Design and layout by Ruth Tott

Printed and bound by Bell and Bain Ltd., Glasgow

Contents

Acknowledgements

With grateful thanks to:

Joy Haynes (Tim's Godmother – sadly no longer with us), who helped write the introduction; Ruth and Paul at Home Farmer, for sticking with us through thick and thin; Rosemary and Dan Champion / The Accidental Smallholder; Paul Courtney / Vigo Presses Ltd; Simon McEwan / Country Smallholding magazine; Richard and Tracey Wilson; John Allport; Tim Evans; Anke Sieker; Richard and Linda Hurst / Richlin Dairy Goats; Sarah Bunker; James Dennis / Diggers and Dreamers; Oli Rodker / Ecological Land Co-operative; Charlotte Oliver / Landmatters Permaculture Community; John and Karen Cooper / Morfa Nefyn Orchard.

And to our families, without whom none of this would have been possible, and in particular to our children, Iestyn, Llinos and Rhian, who have to put up with an awful lot, one way and another.

Photos courtesy of:

Richard Wilson (p. 92, 93, 375, 382); Ian Wilkinson / Cotswold Seeds (p. 131, 139); Irish Moiled Cattle Society (p. 168); Tim Scrivener (p. 168); Southdown Sheep Society (p. 196); Susan Bryden (p. 197); Anke Sieker (p. 249, 253, 254, 258, 260); Carrie Rimes (p. 267); Fotolia © Aless (p. 300); Barbara Rainford (p. 301); Dominic Regan (p. 360); British Association for Shooting and Conservation (BASC) (p. 361); Simon Mulholland (p. 391); Rosie Beat (p. 413); National Farmers' Retail and Markets Association (FARMA) (p. 415); Fotolia © Eagle (p. 419); Ruth Tott (p. 419); Paul Melnyczuk (p. 431, 432, 438); Charlotte Oliver (p. 433, 434), James Dennis (p. 436)

Authors' note

This book has been a long time in the making. We first put pen to paper in 1995, when we were living on Bardsey Island. There was very little recent work on self-sufficiency available at that time, so, had we completed the task, we'd have had an un-distracted audience, and would probably have found ourselves at the forefront of a new revolution. But it was not to be: starting a family, an enforced house move, and taking on our own small farm all contrived to put the project on the back burner.

Since then smallholding has experienced a huge surge in popularity, and every Tom, Dick and minor celebrity seems to have written a book on the subject. We appreciate, therefore, that this piece of work is entering a highly competitive marketplace. However, we differ in so far as that what we write about is what we do, day in, day out, year after year. It's our principal occupation. When we say that something works it's because we know it works, because we've done it, and the illustrations we've used support this claim.

We hope you'll find this book both enlightening and inspirational, although in reality all we've tried to do is provide a set of simple guidelines for anyone wishing to adopt the kind of lifestyle that we are lucky enough to enjoy.

Tim & Dot Tyne,
Ty'n-y-Mynydd Farm, 2016

NB. We make no apology for our apparently random use of both metric and imperial measurements throughout the book. We simply wrote down whichever seemed easiest to visualise at the time, in the hope that other people would be able to visualise it too. For readers who aren't conversant with both systems we've included conversion tables in the appendices.

Introduction

"Perhaps now is the time to relearn how to live within nature's means, as some have tried to demonstrate. Switch off the electricity, turn out the lights, sell the car, grow vegetables, walk to work, bring back the small local school, learn a craft, buy only what you need, make your neighbours your friends and have fun in simple, traditional ways…"
Christopher Lloyd

"The end of the human race will be that it will eventually die of civilisation."
Ralph Waldo Emerson

In the early 1970s London was an overcrowded and polluted city. The dream of a much better life in the countryside seemed remote and unattainable. However, there were a few courageous souls who believed that it would be possible to achieve a self-sufficient lifestyle, raise a family… and survive the journey. My parents were two of these unusual people, and they began to turn this dream into reality in 1976 when they purchased 'The Hollow', a diminutive, semi-derelict thatched cottage in need of a total rebuild, on the very edge of the Halvergate marshes in Norfolk. There followed an almost surreal period of dual existence: the London home – school, work, people, noise – then the mad dash to Norfolk each Friday evening for freedom, fresh air and fun. It took the family more than five years to rebuild The Hollow, and we maintained this double lifestyle almost throughout.

At no time was the contrast more marked than at Christmas. We spent most of our holidays at The Hollow, with friends and relatives rallying round to help with the building work, but Christmas could be rather tricky. For a long time the cottage had no roof, so we lived in a caravan or under canvas but, with my older sisters returning home from university for the festive season, the London house was clearly the most practical focal point for the family. I remember so little about it – I think all the fun must have occurred after I was tucked up in bed! In the morning there'd be a lingering scent of cigarette smoke and red wine, and students snoring on the settee in the heavily curtained sitting room. My childish mind would boggle at the behaviour of the grownups! In due course my sisters moved further afield, creating family circles of their own, and our cottage got its roof. The long-awaited Christmas in the country became a reality. What a difference! The darkness, seldom seen in the city, and the silence, or the howl of a gale sweeping across the marshes, roaring around the wide chimney into which my father had built a cross of iron, to keep the witches out. A great log fire in the open hearth, with the cat's paw print in the brickwork above (I wonder if it's still there?).

Most important of all was the neighbourliness; I don't believe there were more than twenty houses in the hamlet in which we lived, and everybody knew one another well. We'd walk to church on Christmas morning, like everyone else, and there always seemed to be so much time – time to stop and talk, come in for a drink, to throw snowballs at the other children. I remember huge snowdrifts in the lane, and walking miles pulling a sledge to buy peppermints from the shop in the next village, where the shopkeeper had a tin leg and kept Golden Guernsey goats out the back. There were long family rambles across the marshes, often in the company of another couple. The aim was to walk to the Berney Arms Windmill – there was reputed to be a short cut across the marsh – but we never made it!

And then there was the ice skating. My father had a bit of a thing about ice skates – he could never walk past a pair of skates in a junk shop window without buying them! We had two sacks full of skates, of every shape and size, enough to kit out several families, so that when the weather permitted we'd skate in company across acres of frozen flooded water meadows, and along the network of drainage dykes. And, of course, there was Christmas dinner, by this time augmented with home produce. We hadn't yet progressed to the stage of producing our own meat, but the fertile sandy loam of the cottage garden supplied most of our vegetable needs. Pickles, chutneys, jams and preserves were all home made, often from hedgerow ingredients, and on one occasion my mother baked a loaf of bread using flour ground from grains of wheat gleaned from the field next door, where an overhanging branch prevented the combine harvester from cutting a small strip alongside our garden. There was no practical reason for this except to say "we've done it", but it was fun. The loaf, if I remember correctly, was dark and rather brick-like.

Eventually my parents sold the London house, and The Hollow became our full time residence, but only briefly. My father still worked in the city, and in reality it was too far to commute on a daily basis. What's more, with a small baby in the house (my sister Lucy was born just two weeks after mum had taught my younger brother to ice skate on the frozen marshes), the cottage was proving somewhat small for our needs. And we wanted land, and we wanted to be able to keep livestock... and we were on the move again, just after my tenth birthday. We moved into The Old Rectory, Great Oakley, Northeast Essex, in the spring of 1982, on my younger brother's seventh birthday, when Lucy was just 3 months old. Now the family adventure really began! The size of the house was overwhelming, with its many rooms, outbuildings and associated unkempt acres, but what a wonderful place for a child to grow up in.

Initially my father continued to work in London, with my mother doing all the smallholding work, but, in due course, he took advantage of a voluntary redundancy package, and the whole family became totally dedicated to a full-time smallholding and a self-sufficient lifestyle. This was a huge commitment, both physically and, once we started keeping livestock, emotionally too. And, of course, financially. We weren't the only ones though; a strong community spirit existed among many families that were treading the same path as ourselves, and, what's more, smallholders were integral members of a wider rural community. Basically we were all as penniless as each other. There was none of the 'them and us' attitude that is so often seen now

that property prices have pushed smallholdings beyond the reach of many less privileged folk. The 'virtual' communities that now exist online, in the shape of social networking sites and the like, may give today's smallholders a sense of belonging to a group of like-minded individuals but, in reality, many are isolated from the real community in which they live.

Goats were the first livestock to arrive on our holding, closely followed by poultry, and then pigs. The old pigsties were rebuilt and a couple of weaners, purchased locally, were soon rooting happily in the straw. The Rector used to walk through our driveway early each morning, past the pigsty, on his way to unlock the church, and he and my father would sometimes be seen together, leaning on the pigsty wall contemplating the contented little porkers within. I don't know if they discussed God or bacon at these times, but it seemed the very epitome of rural life.

Sheep came a couple of years later, and were wholly my responsibility from the start. In fact, I purchased the foundation stock using a loan from my father, and kept the flock as separate from the rest of the family's activities as I could. I had to provide two lambs per year for the deep freeze, as rent for the grazing. Bagged feed for our animals was fairly expensive (although a mere fraction of today's prices), so we eked out the rations using rolled barley and oats purchased directly from a local farmer. The same farmer supplied us with hay until we were able to make our own.

Obviously it was necessary for each enterprise to generate enough of a surplus to sell through

local markets or at the farm gate, in order to cover the cost of production of everything we consumed ourselves. Starting in a small way a regular customer base was built up for produce such as goat's milk, eggs and vegetables, all of which could be sold directly to the public without any of the complex legislation that today's small-scale producers have to contend with. My mother also made soft cheese and yoghurt from the goat's milk, and mayonnaise from our own eggs, which she sold alongside her other produce. Other smallholders were doing the same thing, and "Goat's Milk for Sale" signs on front gates were a common sight. When legislation became tighter my mother simply circumvented the rules by writing "not for human consumption" on all the goats' milk packaging, and continued to supply existing customers, who were all in the know, of course. Once it was no longer permissible to sell eggs from untested hens at the local market she just baked the eggs into cakes and sold those instead!

With this upbringing, is it any wonder that I've remained passionate about the ideals of self-sufficient living? In fact, apart from the three years I spent at agricultural college (which is where Dot and I met), I don't think there's been any time since my childhood when I haven't been directly dependent on the land for my livelihood. Even during our final year at college Dot and I kept poultry and grew vegetables alongside our student digs.

On leaving college, full of youthful enthusiasm, we moved to Bardsey Island, off the tip of the Llyn peninsula, where I was to undertake the role of island shepherd. For me this was the culmination of a long-held ambition, but Dot, coming from a background rather different from my own, faced a very steep learning curve. In truth, these were our 'formative years', during which we both learnt an awful lot – about ourselves, about each other, and about a way of life to which we remain committed. With no mains services, and often being cut off from the mainland for weeks at a time during rough weather in winter, we had to largely fend for ourselves, and I think we came as near to total self-sufficiency as is possible in this day and age.

All in all we couldn't have had a more testing, or a more fulfilling, four years than those we spent on Bardsey. When our contract ended, and we left to take on our own smallholding on the mainland, leaving the island was like losing part of our lives, but sadly all good things must draw to a close.

What we will always hold is the unique experience and the personal memories, such as winter alone on the island with only one another for company, getting married in the island's tiny chapel, and being airlifted to the mainland for the birth of our son. Perhaps most memorable of all was returning home to the island with our new born baby, in our own boat, with a dolphin playing in the bow wave.

The re-adjustment to mainland life wasn't easy. We found driving particularly unnerving, and for a long time crept around at 25 miles an hour; mains electricity took some getting used to; mains water tasted foul, and trips to town left us with aching feet and legs, having walked on nothing firmer than close cropped coastal turf for four years. However, apart from the fact that the house was rather

small, our new home was probably as near to being ideal as anyone could wish for. Situated well off the road, we had a good-sized yard and useful outbuildings within a 22-acre plot of land. The habitat is diverse, with wetland, woodland, unimproved and improved grazing, rocky outcrops and hedgerows, and we're sufficiently high up to be able to watch what our farming neighbours are up to and, very important to us now, we're able to see the sea from the kitchen window.

We had planned the management of the farm prior to our move, and agreed that the holding must keep us, not the other way around. Plenty of thought was given to whether or not the farm should be organic, and eventually we decided against it. Instead we have adopted a responsible approach that makes a sensible compromise between our own need to make a living, the health and welfare of our animals, and our environmental footprint. Our livestock enterprises were initially based on the stock we brought with us from Bardsey: half-a-dozen sheep, a few goats, a couple of pigs and some poultry. Within two days of moving in we had added a further 45 sheep to our flock, which we sold again in the spring with lambs at foot, thus giving a quick turnover.

From the start, and as we have improved, developed and expanded the farm, we've kept a detailed financial record of each individual enterprise. As the desire to be self-sufficient extends beyond the production of our own food, dredging up largely forgotten memories of lectures in the college computer lab enabled us to design an accountancy and book-keeping programme for our PC. This produces our end of year

accounts, VAT returns and so on to the satisfaction of HM Revenue & Customs, the Welsh Government and the Bank, without recourse to an accountant. The figures at the end of our first year at Ty'n-y-Mynydd showed that our little farm had made a modest profit, and we hadn't fallen out with our mortgage lender.

From this small beginning we've been constantly refining and adjusting our activities, but some years are more successful than others. However, the good times outweigh the bad, and over the past twenty years we've been able to raise our own children on the produce of our own plot of land, in a way that we believe is both economically and environmentally sustainable. Therefore, our over-riding philosophy – that each of our activities must pay its way, and the food we eat should be free – has stood the test of time for three generations of our family, and long may it continue.

Section One
Viable Self-Sufficiency

Defining Viable Self-Sufficiency

"The greatest fine art of the future will be the making of a comfortable living from a small piece of land."
Abraham Lincoln

Use of the term 'self-sufficiency' is becoming increasingly fashionable in the current economic and ecologically-aware climate. At the time of writing, the UK is around 60% self-sufficient in food overall, and around 74% self-sufficient in those foods that can be grown here. However, there are huge variations between food types, and the figures hide the extent to which foods supposedly produced in the UK depend upon imported constituents, such as energy or proteins. Despite the fact that UK self-sufficiency levels have declined since the 1980s, by 'recent' historical standards the current situation isn't unusual: the UK has been reliant on food imports to meet the needs of its population for more than a century. Although we're more dependent on food imports than some comparable EU countries, 68% of our imported food does come from other member states, and the EU as a whole has a very high level of independency.

While national food security is undoubtedly an important issue for politicians, particularly given the way that global population is rising, most of us who think about self-sufficiency are concerned with what it means at a more personal level, producing what we need for ourselves and our families, without always being dependant on others – a wonderful aspiration, but can

it become a practical reality? And, furthermore, can it be a sustained reality?

What is self-sufficiency?

Being self-sufficient is usually taken to mean being reliant on yourself, your labours, and your own resources in order to produce the basics necessary to live. This could cover a very broad range of activities: self-sufficiency in fuel and power might mean growing enough willow to be able to run a biomass boiler for your heating and hot water, or perhaps installing a small hydro set or wind turbine for electricity. You might aim to carry out all the smallholding tasks yourself, such as hedge laying and fencing, rather than calling in a contractor, or perhaps you'll design and construct your own agricultural buildings, thus making you self-sufficient in practical skills. And, in this day and age, self-sufficiency in information technology would be a considerable boon to any smallholder wanting to develop a realistic small-scale farming venture – quite apart from promotion of one's own enterprises, a nice little side-line could be created, building websites or producing brochures and literature for other small businesses. However, the term 'self-sufficiency' is generally used with reference to food. At least, that's the starting point for most people.

Anyone can rustle up a home-produced meal from time to time.

Even within the limited confines of a suburban environment (or with simply a window box and some patio tubs) it's possible to put a surprising amount of home-grown produce on the family dining table. And not just vegetables either – urban poultry keeping is all the rage right now. But could you do it every day, week in, week out, month after month? Perhaps not in suburbia, but with a few more resources at their disposal it really shouldn't be that difficult for a family to exist almost entirely on home-grown grub, all year round. The really difficult bit is achieving this at less than the cost of purchased meals. To the uninitiated this may sound like a slightly contradictory statement – home-produced meals are bound to be cheaper, aren't they? Alas, no. Home-grown food is all too often an expensive luxury, sadly at odds with the ethos of self-sufficiency. Recently I heard of someone spending £400 on a chicken house, and another £200 on accessories for just three hens! I'm sure they were delighted to have fresh-laid eggs for breakfast, but at what cost? Identifying, and being aware of, these production costs, and working out what really is worth doing (in both practical and economic terms) and what isn't, and accomplishing it on a daily basis, year after year, is what we mean by viable self-sufficiency.

Why do it?

Despite the fact that there are big global issues at stake here, the decision to opt for a more self-sufficient lifestyle is generally a personal choice, according to the dreams of the individual. Taken at face value it seems a rather selfish thing to do, as the self-supporting smallholder becomes far more concerned about what's happening on his own farm today than what might happen to the whole world tomorrow. He has to be, if he depends upon it for his livelihood. However, if a greater proportion of the population were to think in this way then perhaps the impending disaster of tomorrow could be averted.

The reasons for making the choice are many and varied, and often have their origins in popular misconception. Strip away those fallacies, and you're left with what amounts to a fairly primitive urge to farm.

As we've seen, any argument on the basis that food could be produced more economically at home is, for most people, a tenuous one (although it can be done). Staple commodities are so cheap to buy in supermarkets that, in most respects, you simply can't compete. The supposed superior quality of home produce is another argument that's often trotted out, but again this (on its own) is a doubtful statement – commercial food production standards are pretty high in the UK, particularly at the top end of the retail market. Take cheese, for example. Dot can (and does) regularly make cheese using the milk from our cows, and very nice cheese it is too, but, even so, we know it's not comparable with some of the high-class artisan cheeses we could buy (if we could afford to). And, let's be honest about it, I should think we've all, at one time or another, politely picked our way through a proudly presented home-produced meal of decidedly dubious distinction.

However, if we put these two arguments – price and quality – together, we're on firmer ground. It ought to be possible for the smallholder to routinely produce

raw ingredients that are at the higher end of the quality spectrum, at a price equivalent to the cheap and nasty supermarket stuff. The rest of it is all down to the skill of the cook...

The fact that we can eat fresher produce if we grow it ourselves is indisputable, and perhaps, to an extent, freshness has become synonymous with quality. Yet if this argument is to hold water we must question why so many pages in books on self-sufficiency are given over to methods of vegetable storage. Once peas have been in the freezer for six months or more, does it really make any difference whether they were home grown or not? Environmental considerations don't always stack up that well either: if we're serious about self-sufficiency on a small acreage then there won't be much of the holding available for non-food producing conservation projects. Having said that, home produce can score pretty well in terms of food miles.

Whatever principled arguments people use in their efforts to justify attempts at self-sufficiency, the ultimate deciding factor will usually be desire – a desire to be free of dependence on others; to do things our own way at our own pace; to eat and live the way we want to; and not be dictated to by the retail sector. But with property prices as they are it can become an expensive whim to follow.

Very few people in the UK find themselves in a situation where they grow their own because they have to, because it is the only realistic way to survive in the conditions in which they live. For those that do (and even this may be a personal choice), it can be a great opportunity to push back the boundaries of what's possible, and

Intensive v extensive

Although the phrase 'intensive farming' conjures up negative connotations, it is a fact that (like it or not) smallholdings are, on the whole, very intensive small farms. Stocking rates tend to be much higher than on larger farms, for the simple reason that smallholders don't have the luxury of the acreage required for extensive systems. Extensive farming is perceived to be a cleaner, greener method, yet it only works by virtue of high acreages and low stocking rates. The same principles cannot be applied to a productive smallholding. However, as John Seymour said, *"It is far better to have a small acreage of land and really do it well, than have a large acreage and scratch over it. It takes very little land to grow the vegetables for a family, if that little land is farmed to the utmost"* and *"everyone who owns a piece of land should husband that land as wisely, knowledgeably, and intensively as possible. The so called self-supporter sitting among a riot of docks and thistles and talking philosophy ought to go back to town. He is not doing any good at all, and is occupying land which should be occupied by someone who can really use it"*. Clearly, then, there's a problem of nomenclature, and in our minds we're burdening the word 'intensive' with images of factory farming and industrial-scale agriculture, when in reality we should be proud of the high standards of husbandry, stockmanship and welfare required in order to produce good yields of healthy crops and livestock from very small holdings.

to learn what's really practical in an everyday situation. Under these circumstances, self-sufficiency must be truly viable.

Our walled garden on Bardsey Island.

In this respect, Dot and I had an ideal opportunity to put these considerations to the test during the years that we spent living on Bardsey Island. Although our primary role was to care for the island's sheep flock, an annual remuneration of just £2000 meant that we had to find other ways to provide for the majority of our needs. We certainly couldn't afford to buy much. The house came with the job, so at least we weren't burdened by mortgage or rent, and we took over a highly productive walled vegetable garden which also contained a couple of apple trees, and other seasonal luxuries like soft fruit and rhubarb. Additional land was available by negotiation, so we ploughed an area for potatoes, and grew barley and root crops to feed our animals. We inherited a collection of domestic livestock from the previous occupants, including a

few 'scrub' goats, lots of Muscovy ducks and a flock of around 40 geese. The goats, although not high yielding, were thrifty and tough, and provided us with sufficient milk for all our needs, without high levels of imported feedstuffs. Home-grown barley was fed on the sheaf, with the straw used as bedding, and the poultry could be fed by the same method. Our sheepdogs lived almost entirely on a diet of wild rabbits. Eventually we had a freezer, and it became feasible for us to rear a couple of pigs each year, thus converting damaged crops, fish offal, spare milk and whey from cheese making into a much appreciated addition to our diet.

Surplus vegetables we sold to visitors, providing a welcome cash revenue which helped with the purchase of those items we were unable to produce, such as loo rolls, flour, sugar and tea. Twice a year Dot crossed to the mainland to go shopping, and, in the meantime, if we ran out we went without. We accepted the fact that during the hungry gap we ate mostly spuds, last year's turnips and curly kale. We produced all our own meat (including bacon, ham and sausages), all our vegetables and soft fruit (although we did once buy in a bag of onions), all milk, yoghurt and some cheese, all eggs, jams, chutneys, wines and beers. Fish, of course, featured highly on our menu, and occasionally we dined royally on lobster and crab. All bread, cakes and biscuits were baked in a driftwood-fired Rayburn, we managed our own water supply, had a generator for electricity and composted all our waste. We had no flushing toilet so that was composted too. We learnt very quickly not only how to do these things, but, perhaps more importantly, what was worth doing

and what was not. I think we came as near to total self-sufficiency as is practical in this day and age, and, interestingly, we managed to save most of our monetary income, which stood us in good stead when we returned to the mainland to take over our own small farm.

We aim for a similar level of self-sufficiency on our current holding, but many times we ask ourselves is it possible, or is it worth it? Mainland life is very different from island life, and we now have additional financial ties and family commitments that didn't trouble us then. Some years we achieve it more nearly than others, but it probably doesn't pay to be too purist – it would be easy to become disenchanted. We believe (quite passionately) that smallholding and self-sufficiency should be a viable career option for young families, and not just the preserve of affluent downshifters and retired professionals, but, for this to be possible some cash income will need to be generated on a regular basis – there are some bills that just won't go away, no matter how far you distance yourself from civilisation. However, there's a very real risk that money worries could end up taking over your life: time spent in off-farm employment means less time available for working the land, thus triggering a gradual shift back to a 'conventional' existence. Therefore it's vital that the self-supporter is able to establish a degree of self-sufficiency that's both appropriate to his situation, and financially justifiable.

If you rear a pig and put the meat in the freezer, you have home-produced pork, but are you self-sufficient in pork? Did you grow all the food that the pig required? Did you kill and

Children and self-sufficiency

Working together as a family unit to put food on the table is a great education for everyone involved, but particularly for the youngsters. We regularly see the results of surveys which tell us that many school children today have no concept of where their food comes from or how it's produced, which is a very sad state of affairs. (Although to be fair, there are also plenty of adults who show a staggering degree of ignorance about food production and farm livestock.)

Growing your own, and getting the kids to help whenever possible and practical, will also teach them to appreciate the amount of sheer hard work that goes into putting meals on the table. A recent study showed that in the UK we throw away 18 million tonnes of food per year, with a monetary value of around £23 billion. Approximately ⅓ of this comes from private households. Living in a society where so much is wasted, encouraging our young people to be thrifty and resourceful can only be a good thing.

Taking an active part in the life of the smallholding connects children very closely to the 'real' world. They learn to understand the process of growing and harvesting crops, the rearing and killing of livestock, and the basics of land management. Importantly, it connects them with the natural cycles of birth, life and death, helping them to develop a proper understanding of, and respect for, natural sexual behaviour, to comprehend the miracle of birth, and the reality that death is final. The smallholding can be a wonderful classroom where many practical applications of theories learnt in school can be explored.

butcher the animal yourself? No? Then are you self-sufficient, or are you just producing meat, at cost? Now, let's suppose that you rear two pigs, with one being sold to cover the cost of rearing them both. It's a trade off. It simply wouldn't be possible, given the resources available to most of us, and the number of hours in a day, to produce and process everything. Therefore we need to be realistic, not only about what we can do, but what is worth doing, and then do it well.

There are many, many things we could do, if we wanted to, and very high levels of self-sufficiency in food and other necessities aren't an absolute impossibility. However, unless we're realistic about what is economically justifiable, striving for self-sufficiency can become a wasteful and time consuming

extravagance. We could, if we wished, grow willows and make baskets to harvest our vegetables, and tan hides to make shoes. This would undoubtedly be jolly good fun, but, if we depended upon it, by the time we'd done these things our spuds would have rotted in the ground and we'd have very sore feet! Instead we recycle old sheep-lick buckets for use in the garden, and we cut down worn-out wellingtons to make galoshes for summer wear.

Changing legislation, unfathomable bureaucracy and high property prices prevent the would-be self-supporter from approaching this way of life with quite the same happy-go-lucky attitude of the 1970s drop outs, but it's still possible to lead a largely independent lifestyle, free from the shackles of regular employment,

providing for one's self and one's family, on a small plot of land.

We cut down worn-out wellingtons to make galoshes.

Getting Started

Career (verb): "to move rapidly and dangerously (usually downhill) in an uncontrollable manner"

Almost without exception, there's an overriding assumption that anyone getting into smallholding is moving from some other more lucrative lifestyle – it seems to be generally accepted that the newcomer will be someone with capital or property likely to have a reasonable income from either pensions or employment. This can make rather demoralising reading for younger people with burning ambitions of self-sufficiency: is it really necessary to spend 30 years or more as a slave to industry simply in order to enjoy your declining years in rural splendour? That's a long time to wait to realise your dreams, and you might not live that long anyway! And what about 'downshifters', that steady trickle of high-salaried, early middle-aged families escaping stressful city lifestyles and opting for a gentler existence? Why go through all that stress in the first place? Well, it all comes down to money. *"Rid yourself of your mortgage,"* advised one writer. Great advice for mortgage holders, but, for anyone wishing to start as they mean to go on, the problem is not so much getting rid of the mortgage, but getting the mortgage in the first place. What bank in its right mind will part with a few hundred thousand pounds on the strength of income predicted from an overgrown veg patch and the sale of eggs from a dozen hens? Affluent downshifters and top-of-the-property-ladder pensioners have effectively pushed smallholding prices way beyond the reach of the first time buyer, forcing the younger generation of dreamers to follow the same stressful route through the city smoke.

So, is there a place out there in the world of self-sufficiency for the 'career' smallholder? Well we think there is, but then we would say that – we've never done anything else!

Start as you mean to go on

In 1993/94, when Dot and I were in our final year at college (aged 20 and 21 respectively), we abandoned halls of residence in favour of renting a house together, some distance out of town. For a few quid a week extra we also managed to rent the small field alongside, and some outbuildings. Part of the field we fenced off to form a vegetable garden, and built a small coop for half-a-dozen hens. The remainder of the field held some store lambs used primarily for sheepdog training (a useful sideline) and a colt foal we'd bought to rear and sell on as a riding pony. The outbuildings were ample for stabling and kennels, and we could easily have added a milking goat and a couple of fattening pigs, had we so wished. We had a hutch full of ferrets and a shotgun apiece, so rabbit, hare, duck, pigeon and pheasant often appeared on our menu (and so too, on one occasion, did an extremely large sea-trout, but perhaps the less said about that the better…). We brewed our own beer, baked our own bread, and altogether enjoyed ourselves immensely! All of this was viewed with some amusement by our fellow students, but we had the last laugh as we watched our colleagues spiralling hopelessly into debt. The rent (for field and cottage together), if I remember correctly, was £34 per week, which was easily covered by doing lambing work during the Christmas and Easter holidays, and I went shearing at weekends in the summer, with Dot wrapping fleeces. At the end of our college course our student grants remained largely intact, ready to finance our next move.

Now, I'm not for a moment suggesting that you blow your diploma in favour of a self sufficient lifestyle, but this story does serve to illustrate the fact that it really isn't difficult to make a start in smallholding, there's no mystery about it, and neither need it require vast capital. (A grant cheque does come in handy though…)

To buy, or not to buy?

Before moving on to the tricky question of mortgages, let's consider some options for getting started without purchasing a holding, although I accept that the ultimate ambition for most folk would be to own the land on which they live.

Land only

If you already have a house in a rural area then it shouldn't be too difficult to rent a piece of land to get your venture off the ground, though you might have to put up with a bit of travelling to and fro, unless you're lucky enough to be offered something right on

Ty'n-y-Mynydd farm - purchased from the bank before it was offered at auction.

your doorstep. Advertising of smaller acreages to let is usually by word of mouth, which is why newcomers to an area are generally the last to hear of what's available – by which time it's usually too late. Failing that, we've found land to let in the classified section of the local paper, and even on a postcard in the village shop window. Larger areas will probably be handled by the local livestock auctioneers, so let them know what you're looking for and they'll keep you informed of what becomes available. Once you've located a suitable patch it may be necessary to put in a tender – you'll be in direct competition with lots of other hopefuls, so do put a bit of effort into compiling a proper application. (Remember, a landowner does not necessarily have to accept the highest bid, should he feel that one of the lower bidders would, in fact, make a more satisfactory tenant.) Get a land agent to come and have a look around with you to advise on the rental value. He may also write a brief report outlining why he believes that to be a fair rent. This will probably cost a hundred pounds, but should be worth it.

Submit a copy of the report with your application, which should contain details about yourself (a sort of condensed CV if you like) and a simple business plan. Also include the names and addresses of a number of referees – for maximum effect the list should consist of a Reverend, a local Councillor, your bank manager and a commercial farmer. The more agricultural experience you've got, the better your chances – landowners are understandably reluctant to hand over the management of their principal asset to a complete novice. The biggest drawback to renting land like this is the likely lack of buildings – you'll not be able to justify erecting a shed on short term rented land, even if the landlord approves. If there aren't any suitable buildings on the land already, or where you live, then use a temporary structure such as a polytunnel for livestock housing. I know of one chap who put up a marquee in the garden for his sheep.

Whole holdings

Long term tenancies of whole smallholdings (house, land and buildings) don't come up very often in the private sector, but you may occasionally see County Council smallholdings advertised. Sadly, though, most local government seems to have sold off its agricultural estates. Council holdings tend to be larger than the average smallholding and are really intended to be 'starter farms', so are most appropriate if you're thinking of using a smallholding as the first step towards a career in larger scale agriculture. Competition for tenancies is fierce, and you'll probably need to have an agricultural qualification (and / or years of practical experience) to stand much chance.

A job complete with house and land

These do crop up from time to time, usually on the big country estates. Scan rural lifestyle magazine ads for *"Wanted, part-time gardener / general handyman"*, then look for the one that says *"in return for cottage and five acres"*. Go for it – you've nothing to lose, but be aware that on an agricultural estate there may well be restrictions on you keeping livestock, for bio-security reasons.

Community projects

One of the best publicised examples in recent years has been the Fordhall Community Land Initiative. Brother and sister team, Ben and Charlotte Hollins, desperately wanted to save their late father's pioneering organic holding from development, and

Derelict properties may provide opportunities if your budget is limited.

launched a nationwide appeal to buy the place. The required sum was raised with only hours to spare. The charitable trust now has some 8,500 shareholders with Ben as farming tenant and Charlotte managing the Fordhall Community Land Initiative. There are ample opportunities for shareholders and members of the community to get involved at Fordhall Farm, through volunteering, attending courses, or simply by making use of the cafe and farm shop.

There are numerous smaller scale community land projects up and down the country, including some city farms and school farms, and a number of nature reserves also have livestock for land management purposes. Most of these will enable you become involved to a greater or lesser degree and, although this may only be on a voluntary basis, it does at least get you a foot in the door. Or you could develop your own scheme in conjunction with a group of like-minded individuals. If you're thinking of running a smallholding or self-sufficiency venture as a community project,

consider crowd funding as a means to raise the necessary capital. Rewards to your backers could include produce from the holding, such as seasonal veg boxes, or free access to farm open days.

Buying a holding

There are a few key points to bear in mind here:

• A mortgage lender need not be a bank or building society. You can enter into a proper legally binding mortgage agreement with a friend, a family member, a business, or anyone who is inspired by your ambitions and has faith in your ability to see it through. I know of several cases where smallholders have been offered mortgage terms by the farmer selling them the land.

• There may be certain tax advantages in having a mortgage agreement with your parents, so do seek proper legal and financial guidance.

• A mortgage isn't required for 'land only' purchases – an ordinary

business loan will do, or you could use an overdraft facility (but that's a bit risky). The main thing is to make the purchase; the debt can be shifted to a more suitable arrangement afterwards.

• It's not a problem to have your house and your land on separate deeds, under different finance arrangements. If you can, try to buy at least one small piece of land outright as soon as possible. This can then be used as security against further purchases without putting your home at risk.

• Although it's very pleasant to drool through the property pages of a glossy lifestyle magazine, you're unlikely to find anything affordable. Get behind the scenes a bit and look for banks selling off property as a result of bankruptcy (and make a mental note not to go the same way as the last poor bugger), derelict properties, or government auctions of abandoned land.

Remember that there is always a cost associated with your use of the land. If you rent the ground you use (or have a mortgage) then this cost will be all too apparent, but if you own your property outright then it's less obvious. In order for any of your enterprises to be justifiable then they must at least produce an output equal in worth to the rental value of the area they utilise, otherwise you might as well let the land to a neighbour and use the money to buy your food elsewhere as cheaply as you can

Have You Got What It Takes?

"Tried and true ways to fail: Too little capital, unfavourable location, uncongenial soil, too large an area, inefficient soil preparation and tillage, lack of feeding, big-headedness, inexperience, city hours, laziness, too many pets and guests."
From Five Acres and Independence by M. G. Mains, B.S., M.A. (1947)

The road to self- sufficiency is a rocky one. It's not the stress-free, easy-going lifestyle that many people fondly believe; It's damned hard work, and very precarious. So, have you really got what it takes? It's just as well to ask the question now, rather than two years hence when all your dreams come crashing down around your ears.

• **Physical constraints:**
Physical fitness is essential, and by this I don't mean the sort of fitness you develop through working out at the gym; I mean endurance; the ability to work ridiculously long hours for very little gain, and sometimes to keep on going beyond the point of exhaustion when 'ordinary' folk are falling by the wayside. A normal working day on the smallholding, at a slack time of the year, might be only 10 hours, but at peak periods, such as lambing, this can easily rise to 20 hours a day, per person. And weekends are just the same. (As for holidays – what are they?) In addition to this, someone still needs to attend to the domestic chores – the cooking, cleaning etc. Inevitably, traditional gender roles are adopted, which, while not exactly 'PC' nowadays, have

stood the test of time. If it works, why change it? Therefore, I unashamedly write that yes, Dot does all the cooking (which she's very good at) and cleans the house (from time to time), and I carry out the equivalent mundane tasks out-of-doors, like scraping up cow dung twice a day through the winter, carrying feed and silage across muddy fields, and doing the milking, come rain or shine. We adopt other roles according to our individual areas of expertise, so, while Dot grows all the vegetables we require, I produce the meat. She harvests her crops; I slaughter and butcher the pigs and sheep - very different tasks, requiring very different mindsets, but by working as a partnership, the whole is complete. In addition to this are the major seasonal activities such as lambing, shearing and haymaking, where we all – children included – work as a team on the same job (although even here, the tasks are naturally broken down into parts that each individual can reasonably be expected to play).

Nevertheless, whichever way you look at it, and however you decide to divide things up amongst yourselves, the fact remains that running a productive smallholding (as opposed to a hobby holding) is an arduous undertaking for the whole family. It's not a way of life I'd advise to anyone whose health is failing to the point that it affects their physical capabilities. Having said that, there's no doubt that it's a healthy lifestyle, and many people new to smallholding find that erstwhile troublesome minor ailments such as eczema, hay-fever

and allergies simply fade away. And it's not just your physical health that's got to be up to the mark; if you're the sort of person who's thrown into depression by repeated disappointments then please – look elsewhere for a career. While the mental stability of anyone who decides to embark on a life of self-sufficiency might be questionable, mental fortitude is essential. Believe me, you will suffer multiple knock-downs along the way, and you just need to get up, shrug your shoulders and carry on. The ability to view each disaster as a positive lesson, rather than a setback, is a must, as is a sense of humour. And you mustn't let money worries get to you, either.

The flip side of the coin is, of course, the fact that a change can be as good as a rest. Smallholding isn't stress free, but it is a different kind of stress. For some folk, who may be beginning to crack under the strain of a conventional high-pressure city existence, the new challenges associated with the change of lifestyle may be just what's needed to lift them out of the rut, and avert a full-scale breakdown.

You must have the backing of your family: without this you are doomed to failure!

• **Financial constraints:**
While some – such as mortgage, loan repayments or rent – are rather obvious, others are less so. It's all too easy to slip into the mistake of considering the grocery bill to be the major item of household expenditure, which will conveniently 'disappear' once a reasonable level of self-sufficiency

is attained. Sadly, this isn't the case. There are a number of other domestic overheads which simply aren't going to go away (but steps may be taken to ease their impact):

NB: Figures given below are based on a family with three dependent children, at 2014 prices, and broadly follow our own experience. Families within walking / cycling distance of schools will be able to make considerable savings, as will couples without children.

Home and contents insurance: Based on the estimated re-build cost of your property, plus the value of your possessions. The premium may be in the region of £10 per week for a fairly small dwelling. If you live in rented accommodation then this ought to be covered by your landlord, although you'd be well advised to at least insure the household contents (i.e. the stuff that is actually yours). Insurance for your smallholding activities is a different matter altogether, although on very, very small holdings your outbuildings and contents may well be covered by a domestic policy.

Council Tax: Banded according to the approximate value of your property. Be aware that some rural properties with small acreages attached have been placed in an inappropriately high band due to their 'desirability'. In our own case, for instance, our 2-bedroom cottage with its small plot of land was given a higher rating than a neighbouring large farmhouse with many hundreds of acres. If this happens to you, then appeal against it. We did, and were successful, but we had to demonstrate that we used our land for agricultural rather than amenity purposes. Even

so, the bill still comes in at £22 per week. For those on low incomes, there may be support available to help cover this, but it's by no means a foregone conclusion.

Domestic heat and light: Electricity (including running fridges, freezers and washing machines), cooking, central heating oil etc. These are costs that you may well be intending to reduce, or even cut out altogether, as you become more self-sufficient – solar power or wind turbine for electricity; coppiced woodland providing fuel for cooking and heating – but the chances are that you'll move into a property that already has these services in place, and you'll use them. Expect to pay as much as £45 per week for the privilege. However, an appropriate proportion of the electricity bill can be allocated to business, rather than domestic, use.

Water: On a modest sized smallholding, you might use just under a cubic metre every day, which, if it's coming from the mains, will cost in the region of £1.35 per m^3, plus a service charge (currently around 9p per day). So you're looking at spending nearly £10 per week on water. As with electricity, part of this should be considered a business expense.

Telephone: Most people would consider this a necessity nowadays. A basic phone and internet package is going to set you back £7 per week.

Vehicle insurance: It's a sad fact that it's more-or-less impossible to manage living in a rural area without a vehicle, particularly if you've got a young family. Not only that, but the chances are that your vehicle will need to be a big one capable of travelling off-

road and towing a heavy trailer. Insurance costs may be as little as £5 per week, but could be much more.

Road Tax: £8 per week.

Road Fuel: Obviously any fuel used for towing a trailer and carrying out other smallholding duties is a business expense. What I'm talking about here is the domestic mileage. The biggest cost, if you live in an out-of-the-way rural area and have dependent children, is the school run. When all of ours were in one school it was bad enough, but as soon as the eldest moved up to secondary school that pushed the total distance travelled up to nearly 90 miles a week! And on top of that there are all the out-of-school activities that require a parental taxi service. Where possible we share these duties with other families, but even so we're looking at spending at least £40 per week on diesel for domestic usage alone (on which we cannot reclaim the VAT, as we do with fuel used for business-related journeys). If we were starting all over again, we'd definitely make more of an effort to explore other modes of transport. If everyone did that then the world would be a better place.

MOT and servicing: If you're of a mechanical turn of mind you might service your own vehicle, and save yourself several hundred pounds a year. Assuming, that is, that there's no major repairs required. Either way you'll need an annual MOT, which, if all goes well, works out at about £1 per week. Generally, though, it'll cost a lot more. Our yearly vehicle maintenance bill is so appalling I can't even bring myself to mention it here.

Groceries: No matter how much

you strive for self-sufficiency, there're some things you're going to want to buy on a fairly regular basis. Loo rolls and other toiletries, for example (I'm told that you can make your own re-useable sanitary towels from yellow dusters, but I've yet to find a woman willing to try it), and certain food products. Assuming that you produce all your own vegetables, meat, eggs and dairy products, you might reasonably expect the weekly grocery bill for a family of five to come in at just under £40. However, you may have to travel a few years down the road to self-sufficiency before you manage to achieve that.

Tot up the figures above and you'll see that it's going to cost you (as a family) a minimum of £188 per week (i.e. about £37.50 per person per week) just to exist. That's without any mortgage repayments (and associated PPI) or rent, and before we've even begun to think of the costs associated with your smallholding activities – vet's bills, animal feed, hay and straw, fencing materials, fuel for the tractor, business insurance, etc., etc. And yet we've already made the assumption that self-sufficiency will make a positive contribution to reducing domestic expenditure. This does highlight how important it is that each enterprise on the smallholding covers its own costs, and that at least some activities generate a small surplus – i.e. you practise the art of viable self-sufficiency.

However, I'm getting ahead of myself rather… The fact is that before you've bought a single pig, or even sown a single seed, you need to be able to meet these domestic obligations. This may mean that at least one member of the family must do some paid work

off-farm, initially at least. Based on the figures I've quoted, four hours a day at the current minimum wage of £6.70 would do it, if you own your smallholding outright. Or you might choose to claim some form of income support to tide you over while you get your fledgling enterprise off the ground. Either way, it's not an insurmountable problem, but nevertheless it is a significant constraint, and it must be overcome from day one.

• **Time management:**
Don't be under any illusions about how much of your time is going to be taken up with running the smallholding. It's basically a full-time occupation, particularly if there's livestock to care for. That's not to say it has to be a full-time job for all members of the family, but at least one of you will have to make it your principal occupation if there's to be any real chance of success. Other work has to be fitted in around the demands of the farm, not the other way around. Do ensure that you've planned for this level of commitment before taking the plunge.

On a day-to-day basis, the sheer volume of work can be overwhelming, and much of this is simply routine stuff that needs doing over and over again – feeding, milking, mucking out etc. Obviously, this changes with the seasons, but there'll always be a certain number of daily chores to attend to, before you can get started on whatever is the main task of the day, whether it be fencing, muck spreading, shearing, hay making, building repairs or whatever. However, the repetitive nature of the morning and evening routine does at least mean that you'll know, reasonably accurately, how long it's going to take and can plan accordingly. Different

families have different ways of tackling the basics – there's no right and wrong way of doing it. In this household I do the morning milking and so on, while Dot gets the kids off to school and attends to some domestic chores. In the evening I'm usually doing the milking and feeding round, while she gets on with cooking our supper. The children also have their own outdoor tasks to attend to both before and after school, e.g. feeding rabbits, poultry and ferrets. Other families may choose to share all aspects of the workload between them, and others may take it in turns to fulfil the various roles. Just do whatever works best for you. The main thing is that you have a regular start time every morning. This should be reasonably early, but not so early that you burn out after a year or two. I reckon if I'm out on the yard at between 7.30 and 8.00 in the mornings that's good enough for a normal day. Sometimes it has to be a lot earlier – for example, if we've got something planned that's going to take up the whole day – and at weekends it's inclined to be a bit later. I usually start the evening chores at around 6.00pm, but this can be much later, particularly in the summer when we might have been busy in the fields all day. It's also important to have clearly defined breaks for elevenses, lunch and tea. At lambing time, in particular, it can be difficult to keep to any kind of schedule, but we do try our best to retain some semblance of order. Even at unpredictable times like this I do try to make a plan of action at the beginning of each day, and then we do our best to stick to it.

At a fairly slack time of year (e.g. when there are no calves to feed), the basic tasks take me about an hour and a half (not including checking sheep in outlying fields, which is usually combined with something else, like the school run) at each end of the day. At busier times it could be double that. Everything else – whether it be work on the farm or other employment – has to fit in around this.

Having broken your day down into manageable sections, you can do the same with the working week. So, for example, you might decide that Mondays and Tuesdays should be spent in the vegetable garden, Wednesdays in the office, and Thursday and Friday working in the fields or carrying out livestock husbandry tasks. The weekends can be reserved for those jobs that require a larger workforce, when more of the family may be around to help. This plan should never be set in stone, as the weather or the demands of your animals may make it unworkable. However, do try to adhere to it as closely as you can.

Separate 'to do' lists can be compiled for each section of the week, which make rather less daunting reading than one great long list of everything. Therefore, when working in the garden, you can put the Wednesday / office list completely out of your mind and just concentrate on the job in hand. If it's a non-office day then be strict – don't turn on the computer and don't answer the 'phone.

Don't overload yourself

It's easy to get bogged down in the daily routine of running a smallholding, with the result that many projects are started but not completed. All too often it's this accumulation of unfinished work that leads to smallholdings having

a ramshackle and rather run-down appearance, which creates a bad impression, and is one of the reasons why smallholders are seldom taken seriously by the wider agricultural industry. And of course, the more jobs you have on the go at once, the less likelihood there is of ever finishing any of them, and other things – like animal health and welfare – start to backslide too.

The answer, I think, is to set a realistic target to undertake one major project each year, and finish it before moving on to anything else. If you manage to complete it ahead of schedule then you can afford to take things easy for a month or two. If, on the other hand, the project runs over time, then simply delay the start of the next one on the list. Try to alternate between large and small, so, for example, in one year you may undertake a major improvement of your farm buildings, in which case in the next year you might content yourself with doing a bit of fencing. Some projects – such as hedge laying or dry stone walling – require only your time and labour, and others (e.g. replacing machinery or buying additional land) take up no time or labour, but require considerable investment of funds. Some, such as erecting a new building or re-fencing a field, need both. Alternate the cash years with the non-cash years, thus allowing you to re-coup some capital. Sometimes it might be necessary to spend time working off the holding in order to fund the next round of improvements.

Be prepared for everything to take twice as long and cost twice as much as expected.

An Introduction To The Land

"Anyone who comes into possession of a piece of land should look upon himself or herself as the trustee of that piece of land". John Seymour.

Agricultural land classification

Agricultural land is classified into one of six grades (1 to 5, with grade 3 being sub-divided into two categories) according to its overall 'usefulness' for farming purposes. In essence, the highest-graded land will be capable of producing a broad range of high-value crops, whereas lower grades will have very limited potential. You will often see the grade stated on particulars of property for sale, and reflected in the asking price.

During the assessment process a number of issues are taken into consideration, and, although there are various ways in which areas of land can be improved, it would not be considered practical or economical to attempt to raise the overall grade due to the influence of fixed factors such as climate and elevation.

Grade 1: This is the highest quality agricultural land, with very few limitations (if any) affecting the use to which it can be put. Consistently high yields of vegetables, salads and fruit are readily attainable.

Grade 2: Very good quality land, but with some minor factors affecting ease of cultivation or harvest. Suitable for most crops, but not as versatile as grade 1 land, nor quite so consistently high yielding.

Grade 3: Moderate to good quality land, with limitations on cropping, cultivation, harvesting and yields.
- *Sub-grade 3a:* Good quality land suitable for consistently producing fairly high yields of cereals, or more modest yields of a broader range of crops (including potatoes, roots and grass), and some vegetables.
- *Sub-grade 3b*: Moderate quality land, suitable only for a restricted range of crops, primarily cereals or grass. A broader range of crops could be grown, but yields would be low.

Grade 4: Poor quality land, with considerable limitations affecting the range of crops that can be grown, and their expected yields. Typically grade 4 land would be used for grass, with maybe some cereal crops and roots grown in better areas for livestock feed. Although reasonable yields of grass might be obtainable, the nature of the terrain may impact on the way the crop can be used.

Grade 5: Very poor quality land suitable only for permanent pasture or rough grazing.

Some of the factors which affect agricultural land classification:

• **Climate:** This is probably the dominant factor in determining agricultural land classification. However, at a local level, aspect (i.e. the direction in which the land faces), gradient and elevation can all have an effect on the micro-climate, creating exposed areas, frost pockets etc., on land that would otherwise score fairly highly.

• **Gradient:** Gradient restricts the use of agricultural machinery, therefore the highest quality land is generally the flattest. For example, for land in grades 1, 2 and 3a, there is a gradient limit of seven degrees.

• **Micro-relief:** Sharp changes in angle, rocky outcrops etc, even on relatively gentle slopes, will have a limiting effect on land use, and therefore affect the grade.

• **Flooding:** The risk of regular flooding will be taken into consideration.

• **Soil properties:**

- **Texture and structure:** These also affect the land's susceptibility to drought and, conversely, waterlogging.

- **Depth:** The depth of topsoil present will affect the type of cultivation that can be carried out. For example, very shallow soils may not be ploughable.

- **Stoniness:** Stony soil causes more wear on machinery, affects the growth of root crops and hinders the harvesting of potatoes. The presence of a lot of stones also reduces the soil's nutrient capacity.

- **Chemical properties:** The chemical properties (e.g. acidity / alkalinity) of a soil are only taken into consideration when they cannot readily be corrected and / or maintained by normal husbandry procedures such as the use of fertilisers or lime. However, toxicity will have a negative effect on grade.

Soil assessment

The types of soil found on your holding may vary considerably between different fields, and even within fields. Knowing what soils are present, and how to manage them, enables you to make best use of each area. Also, on examining the soil, you might come across evidence of previous mismanagement (e.g. compaction) which, if rectified, could increase the cropping potential of your land.

Soil texture and type:

The texture of a mineral soil is determined by the relative proportions of sand, silt and clay in its makeup. Clay has the smallest particles, and sand the largest, with silt lying somewhere in the middle. A mixture of all three is what is known as a loam, which, depending on the dominant particle size, might be described as a 'sandy loam' or 'clay loam', or you might have 'loamy sand', and so on. Most soils also contain some organic matter, with a soil being termed 'organic' when the proportion of organic matter present is from 10-20% (e.g. 'organic sandy loam', which would be a lovely soil to have in the vegetable garden). A peaty soil is one that contains 20-50% organic matter, and anything above that is simply termed peat. Peat such as is found in permanently waterlogged upland bogs is sour, acidic stuff, and no good for anything except rough grazing in a dry summer. Drained fenland peat, on the other hand, is a wonderfully fertile growing medium (and so it should be – it's like pure compost!), although the underlying sub-soil will affect its usefulness in times of drought (e.g. peat fen over clay is much better than peat fen over sand or gravel). There are also chalky soils, which, when clay is present, are known as 'marls'. Again, these are named according to the dominant constituent, e.g. 'chalky' marl or 'clay' marl. In some parts of the country there are old marl pits, where the chalk-and-clay mixture was extracted and spread on the land to improve the texture of soils that lacked these components, and to correct problems of acidity.

Sandy soils are often termed 'light' (i.e. easily worked) soils, but are also 'hungry' soils, in that they don't hold onto nutrients for long. Repeated applications of farmyard manure are required to maintain fertility. However, these soils do warm up quickly in spring, and don't suffer from waterlogging in winter. Erosion may be an issue though, as might drought. Clay ('heavy') soils, on the other hand, are cold and difficult to work early in the year, although they are retentive of nutrients and water, so can produce high yields under favourable conditions. Digging over in the autumn and then allowing frost action to break down the clods can make clay soils more workable, as can applications of lime.

To assess type and texture, you need to take up a handful of moist soil. Begin by rubbing some between your finger and thumb: sandy soil will feel gritty; silt feels powdery or silky; and a clay soil is smooth and slippery. Loams will have a crumbly texture. Peaty soils feel spongy and are distinguished by their very dark – almost black – colour. Next, try moulding your handful of soil into a ball: a clay soil is easily moulded, and will take on a 'polished' appearance when the surface of the ball is smoothed with a moistened finger. Sand, on the other hand, won't hold a ball shape at all. Loam can be rolled into a ball, but it'll easily break up, and can't be smoothed like clay.

Above and Below: Contrasts in land type:
Same cattle, same farm, different fields.

Soil structure

To examine soil structure you really need to dig a small square hole, say a couple of spades width by a spade-and-a half deep. Now have a good look at what you've exposed. (Of course, if your land lies thinly over solid rock, as much of ours does, then you're not going to be able to dig down the required 18" or so. Just do the best you can.)

In a soil with good structure, you'll notice that it's easily broken into clearly defined blocks, with plenty of vertical gaps between them which allow water to drain away, air to circulate, and roots to grow freely and obtain their required nutrients. The blocks themselves are relatively easy to crumble in the hand. Plant roots should be evident at depths of over a foot, and the lump of soil that you dug out should contain at least 10-15

earthworms. The colour and depth of the topsoil is important too: very shallow soils will probably only be suitable for permanent grassland, although the use of surface cultivations may enable you to sow fodder crops or to re-seed with more productive grass species. For vegetable growing you'll need a reasonable depth of topsoil, although on a small scale (i.e. in the garden) you can create this yourself by using plenty of manure and compost, and by carrying in molehills from the surrounding fields. (Sounds daft I know, but we did it and it worked!) Failing this you could build raised beds and fill them with imported topsoil. A dark colour is indicative of high organic content, so darker topsoils are likely to be more fertile.

Poorly structured soils, on the other hand, don't separate so easily into blocks. There are fewer vertical cracks (i.e. the block sizes are much larger), and what cracks there are will be narrow, so drainage and air flow is restricted. Horizontal fissures present a barrier to root growth, and trap water. Rust-coloured patches, or greyish streaks in the soil, reveal areas where waterlogging has been a problem, and this may be accompanied by a foul smell due to the incomplete breakdown of organic matter under anaerobic conditions. Soils such as this are very susceptible to damage by poaching or the passage of machinery when wet, and any such damage will simply exacerbate the problems.

Some structural issues may be the result of previous mismanagement, such as compaction caused by machinery and trampling by livestock, inappropriate ploughing depth, or poor drainage, and as such might be correctable by the

Spreading lime on an acidic soil to correct pH.

use of a subsoiler, sward lifter, soil aerator or mole-plough, depending on the nature of the problem and the depth at which it lies. Spreading lime on acidic soils to correct pH (see below) will also improve their structure as it aids the process by which they are broken down into smaller blocks.

Chemical properties

Essentially what we're looking at here is the pH (i.e. the acidity) of the soil and the presence of three important elements (phosphorus, potassium and magnesium), and the way in which they affect the uptake of nitrogen by plants. There are lots of other micro-nutrients that might be studied in a more detailed analysis, but they won't be identified by a basic soil test kit.

pH: The pH is a measure of acidity (or alkalinity). A low figure represents acidity, and a high one alkalinity. The optimum pH for efficient grass growth on mineral soils is about 6.3, and the majority

of vegetables will thrive at this level too. On peat-based soils the optimum is a little lower, at around 5.5. Potatoes and oats are both crops that'll tolerate fairly acidic conditions (down to about pH 5.0), and, at the other end of the scale, many brassicas are happy to grow where the pH rises above 7.5. A pH that is too low can be raised by applications of lime (which will also improve soil structure).

Different soil types will respond differently to liming, so there's a certain amount of trial and error involved in raising pH to the optimum level. The maximum amount that should be applied at any one time is 5 tonnes per hectare (2 tons per acre, or 0.5 kg per m²), which ought to lift the pH by almost half a unit. However, lime is fairly slow-acting stuff, so you'll have to wait a year before re-testing in order to monitor the effects of your efforts. Reducing the pH of alkaline soils is more difficult, but it can be done by incorporating plenty of farmyard manure and by heavy cropping

(e.g. the taking of several cuts of silage or hay each season from the land in question).

Phosphorus: Represented by the letter 'P' in scientific language, phosphorus, in the form of phosphates, is essential for plant root development. However, it's not only root crops that benefit – good healthy roots on any plant will lead to better overall growth and foliage. The optimum phosphate index is 2, but where pH is less than 5.5 or greater than 6.5, the phosphorous will be 'locked up' and therefore unavailable to plants. Soil phosphorus content can be raised by applications of farmyard manure or 'artificial' fertilisers (such as rock phosphate), but it's important not to exceed levels that can be readily utilised by the crops being grown, as surplus phosphates are easily leached to watercourses, and are harmful to the environment if present in large quantities.

Potassium: Written simply as 'K' in chemical formulae, but known to farmers and gardeners as potash, potassium is essential for strong and vigorous plant growth as it controls water loss from cells and also aids the transport of nutrients from the roots to the leaves. Light soils are most likely to deficient in potash, and, even if plenty of nitrogen and other essential elements are applied, plant growth will be seriously compromised unless the deficiency is rectified. The optimum potassium index is 2, and the cheapest way to raise the level is through generous applications of farmyard manure. On a very small scale (e.g. on individual plots in the vegetable garden), a top dressing of wood ash will help. Excessive use of 'chemical' sources of potassium on grassland, particularly if applied early in the year, can result in too much lush growth.

Magnesium: Magnesium (or 'Mg') is an essential part of the diet of grazing animals, particularly those that are milking heavily. A deficiency leads to the condition known as 'staggers', which is generally characterised by sudden death (which makes treatment tricky, to say the least). The ideal Mg index is 2. Lighter soils are most prone to deficiency due to the fact that magnesium is easily leached out. Where particular fields are identified as having low magnesium levels, it's important to provide supplements for susceptible groups of livestock in spring (e.g. ewes with young lambs at foot and cows at turnout) and autumn (suckler cows in particular), and avoid the application of fertilisers which contain high levels of potassium at these times.

An excess of magnesium, on the other hand, will reduce the efficiency with which plants are able to utilise other nutrients.

Drainage

Most 'improved' agricultural land will have had some kind of drainage system installed at some point in the past, except perhaps in the case of light sandy ground overlying gravelly subsoil, which is, of course, naturally free-draining. At one time there were substantial grants available for land reclamation and drainage works, but this is no longer the case. As a result, many existing field drainage systems have fallen into disrepair, and very few new ones are installed. Therefore, when making an assessment of your land, it's quite likely that in

Main and Inset: Due to poor drainage, this field is unuseable for most of the year.

some fields you'll see evidence of waterlogging in the soil structure (see above) together with clumps of rushes and other wetland plants, and possibly standing water on the surface (depending on the time of year). On areas of ground that are persistently waterlogged, surface water often has an oily sheen, and contains streaks of reddish ooze. There might also be areas of bare ground where grass has simply failed to survive. Unless rectified, the situation will simply get worse every year, and the use that you are able to make of the affected field(s) will diminish considerably. Growing crops will be out of the question, grazing

Evidence of persistent waterlogging.

A relatively minor problem, such as a blocked culvert or drain, will soon lead to deterioration of the surrounding grassland.

will be restricted to summer only, livestock production will fall due to the loss of higher-yielding grass species, and incidence of diseases such as liverfluke and footrot may increase.

Even if the existing un-maintained drainage system is still functioning, you might find its capabilities affected by activities on adjoining land. For example, when we first moved here, the mountainside above us was clothed in mature forestry plantation, and our field drains were just about coping. However, came a day when the trees were felled and the situation changed almost overnight: Without the forest to hold it back, water flowed off the mountainside at a rate that was well in excess of the capacity of our drains and ditches, and a field that was previously merely damp at certain times of year is now covered in rushes, and almost unusable. Likewise, be aware that any drainage activities that you carry out may well have an impact on farms further downstream.

TIP

What you thought were small springs popping up in your fields during wet weather might simply be places where the original drainage system has become blocked, forcing water to bubble up to the surface in search of an easier route.

Drainage function

A drainage system serves two basic purposes: firstly, it must intercept any water flowing onto the land and divert it away somewhere else, and secondly, it must carry off any water that's already on the land, or which falls on the ground as rain and snow, or which issues from beneath the surface in the form of springs.

In essence then, it can be seen that what's required (assuming that the field is of a regular shape, and lies on a slope), is simply an open ditch along the topmost boundary, and another along the lower. However, in real life things aren't generally that simple, and the situation within each field might be very variable, depending on both the micro-relief and the nature of the underlying subsoil and bedrock. In some cases it may be necessary to install separate drainage systems in different parts of the field, and of course you won't want a lot of open ditches criss-crossing your pasture. Therefore, the usual practice is to have a series of parallel underground pipe drains, which run diagonally across any slope, These are linked to a central main drain (also underground, and running straight down the slope), which in turn debouches into an open ditch along the lowest boundary. This is known as the 'herringbone' system. Several herringbone systems might be

needed in each field. Each of the parallel drains serves both of the purposes stated above, carrying water away from the land above it and protecting the land below. In the same way, the open ditch along the bottom of one field is effectively intercepting water that might otherwise have affected the next field down the slope. The network of drains will eventually converge on a stream, which, if it's got sufficient volume of flow, might be put to good use on the holding.

Any springs that rise in the field may need to be contained and piped directly to the ditch, rather than being included in the main network. With a bit of luck, it might be possible to utilise this source for livestock drinking purposes, by using the piped spring water to fill a trough *en route*.

TIP

To locate a hidden system of underground land drains, view the field on a frosty morning. Frost will thaw more quickly above buried pipes, so the whole drainage network will briefly be revealed as green lines against a hoary background.

Installation

Basically you dig a trench, lay a perforated plastic pipe in the bottom, partially backfill with 'drainage stone' (clean chippings or shingle), and finish off by replacing an appropriate amount of topsoil. There does need to be a good fall in the run of pipe, to reduce the likelihood of silting, so where the slope of the field isn't sufficient to provide this you'll need to adjust the depth of the trench along its length.

Main: *Installing a new field drainage system.* **Inset:** *Perforated drainage pipe.*

When excavating a drainage channel or cleaning out a ditch, always begin at the lowest point and work your way uphill. If you do it the other way about then you'll be struggling to dig in an ever-increasing flow of water that's got nowhere to go.

The new field drain discharges into a nearby ditch.

Drainage stone for backfilling over perforated pipe.

Assuming, for the sake of simplicity, that you've dug a trench a foot wide, and that you're going to use a 12" depth of shingle over the pipe, then you'll need about 3½ tonnes of stone for every 20m length. However, make sure you allow some extra, as the dimensions of the trench are unlikely to be exact.

On flat fields, the open ditches around the boundary will need to be particularly deep, in order to facilitate setting the pipe exits low enough to gain the necessary fall. Ideally, you're looking for an absolute minimum fall of 1 in 250, with no significant change

in gradient along the length of the pipe.

The depth at which field drainage pipes should be laid will depend on the nature of the soil, and also on the intended use to which the field will be put. On heavy clay soils, drains should be relatively close to the surface, otherwise water may not succeed in getting through to them. Light soils, on the other hand, can be drained at depths of 3'- 4', and on peaty ground you may need to go deeper still. Where land is to be cultivated, the drainage system needs to be sufficiently well buried that it's not going to get damaged by machinery, but on permanent pasture you needn't go so far down. The last drain that we installed, on grazing land, only required an 18" deep trench. In the bottom of this we placed a 6" diameter pipe, which we covered with 8" of shingle, topped off with 4" of topsoil.

If circumstances dictate that a deep drainage system needs to be installed on heavy clay land then it can be augmented by the use of mole drains. Mole drains

are formed by a tractor dragging a torpedo-shaped tool through the soil at an appropriate depth to open up a channel. In clay soils, mole drains may remain functional for as long as six years. Mole drainage should be carried out at right angles to the direction of the existing pipe drains, with the tool set at such a depth that it passes through the gravel infill as it crosses above the line of each pipe. In certain situations, mole drainage alone may be sufficient, but it's not a long term solution. Pipe drains, on the other hand, may be expected to last 60 years or more.

29

Basic Requirements and Infrastructure

The basic requirements can be crudely broken down into three major components: house, outbuildings and land. How much of each of these assets you require is going to vary according to individual circumstances; land, for an urban smallholder, might consist of lots of patio-tubs and window-boxes, plus an allotment down the road. The number and size of any outbuildings needed is going to depend, to a large extent, on what livestock you intend to keep, and your own housing needs may range from a single room bothy for a single person, to a large and rambling country house for a large and rambling family.

You may be lucky – as we were – and find a smallholding that satisfies all three of these basic requirements from the outset. The fact that we've subsequently knocked down and replaced the main outbuilding, doubled the size of the house, and substantially increased our acreage is neither here nor there; that's just evolution, adapting our working environment to suit our changing needs – our family got bigger, so the scale of our activities had to follow suit.

However, in many cases you might only succeed in satisfying one or two of the basic requirements, initially. This is particularly likely if you're tied to a certain area (perhaps because one member of the family has employment commitments), or have a particularly tight budget. You might have a nice house with a range of outbuildings, but no land,

so you look for opportunities to buy or rent fields nearby. Or you might have land with a house, but no outbuildings, in which case you build some. Outbuildings on land where there's no house perhaps lend themselves to conversion into a dwelling unit, so this type of property shouldn't be overlooked if you're aiming to re-locate. And some folk might choose to start with a completely blank canvas by buying an empty plot of land, in the hope that they'll get planning permission to turn it into the smallholding of their dreams.

Location

Land on the eastern side of the UK is generally (but not exclusively) more productive than that in the west of the country, but the latter is often milder (particularly in coastal regions), and has higher rainfall. Latitude will also affect weather and light conditions, with more winter daylight in the south. However, summer daylight hours increase the further north you go. Obviously there's nothing you can do to change this, but you do need to be aware of the impact it'll have on property prices. Put simply, smallholdings in 'better' areas (i.e. more fertile land etc.) are more expensive. Therefore these tend to be owned by 'lifestyle' smallholders rather than 'livelihood' smallholders, as a self-sufficient way of life isn't going to generate enough revenue to pay for a top end property. Ironically, this means that the families that really need productive holdings tend to end up trying to make a living in

the least productive areas of the country. Rough hill land in the north-west can still be purchased for under £1,000 per acre, whereas the same area of good quality ground in the south-east might set you back as much as £15,000. Whatever price you end up paying you can be reasonably sure it's a safe investment, as the value of bare agricultural land keeps on steadily rising. However, if you're thinking of buying a plot and building your own house then the magic words 'development potential' are going to escalate the price way beyond these figures, although, of course, the possibility for development isn't so great in upland regions.

In addition to the potential productivity of the land that accompanies any prospective smallholding you might be interested in viewing, you're going to have to consider the following:

• Do you have other commitments that limit your search to a specific area? For example, strong family ties, ageing relatives or employment.

• Do you require easy access to road and rail links? Being well connected may negate some of the restrictions outlined above, for example by making commuting a realistic option, and might also be necessary if you want to diversify your smallholding business to include enterprises such as tourism, running courses, opening a farm shop, or providing converted outbuildings for use as offices.

• Do you need to be close to schools? Even if you don't have any children at the moment, you may reproduce in the future!

• Is there a local public transport network? Many rural areas are very badly served in this respect, often making it necessary for families to carry the cost of running several vehicles.

• Can you cope with isolation? If you're a gregarious soul then you'd be wasting your time viewing properties in the back of beyond, no matter how idyllic they appear. This is particularly so if one partner is likely to be working away during the week.

• Are you planning on running a home office-based business? If so, consider aspects such as broadband and mobile phone coverage.

• Would you object to other people having rights of access over your property? For example, sporting rights, public footpaths, open access land, and shared use of tracks, yards and parking areas.

• Could you cope with the maintenance and repair of a run-down dwelling? Houses sold as being 'in need of modernisation' are generally pretty rough, and hence a touch more affordable.

All of these points (and many more besides) impact on the desirability of a property, and hence it's price. If you don't mind living half way up a mountainside in the middle of nowhere, with no internet connection and having to home-educate your kids through force of circumstance, then there are still reasonable-priced properties out there to be had.

Site plan

Layout: In an ideal world, the whole of your smallholding will consist of a single block of land contained within a 'ring fence' (i.e. a stock-proof boundary that encircles the whole place), subdivided into a number of useful paddocks. Having the house and buildings situated at the perimeter is best from a biosecurity point of view, but may not be so convenient with regard to moving livestock to and fro between housing and grazing.

Location of water supply: Having a natural water source that's situated uphill from your house and buildings (and as many of your fields as possible) is a huge asset, as gravity can be used to pipe it to any part of the holding.

Access to fields: Although fit and healthy animals can negotiate awkward slopes and narrow gateways, there may well be times when you need to enter fields in a vehicle in order to bring a poorly animal out. Invariably this will occur at a time of year when ground conditions are at their worst. Hardcore access tracks may need to be installed across difficult terrain. Field gateways should be conveniently sited, and must be wide enough to allow the passage of any machinery required for harvesting whatever crops you're planning to grow (including hay and / or silage).

Kitchen garden: Does your prospective smallholding have a suitable area reasonably close to the house that can be used as a kitchen garden?

Security: It's a sad fact that even in rural areas there's a certain risk from theft and vandalism. This may be increased if your outbuildings are situated at a distance from your dwelling.

Try to avoid letting your head be ruled by your heart! You may be tempted by the picturesque appearance of low-lying meadows in summer, ablaze with wetland wildflowers and teeming with butterflies, but in the winter the reality is rather different. Larger farms generally consist of a diverse range of habitats, soil types and site classifications, meaning that livestock can be rotated around different areas of the holding according to seasonal variations in ground conditions. The smallholder with only a couple of fields may find that all of his available land falls within one category, seriously limiting the overall versatility of the holding. This is going to be a particular problem if those few fields become waterlogged or flooded.

When viewing potential properties, you really must leave those rose-tinted spectacles at home!

THE HOUSE

If you've already got a house, or you can afford to buy one, then that's good. If not, you can build you own. You can build it out of sticks and stones, mud and straw, or more conventional bricks and mortar. The choice is yours, subject, of course, to the deliberations of your local planning department and a whole set of rules called 'building regs'. Thankfully, regional councils are beginning to look more favourably on 'alternative' construction methods than had previously been the case, which is good news for the self-builder, because lower impact often equates with lower cost.

However, do bear in mind that your smallholding isn't only your livelihood – it's your pension as well. One day, when increasing age and infirmity begin to take their toll on your physical ability, you'll want to cash in your asset and 'downsize'. Putting a property on the market that includes a substantial dwelling house is likely to realise far more capital than one with a cluster of mud huts.

Requirements

Apart from the obvious fact that it needs to keep you warm and dry, which applies to any house anywhere, the distinctive requirements of the smallholder are fairly easily satisfied. Only you can determine how big (i.e. in terms of the number of bedrooms, bathrooms etc.,) your home needs to be, but additional things that you will need to consider are:

Large kitchen: The kitchen is so central to family life on the smallholding that it must be roomy enough to permit a wide range of activities other than just basic cooking and eating. Everyone will spend most of their indoor time in the kitchen, so even a big one can get pretty crowded at times.

Designated study or office: Unfortunately, running a small farm generates a considerable amount of paperwork, most of which is a legal requirement. You can't afford to have it all just jumbled up with ordinary day-to-day stuff, so you'll need a couple of filing cabinets, at least, and somewhere to work. Also, if you're running any other kind of

office-based business from home, you'll need space for all that that dictates, too.

Toilet / washroom easily accessible from outdoors: In cases of emergency, you need to be able to access clean water and a first aid kit as quickly as possible without having to traipse through the house looking for things. It also makes it a lot easier to maintain reasonable levels of personal hygiene during busy periods of prolonged outdoor activity, such as lambing time, or when friends and relatives are camping in the garden.

Air-locks on external doors: To get into or out of the house you should have to pass through two doors. Always close one before opening the other to avoid rapid and wasteful heat loss from within. The airlock effect can be created by the installation of a conservatory or closed porch, or by having your back door opening into an unheated utility room or scullery (which is a good idea anyway, see below).

Plenty of 'utility' space for wellies, wet coats, overalls etc.: It's no good relying on a dainty porch to house the accoutrements of a family whose daily life is spent working outdoors, come rain or shine. There's got to be room to kick off muddy boots, disrobe, and hang everything up to dry. And each member of the family will probably need two complete foul-weather outfits on the go (one drying, one for wearing) so that changes can be made part way through the day if necessary. In a big family that adds up to a lot of muddy togs. Something like a large utility room, scullery or conservatory is a must.

Storeroom on the north-facing side of the house: In fact, anywhere between north and east is fine. Ours is actually a small outhouse that stands slightly detached from the main dwelling. The 2' thick stone walls and relatively small windows ensure that the internal temperature remains nice and cool all year round. The storeroom needs to have plenty of shelving for storing of jams, pickles, chutneys etc., and probably space for several chest freezers. You might also need to find room for sacks of flour and potatoes, and large containers full of honey, malt extract and suchlike. A fairly high ceiling is a bonus, enabling you to hang strings of onions, sides of bacon and so on out of harm's way. It's also a good place to hang game or mutton carcasses for maturation. If the storeroom is big enough, you could even have your chopping block here and use it for butchery, in which case you'll also need a hot and cold water supply, and hand-washing facilities.

Versatility: When buying a property, think not only of your current needs, but what your requirements might be in a few years' time: your family may get larger, you may retire from regular employment in order to work full-time on the holding, an ageing relative may need to be accommodated, or you might set up a new home-based business. It would be a pity if, having established a productive smallholding, you had to sell up and move because the house no longer suited. Look for characteristics that make for easy adaptations: is the loft space big enough to be converted? Is there enough clear area around the house to allow the building of an extension? Could a spare bedroom become a study? Is there an outbuilding that could be turned into an annexe? Many small farms have a range of traditional outbuildings that actually adjoin the dwelling house, and, if we were starting all over again, this is one of the things we'd be looking for – extending our living space would then be a simple matter of creating some new doorways.

Obviously anyone who's starting from scratch with a green field site is going to have to consider other requirements such as electricity, water supply and access, but on existing properties these will, to a certain extent, have been provided for. That's not to say they'll be entirely suitable as they are, but will at least serve your needs in the short term.

Build-it-yourself

• **Practicalities:** I have no doubt that anyone who wants to can build their own house: if you haven't got the skills already you'll soon learn them as you go along. However, you do need to ask yourself whether this really is the most practical option. If you've got the capital and can afford to take a year or so off from doing everything else, then self-building is an ideal solution, and hugely rewarding. However, if you're employed full or part-time elsewhere, while also trying to establish a productive smallholding, then most of your waking hours are pretty well tied up, and your building project is going to take ages – years, in fact. Personally, I don't think you could possibly make a good job of caring for crops and livestock while temporarily residing in a static caravan in the middle of a building site. Animal welfare

standards would inevitably deteriorate, particularly during the winter months – you'd be too busy trying to keep yourselves warm, dry and sane. The exception to this would be on a holding that was already well equipped with plenty of outbuildings for livestock and storage purposes.

So, if you do decide to self-build on a part-time basis, or carry out major alterations on an existing property to the extent that your living space is affected while work is in progress, I'd strongly recommend that you hire in skilled labour at certain times, or contract out parts of the job, in order to move the project forward as quickly as possible. Either that or you put your smallholding activities on hold until the building work is complete, and rent out the land to somebody else in the meantime. It's my belief that you need to be settled to be self-sufficient, and there's nothing more unsettling than having nowhere to live.

• **Design:** Although, as I mentioned already, there are a number of alternative construction methods that could be utilised, consider whether these would be practical in the light of your intended smallholding activities. It would be great fun to design, build and live in a 'hobbit hole' or a Celtic roundhouse (I'd like to try it myself someday), but once you get into the business of producing your own meat and dairy products you need areas which are light and airy, easily washable and vermin proof. You don't need much of an imagination to predict what the results of applying a pressure washer to the inside of a mud hut might be…

You also need to consider the

It might be fun to live in a mud hut, but is it practical?

overall visual appearance of your smallholding – if you don't, your local planning department certainly will. A sticks-and-mud dwelling house of unusual dimensions is going to look a trifle incongruous when surrounded by the conventional agricultural buildings that accommodate your animals. Of course, you could also build your livestock housing using mud and sticks, but this is really only going to be practical on a very small scale.

To my mind then, this leaves us with three building material options for the self-built dwelling house: Straw bales, timber or conventional.

As far as the actual design process goes, you can do this yourself. Basically you just draw a sketch (to scale) of what you want. Don't get carried away though, by adding complications such as dormer windows or changes in roof pitch. Not only will these make construction more difficult, they'll add to the cost. Work on simple principles of squares, rectangles and triangles and you won't be too wide of the mark. Your own sketches should be sufficient for the purpose of applying for planning permission and getting quotes for materials, but you'll need the help of a structural engineer to work out the fiddly

Straw bale building at the Centre for Alternative Technology.

Straw bale building

The concept of building with straw bales isn't new, although it's a relatively recent innovation in the UK. There are two main construction methods: framed or load-bearing. In the case of a framed straw bale building, the bales don't carry the whole weight of the roof, and are primarily used to form a highly efficient in-fill for each of the timber sections that make up the structure of the house. However, the framework doesn't achieve its full rigidity until packed with straw, meaning that the bales do contribute to the overall structural strength of the building.

In the case of load-bearing straw bale construction, the bales themselves are the principal building blocks, and are expected to support the full weight of the roof and any internal floors.

A third method uses a substantial framework, with a straw bale in-fill providing insulation but no structural strength. In this respect it's little different from any other timber-framed building method, and some of the cost benefit associated with the use of straw bales is lost.

Whichever technique is used, the inside and outside is generally coated with a traditional lime render, as this is better able to cope with the natural movement and breathability of the straw. Cement-based products tend to develop cracks as the building settles, which may lead to the ingress of water.

We did give serious consideration to the use of straw bales when planning to extend our house, but rejected the idea due to the fact that the bales must be kept dry throughout the building process – in the unlikely event that we might have a sufficiently settled period of weather to raise the walls, we'd more than likely be too busy with haymaking – and also because, in this incessantly damp West Wales climate, we couldn't dispel the image of seeing our house slowly subside into a pile of compost.

bits that are required to comply with building regs. Things like site levelling, the depth of the footings, the thickness of the concrete slab, the route of sewerage pipes, the height of the damp-proof course (DPC), and the dimensions of load-bearing beams. If you get these wrong your house won't necessarily fall down, but you might be asked to pull it down and start again.

Also be aware that your new home may be subject to an Energy Performance Certificate (EPC) inspection at some point, perhaps if you're planning to claim feed-in tariff (FIT) payments on a solar panel installation, or put the property on the market. Factor energy efficiency into your design, and include masses of insulation – under the floor, in the walls, and in the roof.

• **Planning:** You'll almost certainly need to apply for planning permission for your proposed development, but if you're in any doubt about this you can first submit an application for determination of planning permission. This gives your local regulatory department the opportunity to advise you as to whether full planning permission will be required. In certain circumstances, retrospective planning permission may be granted for a building constructed without consent, but it's far more likely that you'd be instructed to demolish it, so it's probably not worth the risk. However, if you're able to demonstrate that you've been using / living in the building, without challenge, for a minimum of ten years (four years in some areas) from the date of completion, then you should be entitled to claim a Certificate of Lawful Use or Development (CLUD). You'll

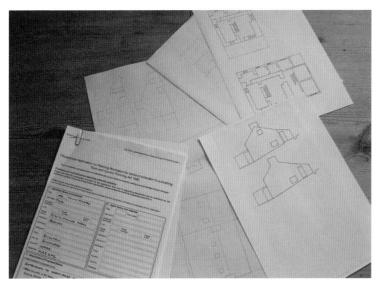

As far as the actual design process goes, you can do this yourself

undoubtedly be required to provide proof of your occupancy, so if you're thinking of taking a gamble and trying to exploit this loophole, make sure you keep accurate records, e.g. dated photographs, receipts for building materials, utility bills etc.

Submitting a planning application is a relatively straightforward procedure using the appropriate forms obtained from your local council. For something simple and uncontroversial such as a modest extension to an existing property, planning permission is likely to be granted quite quickly, although it could be subject to certain conditions (e.g. here in Wales, the use of Welsh slate for roofing may well be a stipulation). Planning controls are in place to protect (amongst other things) the character and amenity of an area, so provided your proposal isn't so outrageous that it might constitute an undesirable visual impact, it should be ok. However, if you live in an Area of Outstanding Natural Beauty (AONB) or some similarly designated area, or if your existing

house is a listed building, there may be additional hoops to jump through, and you might also be required to provide a Design and Access Statement.

If you're contemplating a new-build on a 'green field' site then permission will not be so readily granted, and you may be required to demonstrate that your smallholding activities are a financially viable business, and that it's necessary for you to live on site in order to carry out those activities and / or for animal welfare reasons. This is one of the explanations as to why so many smallholders spend several years in temporary accommodation such as a caravan or mobile home, gradually developing their business to the point that it will satisfy the demands of the planning system.

If your application is refused you have 6 months in which to appeal, and once planning permission has been granted you must commence work within 5 years.

Permission for the conversion of

existing farm buildings to dwelling units has recently become easier to obtain, with the introduction of Class Q to the General Permitted Development Order. This applies to buildings that were used solely for agricultural purposes on or before 20th March 2013, or, if built after that date, have been in agricultural use for a minimum of 10 years. The downside to this is that a successful Class Q application will result in the suspension of your permitted agricultural development rights for a period of 10 years, so if you're also planning on constructing new accommodation for your livestock, you'd better get that done first.

• **Building:** For our own domestic building project we decided to use timber. Reasons for this choice included cost, sustainability, speed and ease of construction, visual appeal, and the fact that it's a material I feel comfortable working with. We employed a local craftsman (sustainable-choice.co.uk), and all the timber was sourced locally too. We would've liked to have harvested the timber from our own trees, but at the time didn't have any that were big enough.

The framework components were cut and shaped in a clearing in the woods about a mile away, and then erected on site. The craftsman was contracted to supply materials and build a 5 x 8.5 metre, two storey, weather-proof shell to our own design, with us then taking over for the internal fitting out. It cost £25,000 (in 2013), which we feel compares favourably with other construction methods. However, this could have been considerably reduced if we'd been able to use home-grown timber, and if we'd undertaken to do more of the work ourselves.

Although it's in the form of an extension to an existing dwelling, it could just as easily have been built as a free-standing unit. Therefore, the following sequence of photographs should be of benefit to anyone thinking of building in this way:

1. Site preparation - there seemed to be an awful lot of digging down before we could begin to think about building up.

2. Setting out the foundations.

3. Building base walls of blockwork onto the new concrete fottings.

4. Meanwhile in the woods, the frame is taking shape. The timber used is larch, in 8" x 8" baulks.

5. Pouring the concrete slab, having first laid down a damp-proof membrane and 6" of insulation. Steel reinforcement mesh was also incorporated at this stage.

6. Beginning to install the framework on site.

7. Most of the ground floor frame in place.

8. With the upper storey timbers and the roof trusses in place, the framework is almost complete.

9. Covering the outside with a water-proof, breathable membrane. This is held in place with 2" x 1" battens, which also provide a fixing point for the external cladding.

10. The internal studwork, fitted within the main timber frame, is made of 2" x 4" rough sawn larch. This is what we'll be attaching our plasterboard to, in order to divide the space up into different rooms. Gaps are left in appropriate places for windows and doors.

11. Re-routing the drainage system that had been disturbed by our initial excavations, with additional pipework to cope with roof water, and plenty of rodding points.

12. Fitting the windows and frames, also handcrafted in the woods.

13. Sheep's wool insulation was used throughout. Here Tim can be seen filling the gaps between the rafters.

14. View from the rear – nearly done.

15. Habitable at last!

OUTBUILDINGS

Most smallholdings seem to fall into one of two categories: those that have an over-abundance of outbuildings, and those that have none. The latter occurs where a smallholding is established on a 'green field' site, perhaps by buying a few fields close to an existing residence, or by purchasing a plot of land in the hope of gaining permission to build. The former are usually what remains when a large farm is divided up and amalgamated into even bigger units. All the best agricultural land is sold off to neighbouring landowners, and the house, together with outbuildings and a few acres, is marketed as a desirable smallholding. In this case, the number and range of outbuildings is likely to be disproportionate to the acreage remaining, providing plenty of opportunities for the resourceful smallholder wishing to diversify.

However, unless there are some relatively modern agricultural buildings on the site, the needs of the livestock keeper may not be satisfied. Historical farm buildings, although aesthetically pleasing and perhaps in keeping with the traditional ethos of the smallholder, were designed and built at a time when our understanding of the welfare requirements of livestock was very poor, particularly with regard to respiratory disorders, and as such many are woefully inadequate for their original purpose. They're also very difficult and time consuming to muck out. Often it makes better sense to convert old farm buildings to other uses, such as holiday lets or workshops, which can help to generate the income stream required to enable a fledgling

smallholding to survive.

Having said all that, many smallholders (ourselves included) do successfully utilise traditional outbuildings for housing livestock, but it's very important to be aware of their limitations when deciding on factors such as what animals to keep in them, how many, in what age groups, and at what time of year. For it to be effective you need to blend aspects of both traditional and contemporary methods of animal husbandry into a workable system, appropriate to the needs of the modern smallholder.

On holdings that do already have more up-to-date outbuildings, the battle may be considered half won. Here the principal challenge lies in making best possible use of the space available in a way that is not only beneficial to your animals, but is easily managed without everything degenerating into a muddle.

Given a large enough shed it may be possible to bring all your 'indoor' smallholding activities together under one roof, which simplifies matters no end if – and it is a big if – you put sufficient forethought into the internal layout of the area available, and ensure proper segregation of the various enterprises (without compromising versatility). It is when one thing spills over into the space allocated to something else that things begin to go wrong. Timing is crucial here, too, so that different activities can be planned to use the same space at different times of year.

For example, you may wish to use your shed to house a few store cattle in the early part of the winter, and then to lamb your sheep. This is excellent as it makes optimum use of the space, but it

does mean that you'll have had to plan the approximate sale date of the cattle 5 months in advance (i.e. when you put the ram in with your ewes).

On the face of it, the 'green field' smallholder might appear to be at something of a disadvantage, but this isn't necessarily the case. Given a blank canvas (and provided that the necessary planning permissions can be obtained, if required), it should be possible to design livestock housing solutions specifically tailored to the range of animals kept. This need not be particularly complex or expensive. It's very nice to have a custom made steel portal agricultural building, if you can afford it (or if there are grants up for grabs in your area), but a more modest 'off-the-peg' model may not be as pricey as you might think. If that's still beyond your reach, you can get by just as well with a basic pole barn constructed from re-claimed materials.

A field shelter converted into a lambing shed for a small flock.

Failing that, there are any number of adaptable temporary or semi-permanent solutions. One couple we met kept their sheep in a large marquee at lambing time. Another friend used his polytunnel to house his early lambing flock in winter, and for growing plants in the spring. Someone else I knew used to move all their free range poultry into the greenhouses for the winter, where they did a grand job clearing up the residue from the year's crops. Pig arks can be used for lots of things besides pigs, and simple field shelters are very versatile too; I recently visited a local smallholding to see just such a structure – erected for horses by the previous owner – neatly converted into a little lambing shed.

Whatever you decide to do, think ahead. Consider what types of livestock (and how many) you may have on your smallholding a few years hence, and plan accordingly. If you're starting from scratch then build as big as you think you'll need (and a bit more) from the outset, and, above all, avoid the gradual spread of an unsightly 'shanty town' of ramshackle huts, derelict caravans and old lorry containers, which is all too common, and only serves to give smallholding a bad name.

Traditional outbuildings for livestock housing

The very nature of many smallholdings means that the outhouses (if any) that accompany them tend to be traditional buildings, built to local designs, using local materials, many years ago. In a lot of cases these are in a poor state of repair, and will not have been used for their original purpose for a very long time. For the smallholder wishing to embark on a new livestock keeping venture, the availability of a range of traditional buildings may appear to provide a perfect ready-made solution to the problem of winter housing for their animals, but unfortunately it's often far from

Building a simple pole barn using a mix of new and reclaimed materials.

ideal. It's not for nothing that these outbuildings have been displaced by more up-to-date structures on the vast majority of commercial farms.

Nowadays animal welfare is the number one priority when designing livestock accommodation, and, while I'm not necessarily suggesting that traditional husbandry methods were inherently bad in this respect, it must be remembered that our understanding of an animal's basic requirements for good health and welfare far exceeds that of our forebears.

Therefore, with the exception of a nasty glitch in the 1970s and early 1980s (when, due to public demand for cheap food, and government incentives, we saw a proliferation of so called 'factory' farms), the standards of welfare for housed livestock have steadily improved over the years, in line with research, innovation and development.

So what is it that makes traditional outbuildings so poor? Ventilation,

primarily, or rather the lack of it. Look at any modern livestock building and you'll see that it's designed with air flow in mind. Often they're open fronted (and sometimes open sided too, being little more than a roof on legs), and what cladding there is, is generally space boarding (or 'Yorkshire' boarding), which consists of 5" wide vertical planks with a gap of about ¾" between each one. (The exact dimensions may vary, provided that the ratio remains in the region of 7:1).

Walls are generally solid only up to a height of 4' to 5'. Apex roofs are often open at the ridge, and gaps may even be left between individual roofing sheets. The whole structure gives an impression of space, light and airiness. Compare this with traditional buildings, which are often fully enclosed on all sides, with minimal provision made for ventilation. Roofs – be they slate or tile – are generally sealed at the ridge, and the 'torching' (plaster between the laths) on the inside effectively prevents stale air from exiting through any cracks

Traditional outbuildings are often far from ideal for housing livestock.

and crevices. Lack of overall height may result in insufficient airspace for the number of animals kept, and if a traditional hayloft is installed above the animals' accommodation then the situation is many times worse. Windows, if any, are usually glazed, and can only be partly opened. The overall effect is pretty gloomy, and the accumulation of warm, moist, germ-laden, stale air results in a very unhealthy environment.

Another consideration is access. Many traditional outbuildings have only standard-sized doorways (or even smaller), meaning that everything that goes in (e.g. hay, straw and feed) must be carried in bit by bit, and everything that comes out (manure – lots of it!) must be physically shifted by fork and wheelbarrow. This was all very well in the days when even a modest-sized holding would have employed a couple of farm servants, but the modern smallholder is usually a part-timer, with the result that routine mucking out is something that's often left until the weekends, or even longer. The inevitable build-up of dung serves only to exacerbate the unsavoury

conditions brought about by inadequate ventilation. An additional downside to poor access is that, in the unfortunate event that one of your animals dies, it can be very difficult to get the body out. In the case of a cow or pony it might even be necessary to cut the carcase up in order to remove it, which could be a distressing experience if the animal was a much-loved family pet.

Another point to bear in mind – one that sort of goes hand in hand with easy mucking out – is that many traditional outbuildings were not designed for loose housing. Nowadays we tend to equate high welfare with a degree of freedom, but formerly many animals (in particular dairy cows and working horses) were kept tied up in stalls all winter, and that's the method of husbandry that these old buildings were originally designed to accommodate. The advantages are obvious – all dung is deposited neatly in the dung passage behind the stalled animals, urine flows away, the animals' coats and bedding stays clean and dry, and mucking out is reduced to a few minutes per day – but you may have moral objections to adopting

these old-fashioned methods. Personally I believe that it's sensible for smallholders to adopt a middle-of-the-road approach, based on aspects of both traditional and modern husbandry methods.

Making use of traditional buildings

Firstly, I think it's necessary to consider whether it's essential to make use of the available range of traditional outbuildings for livestock housing purposes, or whether they can be put to some other (more profitable) use which could help generate the necessary funds required for the construction of a new agricultural building. Many redundant cowsheds have been successfully converted into holiday lets and offices, incorporated into house extensions, or simply adapted for use as a farm workshop or store room. For anyone looking to give up the day job and live full time on their smallholding, the idea of generating an income stream from tourism by utilising an existing asset that's no longer fit for its original purpose is no doubt an attractive one. However, with certain adaptations and considerations, there's no reason why traditional outbuildings shouldn't be successfully used for housing a smallholder's livestock:

Roof: In my experience, the roof of a traditional building is its weakest point. Sooner or later it'll need replacing, thereby giving a new lease of life to the whole structure. It's often prohibitively expensive to restore an old roof to its former glory, so, unless you're actually required to do so, sheet materials provide a more affordable alternative, and require less timber and less skill. However, corrugated metal sheets may result in excessive condensation. Onduline or fibre cement would be better. Remember to leave a good ventilation gap at the ridge, and, if possible, at the eaves too. Also, re-roofing in this way provides an excellent opportunity to include some clear sheets, thus allowing plenty of natural light into an erstwhile gloomy interior.

Walls should be rendered and painted.

Walls: Brick or stone walls should preferably be rendered on the inside to a height of about 5'. The whole interior can be given a coat of white masonry paint. Timber walls can be lined to the same height with something like 'Stokbord'.

Windows: Unless existing windows can be fully opened for ventilation, it's best to remove any glass. If necessary, cover the opening with a piece of weldmesh.

Doors: These should be 'stable' type doors, with the top half always left open. In fact, you don't really need a top half at all. In warm, still weather, the bottom half may need to be left open as well.

Floor: Old cobble or brick floors may look picturesque, but they're an absolute nightmare to keep

clean, and they're not particularly good for hooves, either. What's more, pigs will simply dig them up. If you don't feel like ripping out a traditional floor and replacing it with concrete (it may, after all, be historically significant) then the answer is to cover the existing cobbles with a layer of carefully levelled sand, followed by a sheet of visqueen, before laying a new concrete floor on top. Keep an accurate record of what you've done so that in the future anyone can restore the original floor, should they wish to do so. When laying your new floor, remember to make provision for drainage.

Internal divisions: Don't clutter up the available space with solid partitions. These will simply make the interior appear darker, reduce air flow, and make mucking out even more difficult. Use galvanised gates or hurdles to create a versatile layout that won't detract from the light and airy atmosphere that you're trying to create.

Stocking densities: Keep them low. Be aware that published guidelines for space allowance generally refer to modern buildings. For example, if I was housing sheep in a traditional building, I would not stock them at more than a quarter of the recommended density.

New builds

First and foremost, don't make the mistake of thinking that modern agricultural buildings are only for big farmers. There's no earthly reason why smallholders should be hampered by a lack of suitable facilities, and nor should animal welfare be compromised by a misguided belief that 'old fashioned' is better. The principal

livestock building is the focal point for all smallholding activities (during the winter, anyway), and it's just as well to make sure it's a good one. With a bit of forethought at the design stage, it's possible to bring important aspects of all enterprises together under one roof, with scope not only to house different ages and categories of stock at different times of year, but also to provide storage space for feed and forage, and a machinery workshop as well. Getting it right will take a lot of the drudgery out of routine smallholding tasks, and make a big difference to the quality of life that you're able to enjoy. It will be better for your animals, too.

Cost

There is, of course, the issue of outlay. Many smallholders, whether they run their holding as a business or purely for pleasure, may feel that they cannot justify the expense of erecting a new building. However, steel portal frame buildings are the most popular, and, despite recent hikes in the cost of raw materials, it's still possible, at the time of writing, to buy a 60' x 30' building in kit form for under £5,000. Obviously there'll be construction costs to add on to that, and additional expenditure on block work and concreting, but a building of that size would fully satisfy the entire livestock housing needs of any reasonable sized smallholding or small farm. For those who operate on a more modest scale, there are companies that specialise in supplying smaller agricultural buildings as kits, with a 30' x 20' shed costing in the region of £3,500.

You'll notice, though, that the cost per square foot of the smaller building is more than double that of the larger one, so, as I've mentioned before, my advice would be to 'think big'. You'll never regret having plenty of space under cover, and it would be an awful pity to build a small shed, only to find yourself having to build another one alongside it in a few years time, because your activities outgrew the first. The prices given above do not include VAT, which, at 20%, could be a major consideration for some. Sensible smallholders will be registered for VAT, and can claim it all back from HM Customs and Revenue, which may make all the difference when considering the financial viability of a project of this nature. Another advantage to running your smallholding as a business – no matter how small – is that, in your accounts, expenditure on capital items like buildings can be spread over 10 years in the form of an annual charge. This makes the investment much easier to justify.

Although steel portal frame buildings are the most popular, there are several companies that supply all-timber buildings as kits, fabricated to your requirements, which would be attractive to anyone who'd prefer a more 'traditional' look to their new shed, but, on the whole, these are more expensive.

Whatever the material chosen, the principal benefit of using a kit building is that you know it will be properly engineered, with the dimensions of all members being appropriate to the lengths of span, etc. Basically, this means that all the complicated sums will have been done for you. It will also conform to BS 5502, which will probably be a requirement of planning permission (if needed)

and any grant scheme under which you may be applying for support for the project. Having said all that, there's nothing to stop you starting from scratch and building the whole thing yourself, particularly in the case of very small outbuildings, provided, of course, that you've got the necessary skills and are able to comply with any legislation that may have an impact on the design, location and use of the structure. The most popular type of building for home construction is a mono-pitch pole barn. With judicious use of second hand and reclaimed materials, a serviceable outbuilding can be built on a very tight budget by this method.

Planning permission for agricultural buildings

Planning rules are fairly complex, and their interpretation varies between regions. All cases are dealt with on an individual basis, so don't assume that because a friend or neighbour has been allowed to build something (with or without planning permission) you will be too.

There are certain exemptions that allow you to construct domestic outbuildings that are ancillary to the use of your property, and these may be used for smallholding purposes such as housing pet animals or poultry, birds, bees or other livestock "for the domestic needs or personal enjoyment of the occupants of the house". There are various restrictions to the permitted size of such developments (e.g. must be less that $10m^2$, height no greater than 4m, etc.), and also restrictions as to where they can be located in relation to other structures, such as

the main dwelling house, roads and public rights of way. Exemptions don't apply in designated areas such as National Parks or Areas of Outstanding Natural Beauty.

'Backyard' livestock keepers may find that there's sufficient scope within these guidelines for the construction of suitable buildings, but for most smallholders, the erection of a livestock shed would classify as agricultural, rather than domestic, development. Don't worry, though – this may still mean that full planning permission isn't required. At the time of writing, permitted development rights exist for the erection of agricultural buildings up to a certain size ($465m^2$, but smaller if within 90 metres of any other building, and less than 12 metres high) on holdings of 5 hectares or more, provided that the development is not less than 25 metres distant from a classified road. Limited agricultural development rights also exist on holdings of under 5 hectares (but not less than 0.4 hectares), provided that the development is reasonably necessary for the purposes of agricultural activity on that holding, and that it isn't carried out on a separate plot of land of less than 0.4 hectares (even if that plot does form part of the holding), it doesn't significantly affect the appearance of the property, and it's not within 25 metres of a classified road. Limited development would include the extension of an existing agricultural building, or the erection of a new building within the curtilage of an existing building. Regardless of the size of the holding, if the proposed development is intended to house livestock then it mustn't be within 400 metres of the curtilage of any dwelling (except the dwelling on the holding, or on any other agricultural holding). In all these cases, the best thing to do is to apply to the local authority for Determination of Planning Permission. There is a small fee to pay for this (about £60 last time we applied), but the outcome will state categorically whether or not you need to apply for full permission for your proposed development, or whether you can just go ahead and build it.

In the event that you are refused planning permission for an agricultural building on your holding, you do have the right to appeal against the decision. For smallholders, the hardest part of the process is convincing the authorities that there is actually a genuine need for such a development, so, if you do find yourself having to appeal, I suggest you engage a farming consultant to devise a suitable business plan for your holding that will clearly demonstrate that an agricultural building is essential, not only for economic reasons, but also to the health and welfare of your animals.

A management strategy that included a January lambing sheep flock and an intensive calf-rearing enterprise ought to do the trick – you're not obliged to stick to the plan, so it's purely a paper exercise to get you the permission you want. Once you've got your lovely new shed you can do what you like with it, provided that its use remains within the definition of agriculture for at least 10 years following completion.

Design

To my mind, there are two key factors to bear in mind when planning the construction of a

In sheltered areas, livestock buildings may be open sided.

new agricultural building on the holding – ventilation and versatility. If you get these right, regardless of the size and scale of your smallholding enterprises, you'll find that management is simplified and livestock are much healthier. Generally speaking, the inside of any livestock building (except perhaps where pigs are concerned) shouldn't be warmer than the outside temperature, and there should be plenty of airflow above the animals. However, you don't want draughts at ground level. This is why most farm buildings have solid walls only up to a height of 4' to 5', with some sort of ventilated cladding or space boarding above that. In sheltered areas buildings may be completely open sided, but in most cases only the front (of monopitch buildings) will be unclad, and face away from the prevailing wind. On apex roofs, the ridge should include as many ventilated sections as possible, or even be left open.

To give the level of versatility required by the diverse activities of the average smallholding, I would

Maintain versatility by subdividing the interior of your building using gates.

recommend leaving the interior of buildings as open-plan, without any permanent internal barriers or subdivisions. Pens can easily be set up using gates or hurdles, particularly if hinges have been attached at strategic points to the structure of the building. In larger sheds it helps to have removable gateposts set in sockets in the floor. The exception to this would be when housing is being designed for breeding pigs, where some fairly substantial permanent pens are desirable, particularly if a boar is kept.

The floor of a livestock building

need not be concreted (except, again, where pigs are concerned), provided that it's free draining. However, in the interests of versatility, I would recommend laying a concrete floor – you may want to bring a piece of machinery undercover to carry out maintenance work, and, believe me, it's very frustrating when you drop some small nut or washer on a loose gravel surface.

Portable structures

It's commonly thought that portable structures such as mobile field shelters don't need planning permission. The long-held belief is that, provided that you build your structure on 'skids', you circumvent the rules. Well, I'm sorry to disappoint you, but it isn't quite as simple as that. Largely it's going to depend on what you want to use it for. Horses are a particular case in point: grazing horses counts as agricultural use of land, but as soon as you provide a field shelter or stable, you're no longer simply grazing horses – you're keeping them. Unless they're heavy horses used for farm work this requires planning permission for change of use of the land from agriculture to 'horseyculture'. Once this permission has been obtained then the erection of mobile shelters will not need planning permission (although fixed ones will). However, once you've officially changed the use of your land, you may no longer qualify for permitted agricultural development rights in respect of any other building projects you wish to carry out. Therefore, if you're intending to keep recreational horses on your holding in conjunction with other more 'agricultural' activities, it may be best to try to claim an exemption

for a mobile field shelter or stables on the grounds that it's incidental to your enjoyment of the dwelling house (but do check up on this before committing yourself). Smaller mobile livestock accommodation such as pig and poultry arks are not classified as buildings, so the siting of such items constitutes land use rather than development.

Provided that such use broadly falls within the definition of agriculture, or the animals are purely for the personal enjoyment of the occupants of the house, they should be acceptable in most situations, although local restrictions may apply in certain areas.

Apart from any perceived planning advantages, the principal benefits of mobile structures are ease of construction (no complicated groundworks or foundations) and, of course, portability. The fact that the structure can regularly be moved to a fresh piece of ground is much better from the point of view of animal health and welfare, with less opportunity for the accumulation of harmful pathogens, and less damage to soil and pasture too. Of course, small items such as pig and poultry arks can easily be moved by hand, but larger buildings, like field shelters or stables built on skids, are going to need to be towed to their new location using a tractor. Therefore, unless you've got the means to do this, there's very little to be gained by building such a structure, unless it's purely with the intention of avoiding the need for planning permission on equestrian holdings. On an agricultural smallholding you might just as well erect a more substantial fixed building.

Temporary structures

When considering temporary livestock accommodation solutions I tend to think of polytunnels and straw bale houses, although whether or not polytunnels should be classified as 'temporary' is something of a moot point, as many designs do require concrete footings for the framework. The use of polytunnels for livestock housing (for sheep, in particular) became popular about 30 years ago, and, although they were originally considered by many to be the 'poor man's alternative' to proper buildings, they've stood the test of time. Nowadays there's a whole range of ploytunnels available that have been specifically designed for housing all kinds of livestock, including poultry, sheep, goats and even cattle. At lambing time they provide an ideal environment for the flock, and, once the sheep have been turned out, the tunnel can be put to the more conventional use of growing plants. This sort of versatility and dual use of facilities can make all the difference when considering the financial viability of small-scale farming. A suitable small polytunnel, measuring 18' x 30' (which would be appropriate for housing a modest sized smallholding sheep flock at lambing time) costs in the region of £1,800.

Straw bale houses may not be justifiable in all situations, given the recent high prices of the basic raw material, but if you live in a predominantly arable area they might be worth considering. On a large scale we see straw bale houses being used on outdoor pig units, and the same can be replicated in miniature on smallholdings. We've done it ourselves for both fattening pigs and breeding sows, and it works very well, although the pigs will destroy the whole thing in the end. For sheep flocks lambing outdoors, straw bales can be used individually to provide windbreaks, or can be built up into small huts in which ewes and newborn lambs can be contained. When keeping sheep on my parents' smallholding, I built a fairly substantial straw bale hut each spring, roofed with tarpaulin, which had room inside for several individual lambing pens. Straw bale structures can be burnt after use, which prevents any risk of disease carry over.

HOW MUCH LAND DO YOU NEED?

So how much land to do you need be self-sufficient in most foodstuffs, and to provide yourself with enough of a saleable surplus to help pay a few of the inevitable bills?

This is probably one of the commonest questions we're asked! Unfortunately there's no satisfactory answer, due to the inevitable variation between the productivity of land in different parts of the country. The potential output of a couple of acres in Snowdonia, for example, would be quite different from what you might hope to achieve off the same sized plot in Suffolk.

Taken all round, I believe that we could quite comfortably provide a high level of self-sufficiency for ourselves and our family on 15 acres of reasonable quality ground, managed as follows:

We'd need two cows in order to ensure a year-round milk supply. During the summer these two cows would require around 1½ acres of grazing land. The cows would then be housed over the winter months (roughly 180 days), during which time each would consume about ½ a small bale of hay per day. Therefore, after allowing for a bit extra, 100 bales of hay per cow per year should be enough. It's quite reasonable to expect a yield of at least 100 small bales of hay per acre, so 2 acres ought to be sufficient to provide hay for both of the cows. The calves from our cows would be reared indoors, and sold at around 6 months of age, so wouldn't have any impact on the acreage required, except for the limited amount of hay they'll consume. We'd buy in additional calves to rear on surplus milk.

Our vegetable garden would take up an acre of the land. This should be ample space for growing all of the vegetables and soft fruit required, and there'd also be enough room for a small orchard (with beehives, of course), and a polytunnel.

Another acre would be planted with fast-growing trees, providing a reliable source of renewable fuel. A fifth of these would be coppiced each year, satisfying most of our annual requirement for heating and hot water. Additional supplies of firewood would come from isolated small pockets of natural woodland on the holding (probably totalling around ½ an acre), and managed hedgerows.
A sheep flock would form an integral part of our smallholding plan. A breeding flock of 25 ewes would be a good size for a 15 acre holding, providing lambs not only for our own consumption, but also for sale. 25 ewes will eat about 100 small bales of hay each winter, so another acre must be allowed for growing hay for the sheep. Grazing for the flock in early summer, while the hay fields are still closed off, would be over about 5 acres. Later, after the hay is cut, more grazing would become available, with the aftermath used for fattening the lambs.

If the land were suitable, a couple of acres of cereals would be grown for livestock feed. Two acres could provide us with as much as 4 tonnes of grain.

Pig keeping would be limited to the fattening of two batches of bought-in weaners (in groups of four) each year. These would utilise a spare plot in the garden over the summer, and we'd have an indoor sty for winter accommodation. One of the batches would be for home consumption (two pigs for pork, and two made into bacon, ham and sausages), and the other batch would be sold to help cover costs.

We'd have just a few hens, providing eggs for our own use, and these birds would be able to free range around the farmyard and outbuildings (which I've assumed will, together with the house, take up another acre).
Poultry being raised for meat would be kept indoors.

If you add that lot up it comes to 15 acres.

Fencing and Boundaries

If we were starting all over again, we'd spend our scant reserves on re-fencing the whole farm, even if this meant borrowing additional funds and delaying the start of our livestock keeping venture for a few years. I'd even consider getting a contractor in to do the whole lot in one go. We could always have rented the grazing to a neighbour until we'd recouped enough capital to buy our own animals.

But that's not what we did, and in consequence we have wasted many, many hours rounding up stray sheep, cattle and pigs, and patching holes in our ramshackle boundaries.

Our advice to anyone contemplating buying a smallholding is to factor the cost of fencing into your initial purchase budget, get it done straight away, and save yourself an awful lot of hassle. Otherwise it'll always remain one of those jobs for which there's insufficient time and money, and 20 years down the line you'll still be running after escapees, just like us.

Traditional boundaries

• **Dry stone walls:** Undoubtedly the most effective (and most picturesque) traditional field boundary is the dry stone wall, but then, living in North Wales, we would say that. Clearly, for stone walls to be an option you need to be in an area that has plenty of stones, which generally means the poorer upland regions, where this type of boundary can be seen as a dominant feature of the landscape. Local walling styles will vary according to the nature of the raw material available. A properly constructed dry stone wall will stand untended for centuries, and, provided that it's steep enough sided and has well projecting 'brisket stones' just below the copings, it'll remain stock proof, too. However, once the integrity of the wall is disturbed, whole lengths may collapse. People are the worst culprits – no matter how many gates and stiles you provide, hikers seem to insist upon climbing over any wall that crosses their desired route. I've even seen groups of people walking along the tops of walls to get from A to B. Once the copings have fallen, sheep will launch themselves at the little blip in the skyline, until eventually, amidst a shower of falling stone, they scramble over. It's all downhill from here on. Provided that it's spotted in time this type of damage can be repaired relatively simply, but where larger sections have subsided you'll have to pull the whole piece down and build it afresh. Often a fault will be found to lie in the very base of the wall, where one of the foundation stones has settled over the years until it slopes away from, rather than into, the wall. In this case, everything above it, and to each side, will have become unstable and at greater risk from damage by trespass.

As a basic guide, when rebuilding stretches of wall, every stone you lay must feel like it would rather roll into the wall than out of it, and every uneven surface must slope into the wall, otherwise the next course of stone will simply slide off. Pinners or chock stones can be inserted from the back (i.e. from the middle of the wall, it being built as two faces with a rubble infill) to level things up. In this way, as the wall settles, it simply becomes tighter and stronger. However, rebuilding stone walls is time consuming and, unless you've really got the knack, you may have to do it all again in a few years' time.

Often the demise of a wall begins where a fence post has been knocked in the top, so don't do it.

Three strands of barbed wire alongside a stone wall will help.

Where a large proportion of the boundary is no longer stock proof I suggest you save yourself a lot of bother by simply fencing alongside the old wall. If it isn't too badly collapsed you might get away with 3 strands of barbed wire, strained really tight, with the bottom wire sufficiently close to the wall that your animals can't scramble under it, and the top strand high enough that they won't try to jump it. If, on the other hand, there really isn't much left of the original boundary, a permanent netting stock fence provides the best solution. Again, this should be alongside the old wall. What you mustn't do is to knock fence posts into the top. The only time a fence should run along the top of a wall is when the posts were incorporated as the wall was built, but even then it puts considerable strain on the structure

One interesting variation of stone boundary is the slate fence, seen in the quarrying areas of North Wales. Here, large slabs of slate are simply set on end in the ground, with their tops held together by a twisted wire.

and, more often than not, the demise of the wall begins where there's a post.

• **Laid hedges:** A laid hedge is the lowland equivalent of the dry stone wall, in that a naturally occurring local material is used to create a stock proof enclosure. At the interface between the two styles we have the clawdd, which is a stone-faced earth bank (or an

earth-filled stone wall, depending on your viewpoint,) topped by a hedge, but more commonly the hedge is planted on a low bank formed by heaping up the spoil from an adjacent ditch. The presence of the ditch serves to increase the overall height of the barrier, and provides an additional obstacle to inquisitive animals. Where this type of boundary marks the line between two properties, the official boundary is usually the ditch, with the hedge belonging to the landowner on whose side of the ditch it stands.

The basic process of laying consists of partially cutting through the main stem ('pleacher') of each thorn bush, and carefully bending them over to lie horizontally along the line of the hedge, overlapping one another. Each laid pleacher should lie uphill, so if working on a slope you'll have to start at the top and work your way downwards. Lots of material will have to be cut out of the hedge to leave the main stems fairly evenly spaced, and side branches

47

A traditionally cut and laid hedge.

PRACTICAL SOLUTIONS

Permanent stock wire

No matter how aesthetically pleasing the traditionally made boundaries may be, at the end of the day a permanent wire netting stock fence remains the most practical and secure solution. The trouble is that anyone can put up a wire fence, but not many people can do it really well, and unless the job is done properly you might as well not bother. I see far too many new stock fences that have lost their integrity – and hence their usefulness – in only a few months, let alone years. It pays to get it right in the first place. A good fence has a life expectancy in excess of 15 years, and the addition of a single strand of electrified wire will probably add another decade to that.

Fencing tools

In addition to a brace-and-bit, chisel, spirit level and claw hammer (see page 396), you'll need:

An alloy headed post-knocking hammer: This won't mash up the ends of the posts in the way that a sledge hammer would, although some splitting is inevitable.

A double-handed post knocker: With two people on the job, this is a much better option than a hammer, and won't split the posts at all. If you're handy with a welder you can make your own. The one we've got was made by my father more than 30 years ago, and is still going strong. For really big fencing jobs you might want to hire a tractor mounted post

will need to be removed in order that the hedge doesn't become too wide, and to enable each pleacher to lie comfortably on its neighbour. Where possible, the stems can be roughly woven together. The result may look rather stark, initially, as it often appears that you've cut more out than you've left in. The laid pleachers can be held in place by stakes driven in at right angles to the direction of lay. Ideally these stakes will be cut from the brushwood that's been trimmed out. The final artisan touch is to twist long lengths of briar or withy willow between and around the protruding tops of the stakes, binding the whole thing together.

New growth will shoot up vertically from all along the length of each horizontal pleacher, resulting in a dense network of crossed stems that is more or less impenetrable.

Clearly the hedge will need some protection from grazing stock until the new growth is well established. A properly laid hedge alone will be sufficient for the containment of docile cattle or heavy lowland sheep, with perhaps just a strand

or two of barbed wire alongside for added peace of mind. However, where smaller breeds are kept, the best thing would be to erect a permanent stock fence along one side of the hedge, with the other side temporarily protected by electric wire when required. This would still allow access to the hedge for maintenance. Re-laying may need to be carried out at 10-15 year intervals.

• **Post and rail:** Post and rail fences may look pretty, but really are of no practical use where sheep, goats or pigs are concerned, as the spacing of the rails is generally sufficient to allow these animals to simply hop through the gaps or walk underneath. In order to be fully stock proof a post and rail fence will need wire netting added to it, so you might as well save yourself a lot of expense by simply putting up a proper stock fence to begin with. The same can be said of traditional wrought iron park railings, although these may be an existing historical feature that you'd like to retain.

Using a double-handed post knocker.

Monkey strainer.

knocker, or even get a contractor in to do the whole lot – it may actually work out cheaper in the long run.

A spike: A heavy metal bar, some 5' long, pointed at one end and chisel-headed at the other, is needed for ground breaking, general leverage, and to make a pilot hole for each individual post.

Monkey strainers: For tensioning wire. When putting up stock netting you'll need two sets – one on the bottom strand, and one on the top. Provided these two are sufficiently taught, any remaining slack in the intermediate strands can be taken up using pliers. A parked tractor makes an ideal anchoring point for the monkey strainers, and has the advantage that you can re-position it when working on each section of the fence. Failing that you'll need to get a chain around a nearby tree or some other solid stationary object. At a pinch you can tension the wire back onto itself, but this is never wholly satisfactory

Fencing pliers: Consisting of wire cutters, grips, pincers, spike and

hammer, fencing pliers are the original multi-tool.

A long-handled spade: Just an ordinary digging spade with a slightly over-length handle is fine, although some people do prefer a narrower blade for digging post holes. A small notch cut in the handle makes a handy depth gauge.

A digging tool: The neater the job you make of digging the holes, the more successful you'll be in setting the straining posts securely in place. To this end, a two-handed digging tool (like a giant pair of tongs) is invaluable. Soil that's been loosened by the spike or spade is easily raised from the bottom of the hole using this handy bit of kit, without knocking the sides down or widening it unnecessarily.

Installation

The key to successful fence erection lies in the straining posts. The minimum number

you'll require is one more than the number of coils (or part coils) of wire you're intending to put up, although clearly if the fence line includes gateways, or major deviations from a straight line, you'll need a few extras.

Strainers should be at least 6" in diameter and 7' long, 3' of which must be buried in the ground. Post holes should be dug as neatly and squarely as possible. Use a spirit level to ensure that the post is set vertically, and then – this is most important – put back into the hole every single bit of earth that came out. Shovel it in a little at a time, and tamp each shovelful down hard.

Never be tempted to set straining posts in concrete. Concrete won't bond with the surrounding earth, so, in time, the whole mass will simply rock back and forth in an enlarged hole. And, when the post eventually rots as a result of water pooling on the concrete, and snaps off, some poor devil has to dig the blasted thing out.

Post holes should be dug as neatly and squarely as possible.

The head of the strut should fit snugly into a notch cut in the strainer.

Each straining post, unless flanking a gateway, will require two struts. Generally struts are set in line with the fence, however where corners or deviations to the line are greater than 90 degrees this may not be the case.

Minor changes in the line can be supported by less substantial intermediate strainers which may only need one small strut or stay to counteract the pull of the wire. Struts also need to be about 7' long, though of a lesser diameter than the straining posts that they abut. The foot of the strut should be set against a large boulder buried in a trench, and the head should fit snugly into a notch cut into the strainer to receive it. Nails, if required, shouldn't be inserted until the fence is complete.

If the angle at which the strut leans against the strainer is incorrect, then, as the wire is tightened, the straining post is simply levered out of the ground – this is probably one of the commonest mistakes made by amateur fencers. Really, it shouldn't be a problem except on uneven ground, in which case you could install a box (or 'H') strut. The important point to note in the construction of a box strut is that the twisted wire holding it all together runs from the base of the strainer to the top of the adjacent post, not the other way around. If you get this wrong then the whole assembly will serve no useful purpose whatsoever.

A roll of netting is 50 metres long, so strainers should be set at intervals of no more than 48 to 49 metres, in order to allow sufficient surplus wire at each end of the run for straining and attachment. All wire that's fixed to strainers should be carried right around the post, and joined back on itself;

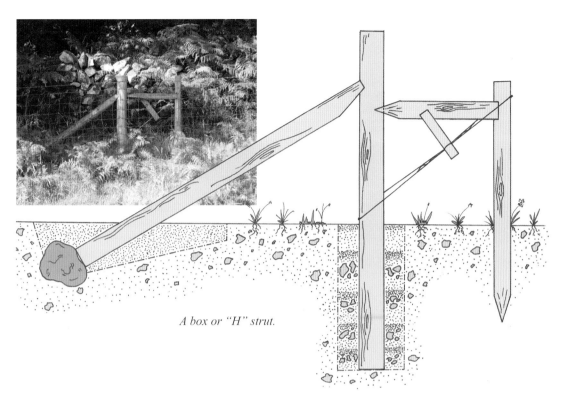

A box or "H" strut.

otherwise the tension of the wire will gradually cause the post to rotate, resulting in the whole fence going slack. Once the strainers are in you can run out and tension the bottom strand of barbed wire, which should be no more than a couple of inches off the ground. This then serves as a guideline for knocking in all the intermediate stakes, at intervals of about 8'.

All stakes and strainers should be tanalised; it's well worth paying a bit extra for this. When rolling out the netting, make sure that you get it the right way up, with the smaller holes at the bottom. This may sound like stating the obvious, but it's surprising how many people get it wrong.

Attach one end of the roll to the appropriate strainer, 2" above the barbed wire (remembering to take it right around the post), then pull the whole lot up tight from the other end using a pair of monkey strainers. When fixing wire to intermediate posts the staples should never be hammered fully home; this allows for a certain amount of 'give' in the fence, and makes it easy to replace an individual post at a later stage, if need be.

You'll notice that fencing staples often have one point slightly longer than the other, in which case the longest point should always be at the top, so the staples penetrate at an angle, preventing rain water from gaining access to the timber at that point. Also, each staple should be skewed slightly, so both points don't enter the same grain; this reduces the likelihood of splitting. The final task is to fasten a top strand of barbed wire some 4" above the stock netting. Beware of over-tightening this; being attached near the top of the posts it'll exert considerable leverage, and, if you overdo it, the rest of the fence will slacken off. If you need to trim any posts to length, make sure that you creosote the tops, and also splash plenty of creosote into notches cut in the strainers.

Electric fencing

Electrified wire provides the ideal solution to most of the smallholder's fencing needs. It's relatively cheap, and quick and simple to erect, and it can be used for both temporary subdivision of paddocks and for more permanent installations.

Flexinets, made from polywire, are ideal for splitting up larger areas of grazing on a short-term basis, for the purpose of rotational grazing. Be aware, though, that horned sheep or goats grazing close to the netting can easily get caught, and also that this type of fence may pose a risk to very young lambs or goat kids, as they're inclined to get tangled up in it. Once they're used to it, it's ok, but you'll need

51

Electric netting is ideal for temporarily sub-dividing fields.

to check on them fairly frequently to begin with.

Temporary electric fences consisting of a number of single wires are a cheaper option. Their efficacy is much improved if they can be erected in front of a visual barrier such as a hedge or bank. Permanent high tensile electric fencing can be usefully installed alongside existing traditional boundaries that are in a reasonable state of repair. Very few intermediate posts are required, so this makes a very unobtrusive fence which preserves the aesthetic appearance of the existing boundary while providing full security.

With the exception of permanent high tensile wire, most electric fence installations can be powered by a battery or solar energizer, giving total versatility. However, if your land is in a relatively compact block I'd strongly recommend that you invest in a mains powered unit, with insulated cables run out to various parts of the farm.

Gates and stiles

• **Gates:** Traditional wooden five-bar gates look lovely when they're new, but when they're old and starting to sag, or if they warp so the latches won't catch, you'll curse them. Some grant-funded countryside management schemes will insist upon the installation of timber gates, but, on the whole, galvanized metal gates are a better bet. They're remarkably good value for money, and are extremely versatile – you can easily lift them off their hinges and use them temporarily elsewhere, perhaps for setting up handling pens or for sub-dividing a building when housing your livestock during winter.

Half-meshed gates are handy as smaller animals can't hop through between the lower bars, but you may find that ear-tags get caught and pulled out, and that male lambs of horned breeds tend to break their horns on them.

Field gates should, wherever possible, be hung so that they can swing both ways, and when moving livestock between fields you should always open the gate

away from the animals. If the gate will only open the wrong way then it's best to lift it off its hinges and lay it aside while the flock or herd passes through.

• **Stiles:** If you suffer a situation where the public are allowed to wander freely over areas of your farm then, in order to prolong the life of your fences, you may need to install at least one stile for every roll of wire erected.

Popular crossing places should have ladder stiles. At these points, barbed wire should be protected by encasing in a short length of alkathene pipe. The upside to this is that it also makes it a lot easier for you to get around your own property.

Ladder stile.

Official footpaths may require kissing gates, in which case I suggest you fit a piece of bungee cord to ensure that they close properly.

Section Two
Crops and Garden

Kitchen Garden

"It takes very little land to grow the vegetables for a family, if that little land is farmed to its utmost"
John Seymour

The kitchen garden is – or should be – the most productive acre on the holding. Ok, so not everyone has got a whole acre to give over to the production of vegetables for home consumption, but the principle remains the same, regardless of the size of the plot – the output per square metre in a well managed garden is likely to far exceed what can be achieved elsewhere on your small farm, particularly if you're able to integrate your vegetable growing activities with other enterprises such as poultry, beekeeping, or even grazing livestock and pigs.

Location

On most smallholdings there won't be a great deal of choice as to where to locate the kitchen garden. However, if you're starting with a 'blank canvas' and find yourself considering several potential sites, all suitably close to the house, there are a number of factors to take into consideration:

Aspect: A garden on a south-facing slope is going to get a lot more sunshine and warmth than one that faces north. In a good summer this won't make a significant difference, but during poor weather any plants on a north facing slope will struggle, and extending the growing season with a view to all-year-round production may prove impossible. Overwintered crops would suffer too.

While we're on the subject of aspect, it's also worth pointing out that your rows of crops should, where possible, run north to south, rather than east to west, to ensure that individual plants obtain the maximum amount of sunshine during the course of a day, and don't excessively shade one another.

Shelter: Unless you're extremely lucky and move to a property that has a walled garden (as we did when we went to Bardsey) then shelter is something you're going to have to think about; high winds can really wreak havoc among your crops. Our vegetable garden faces roughly south-east, and our prevailing wind direction is south-westerly. Good protection is provided from that direction by the farmhouse and outbuildings, and the other boundaries consist largely of mature mixed hedgerows (primarily blackthorn, hawthorn and elder). Bear in mind that hedging plants will pull water and nutrients from the soil, so, if utilising hedgerows as windbreaks, leave quite a wide gap between them and the plots, otherwise you may find that your vegetables are starved. Trees can provide good levels of shelter, but be aware that having woodland adjacent to the vegetable garden provides excellent habitat for all the wildlife species that have got their beady eyes firmly fixed on your crops! Tall barriers also create shade; while some plants will tolerate this to a certain extent, others won't cope so well with low light conditions. You might need to take this into account when deciding where to site individual beds within the garden, and when planning your rotation. Trees and hedges take time to establish, so if you're starting from scratch you may need to provide temporary shelter, such as windbreak netting, wattle hurdles or panel fencing. An improvised barrier of old pallets or recycled corrugated iron nailed to wooden posts would do the job in the short term, despite looking hideous.

Access: Apart from the obvious fact that you need a clear route from the garden to the kitchen, with maybe somewhere *en route* to stop off and wash the soil from root crops etc., you might also need to gain vehicular access to the plot from time to time. Walled gardens may not score so well here. Our wonderful garden on Bardsey was accessible only via a narrow gateway and a series of steep and slippery slate steps, which ruled out the use of any kind of machinery that couldn't be carried by hand, and meant that even a loaded wheelbarrow presented a considerable challenge. Manure could be forked over the wall from a trailer parked in the adjacent field, and I suppose that, had we had a tractor with a front-end loader, we could have simplified this operation.

Good access to the garden enables us to rotavate the plots with the tractor.

Our current garden not only has a small pedestrian / wheelbarrow sized entrance leading almost directly from the back of the house, but no less than two 8' wide field gates giving access from different directions. I can drive in with the tractor to dump manure on the plots, to do rotavating, or to cut the overgrown grass in the orchard, and we've had a JCB in there to install some drainage and to excavate a small pond. We can get large items – such as poultry houses or pig arks – in and out with ease, and at times have even allowed our cows admission to graze off a fallow area. In fact, so important do we consider this degree of access to be that we've also taken it into account when designing the layout of the plot and the type of vegetable beds that we use (see page 57).

Soil Type and Structure

Having assessed the type and structure of the soil in the garden (see page 24), consider not only how to keep it in good heart, but also how you could improve it – there's a lot more scope for improving the soil on your vegetable plots than in your fields. You may find, as we did, that your chosen site for a kitchen garden is remarkably short of soil of any sort. We initially used our pigs to clear away the turf and weeds on each area that we wanted to turn into a vegetable plot, and then spent a lot of time picking up stones and removing some largish boulders. It was only once we'd done all this, spread some muck, and tried to rotavate it in, that we realised how little soil there really was – just a couple of inches (if that) overlying shale, rubble and solid rock. The machine juddered and scraped its way over the underlying rock, broke up the muck into little bits, and that was that. We planted spuds by heaping a bit of crumbled muck over each tuber. They grew. Earthing them up was a bit of a joke as we had no earth. We collected molehills from the surrounding fields and thus rowed up our crop. It worked. The molehills were a reliable source of good quality clean topsoil. Every year we've carried more muck into the garden; not bucketfuls, bagfuls, or even barrowfuls, but tonnes, together with the contents of the compost heap. Now, 17 years on, and despite still being full of stones, the growing medium is dig-able to about 18", and gives us a decent harvest on a regular basis. This is all the more satisfying when we consider that we created it. However, continuous cropping places a heavy burden on the soil, and it'll rapidly become depleted if it's not looked after. Muck and compost are the key tools – they'll improve the drainage of heavy soils, increase the water holding capacities of very light ground, and provide nutrients for plants to feed on. They'll benefit the overall structure of the soil as well. This is vital if plants are to thrive; in a poorly structured soil they'll struggle to put down a good root system and access to nutrients will be compromised. Earthworms also play an important role in maintaining good soil structure – their activities improve drainage and aeration, and by feeding on decaying material they convert it into forms that provide valuable nutrition for your growing plants. Healthy soils have healthy earthworm populations – each spadeful of earth should contain at least half-a-dozen.

Compaction has a negative effect on soil structure, so don't walk on your plots if you don't have to, especially when they're wet. Unless you have narrow beds that can be worked entirely from the paths, regular cultivations can help alleviate compaction, particularly on heavy soils, by providing air pockets and drainage channels where previously there were none. Roughly digging the ground over the winter allows the weather to break up lumps, and renders the soil workable. Personally we like to dig when the ground is lightly frosted, i.e. when the surface is crispy, but still soft underneath.

Rough digging over the winter allows the weather to break up lumps and renders the soil workable.

Many gardening books recommend double digging from time to time, but we have never done this, partly because it sounds like horrendously hard work, and also because our soil probably isn't quite deep enough yet.

At times when you do need to walk on your vegetable plots, for example, when weeding, watering or harvesting, lay a plank of wood between the rows and stand on that. It'll help spread your weight and reduce the risk of soil compaction.

Soil pH

Problems may occur if your garden soil is too acidic, or, more rarely, too alkaline. Indications of acidity include a 'sour' look to the soil, with moss growing on the surface and the presence of certain weed species that prefer these conditions, such as docks, bracken, plantains and thistles. Acidity can be corrected to some extent by adding lime to the soil. A slow acting form, such a ground limestone or calcified seaweed, is generally preferable to hydrated or 'slaked' lime, but because it doesn't take effect so quickly you do need to plan ahead as to where and when to apply it. Don't spread lime and manure at the same

time as this can cause a chemical reaction that results in some of the nitrogen in the muck being lost as ammonia – leave at least a month between applications. Applications of lime also have a positive effect on soil structure.

TIP

Soap contains a high level of phosphates, so if you recycle your 'grey' water for use in the garden you'll be providing your plants with plenty of this essential element.

Alkalinity is usually found in chalk areas, and is difficult to correct. Adding manure will help to lower the pH, as will digging in acidic compost such as that made from rotted pine needles or bracken. However, it's likely to be an ongoing problem that you may be able to control, but not cure. To some extent you need to learn to live with it, perhaps by avoiding growing crops that really don't thrive on alkaline soils, such as rhubarb.

Water

Even in our moist climate the crops in the kitchen garden will need to be watered during the summer months. This can be extremely time-consuming, particularly if you have light soil and a large plot. When planning the location and layout of the garden, ensure that there's a reliable source of water nearby that can be conveyed to each plot with the minimum of hassle. If you've got sufficient water pressure then an irrigation system may be useful early in the season, when plants are still small. In the interests of self-sufficiency we used to pump water from our own spring for this purpose, until we realised that the cost of running the pump exceeded what we would have paid for the same amount of water directly from the mains supply. Needless to say, we soon gave up on that. Another downside is that sprinkler systems aren't very efficient as you end up watering an unnecessarily large area, and they're not much help later in the summer either, when water falling on the dense foliage of the crops tends to evaporate before it can do any good. However, if we had an unlimited supply of free water at a suitably high pressure I think we'd go back to it, particularly for crops grown under cover (e.g. in a polytunnel) where evaporation losses aren't so significant an issue, as all the water remains within the covered area.

For irrigating larger areas a hosepipe is essential.

 TIP

There's no point watering your plants during the heat of the day, as most of it will simply evaporate before it gets a chance to do any good. Evening is the best time, as it's then got all night to soak in.

Now we have a mains water standpipe in the garden. For small jobs such as settling seedlings, or for wetting the soil prior to sowing, a watering can with rose is ideal, but for irrigating larger areas a hose pipe (or possibly several linked together) is essential. It's helpful to have a sprayer attachment that fits on the end of it so that the flow of water can be regulated and adjusted to suit the task in hand, and so that it can be temporarily turned off without having to walk all the way back to the tap.

TIP

I once read an article, written by Bob Flowerdew I think, in which it was suggested that a small reservoir to supply the garden could be built using a retaining wall of old car tyres (stacked in a staggered formation) lined with plastic sheeting. Whether precipitation alone would be sufficient to keep the reservoir topped up I don't know, but it sounded like a very sensible idea to me, particularly as the tyres could be filled with soil and compost, giving a series of plantable terraces around the whole of the outside of the structure.

We appreciate that the use of mains water in the garden is far from ideal, and should be seen as a temporary measure. Where a spring or some other natural water supply can be found uphill from the kitchen garden, it ought to be a relatively simple matter to pipe it to a holding tank in a convenient location, or water from a lower level source could be transferred by the use of a hydraulic (i.e. water-operated) ram pump, which,

once primed, will run more or less indefinitely (see page 377). All roof water from both house and outbuildings ought to be collected as well, and can be gravity-fed to the garden if the lie of the land allows it. On the other hand, where alternative energy systems have been installed (e.g. wind turbine or solar panels) resulting in cheap / off-grid power, the use of electrical pumps to shift water around the holding may well be a sustainable option.

Layout

The available area will need to be divided up into a number of different plots or beds. We recommend that you have at least four, but preferably five. This makes things a lot easier when you come to work out your crop rotations. The size and shape of the beds will depend not only on the size and shape of the garden, but also on how you want to work them. Long narrow beds would enable you to tend your crops without walking on the cultivated area, which can help to preserve soil structure. If you have tractor-mounted machinery, it makes sense to set up your plots so that your implements can be used efficiently, or if you're using pigs to dig over the ground then each plot should be of appropriate dimensions to allow this.

The key consideration is flexibility, with the space being kept as free as possible from any fixed features. Our vegetable garden doesn't contain any raised beds or hard paths, and all permanent plants such as shrubs, fruit bushes and herbs are situated such that they don't impede access to the plots. Items such as compost bins and poultry houses are either temporary or portable. This enables us to access any part of the garden with the tractor by simply driving over the plots, if necessary. Primarily this is for the purpose of bringing in manure, but it also allows us to use tractor-mounted implements to take some of the backbreaking work out of cultivation. During the growing season, when the presence of crops in the ground may make it difficult to manoeuvre the tractor without causing damage, we're able to use a small garden rotavator in tighter spaces, again without any issues of having to lift it over or around fixed obstacles to gain access to the individual vegetable beds. Another big advantage to this versatile approach is that at any time, any one of the five plots that happens to be fallow (or from which the crops have been harvested) can be securely enclosed by electric fencing and used for pigs, poultry or grazing livestock. This enables us to fully integrate the garden activities with our other smallholding enterprises, and makes the most efficient use of the space that we have.
If we hadn't been intending to incorporate livestock into our garden plan then the plots might have been laid out differently,

Carrying well-rotted farmyard manure to the garden.

Temporary electric fencing enables us to use pigs to dig over a fallow plot.

perhaps in the form of long thin strips, with each being the same width as the tractor-mounted rotavator. This would have enabled us to cultivate any one of the plots in a single pass.

Farmyard manure (FYM)

The importance of adding organic matter to the garden on a regular basis can't be overstated. General mixed farmyard manure is fine, but it's better not to put fresh muck on the plots unless some time is going to elapse before crops are sown (e.g. muck spread in the autumn can be left over winter before planting in the spring). In an ideal world, you would use manure that had been stored under

cover to minimise the leaching of nutrients, but this may not always be practical. Muck containing a lot of straw or wood shavings (such as you might get if you keep stabled horses) will need to be rotted for a long while before applying to the garden, otherwise it'll take up nitrogen from the soil as part of the decaying process before it's released again later as decomposition progresses. This type of manure isn't particularly nutrient rich anyway – around 0.6-0.7 % nitrogen – but it's valuable for its provision of bulky organic matter. Poultry manure and rabbit droppings are also best composted before application to the garden, but for entirely the opposite reason – they're both extremely rich, and there's a risk of scorching your plants due to the very high nitrogen content if they're applied fresh. It's also worth noting that poultry manure is rather alkaline, so if you've got a problem with acidity on your plot, composted chicken droppings may simultaneously boost fertility and raise soil pH.

Green Manures

These are crops grown specifically for the purpose of improving soil productivity and structure. They can be sown wherever there's an empty patch of soil, rather than leaving it fallow. The plants take up nutrients and hold them within themselves, avoiding the risk of leaching, and their root fibres bind the soil together, reducing the likelihood of erosion. A number of different crops can be used in this way, and while they'll all carry out the functions mentioned above, some species will also fix nitrogen, and those with longer roots may draw micronutrients up from deeper in the soil. If allowed to flower they can attract beneficial insects to the garden, and provide additional forage for your bees. When the ground is needed for food crops the plants are cut down, left to wilt for a day or two, and then dug in to provide bulky organic matter. However, green manures do take a little time to break down in the soil, and it has been found that the decaying plants can inhibit seed germination. Bearing this in mind, it's advisable to leave about four weeks between digging in the green manure and sowing a subsequent crop. On the other hand, transplanted seedlings should be ok to put in straight away.

Compost

Good compost – and plenty of it – is an essential part of the kitchen garden. Everyone should have a compost heap. All households and gardens produce a certain amount of organic waste and, although a proportion of it can be recycled through the guts of your livestock, there'll still be plenty of stuff left over to go on the compost heap. As a general rule, if something has lived at some point, in some form, then it can be composted, although in the interests of health and hygiene you might not want to

Good compost is an essential part of the kitchen garden.

put all your waste products on an open heap.

There are two main ways to make compost – aerobic (hot) or anaerobic (cold). Being fundamentally lazy we prefer to make cold compost, because it's easier. However, it does take longer, can leave weeds still viable, and may not kill off plant diseases that could potentially infect future crops. Bearing this in mind, there are a few things that we avoid putting on the cold compost heap, in particular potato haulms and onion skins. We also tend not to put any meat or bones on the heap, as they'll attract rats, cats and other vermin. Any woody plants are also best avoided, unless you've got the means to smash them thoroughly before adding to the pile. In coastal areas seaweed was traditionally gathered and composted, and it would be beneficial for you to

Two compost bins side by side, made from old pallets.

add some to your heap, should the occasion arise. However, in our experience, seaweed has become more difficult to use in the garden due to the amount of waste plastic it contains, much of which isn't initially evident.

We make a square bin out of old pallets and start the whole process off with a barrow load of manure in the bottom. Stuff is then added to the heap as it becomes available. Kitchen waste goes on, weeds are added whenever hoeing or weeding is done, and the men in the house are expected to pee on it. Women can do this too, if they wish, but it's a bit more awkward for them. Providing a bucket alongside the heap might help. When we lived in a house that didn't have a flush toilet, we had a 'bucket and chuck it' loo, so the contents of this were added to the compost heap as well. After each emptying of the bucket the heap would be topped off with a fairly thick layer of grass clippings or similar material, to deter flies and reduce smells. Even so, if you're following this system, you'll want to site your compost bins at the farthest end of the garden from the house.

We find that a pallet-sized bin initially fills up quite quickly, but once the composting process gets going the bulk begins to reduce, and the heap settles down at more or less the same rate at which fresh material is added. Occasionally it's necessary to level the top of the heap and tread it all down a bit. It usually takes a year to fill the bin to the point where we really can't add anymore, at which point it's topped off with something like a load of lawn clippings or a barrow or two of farmyard manure, and maybe a capping of earth. Sometimes we plant marrows or pumpkins on the top. We then start a new heap in another bin, and another one the year after, and by the end of the third year the contents of the first bin should be ready to use.

If you want to speed up the whole process you'll need to make aerobic compost, which involves a bit more work. The aim is to gather together a whole load of compostable material at once, and then subject it to conditions that'll encourage rapid decomposition. The hot compost heap needs plenty

of air circulation, both through the sides and at the bottom, so a pallet-type bin is ideal for this as well. Put some twiggy material at the bottom, rather than manure, to allow air in at the base. Your compostable material needs to be well mixed up before it goes in the bin, and it should be fairly moist, so you may need to water it as you fork it in. Pee on it too, if you like, as urine is a great activator. Within a few days the compost will begin to get hot, indicating that all is well. After a couple of weeks, by which time it'll have cooled down quite a bit, empty the bin, re-mix the compost, and pile it all back in again. If it seems dry, wet it, and if it looks too soggy, add some more dry material. The heap will probably warm up again, and as it cools down for a second time, repeat the mixing process. Keep on doing this until it no longer heats up. In warm weather the compost should be ready to use in about four months, but in winter it may take longer.

In reality there's no right or wrong way to make compost, and you'll probably develop a method of your own that lies somewhere between these two extremes.

Home-made compost can be used to add organic matter to the soil, it can be sieved and used in pots and

seed trays, and it can be used as a mulch. However much you make you probably won't have enough, so use it wisely.

Mulching

Mulching basically just involves covering the soil. The use of inorganic mulches, such as plastic sheeting or ground cover fabric, particularly over winter, protects the area covered from weather damage due to excessive rain and wind, reducing soil erosion and preventing soluble nutrients from being washed away. At the other extreme, mulches are used to help retain soil moisture during dry periods. Inorganic mulches are also particularly useful as weed suppressants. We use black plastic silage-clamp sheeting over any empty vegetable plots, weighed down with old car tyres. This kills off any weeds that try to come up, due to the absence of light,

Black plastic sheeting covering a vacant plot.

TIP

Although black plastic doesn't sound very environmentally friendly, it's amazing how much wildlife takes up residence beneath it during winter – in particular grass snakes, slow-worms and toads, all of which are very welcome in our garden. And, of course, we re-use the same sheets of plastic year-on-year, so there's little waste.

Runner bean plants mulched with lawn clippings.

Folding back the plastic in the spring - only minimal cultivation is required before planting.

Fruit bushes mulched with old cardboard and straw.

and allows earthworms to work away undisturbed by the weather. Sometimes we spread manure over the plot before laying down the plastic sheet. When we peel back the cover in the spring the soil needs very little preparation prior to planting – often little more than a single pass with a hoe.

Any of the materials already mentioned as being suitable for adding organic matter to the soil can also be used as mulches, but ideally they should be partially composted first, otherwise there's a risk that nitrogen will be taken up from the soil during the decomposition process. Woodchips are particularly bad for this, so it's probably best not to use them in the garden at all. Don't tread mulches down – leave plenty or air gaps which will help to keep the soil warm and allow rain to drain down slowly into the earth. We find that grass clippings make a good mulch, but are best left to dry for a few days before applying, otherwise they tend to pack down too tightly as they settle. Organic mulches can be applied pretty thickly, provided that the plants you're working around are not completely buried. Compost should be at least 1" thick, but lighter, more airy materials such as straw or lawn cuttings could be laid as much as 6" deep.

Some types of organic mulch provide very little in the way of nutrition for the soil, and are used primarily as weed suppressants and ground protectors. Cardboard, newspaper and old woollen carpets would fall into this category, and are particularly useful under and around fruit bushes.

Soil Preparation

There are two types of soil preparation to consider here. Firstly, the initial groundwork you'll need to carry out if starting with a virgin plot – perhaps formerly part of a grass field – and, secondly, the annual preparation required for the planting of your crops. I've already described how we created our garden in the wake of the sterling work carried out by our pigs, but that's just one method. There are others:

Mulch: If you're in no hurry you can spread a thick layer of manure over the areas you want to use as plots and cover them for a full twelve months with a heavy inorganic mulch such as ground cover fabric, plastic sheeting or old carpets. When you remove the mulch you should find that the all vegetation has died, broken down, and, together with the muck, been pulled into the earth by worms. You should then be able to dig or rotavate the area, tidy up the edges, and start sowing. However, if the ground was infested with perennial weeds, such as couch grass, docks or stinging nettles, rotavating might leave you in a worse position than before you started. Any remaining surviving roots of these species will be chopped up into little pieces by the rotating blades and suddenly, instead of there being just a few viable weeds, there will be many hundreds. Hand-digging for the first few seasons, and manually removing any bits of root you encounter, may be the only way. Or use your pigs for the initial weed clearance, but you'll have to stock them pretty tightly to be sure that they'll do a thorough enough job. Once the pigs have done their bit, and been moved onto the next plot, get busy with the manure, the compost, the mulches, and so on.

Lazy beds: Lazy beds are an option that you might consider if you want to make a quick start. They're ideal for growing potatoes, and are an alternative way of breaking new ground while you're waiting for the plastic or the pigs to do their stuff on the rest of the garden. Mark out a strip about 6' wide (the length is up to you) and put a 3' wide layer of well-rotted farmyard manure in a line down the middle. Place your seed spuds on top of the manure in their growing positions and cover with another layer of muck. Next, remove the turf from the 18" wide strip along each side,

A small garden rotovator is useful in tighter spaces.

turning it over onto the manure, grass side down. Now dig out the newly exposed soil on either side of the bed and heap it on top of the inverted sods. As the spuds grow, the turf will break down, providing additional nutrients for the crop. Once the potatoes are harvested, level the ground, and you should find that you have a neat 6' wide plot. If you want your final plots to be wider than this, just prepare several lazy beds adjacent to one another.

Annual preparation: On an ongoing basis, we use our sheets of black plastic weighted down with old car tyres to cover the plots when they're not in use, either wholly or partially, and find

that this keeps the ground in good condition. As a result it needs very little preparatory work for each crop. If we need to incorporate large amounts of manure quickly, or have a plot that's become compacted through being exposed all winter, then we use the tractor-mounted rotavator, or, for smaller areas, a garden rotavator. Apart from forking over some areas in frosty weather we seldom do any digging; it's far too much like hard work.

Feeds

If your soil is in good heart, and is regularly replenished by liberal applications of organic matter, the majority of crops won't need any additional feed. However, there are some, such as marrows and cauliflowers, that are particularly hungry, and these may require an extra boost in order to develop their full potential. You can purchase general purpose fertilisers relatively cheaply, which are quick and easy to apply, but as a gardener aspiring to self-sufficiency, it seems right to source or make your own plant feeds whenever possible:

Soot: If you have an open fire, or a solid fuel stove or range, you're going to need to sweep the chimney at some point. Don't throw away the soot; spread it on the garden. It's best to allow it to stand for three months before using, as sulphur compounds accumulated within it could increase the soil's acidity. Soot is high in nitrogen, is a good soil conditioner and, because of its dark colour, can help the ground to absorb and retain warmth.

Wood ash: A useful source of potash. Collect the contents of the wood burner's ash pan during the winter, together with the residue of any bonfires (provided that you were only burning plant material and not general rubbish), and apply to the garden in the spring. Potash is highly soluble, so only put it down when the target plants are growing quickly. It's particularly good for fruit bushes, but is also helpful wherever you need to raise the soil pH a little (e.g. when growing brassicas in areas where club root is a problem). Alternatively, both soot and wood ash can be added to the compost heap.

Liquid feed: The simplest involves soaking all the goodness out of a shovelful of manure. Put the manure in a permeable bag of

Comfrey leaves can be used to make a liquid fertiliser.

some sort, such as a hessian sack, tie the top firmly, and dunk the whole thing into a big tub of water. Leave to soak for ten days or a fortnight before removing the bag (the contents of which can go on the compost heap). The resulting liquid can be diluted (if necessary) until it is the colour of weak tea, and then applied to needy plants. Nettles can also be put to good use; cut them in the spring when they're at their most nutritious, half-fill a bucket with the cuttings and cover with water. Leave until it gets pretty smelly then strain and use straight – no need to dilute. If you're planning to use your nettles for brewing beer (see page 327), grow some comfrey for making plant food instead.

Comfrey: (See also page 251) Easily cultivated, deep-rooting and happy in partial shade, comfrey is grown primarily for its leaves, which are not only high in potash, but also contain nitrogen and phosphates. The leaves can be harvested several times a year, although the plants may need a top dressing of muck from time to time to keep them growing well under a frequent cutting regime. Leaves can be wilted and used directly as a nutrient-rich mulch or, more commonly, they can be made into liquid feed. Simply chop up the leaves and put them in a watertight container (preferably with a tap or drain plug at the bottom). Pack them down tightly and place a large stone or weighted board on top, then cover the container. Leave it for about a month. Drain off the juice and store in airtight containers, such as empty plastic pop bottles. It's powerful stuff, so dilute 1 part comfrey liquid with 20 parts water before use. The decayed leaves can be tipped out of the tub and used either as mulch or put on the compost heap. If you haven't got enough comfrey leaves to make the feed you can mix them with chopped nettles as an interim measure, while you go out and source some more comfrey plants or wait until the autumn to lift and divide the plants you've got. We got our plants via freecycle.

Planning for an All-Year Harvest

Despite the fact that in our temperate climate it's perfectly reasonable to expect to be able to gather crops from the garden at all times of year, there seems to be a popular image of the smallholder or allotmenteer busily harvesting his vegetable crop during late summer / early autumn and storing it away in readiness for the lean winter months ahead, rather like a squirrel hoarding nuts. It's quite normal to see the storability of a particular vegetable variety used as a selling point by seed companies, and often large sections of gardening and self-sufficiency related publications are given over to advice on the storage of produce. However, the immense satisfaction of seeing the harvest safely gathered in often turns to intense disappointment when the time comes to make use of the crop

so lovingly preserved: a single rotting spud in a clamp or sack will soon lead to the deterioration of surrounding tubers, and, if left unchecked or undiscovered, huge losses can occur. Marrows and other squashes tend to explode by around Christmas time, and when one goes, others will surely follow. Root vegetables stored in dry sand become shrivelled and unpalatable, and the slightest dampness will quickly ruin whole strings of onions – a real problem if you live on the coast or, as we did, on an offshore island, where the salt-laden atmosphere renders it almost impossible to keep anything really dry. The storage of a large quantity of vegetables is a risky business, and not something that we would wish to be dependent upon.

For many, the chest freezer has

become an essential tool when dealing with summer vegetable gluts, but this is an extremely expensive way to preserve low-value products. A freezer costs a lot to run, so reserve the space for higher value stuff – meat and soft fruit – and leave the vegetables in the ground. Vegetables, on the whole, don't take kindly to being frozen (the exceptions to this being peas, sweetcorn and some types of bean) and, in reality, bags of frozen veg often work their way down to the bottom of the freezer where they will sit until next year (out of sight, out of mind) when they are hauled forth into the light of day and chucked to the pigs in order to make room for the current year's crop. It would have made more sense to have given them to the pigs in the first place. If you must freeze vegetables, process them first into soups or purées as they'll take up less space and suffer less freezer damage.

However, better by far than either freezing or other preservation methods is to plan your vegetable cropping in such a way as to be able to harvest a useful range of fresh produce from the garden at all times of the year, and cut out the storage issue altogether. By good planning gluts can usually be avoided, but, at certain times, a surplus is inevitable. Some vegetables can be turned into pickles and chutneys (or even jams and marmalade) and the remainder sold to cover the cost of seed purchases, or bartered among friends and neighbours. Any odds and ends left over will do for stock feed. Above all, don't waste anything.

Pumpkin marmalade

The following recipe for pumpkin marmalade beats the ordinary Seville orange stuff into a cocked hat in my opinion, and is certainly the best use for pumpkins we've ever come across (apart from hollowing them out and putting candles inside). We got it from a book called *Best-kept Secrets of the Women's Institute – Jams, Pickles & Chutneys* by Midge Thomas:

Ingredients

1.5kg pumpkin, peeled, seeds and fibre removed, and sliced.
1 litre water
675g oranges, halved and sliced thinly (ordinary eating oranges are fine for this)
675g lemons, halved and sliced thinly
80g fresh root ginger, shredded finely
1.3kg granulated sugar

Method:

Place the pumpkin in a large pan with the water, oranges, lemons and ginger, bring to the boil then simmer for 45 minutes to an hour (until the citrus peel is very soft). Add the sugar, stirring until dissolved, return to the boil then cook over a medium heat until the mixture is thick enough for a wooden spoon drawn through the centre to leave a clear channel. Pour into cooled, sterilised jars and seal.

Pumpkins growing on the muckheap.

Crop rotation

You'll undoubtedly have read about crop rotations, vegetable groups, and how long to leave the ground between growing plants of the same type. Every gardening book (and there are lots) will tell you something slightly different, but, whatever the system, the basic principles remain the same:

• Don't plant the same crop in the same ground two years running.

• Try to avoid following crops being of the same vegetable group.

• The crop being harvested should leave the soil in a suitable condition for the next crop to be sown.

• There should be provision within the rotation for the ground to be rested (fallow, green manure, short term ley, etc.).

Our own method of rotation, using four good-sized plots, is simplicity in itself, and seems to work well.

Based entirely on the relative sowing / harvesting dates of the various crops, everything revolves around the early potatoes, which are the first thing to be planted in the spring. Each year, the order in which subsequent crops are sown or planted out is more or less the same – onions and shallots are usually next, followed by broad beans and early peas, and so on.

So long as the early potatoes are planted on a different plot each year and the following crops are sown in the same order (i.e. in the same position relative to the location of the spuds), there's not much chance of the same things ending up in the same place year on year. Once a plan is drawn up it can be followed each year, so in the second year plot one becomes plot two, plot two becomes plot three, and so on up to plot four, which takes the place of plot 1.

See following 4 pages →

Common vegetable groups

Alliums: Onion family (e.g. onions, leeks, garlic)

Brassicas: Cabbage family (e.g. cabbages, turnips, radishes)

Legumes: Peas and beans

Umbelliferae: Carrot family (e.g. carrots, parsnips, parsley)

Solanums: Tomato family (e.g. potatoes, tomatoes, aubrgines)

Cucurbits: Cucumber Family (e.g. courgettes, pumpkins, cucumbers)

	Sow Direct	Sow in Modules	Plant Out	Harvest	
MARCH	Early Potatoes Shallots				
APRIL	Onions (Sets)	Celeriac Late Leeks	Onions		
MAY					
JUNE		Sprouting Broccoli Cauliflower	Celeriac Late Leeks	Potatoes	
JULY	Spinach Beet Winter Radish Beetroot Maincrop Carrots			Shallots	
AUGUST	Winter Salads Turnip	Spring Cabbage	Sprouting Broccoli Cauliflower	Onions	
SEPT	Corn Salad Spring Greens Winter Lettuce Spring Onions			Spinach Beet	
OCT	Overwinter Broad Beans Overwinter Peas Cauliflowers		Spring Cabbage	Spinach Beet Winter Radish Turnip Beetroot Maincrop Carrots	
NOV				Spinach Beet Winter Radish Turnip Maincrop Carrots Celeriac	Winter Salads Corn Salad
DEC				Spinach Beet Winter Radish Turnip Maincrop Carrots Celeriac	Winter Salads Corn Salad
JAN				Spinach Beet Winter Radish Turnip Maincrop Carrots Leeks	Celeriac Winter Salads Corn Salad
FEB				Spinach Beet Winter Radish Turnip Maincrop Carrots Leeks	Celeriac Winter Salads Corn Salad Spring Greens

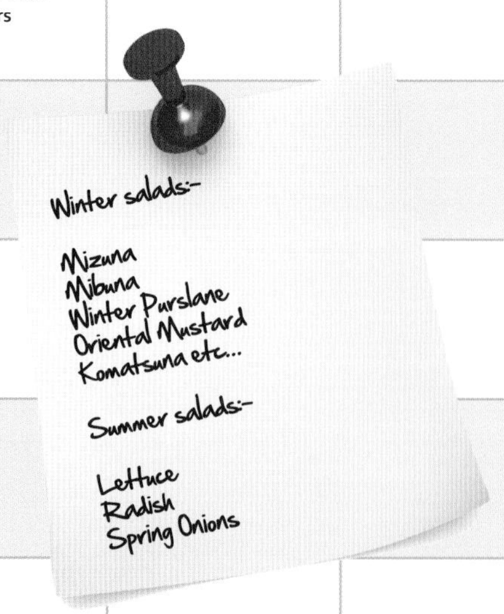

Winter salads:-

Mizuna
Mibuna
Winter Purslane
Oriental Mustard
Komatsuna etc...

Summer salads:-

Lettuce
Radish
Spring Onions

From Plot Four

Go to Plot Two

	Sow Direct	Sow in Modules	Plant Out	Harvest	
MARCH		Summer Cabbage Celery		Spinach Beet Winter Radish Celeriac Maincrop Carrots Leeks	Sprouting Broccoli Winter Salads Corn Salad Spring Greens Spring Onions
APRIL		Runner Beans Courgettes Marrow Sweetcorn Early Leeks		Spinach Beet Winter Radish Celeriac Leeks Spring Onion	Spring Cabbage Sprouting Broccoli Winter Lettuce Cauliflower Spring Greens
MAY	French Beans Peas Turnip		Spring Cabbage Celery	Spinach Beet Celeriac Overwinter Peas Winter Lettuce Cauliflower	
JUNE	French Beans Summer Salads Peas		Runner Beans Courgettes Marrow Sweetcorn Early Leeks	Overwinter Broad Beans Cauliflower	
JULY	Summer Salads Peas			Turnip French Beans Courgettes Summer Cabbage Runner Beans	
AUGUST				Turnip Courgettes Marrows Runner Beans French Beans	Summer Cabbage Peas Summer Salads
SEPT	Japanese Onions			Courgettes Marrows Runner Beans French Beans Summer Salads	Peas Summer Cabbage Sweetcorn
OCT	Garlic			Courgettes Marrows Sweetcorn Peas Summer Salads	
NOV				Celery Early Leeks	
DEC				Celery Early Leeks	
JAN				Celery Early Leeks	
FEB		Spring Cabbage			

From Plot Four

Go to Plot Three

PLOT 3

	Sow Direct		Sow in Modules	Plant Out	Harvest	
MARCH	Early Peas Spinach Beet Turnip Corn Salad Early Carrots	Broad Beans Beetroot Kohl Rabi Summer Salads		Early Cabbage		
APRIL	Broad Beans Summer Salads Jerusalem Artichokes	Early Carrots Parsnips Peas	Brussels Sprouts			
MAY	Summer Salads		Swede Kale	Brussels Sprouts	Corn Salad Summer Salads Baby Turnips Early Cabbage	
JUNE			Winter Cabbage Calabrese	Swede Kale	Spinach Beet Beetroot Kohl Rabi Corn Salad Summer Salads	Early Peas Japanese Onions
JULY				Winter Cabbage Calabrese	Broad Beans Spinach Beet Beetroot Early Carrots Kohl Rabi	Peas Summer Salads Garlic
AUGUST					Spinach Beet Beetroot Early Carrots Summer Salads	
SEPT					Spinach Beet	
OCT					Spinach Beet Swede Calabrese	
NOV					Spinach Beet Parsnip Swede Kale	Brussel Sprouts Winter Cabbage Jerusalem Artichoke
DEC					Spinach Beet Parsnip Swede Kale Jerusalem Artichoke	Brussel Sprouts Winter Cabbage
JAN					Spinach Beet Parsnip Swede Kale	Brussel Sprouts Winter Cabbage Jerusalem Artichoke
FEB					Spinach Beet Parsnip Swede Kale	Brussel Sprout Winter Cabbage Jerusalem Artichoke

Go to Plot One

Go to Plot Four

	Sow Direct	Sow in Modules	Plant Out	Harvest
MARCH				Spinach Beet Kale Winter Cabbage
APRIL				Spinach Beet
MAY				
JUNE				
JULY				
AUGUST				
SEPT				
OCT				
NOV				
DEC				
JAN				
FEB		Maincrop Onion (from Seed)		

PIGS

CATCH-CROP

MUCK

Go to Plot One

One strategy you'll often see recommended involves using a different plot of the four in turn for each vegetable group each year (usually spuds followed by legumes, then brassicas and finally roots, before returning to spuds and starting all over again), but, while it looks like a perfect rotation on paper, in reality it's not particularly practical due to the varying space requirements of each crop. For example, legumes should follow potatoes in the rotation, but the spuds will have taken up a far larger area than you'll require for your peas and beans. Conversely, you could easily be left with insufficient space for your spuds if they're following a crop that uses a smaller area, which most do. Not only does our system overcome this issue, it provides us with fresh vegetables to harvest at all times of the year. (See pages 66 - 69)

If it's your intention to grow maincrop potatoes in the vegetable garden then you'll need to insert another plot into the rotation between plots three and four, and utilise five plots on a five yearly cycle. However, maincrop potatoes are a very low value crop that ties up a whole plot of land for the entire growing season, so it's difficult to justify giving over space in the vegetable garden. What most people round here seem to do is to plough a small strip in a field for their maincrop spuds. By using a different strip each year any potential problems of disease carry over are avoided. (Onions are another low value crop that takes up a lot of space, so it's might be a good idea to move these out of the garden and into the field as well, together with carrots). Another alternative worth considering is to grow enough early varieties of potatoes to see you through most of the year. This

Field scale vegetables

Unless your plans include semi-commercial market gardening, perhaps in order to supply produce to a farm shop, box scheme or market stall (in which case you're probably moving outside the scope of this book), you should have no problem satisfying all your culinary needs with the output of a modest-sized kitchen garden. However, there are some crops which, by virtue of their low-value and high-space requirement, may not justify inclusion in the rotation. Chief amongst these are maincrop potatoes, onions and carrots. These are dietary staples, which means you're going to need to plant an awful lot of them if you're going to have anywhere near enough. Therefore, better use of space may be achieved by growing them on a field scale, rather than in the garden. If you're ploughing and cultivating a field for cereals (see page 122) then it's a simple enough matter to plant a few rows of spuds and other vegetables along one edge. This is precisely what we did on Bardsey, when growing barley to feed our pigs, goats and poultry. Otherwise you'll need to temporarily fence off a strip in one of your grazing fields. By using a different strip each year, and subsequently reseeding it with grass, you'll not only avoid any carry over of vegetable diseases, but improve your grassland too.

If you don't fancy ploughing you could spray off the existing vegetation and simply rotavate the strip, but it may take several passes with a fairly hefty machine to produce a sufficiently fine tilth. For ease of management and harvesting we found it simplest to raise the soil up into ridges and plant spuds, onions and carrots directly into the tops of those. We used a potato ridging tool, which mounted on the 3-point-linkage of the tractor, and created several ridges in one pass. Similar but smaller implements are available for attachment to two-wheeled garden machines.

has two advantages: Firstly, you can usually have all your earlies dug by the middle of July, freeing up the plot for another crop, (and contrary to common belief, most early potato varieties do actually store pretty well), and, secondly, you'll avoid the dreaded potato blight, as all your spuds will be safely lifted before the blight season begins.

Pumpkins and other winter squashes are another crop which isn't in our rotation plan as they take up too much space sprawling all over the place, so we grow them on the muckheap – they love that growing medium and

can romp around to their heart's content. The dense covering of foliage also helps prevent nutrient losses from the rotting manure by slowing down the passage of precipitation.

Additional tips for year round cropping

• There's considerable leeway in sowing dates beyond what is given on the seed packets. For example, we sow calabrese in June, some two months after the date given on the packet, to harvest in late October / early November. 'Early' peas (recommended sowing date

Chives and their flowers can be used in salads at a time when onions are scarce.

• Turnips grow quickly and make a good 'catch crop'. The tops of autumn-sown turnips will provide useful greens when nothing much else is available.

A fresh crop of greens sprouting from the cut stump of a cabbage plant.

• When harvesting cabbages, don't pull up the whole plant. Slice the head off carefully, leaving the root in the ground, then make a cross-shaped cut in the top of the stump. A fresh crop of greens will spring up from this, which can be harvested on a 'cut-and-come-again' basis for many months to come. If the plant runs to seed in the spring you can pick and eat the flower spears like sprouting broccoli and use the leaves from the stems.

• Don't forget the edible weeds which are very useful during the 'hungry gap'. Stinging nettle tops can be used as a spinach alternative (or to brew beer), chickweed makes a good base for salads, and dandelion shoots can be blanched – the resulting crop will look just like seakale and can be used in place of chicory.

• Sprouting broccoli, small spinach leaves, cabbage, grated turnip and celeriac are all good in winter salads.

March / April) can be sown in early July to give fresh garden peas in October.

• You may not have any pigs to clean up the fourth plot, in which case you could move a chicken ark over the ground, or perhaps graze it (geese would do the trick, although we have used a cow) – anything to give the land a bit of a break from cropping. Alternatively, sow with a green manure crop or put down muck then cover with black plastic.

• Maincrop onions harvested in mid August, even if they store well, will be getting rather soft by the following April. Therefore you should also plan to grow autumn sown onions, spring onions, Welsh onions, chives and leeks for a succession of harvesting dates.

• Start harvesting 'baby' roots (beet, carrots etc.,) by the end of May.

• Remember you can eat thinnings.

positions when large enough. All require a fertile soil, and it's best to apply a bit of lime before planting out seedlings.

Brassicas are happiest in fairly firm ground. At a pinch they will grow in the patch that you dug the early spuds from, but try to avoid putting sprouts and cauliflowers where the soil is loose – you are far more likely to end up with blown sprouts and loose cauliflower heads.

Brassica pests

Deter cabbage root fly by covering the ground immediately surrounding newly-planted brassicas with carpet underlay or similar.

Growing Tips

This is not a gardening book, so we haven't included detailed guidance on the cultivation of vegetables. What we have done is to provide a series of notes and tips based on our own experience of growing these crops. In some cases these may differ from what's commonly recommended. Additional information relating to seed rates, sowing depths and general husbandry can usually be found on the backs of seed packets.

BRASSICAS

Virtually all brassicas will do best if sown in modules or trays and then planted out to their final

Brassica seedlings growing in modules.

We're using remnants from an old rubber pond-liner for this at the moment, which is ideal. Using a piece about 6" square for each seedling, cut three quarters of the way in from one edge, and then make two more small cuts at right angles to the first, in the centre of the material, to form a cross. Place these collars around the stems of every brassica plant to protect against the fly. Curly kale and swedes don't seem to be so badly affected as some other types of brassica, but Calabrese are particularly susceptible.

Watch out for mealy aphid – at a distance they look like a greyish, mouldy patch on the plants. They'll cause distortion and yellowing of the foliage, and retarded growth. They can be treated by squashing, spraying with a water jet (to blast them off the plant), derris dust (no longer available in the UK), soft soap sprays, and sprays containing pyrethrum.

Caterpillars can make a real mess of your plants, but we find that they rarely cause so much damage that the crops don't recover or can't be eaten (unless the plants were very young when attacked). They're best controlled by squashing the butterfly eggs, which are laid on the undersides of leaves, or by hand picking them off the plants. We have tried to deal with them by spraying with slightly soapy water, and some people swear by using a smelly concoction made with rhubarb leaves. Another option is to cover the crops with an insect-proof barrier such as netting or fleece. Coloured brassicas (red cabbage, red kale etc.,) seem to be less attractive to the cabbage white butterfly than their green counterparts.

Flea beetles may attack your seedlings as they emerge. Generally they'll recover well enough without treatment, but radishes and turnips seem to be particularly susceptible. We used to treat ours with derris dust before it was withdrawn from sale. Derris was an organic product, and as yet there doesn't seem to be a suitable natural alternative.

If you're unlucky enough to have club root fungus in your soil, the lime you spread at planting will help to inhibit it. There are a number of brassica varieties available nowadays that are able to tolerate club root, so grow these in preference. If your soil doesn't carry this disease, try to keep it that way by **never** purchasing brassica seedlings unless you're absolutely certain that they've been grown in clean compost. Avoid gifts of spare seedlings from your neighbour's allotment at all costs.

Sprouting broccoli

This always used to be a late winter / early spring vegetable, from a May sowing the previous year, but recent plant-breeding developments mean that it's now harvestable over a much longer season. Winter varieties will continue cropping for ages, provided that you keep on picking, and with the introduction of a summer sprouting variety you could, potentially, be eating fresh broccoli for ten months of the year. We find the April cropping varieties particularly welcome at a time when most of the winter brassicas are finished, but before the new season crops are ready, during the hungry gap. Broccoli is excellent steamed, used in stir fries, or raw in salads, and even if the florets have opened up a bit before you get around to harvesting them, they're still perfectly good to eat.

One downside is that the plants don't make very efficient use of space, which is something to consider if you only have a small plot.

Recommended varieties: Early Purple, Claret (F1). The F1 hybrids have very high quality spears, but the cropping period is shorter.

Purple sprouting broccoli.

Calabrese

It can be quite difficult to grow good quality large heads of Calabrese, but persevere, as it's quite delicious. The main heads will 'go over' quite quickly, so cut them as soon as they look ready. Once you've harvested the main head, leave the plant in the ground and it'll produce a quantity of smaller side spears that you can cut for the kitchen.

Give the Romanesco varieties a try if you fancy something a bit different; not only do they look fantastic, but the flavour is excellent too.

Brussels sprouts.

Brussels sprouts

Choose varieties that will take you right through the winter season. We usually grow two types, one early and one late season variety, making doubly sure that there will be home-grown sprouts to accompany our Christmas dinner.

If your plants grow very tall, and your vegetable patch is in a windy spot, you might consider staking them to keep them upright. Regularly remove any lower leaves that turn yellow, which helps to maintain good airflow around

the main stem, where the buttons form, and reduces the likelihood of your sprouts going mouldy. Start picking from the bottom up, as soon as the sprouts become large enough. After harvest you can cut the leafy top off the plant and use it like cabbage or spring greens.

Recommended varieties: Brontë (early), Doric (mid / late season). Almost all of the varieties found in seed catalogues are F1 hybrids. In our experience these are far superior to open pollinated types.

Winter ccabbage.

Cabbage

Choose a range of varieties to ensure that you're always able to harvest cabbages in one form or another. Despite what I said earlier about disregarding the sowing times stated on seed packets, cabbages do seem to be quite date sensitive, so follow sowing and planting dates quite carefully for best results.

Spring greens / collards can be sown late August / early September to give tender spring greens for harvest from mid March. Unlike other brassicas, these do well enough when sown direct. If you prefer to use modules to start off your spring greens, don't put them in the greenhouse; leave

Spring greens.

them outside to germinate. These seedlings need to be tough if they're to survive the winter.

Red cabbages are great. Although they're often eaten pickled, you can use them just the same as green cabbage for extra colour on the plate.

Recommended varieties: Kilaton (summer / autumn), January King (winter), Frostie (spring greens).

Cauliflowers

It's hard to beat the satisfaction of harvesting a perfect cauliflower, but they're quite a demanding crop to grow well. The plants like firm soil and ample light, and mustn't be allowed to run short of water or nutrients, or suffer any kind of setback. General requirements are as for other brassicas, but try not to sow / plant too many at once, otherwise you may find yourself with a dozen cauliflowers that all need eating at the same time. Just sow half a dozen, and then a few more a couple of weeks later, and so on. If you do find that you've got more than you can cope with you may be able to store a mature

Cauliflower.

Curly kale.

cauliflower for a limited amount of time by pulling up the whole plant and hanging it upside down in a cool frost-free shed.

As with other brassicas there are plenty of varieties to choose from, so it should be possible for you to have cauliflowers at whatever time of year you want them, provided you plan ahead. We usually grow two varieties: one mid / late summer heading (which is used, amongst other things, for making piccalilli), and a winter type to head in late April and May from a sowing the previous spring. These do take up space on the plot for a long time, but they're very welcome when they mature as there's so little else about at that time of year.

Recommended varieties: Mayflower (late winter heading), Nemo (late summer heading).

Kale

This very hardy and reliable brassica is used primarily for winter leaf production. Management is as for other brassicas, but kale can be sown later in the season without compromising the crop. June sowing would not be too late.

Another advantage that kale has over some other members of the cabbage family is that it's less attractive to caterpillars and slugs / snails.

Harvest a steady supply of leaves from October through to March, when the plants will start to bolt. You can then gather the developing flower shoots and eat them as sprouting broccoli, effectively getting two crops from the same plant.

Recommended variety: Dwarf Green Curled – this variety is good for exposed sites, and is able to cope with poorer soil conditions.

Radishes

This really quick growing salad crop can be ready in as little as 3-4 weeks after sowing. Radishes are always one of the first crops we sow each year, usually under cloches, and the first new season vegetable to be harvested. They need to be sown little and often – half a row every week to ten days or so – as they have a tendency to go rather hot and woody if they're allowed to over mature.

This sowing policy means that you should finish harvesting each batch before they go past their best, and just as the next lot are ready. To extend the harvest period, choose a variety that has been bred to grow to larger sizes without deteriorating.

Radishes don't warrant a special place in your rotation because they're in the ground for such a short period of time, and you can just squeeze a half row in here and there, wherever you have room. For example, if you sow a couple of rows of peas, you will have to leave about 2'6" between rows. However, while the pea plants are small they don't require the whole area, so you can sow a row of radishes down the middle. By the time the peas do need the space the radishes will have grown, matured and been harvested.

Recommended varieties: Ilka, Pink Beauty.

Swedes

Remember to treat swedes as brassicas (which is what they are) rather than roots – sow in modules and plant out when big enough. This seems to be far more successful than direct sowing.

There's no need to sow swedes particularly early in the year – May or June will be quite soon enough. The modules can be left outdoors for germination, which removes the need to harden the seedlings off before planting out. Leave plenty of space (6"- 9") between each seedling when planting out, otherwise the developing swedes will remain stunted and small.

Swedes are particularly prone to boron deficiency, which manifests itself as browning and sogginess within the root.

Swedes are frost hardy, so can remain in the ground and be harvested fresh from the plot as required. The first should be ready in early November, and they should stand well over the winter. However, they'll become increasingly tough and woody as spring approaches. Any plants remaining in the ground at this stage (perhaps those that failed to develop a decent sized swede) will throw up a lot of new leaf growth, which can be harvested and eaten as cabbage.

Recommended variety: Ruby.

Turnips

A much underrated vegetable. Like swedes, turnips are brassicas masquerading as root vegetables. However, unlike other members of the cabbage family, they prefer to be sown direct.

An early variety such as 'Snowball' will give a crop of sweet, tender roots in as little as eight weeks from a mid March sowing, and they can be grown as a 'catch crop', utilising space between larger, slower maturing plants. They're best harvested small as they can become woody as size increases.

Sow the tiny seeds as thinly as you can, and thin out the seedlings to about 4" for early crops. A winter hardy maincrop variety sown in late autumn can be over-wintered to provide a crop of green leaves

Swedes (with leeks behind).

from March, when other leafy stuff is beginning to get a bit scarce.

Recommended varieties: there are lots of new varieties offering improved eating quality, but a few of our favourites are Market Express (early), Snowball (early), Golden Ball (maincrop).

TIP

When you discover a variety of any particular type of vegetable that does well on your land, stick with it. This is particularly the case with brassicas. It's fun to experiment with different crops, but don't bank on them feeding you.

ROOTS

Roots shouldn't be grown in soils that have been recently manured, so they tend to fit in towards the end of a rotation. Lighter soils are generally the best, but preferably not too stony.

Beetroot

Don't plant huge quantities of beetroot unless you're really keen on them. A little goes a long way. We usually grow far too many. Choose monogerm varieties (which produce only one plant per seed cluster) to reduce the need for thinning. They're usually sown direct in the ground, but can be germinated in modules if you prefer. However, care must be taken to transplant the seedlings without root disturbance. Once established they're a pretty trouble-free crop to grow, but watch out for boron deficiency (as outlined for swedes).

Beetroot can be harvested at any size, depending on what you're going to do with them – you'll want little ones for pickling and for use in salads, and much larger roots for cooking and making chutney. The latter can remain in the ground throughout the winter, to be lifted as needed.

When harvesting beetroot, remove

Beetroot still in the ground, late winter.

Carrot fly

This is by far the worst pest of carrots, and if you do nothing to minimize its activity it can decimate your crop.

There are various measures that can be taken to reduce the amount of damage caused by carrot fly, so choose whichever options suit you and your garden best. Our preferred methods are to sow a fly resistant variety (usually Resistafly) in June, thus avoiding the first generation of flies, and to sow sparingly and carefully so as to avoid thinning, if at all possible. Although we do get some carrot fly damage, it doesn't usually become apparent until late on in the autumn, and even then it's rarely so bad that a carrot is completely unusable.

Another option is to surround your carrot bed with a low barrier of about 2 to 2'6" in height, made from insect mesh or fleece. Apparently these pests only fly close to the ground, so putting a barrier around the carrots should prevent the flies from gaining access to them in the first place. Another option is to grow your carrots in containers that raise them high enough off the ground to keep them out of the flight line of the flies.

Alternatively, cover the whole crop with fleece or an insect proof mesh.

the leaves by twisting them off rather than by cutting – this reduces 'bleeding'. Also try to avoid damaging the skin for the same reason.

Cook large beets by washing then wrapping each one in tin foil and slowly roasting in a low oven. We leave ours in the bottom of the Rayburn top oven on idle overnight, which is much easier than boiling them for hours on end.

Recommended variety: Boltardy

Carrots

Carrots are a dietary staple, so grow plenty. Fairly light, sandy soils will give best results, but if your ground is less than ideal, or full of stones, try stump-rooted varieties or quick-growing ball type carrots. To grow longer roots on unsuitable soil, try planting into ridges.

Carrots can be sown at quite close spacings without suffering. We usually make our rows 6"-8" apart. Provided that there's sufficient room to hoe between

With carrots, we have found that closer spacings give better crops.

the rows, that's enough. In fact, we've found that closer spacings invariably give better crops of carrots.

Take great care to sow the seed very thinly. Carrot seeds are tiny, so this can be quite difficult, but you do need to try to avoid having to thin the seedlings, if possible. Otherwise the smell of the seedlings you remove will attract the dreaded carrot fly, and you could lose your crop.

Recommended varieties: Resistafly (maincrop), Nantes 5 (early).

Parsnips

A really useful vegetable in that it can be left in the ground all winter without coming to any harm. Indeed, it's often said that the flavour of parsnips improves once they've been frosted. They have a long growing season, so you need to set aside a patch of ground for an extended period, but, having said that, you can pack quite a lot of plants into a small space.

Parsnips are very slow to germinate, so if you're sowing directly into the ground, mix in some radish seed as well. Radishes germinate and mature very quickly, so the emerging seedlings will mark the row for you (so you don't accidentally hoe everything up), and will be harvested long before the parsnips need the space. In common with other root crops, parsnips don't like to be transplanted, so either sow directly as described above, or alternatively sow into old toilet roll middles filled with compost, then plant out the whole tube once the parsnips are growing well. Initially sow two seeds per tube, but remove the weaker seedling before planting out.

Traditionally, parsnips have been sown very early in the year, sometimes as early as February, but we prefer to sow them later (mid March, or even April), particularly if sowing direct. These later sown plants easily catch up, and may even overtake those that were sown earlier.

Recommended variety: Gladiator.

TIP

Parsnip seeds have little wings on them and are very lightweight – avoid sowing them in windy conditions.

Parsnip canker

This fungus enters through small cracks around the crown of the root and causes brown areas to form, which subsequently rot. The best way to avoid it is to grow a resistant variety, and to be fairly strict about crop rotation.

Parsnips can also suffer with carrot fly, but not to the same extent that carrots do.

LEGUMES

All legumes like lots of organic matter in the soil, so grow them following a crop for which the land has been mucked. We put them on the plot that had spuds on it the previous year.

Leguminous plants have nodules in one their roots which are able to fix nitrogen from the air, so it's a good idea, when they've finished cropping, to cut the tops off and leave the roots in the ground to continue their nitrogen fixing activity. This increases soil fertility for the next crop in the rotation.

Broad Beans

This hardy crop is one of the first new season vegetables to be ready to harvest in our garden, so is always very welcome. Although often started in pots or modules, we find that it's best to sow broad beans direct. Grow in staggered double rows as they can get quite tall – this arrangement gives the individual plants more support and shelter. Extra support can be provided, if required, by pushing in some stout poles at the ends of the rows (and mid way along

Although broad beans are often started in pots, as shown here, we usually sow ours direct.

Broad bean plants in flower, supported by strings.

if needed), then tying strings all the way round each double row at height intervals of 6"- 8".

Sow spring varieties as soon as soil conditions allow. Watch out for mouse damage as the young shoots emerge. If necessary, cover each plant with an old jam jar until it's big enough to survive the attack. We've done this in the past, and it does keep the rodents at bay, but you have to be quite careful to harden the plants off afterwards, by weaning them from the jars gradually. The extra warmth provided by the jars makes the plants very delicate, and they are liable to get blasted if you expose them to too much weather too soon.

Harvest the first pods while small and tender and eat as mange tout then allow the rest to mature for shelling beans.

Shelled broad beans are one of the few vegetables that will freeze well, and are welcome in the winter months. We've never bothered to blanch before freezing, and haven't encountered any problems as a result. Don't freeze broad beans with their pods (as for mange tout) or they'll go black where they've been cut.

Recommended varieties: 'Bunyards Exhibition' is a reliable cropper, suitable for use as mange tout and also for producing shelling beans. It does grow quite tall (about 4'), so if your garden is in an exposed location try 'The Sutton', which only grows to about 18". Autumn-sown varieties such as 'Super Aquadulce' can survive the winter well enough without protection, but you will get earlier spring crops if you cover them with cloches.

Broad bean pests

Black fly will probably infest the growing points of your mature broad bean plants. Pinch out the tips if you like (you can eat them like spinach), or you could try blasting the aphids off with a jet from the hose. Spraying with soapy water can be quite effective too. Chocolate spot is another common problem. There's no cure for this, but the plants should still crop well enough. Try planting a bit further apart to avoid chocolate spot next year.

French Beans

There are two main types of French bean: dwarf and climbing. The dwarf varieties are compact, bushy plants about 18" tall, grown in rows with about 5" between plants. Climbing French beans need some sort of support, like runner beans. They're harder work than dwarf varieties, but will give a bigger crop.

Don't sow French beans outdoors too early as they're susceptible to frosts and rot. You can get an earlier start by sowing in pots under cover, and transplanting when the weather warms up. Start harvesting once the beans can be snapped in half, and keep picking regularly to encourage further pod production.

French beans freeze well. They just need topping and tailing first.

Recommended varieties: Cobra (climbing), Montano (dwarf).

French bean pests

Slugs find French bean plants extremely attractive, so make sure control measures are in place. Blackfly can also be a nuisance.

Slugs and snails

Slugs and snails are the bane of gardeners everywhere. If you have a sandy soil they may be less of a problem, as they don't like the gritty texture. There are various control methods available, and everyone needs to make their own choice as to what's appropriate to their situation. Beer traps are favoured by some (although it strikes me as a waste of good beer), and others swear by going out with a torch at night and collecting them up. We have such vast numbers of slugs and snails that the aforementioned methods wouldn't even begin to make inroads. After having had whole crops wiped out by marauding gastropods, we find that we have no option but to use slug pellets. Remember that the whole purpose of the exercise is to feed your family rather than the slugs, so it doesn't pay to be too 'holier-than-thou' about it. We use them sensibly, and in accordance with the manufacturer's recommendations, and haven't noticed any evidence of damage to birds, frogs or toads (of which we have plenty) as a result. We've also seen a considerable increase in the number of slow-worms in the garden in recent years.

Runner beans

In terms of the amount produced per square foot of ground, you would be hard pushed to beat the runner bean as a crop. This means they're good in small gardens, as the plants make excellent use of vertical space. However, unless you specifically grow a short variety (such as 'Hestia'), runner bean plants must have support, as they'll easily run for 8' or more. The usual method is to grow them up bamboo canes. We always put ours into a wigwam shape, with eight canes to each one, as we feel this is the most sturdy arrangement for our relatively windy site. However, the plants can get rather congested around the top of the canes, making it harder to pick the beans, and sometimes causing distortion of the pods. On more sheltered sites, runner beans can be grown in straight rows, with the plants climbing up strings or canes attached to a ridgepole running between uprights positioned at the ends of the rows. This method gives each plant more space and light.

Main: Bamboo cane 'wigwams' for runner beans.
Inset: Growing sweet peas with your runner beans may encourage pollinators.

Runner beans should be harvested regularly, to ensure that they continue cropping.

Runner beans are a hungry crop, so make sure the soil contains plenty of organic matter. Being frost tender they're usually sown in pots or modules for transplanting, but alternatively they can be sown direct from mid May. Another batch sown in mid June will provide a later crop, ready to harvest when the first lot have just about finished. Don't sow too many though, or you may be completely inundated with beans. We find that 40 plants is ideal for a family of five, and that gives us enough for eating fresh and for making into chutney. You can freeze surplus runner beans, if you want to, but we wouldn't consider growing extra beans specifically for this purpose.

Use a heavy mulch (such as lawn clippings) around the plants to help conserve moisture and to suppress weeds, and water liberally once the flowers start to set. White-flowered varieties are said to set better than red flowered in dry weather, but we haven't noticed any discernible difference between them. Having said that, we don't get much dry weather around here, so perhaps it wasn't a fair comparison. Pinch out the growing tips of the runners when they reach the tops of the canes – this causes more growth to come up from the bottom. Once they start cropping, runner beans must be picked regularly to ensure a long season.

Leaving beans to mature on the plant will stop the formation of new flowers, meaning no more beans. Encouraging pollination will help increase the crop; apparently, runner beans aren't particularly attractive to bees, so it's been suggested that growing some climbing flowers, such as sweet peas, amongst the bean plants may help to draw them in.

At the end of the season you can leave some mature pods on the plants to dry. Shell them after picking, and finish drying by the Rayburn. These dried beans can be used in winter stews, but they do take a lot of cooking.

When the plants have finished cropping, cut the tops off and leave the roots in the ground to continue fixing nitrogen over the winter months. Technically, runner beans are perennials, and if you leave the roots in the ground and protect them well from frost, they will re-grow and crop again the following year. We haven't tried this, but it might work if you live in a particularly mild area.

Recommended varieties: Look for varieties that offer heavy crops of beans in a range of weather conditions. We particularly like White Lady (white flowered) and Galaxy (red flowered).

Peas

Peas aren't the most straightforward of crops to grow, but as the result is so vastly superior to either the frozen or tinned version, it's worth making the effort and growing plenty to be eaten straight from the garden. If you choose your varieties well and plan your sowing carefully, it should be possible to harvest fresh peas from late May / early June, right through to late October. Sow early varieties in March for crops in June, and plant another batch a couple of weeks later. Maincrop peas can be sown in April (along with another row of earlies) to carry you through the main part of summer. Sow a few more 'earlies' in July to give fresh garden peas in October, and overwinter hardy varieties sown in mid October

Pea plants growing up recycled plastic netting.

should give you a crop to harvest in late May. They like a soil with plenty of organic matter, so try to use a plot that has been mucked during the last 12-18 months.

All pea plants will need support of one sort or another. Older varieties often grow up to 6' in height, so have a think about how you'll hold up the crop before committing to grow it. Twiggy hedge trimmings (known as 'pea sticks') have traditionally been used as supports, but we've never had much luck with this method. The combined weight of the crop and the force of the wind contrive to flatten the whole lot, causing damage and wastage, and making harvest very difficult.

For the last few years we've recycled the plastic netting off our silage bales to support the peas, and found this to be more successful. Having knocked in a fence post at either end of the row, the strip of netting is stretched between the two, with a length of baler twine top and bottom to keep it reasonably taught. A few extra supports (short lengths of bamboo) may be needed at various points along the row to prevent the net

from sagging. The best time to put the netting in place is just after the peas have come up, but before they grow more than a few inches tall. On exposed sites, choose shorter varieties.

Once the pods start to mature, pick regularly – at least every other day, if you can. As with other legumes, any mature pods left on the plant will slow down or stop the flowering process, causing your harvest to draw to a premature close. Semi-leafless varieties are a good bet as it's easier to spot the pods, reducing the risk of any being left on the plants. You also get fewer problems such as mildew with these types, due to better air circulation.

When you're removing the dead haulms at the end of the season, try to leave the roots in the ground as they'll continue to fix nitrogen from the atmosphere, which will benefit the following crop in your rotation.

Recommended varieties: Kelvedon Wonder (early), Boogie (maincrop, semi-leafless).

Pea pests

Mice and birds are the most likely causes of losing young plants. Mice will dig up the germinating seeds when they are full of sugars, and birds attack emerging seedlings. Birds can be deterred by starting the plants off under fleece, or placing assorted twigs, strings or tape over the rows to keep them off. Pigeons are probably the worst avian pest where peas are concerned, but at least you can shoot and eat them!

Minimise moulds and mildews by not sowing seeds too close together, allowing plenty of space between rows, ensuring good airflow around the plants, keeping them weed-free, and growing semi-leafless varieties.

If, on shelling your peas, you find that they're maggoty, then they've been attacked by the pea moth, which lays tiny, transparent eggs on the plants. The resulting maggots migrate to the developing pods and burrow into the peas. The surest way to control them is to grow the crop under a tent of horticultural fleece, but this isn't always going to be practical. Damage can be minimised by growing only quick-maturing cultivars for early and late crops, thus avoiding the moth's most active months of July and August.

ALLIUMS

Onions

Onions are a low value crop that takes up a lot of space for the whole summer, so it's quite a good idea to move these out of the garden and into a field strip. If you only have a small plot, without the luxury of a field, you might decide to use the space for growing something else and buy in whatever onions you require, as they're so cheap.

Onions like fertile ground that has been recently manured. They can either be grown from sets, which are immature bulbs that have had their growth artificially halted, or from seed. Seeds are cheaper to buy than sets. Growing from seed is a longer, trickier job, but gives heavier yields. Sow one or two seeds per module in February and don't keep them too warm, or the resultant plants are likely to bolt. Plant out when the seedlings are growing strongly. Growing from sets is much simpler – just poke the root end in the ground, and away you go. Plant when soil conditions allow, but late March / early April is probably soon enough. We've planted sets as late as early May, and still had a useful crop. Autumn sets can be planted in early September and over-wintered, giving a fresh harvest from mid May.

Whether planting sets or seedlings, space them 6" apart, with 12" between rows, unless you're trying to grow particularly large onions, in which case give each one a bit more room. Take particular care to keep the plants weed-free from mid July onwards, as they need as much sunshine as possible to dry the skins and shrivel the stems

Dot planting onion sets.

prior to lifting. Loosening the soil around each bulb a week or two before harvest also helps in this respect.

Ideally, store in bunches or strings, or in net bags or on mesh trays, in a frost-free place with low humidity. Theoretically, if the conditions are right, and if you've chosen varieties that are noted for their storage properties, they might keep until April or May the following year. We always have difficulty storing onions as the air around here is so damp, so we've also tried freezing (which tends to taint the whole contents of the freezer) and drying.

Recommended varieties: Turbo (maincrop), Radar (over winter).

Dried onions.

Onion pests

White rot is one of the most serious problems you're ever likely to encounter in your garden. It manifests itself by turning the onion plant's leaves yellow and causing them to wilt. White mould appears around the base of the bulb and, as the fungus spreads, black fruiting bodies develop. There is nothing you can do to save the onions – the best thing is to pull up and burn anything you suspect might be infected. Don't throw them on the compost heap, whatever you do. The fungus is extremely persistent, and can survive in soil for up to 8 years, so you shouldn't accept free gifts of topsoil or home-made compost from elsewhere, no matter how short of these basic resources you may be. Once your garden is infected, the only option, if you really want to grow onions, is to use a completely fresh patch of ground. Leeks seem to be less susceptible.

Initially, onion rot can be confused with onion fly, which also results in the leaves turning yellow and wilting. The difference becomes obvious when you pull up the plants, as onion fly maggots will be visible at the base. Growing under mesh will prevent the flies accessing the onions in the first place. Onions grown from sets are less likely to be attacked than those started from seed.

On the plus side, slugs won't touch onions.

Main: *Shallot sets.*
Inset: *Onions ready for harvest.*

Shallots.

Leeks in winter.

Shallots

Almost always grown from sets (similar to, but larger than onion sets), except where bulbs are being grown for exhibition purposes. Each set subdivides as it grows, producing a cluster of between 2 and 12 shallots. Five or six is the ideal. They can be planted fairly early, from late February or early March, if conditions allow, and will be ready to harvest before your onions, thus bridging the gap between autumn-planted sets and maincrop.

Storage and care of shallots is as for onions, although we generally pickle all of ours, which we find preferable to growing a specific variety of pickling onion.

Recommended variety: Topper.

Garlic

This is almost as essential as onions in the kitchen, but it's doubtful if it's worthwhile growing your own. Garlic for planting may cost almost £5 for 20 cloves,

which, allowing for some losses, will generate 18 bulbs, so they work out at around 28p each. Bulbs of garlic can usually be purchased for less than this in supermarkets, and, although it grieves me to say so, I have to admit to finding the flavour of home-grown garlic inferior to bought bulbs.

Ideally, garlic needs to be planted in the autumn for a successful crop. Put individual cloves in the ground about 6"- 8" apart in mid / late September. Lift once the foliage turns yellow, from mid July (if autumn planted). Dry and store as for onions.

Leeks

Although leeks take up the ground for a long time, each plant doesn't need much space, so you can fit a lot of them in to a relatively small area.

Best sown under cover in March / April, in deep seed trays (recycled fruit punnets), although you could sow them in a seed bed if

you prefer. Germination takes a couple of weeks, and once they're growing well they can be put outside and hardened off. They're pretty tough. If you've sown the seeds too thickly you can prick some out into another tray to give them a bit more room. There's no particular hurry to get them planted out in the garden, as they can tolerate being in trays for a long time. However, if this is the case, you might need to feed them, as the nutrients in the potting compost will only last for about 6-8 weeks. We don't usually plant ours out until late June, which is early enough for this slow-growing vegetable. It's often suggested that you should cut off the tops of the leaves and trim the roots at the time of planting out, but I've never been able to understand the logic of this. Having tried it, I can honestly say it makes no difference to the success or otherwise of the resulting crop, so now we don't bother.

To plant out, make a series of holes, about 4" deep with a dibber. If the ground is very dry and the holes keep collapsing, water the surface first and this should help. Drop a leek plant into each one, but do not backfill – just pour water in until the hole is full then leave the plants to settle. The first leeks may be ready to harvest as early as mid September.

Any leeks remaining in the ground in the spring will start to bolt, but you can still use them by slicing them lengthways and removing the flower stem, which is really tough and woody. The rest of the leek will be fine to eat. Very often we're still harvesting leeks in May.

Recommended varieties: Autumn Giant 3 (early season), Giant Winter 2 (late season).

Leek pests

Leeks are susceptible to most of the same pests and diseases that bother onions, but generally are not so severely affected that the crop is unusable. The main one to look out for is rust – seen as reddish blotches on the leaves. Plants can die if the attack is severe. Rust-infected plants should be removed and burnt, and leeks should be grown elsewhere on the plot for a year or two to minimise the chances of recurrence. The best option, if you have had problems with rust, is to grow a resistant variety.

Spring / Salad Onions

These are essentially onion varieties specifically developed for harvesting as immature plants, with very little bulb and a milder flavour than standard onions. Sow fairly thickly in open ground.

Thin to approximately one plant per inch and use the thinnings in a salad, like chives.

As with most other salad crops, sow small amounts on a regular basis, to ensure a steady supply of prime plants for use in the kitchen. They should be ready about 12 weeks after sowing.

If any become too large and strong flavoured to use in salads, just treat them in the same way as standard onions for culinary purposes.

They're susceptible to all the same pests and diseases as the other alliums, but may not be as badly affected as they're in the ground for a much shorter period.

SOLANUM FAMILY

Potatoes

Spuds are a good crop for breaking up previously uncultivated ground. You may have problems with wireworm in the tubers for a year or two if the land was previously down to permanent grass. On virgin ground, lazy beds (see page 62) may be a good option for getting started. Either way, you'll need plenty of muck.

Spuds can be planted in mid March, with the earliest varieties ready to begin digging up by the end of May. (But don't panic if you didn't get your potatoes planted at the right time because you were too busy with lambing – just get them in the ground as soon as you can afterwards. If you've opted for earlies and second earlies you'll still get a decent crop, even if they're not planted until May.)

For best results, seed potatoes of early varieties should be chitted.

Seed potatoes and dibber.

This entails putting the tubers in a light, airy, frost-free place, rose end uppermost (egg trays are handy for this), and leaving them to grow sprouts. Ideally, put them in the ground when the sprouts are about 1" long, although in practice it doesn't matter if they're a bit longer.

To make your seed spuds go further you can cut any larger tubers in half before planting, provided that each half has strong sprouts. There's no need to chit maincrop seed potatoes.

Traditionally, spuds are planted by laying the tubers at appropriate intervals in a shallow trench, which is then covered over by running a ridging tool up between the rows (or using a draw hoe, on a smaller scale). Alternatively, just make a hole with a dibber, drop the spud in and cover over. That's how we do it, anyway. You do need to ensure that the tuber goes right to the bottom of the hole (you don't want a pocket of air underneath it), and be especially careful not to knock off the sprouts. Early varieties should be planted 12"- 15" apart, with a minimum of 18" between rows. Second earlies require 15" between plants and 24" between rows, and for maincrop you should allow 24" between plants, with the rows being 30" apart.

As the plants grow, earth up into ridges, if possible. This protects the stems from damage, and results

The spud planting team at work.

Earthing up the rows.

Potato blight

Potato blight deserves to be taken seriously, because it can decimate your crop and ruin all your spuds in storage as well. Blight initially causes brown splotches to appear on the leaves, the underside of which have a white, furry coating. It should be possible to avoid the worst of it by growing only first and second early varieties, as these will be out of the ground and stored before the blight season begins. Makes sure that you only plant blight-resistant varieties, particularly if growing maincrop spuds, and earth up well.

If your plants do get blight you should cut the foliage down at the first sign of disease, take it away, and burn it. Leave the spuds in the ground for at least another three weeks, which gives an opportunity for the blight spores to die on the soil surface before you disturb it. Then lift all the tubers and store.

Blight can be delayed to some extent by spraying the foliage with a fungicide every 10-14 days from early July onwards. Previously Bordeaux mixture would have been used, but due to toxicity issues associated with copper it was withdrawn from sale in February 2013. You could also sign up to the blight warning website (blightwatch. co.uk) to get regular emails and texts telling you when potato blight is likely to be found in your locality.

in fewer green spuds (which are inedible) amongst your crop.

Potato plants produce a dense canopy of leaves which will shade out most weeds, but often we find an early harvest of chickweed between the rows, which we use in salads.

If you do grow maincrop spuds, these can be left in the ground and lifted as required right through to late February / early March. You will need to have grown a blight-free crop of a slug-resistant variety on fairly light soil for this to be a success. The rows should be well earthed up, and perhaps protected using straw or bracken.

Recommended varieties: Accent (first early), Charlotte (second early).

Freshly dug new potatoes.

Tomatoes

If you're in the southern counties of England, you might consider growing tomatoes outdoors. Being closely related to potatoes, tomatoes can be decimated by blight too, so use a blight-resistant variety such as 'Ferline'. Any further north and you would be better off to grow them under cover (see page 96).

CUCURBITS

Courgettes

You won't need many courgette plants – 3 or 4 should be plenty – as they're simple to grow and are usually prolific croppers. It's all too easy to end up with a glut of this particular vegetable.

Courgette plants are frost tender, so ideally sow undercover in pots in April, with a view to transplanting when all danger of frost is past (early June). They're heavy feeders and like a good deal of well-rotted muck in the soil. Prepare the ground for planting by digging a small hole (a spade width square and a spade depth deep) for each plant, and filling it with manure. Put all the soil back on top, creating mounds, and plant a seedling on each one. Provide some protection from wind for the first few weeks, as the plants are rather inclined to snap off at the base of the stem. We place an old lobster-pot funnel around each one, until well established.

Once the plants start fruiting, pick courgettes as often as you can. They're best harvested small, when the flavour is excellent and the skins are at their thinnest. If you do let some get too big, you can cook them in pies, curries, stews and

Corgettete plants. At left of picture are the recently removed funnels that were protecting the young plants from the wind.

soups, and if they get really huge just use as marrows.

Recommended variety: Sylvana.

Courgette pests

The disease you're most likely to come across is cucumber mosaic virus, which causes mottling of the leaves, poor growth, reduced yield, and, in severe cases, death of the plant. There is no treatment for the condition, but it can be prevented by growing resistant varieties. The virus is spread by aphids, so growing plants under insect netting should also thwart potential infections.

Courgette plants are also very susceptible to slug damage.

Marrows, Pumpkins, and Squash

General cultivation for these is much the same as for courgettes, but some marrow varieties and most pumpkins and squashes are trailing in their growth habit, and as such take up a lot of space. Therefore, if you're planning to plant these in a small garden, make sure you choose bush varieties. Trailing varieties will grow really well on a maturing compost heap, or on the farm muck heap. They're all heavy feeders, and like the rich dampness of these sites.

It's quite a good idea to place an old floor tile, piece of glass, slate, or similar under the flower end of developing fruits, to keep them off the ground and prevent rotting. Marrows should be harvested as soon as they reach an appropriate size (you can realistically expect to get 6-8 good sized fruits off each plant), but pumpkins and winter squash should be left on the plants as long as possible before cutting, to allow their skins to harden.

We usually leave them until late October, but more important than a particular date on the calendar is to cut them and carry in before the first frosts.

It should be possible to store marrows and pumpkins until Christmas or New Year on racks in a frost-free, dry shed, but it's better, I think, to process them as soon as possible.

Recommended Varieties: Badger / Tiger Cross (marrow), Jack of all Trades (Pumpkin).

Jerusalem Artichoke plants.

Cucumbers

Living where we do we've never tried growing cucumbers outside, but have enjoyed considerable success with them in our conservatory (page 97).

MISCELLANEOUS CROPS

Jerusalem Artichokes

Frequently referred to as 'fartichokes' for obvious reasons, this trouble-free crop can largely be left to its own devices. It's a good idea to grow them on a plot which will be used for your pigs in the following year, as it can be very difficult to harvest them cleanly. The pigs will grub up and consume any remaining tubers, which would otherwise re-grow with vigour and smother any subsequent crop. In fact, John Seymour recommended growing artichokes specifically for pigs, to be fed *in situ*.

Recommended Variety: For easier preparation in the kitchen, grow a less knobbly modern variety such as 'Fuseau', which are wonderful roasted with pork. Curiously, though, they turn the dripping black.

 TIP

The dried stalks of Jerusalem artichokes make excellent kindling. Gather them on a crisp, frosty day, break into short lengths, and store under cover until needed.

Celery

Stick to growing self-blanching varieties – traditional trench celery needs a lot of work in terms of soil preparation and care while growing. Both types prefer moist soil with plenty of organic matter. Celery seeds are notoriously difficult to germinate, so they need to be sown indoors, in the warm, and then carefully hardened off before planting out in mid / late May, once the risk of frost has passed.

The season for fresh home grown celery is quite short, but the trench grown varieties do tend to be hardier than the self-blanching types.

Recommended variety: Octavius.

Celery pests

Celery leaf fly will cause blistering on leaves, and results in stunted, bitter stems. It usually begins on small seedlings, so make sure that you don't plant out anything with suspect marks on the leaves. If your plants do develop this problem, pick off and destroy the affected leaves as soon as you spot them.

Celery leaf spot is a seed-borne disease, so is best avoided by using good quality seed rather than home saved.

Lettuces grown from a pack of mixed seed.

Lettuce

Quick and easy to grow, with results that are guaranteed to be superior to anything you can buy. In our experience, loose leaf and cos varieties are a better choice than iceberg and butterhead lettuces. They seem to be more tolerant of differing soil types and growing conditions. Lettuces need plenty of water, but do not like to be waterlogged, so a free-draining soil with plenty of organic matter worked in is best.

Sow in modules then harden off and plant out once the seedlings are big enough to handle without damaging them. Early in the year they can be germinated under glass, but later in the season it's best to leave the seed trays outside. Lettuce seeds won't germinate if the soil temperature is too low or too high. About 15°C is ideal. Also bear in mind that the seeds are tiny and need light for germination to occur, so don't sow them too deeply. Quarter of an inch is enough. Sow little and often – just a dozen seeds every couple of weeks should give you a steady supply of lettuces throughout the summer.

They don't like hot weather, and are rather inclined to bolt if they overheat or dry out. If they do start to run to seed, they tend to be rather too bitter to eat in salads. There's no need to waste them though, as they can be made into soup. Two bolted lettuces make enough soup for the whole family, but if you don't fancy that you can always feed them to your livestock.

Lettuces can also do well in colder conditions, if grown under cover, so it should be possible to harvest home-grown lettuce for a significant proportion of the year.

Recommended varieties: there's a huge choice of lettuce varieties available, and you can have fun trying lots of different types. We find that the lettuce seed mixes offered by some companies are particularly good value.

Cutting salad leaves with the kitchen scissors.

Lettuce soup

This is an extremely useful way to use up a glut of lettuce before they all bolt. Freeze in handy meal-size blocks – excellent for providing a hot dish quickly during lambing when you haven't had time to cook anything else. The recipe is equally good with spinach – use 1lb spinach leaves in place of the lettuce:

Ingredients:

1 large or 2 small lettuces
1 clove garlic
1 large onion
2 pints chicken or vegetable stock
4 oz red lentils
Seasoning

Method:

Chop and fry the onion and garlic until soft then add the lettuce. When sweated down by about half, add the stock and lentils, bring to the boil and simmer for 45 minutes. Liquidise, season to taste and stir in a bit of fresh cream, if you like.

Lettuce pests

Lettuces suffer from a number of mildews and rots. There are varieties that have been bred for resistance, so if you've had problems in the past these would be worth a try. Generally, though, if the plants are healthy and growing strongly they will be able to cope with the challenge of disease.

Aphids also cause problems, including spreading lettuce mosaic virus. If spotted, blast them off with a strong jet of water, or you could consider spraying with a soft soap solution or a pyrethrum based product. If the problem's really bad you might have to grow your lettuces under insect mesh in future.

Salad Leaves

Strictly speaking these are not a separate vegetable category, but as so many seed suppliers now offer seed mixes they're worth mentioning here. Basically they're a selection of leafy plants that are ideal for harvesting when small and immature, primarily for use in salads and stir fries.

These mixes can be grown in pots and grow bags at either end of the season, or directly in the ground when it's warmer.

Sow a few at a time, on a regular basis. Don't sow too thinly, and keep weeds under control. They're best harvested on a 'cut-and-come-again' basis, using a pair of scissors. The first cutting may be possible within three weeks of sowing, and you may get three successive harvests from each batch of plants before they run up to seed.

In spite of your best efforts you might find yourself harvesting weed seedlings along with the salad leaves, but this isn't a major problem as most are fairly palatable anyway.

Spinach / spinach beet

We hardly ever grow true spinach. Instead we grow spinach beet, also known as perpetual spinach, which is a much simpler, low maintenance crop, which seems to do well wherever you plant it. In the kitchen there's nothing you can do with true spinach that cannot be done just as easily using the alternative. Connoisseurs may notice that true spinach leaves are slightly finer in texture, and perhaps have a flavour that is a little more refined, but the difference, in my opinion, is insignificant.

The big advantage of using perpetual spinach is that it has a very long growing season. One sowing in the spring, and perhaps another in late summer, should give you almost a year-round supply of fresh green leaves, as it's

Perpetual spinach.

TIP

Sow some nasturtiums about the place – the leaves and flowers can be used in salads, and the seeds can be pickled like capers. Blackfly and caterpillars love nasturtiums, so hopefully will leave your other crops alone.

winter hardy and will continue to grow slowly throughout the colder months.

There's a tendency for the plants to bolt during dry weather, but if they do, just break off the emerging flower head and keep picking. You can even harvest the leaves that form up the flowering stem.

Recommended variety: perpetual spinach.

Sweetcorn

The big advantage to growing your own sweetcorn is the reduction in time between harvest and cooking – this is why home grown corn-on-the-cob tastes so much better than anything you can buy.

Here, we struggle to ripen our sweetcorn except in a particularly good summer, but we plant some every year, and hope for the best. We might have more success if we were to grow it in a polytunnel, but pollination would need to be assisted.

Unless you live in the south, choose an early variety, and sow indoors to give the plants a flying start. However, don't sow too early unless you've got space to keep

them indoors until they're quite big, otherwise they'll be ready to plant out before the danger of frost is past. We usually sow ours at the beginning of May, but may try sowing a week or two earlier in future. For growing in exposed locations, look for short-stemmed varieties of sweetcorn.

Sweetcorn seedlings grown individually in cardboard loo roll tubes.

Sweetcorn doesn't like having its roots disturbed, so plant in modules to minimise this. We sow ours in toilet roll tubes, then the whole lot – tube and all – can be planted out, and there's no resultant check in growth. Sweetcorn is wind pollinated, so plant out the seedlings in a block formation, rather than in a row.

Planting out, loo roll and all.

Give each plant plenty of room – about 18" square should be enough. You can utilise the space around each plant to grow other crops at ground level. Something of a sprawling nature such as pumpkins or squashes would do well in this situation.

Home grown corn-on-the-cob tastes so much better than anything you can buy.

The crop is approaching ripeness when the tassels on the ends of the cobs turn dark brown. At this stage, pull back the covering leaves and squeeze the juice from one kernel. If the liquid looks creamy or milky, then the cob is ripe. If the liquid is clear, it needs a bit longer. If it's thick and floury you've left the cobs too long and the kernels will be full of starch rather than sugars. If you don't manage to ripen the cobs, don't worry – your pigs, poultry and goats will love them.

Greenhouse and Polytunnel

Producing crops under cover widens the scope of our gardening activities. Not only does it extend the growing season, it also extends the range of crops we're able to grow. Therefore, most kitchen gardens would benefit from some sort of indoor growing space. However, there's a price to pay: obviously there's the initial purchase and construction cost to bear in mind, but also consider that plants grown indoors will require far more care and attention, as they exist in an artificial environment. Issues such as feeding, ventilation and watering are crucial, and could, potentially, become a chore.

If you have the money and the space you should consider building both a polytunnel and a conservatory / greenhouse, but if it's a case of having to make do with one or the other, think about what you're aiming to achieve then choose accordingly. One thing that applies whichever you end up with is this: Get yourself the biggest structure you can afford and have room for. If you don't, you'll very soon find yourself wishing for extra space.

Greenhouses and conservatories

Building a greenhouse or conservatory can be a costly exercise when you take into account the limited amount of

Conservatory

Every house should have a lean-to style conservatory, preferably facing due south (or thereabouts). Not only does this provide you with an ideal area to start off seedlings in the spring and to grow tender plants that wouldn't thrive outdoors, it also gives you additional living space, somewhere to kick off wet wellies and waterproofs, creates an airlock between the house and the wide world beyond and, of course, makes a solar wall out of the part of the building against which it's constructed. Even in winter sunshine the inside of a conservatory can get fairly warm, and this excess heat is absorbed by, and stored in, the thick masonry wall of the house, only to be released later as the external temperature drops. The effect is increased if you paint the external wall of the house (the bit that's inside the conservatory, anyway) black, but this might not be so aesthetically pleasing.

extra growing space that you get for your money. Because of this, they tend to be used for high value, tender crops such as tomatoes, cucumbers or peppers, and also for propagation. The expense is far more justifiable if the resultant structure conveys other benefits, such as in the case of a conservatory that also extends your living space.

There are a number of variables that impact on cost, such as size, design, and frame type, and also whether you opt for glass or polycarbonate. Purchase costs per square foot can vary from £8.50 to

Most greenhouses have only one door, which fails to allow a through movement of air.

£30 for a greenhouse, and between £14 and £30 for a very basic conservatory.

Size: The cost per square foot will be higher for a smaller structure.

Design: A simple lean-to type greenhouse or conservatory will be cheaper on a cost per square foot basis than a freestanding or complex-shaped design. It also has the advantage of additional shelter, making it less vulnerable to storm damage. A lean-to greenhouse needn't be built against your dwelling – it could just as easily adjoin an outbuilding or garden wall.

Frame type: Greenhouse frames are usually aluminium, whereas conservatories tend to be made of uPVC these days. Alternatively, either can be built from timber, but this may cost up to 50% more in the case of hardwood. Traditional greenhouses and conservatories may have steel frames. Timber frames always look nicest, but will require considerable maintenance. Aluminium or uPVC require little more than an occasional wash down.

Glass: Traditional glass is prone to breakages, but it's cheap to replace and will give the best light levels. Polycarbonates are more costly, but are safer. In fact, I would suggest that you use polycarbonate or toughened glass on safety grounds if there is any likelihood of children coming anywhere near your greenhouse. Modern conservatories have sealed double-glazed units, which are proportionately more expensive. Wherever a greenhouse or conservatory buts up against another building, the roof should always be of polycarbonate rather than glass, to reduce the likelihood of potentially dangerous breakages caused by slates or roof tiles slipping down from above.

Ventilation: Greenhouses can get very hot, very quickly, so you must ensure that there'll be adequate ventilation for your plants. Most freestanding greenhouses have only one door, which fails to allow a through movement of air, so roof lights are essential. Unless you're going to be on hand all the time to open and close these as required, you probably need roof lights that vent automatically in response to

changes in temperature. However, the mechanism isn't expensive.

We have a timber-framed lean-to conservatory the whole way along the front of our house. In the spring it's a plant nursery; during the summer and early autumn we use it for growing a range of tender crops (primarily tomatoes and cucumbers), and during the winter we stack it full of firewood and use it as a dumping area for muddy boots and wet coats. Its versatility means it's used all year round, which is what makes the initial outlay justifiable.

Polytunnels

Polytunnels are essentially giant cloches, and have huge potential to extend the length of the growing season by providing a protected environment for a wide range of crops. They tend to be larger than either greenhouses or conservatories, but are less permanent and considerably cheaper. A basic model could cost as little as £2.50 per square foot. This makes them an ideal choice for the protection of lower value crops. Unless you decide to

A suitable small polytunnel for the kitchen garden.

concrete the metal framework in place, a polytunnel can be re-sited from time to time, which reduces the risk of disease build up in the soil, and can add to the structure's versatility. Polytunnels are also commonly utilised for livestock housing (in particular for lambing sheep), and for forage storage if there are times when they're not required for growing vegetables. The interior of a polytunnel can get very hot in summer, and rather humid. These internal conditions can encourage the proliferation of pests and diseases, so you need to be particularly vigilant in order to keep your crops healthy, and pay attention to air flow. With no place for roof vents, doors at both ends are an absolute must. Some tunnels are covered partly (or even entirely) with mesh rather than plastic, which overcomes the ventilation problem to a degree. If you have any choice in the location of your tunnel, placing it so that it runs from north to south, rather than from east to west, will help to keep the temperature down to a manageable level.

A polytunnel is extremely vulnerable to wind damage, and the key to minimizing this is to ensure that the plastic cover is kept in good condition. Inspect it regularly for small holes and tears, and repair them immediately. Snow also presents a problem, and, if it's allowed to accumulate on the cover, could even lead to the total collapse of the tunnel. It should be possible to remove it with a soft brush, either from the outside, or by pushing gently upwards from the inside. The plastic cover will also need to be given a wash from time to time with a soft broom and a hosepipe, to remove dirt and algae. If well cared for, you can reasonably expect the cover to last at least 4–5 years.

Cloches / cold frames

In essence, these are miniature versions of polytunnels and greenhouses, offering versatility and mobility, although only for limited periods at each location (i.e. until the crop begins to outgrow the available space, or until harvested).

The primary considerations are that they should let plenty of light through, be simple to put together and take apart, and allow adequate ventilation while being sturdy enough to stand up to the weather without blowing away. The tunnel style of cloche meets most of these requirements. It should be possible, in most areas, to make use of them through all four seasons. In spring they warm the ground, provide protection for seedlings and to harden off young plants; over summer they can be used to give 'difficult' seeds such as French beans a good start; autumn uses include protecting salads and late summer-sown crops as the weather deteriorates; and over winter they will protect winter salads and give shelter to autumn sown over-wintering crops for a spring harvest. In addition, cloches and frames can be used inside a polytunnel or unheated greenhouse to protect particularly vulnerable plants.

Water

Where narrow cloches are used outdoors, any rain falling on them runs off the cover and soaks into the ground on which they stand. Provided that the soil has sufficient levels of organic matter, moisture should percolate through to the roots of the plants beneath the cloche. Similarly, during a dry spell, the same effect would be created if you were to pour water over the top of the cloche. However, this isn't really relevant to wide cloches and frames, or where the seedlings have yet to put down a root system. In these cases, provision needs to be made to enable you to apply additional water beneath the frame or cloche. With frames it's a simple matter of lifting the lid, but cloches can be a bit more awkward.

Tunnel cloches are commonly used by gardeners, particularly over salad seedlings, but if purchased ready-made they're very expensive for what they are. However, you can easily make your own from corrugated perspex roofing sheets, available in suitable lengths from a builder's merchant. Simply fold them over and hold in place with wire hoops. Although not exactly what you'd call cheap, they're a lot less costly than ready made cloches, and if you look after them they'll last for years.

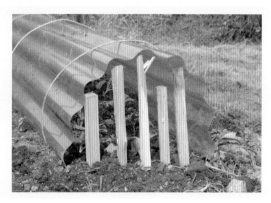

It's a good idea to keep a container of water in your polytunnel or greenhouse to ensure that the water you're using on your plants is at an appropriate temperature. Better still would be to harvest rainwater from the roof of the structure, and divert it to a butt on the inside.

Drain all the water out of your irrigation system before cold weather sets in. If you leave water in it and it freezes, the pipes, valves, and sprinkler heads may be damaged.

In the greenhouse or polytunnel there'll be no water except what you provide. In a small greenhouse, watering by hand isn't going to be too onerous a task; we water all the plants in our conservatory using a watering can, and it's not a big job. However, in larger structures, providing adequate water becomes a far greater issue, and may require something a little more efficient than a watering can. At the very least, you'll need a tap and a hosepipe inside the tunnel. Alternatively, you might want to consider an irrigation system. The most common are soaker hoses (which are laid on the soil at set distances, and gently leak water onto the ground) or overhead sprinklers (which are designed to imitate light rain). Neither option is desperately expensive, and having one or the other is almost essential in a larger polytunnel.

Pests

Aphids: Aphids will attack almost any under cover crop, given half a chance. They'll have a go outdoors too, but are less likely to reach such high numbers due to weather conditions and natural predators (such as ladybirds). They suck the sap out of the plant, causing puckering of leaves, withering and general debilitation, and also carry various viruses which can further damage your crops. In addition, they excrete a sticky substance known as honeydew, which may lead to the development of sooty mould on the leaves. Aphids can be controlled by simply squishing them under the thumb where small numbers are concerned, or by applying a soft soap or pyrethrum-based spray.

Whitefly: These are tiny, moth-like flies that feed on plant sap, causing yellowing and damage to the leaves. They're particularly fond of tomatoes, and can reach

Biological pest control

Biological control uses natural enemies to control pests. The technique is mainly used in greenhouses and polytunnels, and involves the introduction of predatory insects, mites, parasitic wasps or nematodes that attack the pests with fatal consequences. Some biological controls, particularly nematodes, can also be used outdoors.

plague levels in greenhouses if you don't remain vigilant. They may be controlled using soft soap as for aphids, but can develop resistance to chemicals quite rapidly, so beware of being too trigger-happy with the spray bottle. Hanging a sticky trap among the plants can help monitor the population (as well as catching and killing them), giving you information on how quickly the pests might be multiplying. The biological control for whitefly is a small parasitic wasp which attacks and kills the larvae.

Red Spider Mite: Another small sap sucker that can cause huge amounts of damage to greenhouse crops. Usually found on the undersides of leaves, the first sign you're likely to notice is mottling on the top surface, followed by progressive loss of colour and curling at the edges. Heavier infestations will result in leaf loss, and in these cases fine silk-like webs can often be seen on the underside of the affected foliage. They breed quickly, and rapidly develop resistance to chemical treatments. Biological controls are available, but require minimum temperatures in order to work, so can't be used effectively at the ends of the growing season. Given that the mites thrive in hot, dry conditions, one of the best control methods is to keep humidity levels up in the greenhouse, by regularly damping down paths and misting plants. We had terrible trouble with spider mites for a few years, during which time they managed to kill our fig tree, peach tree and grape vine, all of our aubergine plants, and seriously reduced our cucumber yield. We eventually managed to overcome the problem by removing all plants (and plant material) from the conservatory for a full six months, and giving the whole place a jolly good clean.

CROPPING

Tomatoes

We recommend growing at least two varieties – one that produces larger fruit, suitable for slicing and cooking, and a smaller, cherry type for use in salads (and for eating straight off the bush as you walk past!). Plum tomatoes we wouldn't bother with, as tinned tomatoes – a store cupboard staple, and essential ingredient in bolognese and other pasta dishes – are so cheap. Save your growing space for higher value varieties.

Don't sow tomato seeds too soon, unless you're able to grow the seedlings on in sufficient warmth. The seeds need a temperature of at least 21°C to germinate, so use a propagator or a sunny windowsill to get them started. Mid March is probably early enough for most situations.

Sow in modules and pot on into 3" pots when the first true leaves are showing. Plant out to final positions when the plants are strong and sturdy, and the roots are filling the 3" pot, but before they become congested. Make sure they get plenty of light to prevent them from becoming leggy.

Plants may go directly into the greenhouse or polytunnel soil, but can be grown just as successfully in pots or growbags in a conservatory, as we do. Growbags are usually recommended for up to three tomato plants, but you'll get better results if you only put two in each bag.

Pots used for growing tomatoes do need to be fairly large – about the size of a three-gallon bucket will be fine. Empty sheep-lick buckets with holes punched in the bases are ideal. Containers don't have to be pretty, just functional.

If you've opted to grow indeterminate varieties (these grow upwards on a single main stem until you stop them by nipping out the growing point) you must provide adequate support for the plants, particularly once the weight of the fruit starts adding to the burden. One of the most effective means of support, where the plant is growing directly in the soil, is to bury one end of a length of string underneath the root ball when planting out, and then run the other end up to a hook in the roof or to

A heavy crop of tomatoes just beginning to ripen.

an overhead line stretched high up along the length of the greenhouse or tunnel. If growing in pots or growbags, run a string down from the roof and tie it firmly around the lip of the pot or under the growbag. As the plants grow, twist them around the strings.

Indeterminate varieties need to be encouraged to develop fruiting growth rather than too many leaves, and this is generally done by nipping out any side shoots that grow in the angles between the main stem and the leaves. Also watch out for and remove any shoots coming out near the base of the main stem.

Determinate tomatoes don't need support, and side shoots should be left intact as the plant's habit is naturally bushy. These varieties do particularly well in pots and hanging baskets. They're usually cherry sized fruits, and are lower maintenance than other types. Feed regularly with a proprietary tomato feed or home-made liquid fertilizer once the first truss of fruit has set. Tomato plants can produce an awful lot of fruit, but they need a plentiful supply of nutrients in order to fulfill their potential.

Blossom end rot

Blossom end rot results in a dark patch forming on the flower end of the fruit, and renders it inedible. The disease is caused by insufficient and irregular watering, so take care never to let the compost dry out. Some varieties are more susceptible than others.

Good pollination is essential for successful cropping, and the best tomato pollinators in the UK are bumble bees. Honey bees will work tomato flowers, but don't find them particularly attractive.

Removing the lower leaves from plants as they turn yellow can hasten ripening, but don't fret if your tomatoes are still resolutely green at the end of the season – you can pick them as they are, and ripen them on a sunny windowsill. Alternatively, use them to make chutney.

Recommended varieties: For many years we've grown the same two varieties, 'Shirley' and 'Gardeners Delight', which have proved consistently reliable. More recently we've also grown an early fruiting heritage variety, 'Bloody Baron', which extends the period

over which we have fresh tomatoes to eat.

Cucumbers

For ease of cultivation, choose an all female F1 hybrid greenhouse variety. Cucumber seed is very expensive, so you need the reliability of an F1 to justify the cost.

The seeds are sown on edge, individually, in pots in April. They need to be warm for germination to occur, so use a propagator if you have one. Remove the lid of the propagator as soon as you see the seedlings pushing up, in order to reduce the humidity. Pot on into 5" pots when the seedlings have three or four leaves.

Take great care when watering cucumber seedlings / plants: although they need plenty of water, they don't like to be wet around the base of the stem, and can be prone to rotting off here if the compost is too soggy.

When they're ready to move to their final cropping positions, transfer each plant to an 7" pot with the bottom removed, and sink it a couple of inches into the soil or compost in your growbag, pot or bed.

Water well and often, but don't pour water into the 7" pot. Instead, apply water to the soil or compost in which it sits. This helps to keep the stem dry, and hopefully prevents rot.

Despite the fact that the stem base needs to be kept dry, cucumbers do like humidity, so mist the leaves with water daily, or maybe even several times a day in hot weather. Alternatively, damp down the paths around the plants to help

create a humid atmosphere. Feed with an appropriate feed, at least once a week, and as soon as the first cucumbers are ready, start cutting them, and keep on harvesting on a regular basis in order to ensure continuation of supply.

If placed under stress, all female varieties may occasionally produce male flowers. These need to be removed otherwise you may find that your cucumbers are rather bitter.

Cucumber pests

Various mildews may develop on cucumber leaves – we tend to get the powdery type on ours. It's easy to spot, the name gives a pretty good idea of what you're looking out for.

The conditions that favour powdery mildew are detrimental to red spider mite, and the mildew is definitely the lesser of the two evils.

We used to use yellow sulphur as a control for mildew on cucumber plants. However, although it's still available over the counter as a soil conditioner, it's no longer licensed as a fungicide. There are no other chemical controls available.

Aubergines on the conservatory windowsill.

Aubergines

Unless you live in a sheltered spot in the south, aubergines should be considered as a greenhouse or polytunnel crop. The plants need good light conditions and high humidity in order to thrive.

Aubergines require similar conditions to tomatoes for sowing, germination and early growth. Pinch out the growing point when the plants are about 12" tall to encourage the development of side shoots and a sturdy structure. If you're trying to grow aubergines of a reasonable size, it's a good idea to limit each plant to four or five fruits. They should be ready to harvest from late summer, but make sure you pick the fruits before the skins lose their glossy sheen.

Aubergine plants are very susceptible to red spider mite, so do ensure that your greenhouse is free of this pest.

Capsicums and chilli peppers

These are tender crops that we've never had a great deal of success with. Good levels of light are more important than a fertile growing medium. Choosing a European variety that produces thinner walled fruit might be more successful if your growing conditions are less than ideal, as they tend to be more tolerant of lower temperatures and poorer light levels.

Chilli peppers.

In some situations you may be able to grow the plants to maturity outdoors, although they'll definitely need to be started off undercover – a temperature of 21°C, or thereabouts, will give the best germination. You may well need to use a heated propagator in order to achieve this. Alternatively, leave sowing until the weather warms up a bit.

If the plants develop a rather straggly and leggy habit, pinch out the growing points when they are about 15" high to encourage bushy growth. Support may be needed, in which case a cane pushed into the

pot next to the plant and loosely tied to the stem will do. The plants are sometimes quite brittle, so an individual branch carrying a number of fruits may also need to be supported in some way to avoid it breaking.

Feed as per tomatoes.

Peppers can be harvested when green, yellow or red, depending on the degree of ripeness required. When fully ripe (red), the flavour is sweeter and / or hotter.

CONTAINER GROWING

The number of vegetable seed varieties now bred specifically for container growing is a clear indication of the increasing popularity of this method of gardening. The attraction is obvious: the use of pots has made home production accessible to virtually everyone, even if the only space available is a small patio or urban balcony. While it's unlikely (but not entirely impossible) that operating on this scale will achieve total self-sufficiency in vegetables and fruit, these 'micro holdings' can make a significant contribution to a household's domestic economy, particularly if growers concentrate on crops that are costly to buy.

Container growing needn't be restricted to those with limited space; the larger scale gardener may choose to use pots, containers and grow-bags within the sheltered confines of a greenhouse or conservatory, as we do with our cucumbers and tomatoes. In the conservatory we have no other option, as the tiled floor precludes any other method, but in greenhouses it's more common to have soil-based beds or borders. However, repeated heavy cropping eventually leads to nutrient depletion and the accumulation of pests and diseases. Rather than dig out the beds and import fresh soil, container growing may be the way forward.

For the urban gardener, possibly restricted to patio growing, there's a remarkable range of vegetables that can be cultivated in what initially might appear to be a rather limited environment. Patios, by their very nature, are often sheltered sun-traps, which may mean that crops normally required to be grown under cover will thrive perfectly well outdoors.

Making the most of the available area is a top priority, so use vertical spaces such as walls and fences by installing trelliswork and hanging baskets. Flat roofs might also provide additional space, although be aware of potential structural issues, as the combined weight of your pots and their associated compost could be considerable. Plants of varying heights can be used to 'layer' the growing space, with taller crops such as indeterminate tomatoes at the back (perhaps tied to a trellis for support), medium height crops (e.g. dwarf French beans) in front of the tomatoes, and low-growing salads in grow-bags at the front. With a bit of imagination and ingenuity there are many possibilities.

When it comes to choosing containers, you can be quite creative. Of course, you could pop down to the garden centre and spend quite a lot on pretty glazed pots, or a bit less on plain terracotta ones, but a plastic bucket will do just as well, provided you knock a few holes in the bottom. In fact, you can use pretty much anything, as long as it can be adapted to provide adequate drainage and will hold sufficient compost for whatever you want to grow in it – old bath tubs, ceramic sinks, chimney pots; the list is endless. And don't discount grow-bags; they're not pretty by any stretch of the imagination, but they're very useful, fairly portable, and relatively inexpensive.

Pot grown crops

Theoretically, you can grow virtually anything in a pot or container that you can in the garden, and a quick perusal of the seed catalogues will show you that there's a wide range of varieties ideally suited to being cultivated in this way. However, given that there's a lot of work and a certain amount of extra cost associated with pot-grown plants, it makes sense to use this method for crops that are either high value, especially tender or extra early, or where disease problems make it impossible for you to grow them in open ground.

Tomatoes: All types of tomatoes can be successfully grown in pots. There are even varieties suited to hanging baskets (e.g. 'Tumbler', a determinate cherry variety).

Cucumbers: These crop quite well in pots and grow-bags, but they must be well supported, so putting them alongside a fence or over a trellis is probably the best option. If they're to be grown outside, choose a standard type rather than an all-female F1 variety.

Herbs and spices: A wide range of fresh herbs and some spices will grow well in pots, and they are a popular crop for window boxes too. Concentrate on those that you use regularly in the kitchen.

Leafy salad crops: Baby salads can easily be grown for 'cut-and-come-again' cropping, allowing you to gather a succession of harvests from the same limited space over the course of a growing season.

Blueberries: These are usually grown in pots as they require an acidic growing medium, which is easier to provide in a container than in a bed.

Strawberries: Well suited to growing in containers, and pretty much any variety will produce a decent crop on a patio, but choose an everbearing type for hanging baskets, with three or four plants per basket.

Chilli peppers: Ideally suited to growing in conservatories and on patios. Under ideal conditions, a single plant growing in a 10" pot could yield as many as 100-200 chilies. Varieties suitable for hanging baskets are also available.

Aubergines: Although generally considered an under cover crop, aubergines can be grown outdoors on a sunny, sheltered patio. Varieties have been developed specifically for container growing.

First early potatoes: You'll need a good-sized pot for these – at least a 3-gallon bucket for each seed tuber. Alternatively, grow five or six plants in a dustbin. The 'gradual top up' method works well here: plant the seed spuds in compost at the bottom of the dustbin, then earth up the plants as they grow by gradually adding more compost, until the top of the bin is reached. New potatoes should develop throughout the full depth. Harvest by emptying out the entire contents of the bin.

Carrots: Although a low-value crop, and generally not appropriate for container growing, you might like to give it a try if you're seriously troubled by carrot root fly. Choose short or stump rooted varieties, and raise the pot at least 2' off the ground, placing it above the height at which the flies travel.

Nasturtiums and marigolds: Edible plants and flowers add colour to your growing space, and to your salads.

Crops not worth growing in pots or containers would include those which occupy space for an extended period, for example many brassicas (in particular purple sprouting broccoli, sprouts and winter cauliflowers), most root crops and leeks, and also really heavy feeders such as marrows and pumpkins (which would probably take up too much room anyway). Maincrop potatoes wouldn't be worth bothering with either.

Crop management

Striking the right balance between drainage and moisture conservation is the key to getting good results from container growing. Prepare pots well by putting a layer of small stones, gravel or broken crockery at the bottom, to prevent compost from blocking the drain holes and allow the free passage of excess water. The choice of growing medium is also significant: garden soil is usually too heavy, and is inclined to become compacted. Compost is generally preferable. We purchase peat-based compost for containers, although if intending to fill a pot for long-term occupancy, such as

in the case of a grape vine or a small fruit tree, we use a soil-based product. These are more expensive, but better suited to perennials due to their nutrient retention capability and reduced susceptibility to drying out. On the other hand, drainage is harder to get right in soil-based products, and the filled pots can be weighty (which may be a problem if you're intending to stand them on raised structures or flat roofs). There's no reason at all why you can't fill your containers with home-made compost, although we find that we use all the compost that we make on the garden itself, so never have enough left over for filling pots.

It's important to remember that any plant grown in a restricted environment will be entirely dependent upon you for water and food, once the initial reserves in the compost have been used up, so care must be taken to feed regularly, and to ensure that the growing medium is kept moist at all times, without allowing it to become waterlogged. Water requirements will vary enormously depending on the size of the plant, the dimensions of the pot, ambient temperature, rate of growth, and the time of year. Our principal container-grown crop is tomatoes, which we check regularly and water as necessary, which, in hot weather, may be twice a day. Grow-bags are notoriously difficult to keep moist, and actually getting the water to the compost is tricky as it's enclosed in plastic. To get around this, we cut a small hole in the bag next to each plant and partially bury an empty 3" flowerpot in the compost, which provides us with a watering point. Liquid feeds can be added to the water as required (see page 63).

Due to the limitations imposed

upon them, plants grown in containers are more vulnerable to extremes of temperature. Summer crops may suffer from excessive heat, so ensure they're well-ventilated, and keep the roots cool by making sure they're always well-watered. If you have plants in containers outdoors, be aware of the drying effect of the wind, which can rapidly deplete water levels in compost. Pot plants are also susceptible to getting blown over in strong winds due to their often rather top-heavy nature.

Any container-grown perennials that are outside in winter are at risk from frost, as the compost in pots will freeze far more readily than the soil in the garden, so provide protection by either bringing them under cover, or wrapping the pot in some sort of insulating material such as bubble wrap.

Recycling

It should be possible to re-use spent compost and the contents of grow-bags. For example, having used a grow bag to produce a crop of tomatoes during the summer, the following spring you can remove the top of the bag and grow cut-and-come-again salads in it. Once these are finished, spread the spent compost on the garden, or add it to your compost heap. In this way you're making best use of resources and can assuage any sense of guilt you may feel at having bought the compost in the first place.

Soft Fruit

S oft fruit should be grown by every gardener, even those operating on a very small scale.

The period from planting to harvesting can be quite short – as little as six months in the case of strawberries – and almost all types produce a crop in their second season. Most bush and cane fruits will have a productive lifespan of around 10 years, after which yields will naturally decline. However, propagating replacement plants is quite straightforward. They're undemanding to care for, and are generally fairly forgiving of neglect.

An ideal spot for the soft fruit bed would be in a south-facing area, slightly higher than the surrounding ground, and free from frost hollows. A gentle slope is good, as it allows all the plants to catch the sun without casting excessive shadow on neighbouring bushes. Most soils will be ok, but in the case of very light or particularly heavy soils you'll need to add plenty of organic matter. You can improve the soil you have, but only up to a point, so bear this in mind when deciding what to grow, and where to grow it. For example, blueberries will thrive in an acidic soil, but if your land tends towards neutral they can be grown in pots instead.

There are an increasing number of hybrid fruit bushes available now, but we tend to stick to the following old favourites:

Blackcurrants

Blackcurrants seem to be able to put up with a certain amount of mismanagement, which is useful if you're short of time, or when other circumstances come between you and your garden. Our blackcurrant bushes don't crop as heavily as perhaps they should, but because we're not short of space this isn't really an issue – we just have more bushes.

• **Site:** More tolerant of wet conditions than many fruit, but they do like a soil with plenty of organic matter worked into it. A sunny location is best, although light shade can be tolerated without too much impact on yields, and some shelter from the wind is preferable. Blackcurrants flower quite early in the season, so be particularly careful to avoid planting in frost pockets.

• **Planting and establishing:** As with all soft fruit, plant during the dormant period if they're bare-rooted. On the other hand, it should be possible to plant pot-grown specimens at any time of year. However, the only time we've tried this it wasn't a success, so our advice is to stick to winter planting. Allow about 5' of space in each direction around the bush, and dig a big enough hole to take the roots comfortably. Aim to settle the plant in about 2" deeper than it was in its previous location. As you replace the soil, it's a good idea to mix in a couple of handfuls of bonemeal – it's high in phosphates, which are important nutrients for root development. Once the earth has settled around the plant, trim back all the branches to within 2" of the ground, which encourages new stems to grow up from below ground level. As a result you won't get a crop until the second season, but your bush will have a chance to get really well established before it has to cope with the stress of fruiting.

• **Care:** Beyond keeping weeds under control (use an appropriate mulch – see pages 60 - 61) and regularly watering during the first year or two, a good annual dose of muck and perhaps a top dressing of bonemeal in the spring should be all the care your blackcurrant bushes need.

• **Pruning:** None needed until the first crop has been harvested. Subsequently, cut out approximately ⅓ of the branches every year to encourage new growth. Blackcurrants fruit best on wood that grew during the previous season, so the aim is to keep the bush young.

• **Harvesting:** Blackcurrants, as the name suggests, are ready to pick when the currants turn black. They're fiddly little things, so it can be quite a time-consuming job – a good task for small children. If you're lucky, all the currants on an individual string will come ripe at the same time, so you can pick the whole string and then strip the berries off with a fork. Gather them on a dry day, and once harvested they'll keep pretty well in the fridge, possibly for as long as a week. Any longer than this, though, and you'd be better to put them in the freezer for later use. Blackcurrants can be eaten fresh, in which case they're best combined with other types of fruit, as their flavour can be quite strong. They're also excellent for making jams and jellies, and for the production of wines and cordials.

• **Propagating:** Assuming your blackcurrant bushes are healthy, it's very easy to grow new plants. Our first attempt at propagating them was spectacularly successful; we simply took a load of cuttings in the autumn after the leaves had dropped, poked them in the ground, and left them to it. Every single one rooted and grew. When we moved house shortly afterwards we dug up all the young

Blackcurrents pests and diseases

There are two main problems to keep an eye open for with blackcurrants: big bud and reversion virus. The mite that causes big bud is a microscopic pest which takes up residence in blackcurrant buds. Its effects are most easily seen in the late winter and early spring when the bushes are leafless, and it causes the buds to become enlarged and distorted. If the problem is only affecting a few buds they can be picked off and disposed of, well away from the plants, but if the bush is badly attacked it may be necessary to dig up and replace the whole thing.

Reversion virus can be difficult to identify, the main symptom being a gradual decline in the vigour of the plant; fruit yields will drop, the leaves become smaller, and the bush may look as if it's lacking nutrients. As the virus progresses, the leaf structure begins to change, becoming simpler, with fewer serrations along the edges. There's no cure, and the only course of action is to grub the bush out and replace it with certified virus-free stock. Evidence suggests that the reversion virus is spread by the big bud mite, so if you're prompt in your treatment of big bud, your plants may escape reversion.

We've never really had any trouble with birds taking the blackcurrants, probably because they're always too busy stuffing themselves in our redcurrant bushes a bit further along the plot.

plants and used them to create a new fruit patch in our virgin kitchen garden.

Cuttings should consist of a 12" length of the current season's growth, snipped off immediately below a bud. You should also take the tip off the cutting just above a bud with an angled cut. Push the cutting into soil that's not too heavy or waterlogged, leaving just the top two buds above ground. Leave for twelve months before transplanting to a permanent location.

Redcurrants

• **Site:** Much the same as for blackcurrants, although redcurrants are less tolerant of wet ground.

• **Planting and establishing:** Prepare the planting hole as for blackcurrants. Redcurrants are

grown on a 'leg', so remove any shoots from the bottom 6"- 9" of the main stem. Once the bush is *in situ*, cut back all the remaining branches, including the central leader, by half. (This may have already been done if you're purchasing from a nursery or catalogue). Leave about 5' to 6' between bushes.

• **Care:** Easy to look after – just an annual dressing of well-rotted muck, and keep the weeds down.

• **Pruning:** Unlike its black cousin, the redcurrant fruits on old wood, so bushes have to be pruned quite differently. Ideally some summer pruning should be carried out, in addition to the main winter cut back, but to be honest we've never bothered to do this. It would be omitted anyway if the bush had not had a particularly good year. Winter pruning needs to be done while the bush is dormant, but not

Redcurrant bush mulched with straw.

Unripe currants.

Redcurrent pests and diseases

Without netting the fruit we would very rarely manage to harvest any quantity of redcurrants. Blackbirds go mad for them, which is probably why they leave the blackcurrants alone. In fact, everything seems to love the redcurrants. Quite apart from the blackbirds – who're undoubtedly the main culprits – we've had them stolen by pheasants, badgers, and even our own chickens.

The only other pest that's troubled our redcurrant bushes is the currant blister aphid, which lives on the underside of leaves and causes raised, often coloured patches on the upper face of the leaf, but doesn't seem to affect the plant unduly.

the wrong direction and spoiling the general shape of the bush. Finally, cut back any side shoots growing out from the leader to about 2", ensuring that there are a couple of healthy buds on the bit you leave behind. If you decide to summer prune as well, simply pinch out the side shoots to about 5 leaves in late June or early July.

If you're really tight for space, redcurrant bushes can be successfully grown as cordons, but the pruning required for this is much more complicated, and beyond the scope of this book.

during wet or frosty weather. A January weather window usually provides the required opportunity.

Dealing first with the main branches, or leaders, cut back the previous season's growth by half. You should be able to identify the younger growth as it'll be a paler colour than older wood. Cut back to an upward facing bud, and the following year's growth should sprout from it. Also remove any old or diseased stems, together with branches that are growing in

• **Harvesting:** Redcurrants generally have a much sharper flavour than blackcurrants, and the main reason we grow them is to make redcurrant jelly, which is simply the best accompaniment to roast mutton or game. Also, being loaded with pectin, redcurrants are very useful for adding to jams made with other fruits, to aid setting.

• **Propagating:** They're propagated in essentially the same as way as blackcurrants,

usually from hardwood cuttings in the autumn, the only significant difference being that you remove all the buds except for the four or five uppermost, and then ensure that the lowest remaining bud is at least 6" above ground level. This should give a 'leg' to the new bush. We've also successfully produced new plants by layering branches over the winter, then separating the rooted section and replanting in the spring; not exactly 'by the book', but it worked!

Gooseberries

A seriously under-rated fruit, with many sweet and juicy modern varieties a vast improvement on older types.

• **Site:** Full sunshine is preferred, although some shade is tolerated. Avoid frost pockets where possible.

• **Planting and establishing:** As for redcurrants.

• **Care:** As for redcurrants.

• **Pruning:** Winter pruning of gooseberries is as for redcurrants. However, gooseberries will really benefit from summer pruning as well, much more so than redcurrants, so give priority to the goosegogs if you're pushed for time, and you'll be rewarded with a higher yield the following year. Summer pruning is quite simple – just pinch off the young lateral side shoots to five leaves in early July.

• **Harvesting:** Ripe gooseberries have a bit of give in them when squeezed between finger and thumb. In addition, red varieties should have changed colour, with some being nearly black before they're ready. Just eat a few to assess their readiness; they should be sweet, but with a bit of crunch. Unless you've let them get over-ripe, the fruits are fairly robust, so there's no need for delicate handling. Just pick them straight into a suitable sized container and take them to the kitchen for topping and tailing before use. If you've got more than you can reasonably use, they freeze well. We usually freeze them in 1lb batches, which is enough for baking a crumble, and simplifies the business of calculating the right quantity for jam or wine making.

Ripening gooseberries.

• **Propagating:** Usually propagated from cuttings in late summer or early autumn. Take a cutting about a foot in length from the current season's growth, snipping it off just above a bud with a straight cut. Remove all buds from the lower half of the cutting, leaving at least three at the top. Stick them in the ground and they should grow away, ready to plant out as young bushes the following winter. Gooseberries can also be reproduced from layers; you'll get a healthy bush, but it won't grow on a leg as it should.

Gooseberry pests and diseases

The bushes tend to be pretty resilient and trouble free. However, keep an eye open for the gooseberry sawfly caterpillar – a striking looking bluish green grub with black spots. These pests can completely defoliate a gooseberry bush, which has a major impact on the health and vitality of the plant, and will badly affect yield. You can't really mistake them for anything else, so if you see one, squash it. Alternatively, if you notice that your bushes have got leaves missing, have a good look, and keep looking until you find the culprit.

The other main problem to watch out for is gooseberry mildew. The first sign of infection is a white, powdery mould appearing on the leaves and young shoots. If you don't spot it at this stage, the fruit will develop similar white patches, which subsequently turn into a brown felt-like covering over the berries. The best treatment is prevention; keep the centre of the bushes open and well pruned, allowing air to circulate. Overcrowding provides ideal conditions for mildew to develop. Prune out diseased shoots after the fruit has been harvested. Affected fruit can be eaten after the mould has been rubbed off, but they tend to go brown when cooked, so aren't particularly appetising. Gooseberry mildew can be controlled by applying a garden fungicide, but it's much better to avoid it in the first place through good management.

Harvesting raspberries.

Raspberries

Raspberries are a crop with which we've had mixed success. They grow on canes rather than bushes, and in our experience need a bit more care than other soft fruit in order to be successful. We started our raspberry stock by splashing out on a fruit collection from one of the seed catalogues, consisting of an early variety, a mid season type, and an autumn fruiting cultivar. I can't remember the names of the first two, but I do know that the autumn canes were called 'Autumn Bliss'. Raspberries generally have a productive lifespan of 10-12 years, but they propagate so easily that once you've got some you need never be without them again.

• **Site:** Because canes are slightly more delicate and prone to damage than bushes, raspberries need to be put in a spot where they'll be reasonably sheltered from strong winds and, in keeping with most other soft fruit, they prefer full sun (although they will tolerate partial shade). A slightly acidic soil is best, but, more importantly, the ground mustn't be too wet or

they're likely to turn up their toes and die. Try to plant the rows of canes running from north to south, in order that they benefit from maximum summer sunshine.

• **Planting and establishing:** A winter job, in keeping with the planting of other soft fruit. The ground needs to be well prepared before planting canes, so clear it of perennial weeds, and dig in some well-rotted muck. Adding a bit of bonemeal will promote root development and help the plants get established more quickly. Dig a shallow (3"- 4" deep) trench, about 18" wide. Place the young canes in the trench about 18" apart, taking care to spread the roots out evenly. Replace the soil and firm well. Once they're in the ground, cut each cane down to about 12", which encourages the formation of new shoots from the base. This new growth forms the canes that will bear your first crop of raspberries.

• **Care:** The tall and somewhat fragile nature of raspberry canes means that they require support. They can grow up to six feet high, and when laden with fruit can be top heavy, so are susceptible to wind damage if not held up in some way. Ideally you should install a set of wires for the canes before you plant them. This needn't be complicated – a sturdy post at either end of the row, with lighter weight intermediate posts approximately every 10' to 15' will do for summer fruiting varieties. Stretch three or four wires fairly tightly between these posts, with the top wire about 5' above ground level. Rather than wire we use plastic-coated washing line; this is easy to pull tight between the posts, lasts a long time (if you use the type with a polypropylene core), and is less

harsh on the canes than wire. It'll stretch and sag over time, but it's relatively simple to re-tension. Autumn fruiting varieties can manage without support, but will benefit from it all the same. In this case, put two posts about 18" apart at each end of the row (and intermediates, if required), and run the wires up one side of the row and down the other, creating a long, narrow box shape. Encourage the canes to grow between the pairs of wires, which will help them stay tidy and upright. Keep the area weed free, but try not to disturb the roots, as this tends to result in excessive production of new canes. Pull out any 'rogue' canes that grow up away from the rows – if left to their own devices they'll spread and take over much of your garden.

• **Pruning:** Most raspberry varieties fruit on wood from the previous season, making it a two-year cycle of growth and pruning. Basically, all you need to do is to cut out, at ground level, the canes that have produced fruit, leaving just the young canes to produce next year. You can do this as soon as they've finished fruiting, but we usually leave it until winter when the plants are dormant. Do be careful though, as sometimes canes will produce a small amount of fruit in their first season and will go on to give a full crop the following year. In the first couple of seasons we made the mistake of cutting these down, and then wondered why we had such a meagre harvest in the next season. You can usually tell the difference by looking at the colour of the stem; older canes are quite brown, and newer growth is much greener. You might need to thin the canes out a bit once well established. A cane every 3" or so is enough. Reducing overcrowding will result in bigger, better quality berries. Autumn varieties, which will fruit from September right through to November, are usually 'primocanes', meaning that they fruit on the current season's cane. Each spring the whole lot can be cut down to the ground, ready for the next crop.

• **Harvesting:** Raspberries are ready to harvest when they're fully coloured, but still quite firm. They should only be picked when dry, otherwise they deteriorate very rapidly, and go mouldy before you've had a chance to do anything with them. They need to be handled gently, the aim being to leave the central plug and the stalk on the plant. If the berry is ripe it should pull off easily enough; if it doesn't, leave it another day or two. Shelf life is very short, so either eat, process, or freeze them as soon as you can. They're good in pies, crumbles, fresh with lashings of cream, in cakes, bakes, sorbets, ice-cream, jam or wine.

• **Propagating:** Expanding your stock of raspberry canes is simplicity itself: simply lift a cane that's surplus to requirements, cut its roots to remove it from the parent plant, and replant in the desired location as outlined above.

Blackberries and loganberries

Cultivating blackberries in the fruit garden is, in my opinion, a bit of a waste of space. Going blackberrying is a time-honoured autumn tradition, and a large quantity of fruit can be gathered in a relatively short period of time from the hedgerows around the farm. However, if the only wild blackberries you have access to are roadside plants, or on popular dog-walking routes, you might consider planting a thornless variety in the fruit garden.

Loganberries have the same growth habit and requirements as blackberries, so it makes sense to consider them both together.

• **Site:** Given that brambles seem to thrive virtually anywhere, it would seem reasonable to assume that blackberries and loganberries are not too fussy about where they grow. They'll tolerate some shade, and will do well enough in places where the drainage would be too poor for other types of soft fruit. However, choosing a location with more favourable growing conditions will give better crops.

• **Planting and establishing:** Best planted in early spring before the season's growth begins. Dig out a good sized hole that'll comfortably hold the root ball, and carefully position the plant therein. Take care when handling not to knock off any of the embryonic buds – these will grow into canes in the spring. Firm in using soil enriched with a bit of compost and some bonemeal. The usual guidelines for the care of young fruit plants apply – keep them weed free and water from time to time in dry weather. Allow 10' to 12' between plants.

• **Care:** If the summer's particularly dry, they'll benefit from occasional watering, especially during the time the fruit is swelling. Keep weeds in check to maintain good air circulation around the plants and reduce competition for nutrients; applying a thick manure mulch in the spring will help with this. Any shoots that emerge too far from the base of the plant should be removed to keep the area tidy and make weeding easier.

• **Support and pruning:** These plants are like raspberries in that they produce fruit on the previous season's growth, and the same arrangement of support wires

---

Raspberry pests and diseases

Raspberry mosaic virus is probably the commonest and most serious disease that you're likely to come across. Leaves become mottled yellow, curling downwards at the edges, and the fruit is dry and crumbly. There's no cure, and affected canes must be pulled out and disposed of to reduce the chance of the virus spreading. The level of risk can be minimised by buying certified virus-free plants to get you started, and if you need to expand your raspberry stocks, don't accept home-grown canes from elsewhere; either buy in new certified plants, or propagate from your own healthy ones. Most plant viruses are spread by aphids, so keep an eye out for them and control as necessary.

If you're finding maggots in your raspberries, then it appears that you have a problem with raspberry beetles. The grubs are usually found at picking, in the middle of the fruit, as they feed on the central plug and move down to the soil to pupate later in the season. They can be controlled using a pyrethrum garden pesticide, or you might consider using a raspberry beetle trap, which works by attracting then capturing the adult beetles as they emerge from the soil in the spring, thus preventing them from laying eggs on your canes. Traps cost around £20, and a single unit will protect up to 50 square metres.

suggested for standard raspberries will also suffice for blackberries and loganberries. The growth habit, however, is completely different, with the canes being very long and flexible. The current season's new shoots should be tied in to the wires as they grow. One option is to run all the new growths along the wires in one direction, leaving them in place to fruit in twelve months' time, and the following year to send the young shoots in the opposite direction. Cutting out the old stems when they've fruited makes room for the next lot of canes. However, this method takes up a fair amount of space, and you'd probably need to leave more than the previously suggested distance between plants if you were going to do it this way. It's definitely the simplest option though, as you won't need to move and retie canes over the winter months. Another option, where space is limited, is to tie all the new shoots in a bundle to the top wire as they grow. Then in winter, when the fruited canes have been removed, retie the young canes to the lower wires, spreading them out a bit as you go. Only having canes going in one direction does mean you can get more plants in the space available, but the downside is that you can't really have as many fruiting canes per plant (only 4-5, as opposed to 6-8 if the first method is adopted). Overcrowding leads to poor air circulation, the development of moulds and diseases, and uneven ripening.

• **Harvesting:** Pick when the fruit is well coloured and soft. It must be absolutely dry, otherwise it'll go mouldy more quickly than you can use it. Eat, use, or freeze as soon as you can.

• **Propagating:** Multiplying

your stock of blackberries and loganberries is simplicity itself. They reproduce themselves with remarkable ease from tip layers in the same manner as wild brambles. The biggest problem you will have will be keeping them under control – any cane tip that's left touching the ground in autumn will sprout roots, and grow up as a new plant in the spring. If you want it, just dig it up and replant it in the space allocated for it. Otherwise, give it to the pigs or chuck it on the bonfire.

Blackberry pests and diseases

Blackberries and Loganberries are generally pretty trouble free. The only problem we have encountered is a bit of mould on the fruit from time to time.

Rhubarb

Although technically a vegetable, rhubarb is usually thought of as a fruit, so it's appropriate to deal with it here. Generally considered to be a very tough plant, rhubarb is often rather neglected by gardeners in favour of those that need more care. However, if you do look after it well, and give it all the attention it deserves, you'll be rewarded with heavy crops of rhubarb sticks at a time of year when there's no other fresh fruit to harvest.

• **Site:** Rhubarb isn't particularly fussy about soil type except where the ground is alkaline, in which case it won't thrive at all. It can tolerate some shade but, in keeping with most other crops, it will do better if provided with ample sunshine. Also avoid planting in places which might become waterlogged in winter.

Although usually grown in the garden rather than the orchard, rhubarb is a perennial crop, so don't plant it where it could obstruct other activities. There's no reason at all why you couldn't locate the rhubarb bed somewhere completely different, such as in a border by the house.

• **Planting and establishing:** Rhubarb needs to be planted in ground that has been heavily enriched with manure and compost, as it's a gross feeder. Dig the muck in well, preferably in the autumn, ready for planting in the spring (February or early March). Dig a hole big enough to comfortably hold all the roots and set the rhubarb crown in it. Fill in and finish off so that the top of the crown is just below the surface of the ground. Firm the soil and water a little to settle it down. Allow at least 3' between each plant, or more if you have the space. Don't harvest any sticks in the first year, giving the plants time to get established and build up root reserves. Keep moist during the summer months, and use a mulch to keep weeds to a minimum. A dose of muck in the autumn will make sure that they're in good shape for harvest the following spring.

• **Care:** Keep an eye open for any flower stalks that the crowns send up. They're attractive, but will reduce vigour, so it's best to cut them off at ground level. Beyond occasional watering and a good top dressing of manure each year, rhubarb should pretty much look after itself. The exception to this would be in the case of 'forced' rhubarb, where it's encouraged to crop earlier, producing sweeter, more tender sticks of fruit. This involves not only triggering the plant into growth earlier in the year

Tender young rhubarb sticks.

Rhubarb pests and diseases

Pretty trouble free, really. The only significant problem you're likely to encounter is crown rot, the name of which is self-explanatory. There's no cure, so dig up and dispose of affected crowns. It's caused by a fungus which has a few years persistency in the soil, so if you want to replace the diseased rhubarb, you'll need to find a new spot for it.

than would normally be the case, but also making it grow in the absence of light. To achieve this cover the crown with an upturned bucket, a large drain pipe or an old chimney pot, packed all around with fresh muck. It'll then send up tender new growth which can be harvested as soon as it's large enough. Forcing is extremely draining to the plant, so you should never force the same crown two years running. In fact, it's better not to pick at all from a plant that

was forced the previous year. Because of the burden placed upon the plant, and the need to allow it to recover, we've never bothered to force our rhubarb.

• **Harvesting:** Use your judgement to pull sticks when they're big enough to be useful in the kitchen. Don't harvest too many from one plant at a time, and never all of them. Remove by grasping the stem quite near to its base and giving a sharp tug downwards and away from the plant. It should come away cleanly and without snapping the stem. Chop off the leaves (which are poisonous) and add them to the compost heap. Rhubarb needs cooking before eating, and can be used to make a range of pies, puddings, jams and wines. Don't harvest any sticks after the middle of June, giving the plant a chance to recover before cropping next year.

• **Propagating:** Rhubarb can be grown from seed, but the results are very variable. The usual way to increase your stock is to dig up a

large, healthy crown in early spring when it has a number of small shoots showing above the ground surface, chop it in half with a sharp spade (making sure that there are shoots on both halves), and then replant. You can cut it into more bits, but the smaller the pieces you use, the harder it will be for them to develop into strong plants, and the longer it will be before you can harvest a meaningful crop.

Strawberries

Everyone should have strawberry plants, even if it's just one or two in a pot. The first ripe strawberry is the herald of summer, and if you plan your varieties carefully, it's possible to have strawberries for picking over an extended period. Our first strawberry plants were given to us by a friend whose husband was a keen gardener. They did really well, but didn't last long: a family of escapee pigs rampaging through the garden made a bee-line for them, and ate the whole lot. (In fact, over the years quite a few of our strawberry plants have met the same fate.)

• **Site:** Strawberry plants are somewhat fussier that many other types of soft fruit, preferring a sunny, slightly sheltered site, and fairly well drained soil. A cold, waterlogged soil in spring will retard their growth and fruit development, resulting in later, poorer quality crops.

• **Planting and establishing:** If your soil is inclined to be a bit soggy (even after the addition of organic matter), consider growing strawberries above ground level on a raised area, or in some way that generally improves drainage and warms the soil. With this in mind we grow ours in old car tyres. By laying the tyres on the ground and then filling them with a mixture of soil and compost, we're creating temporary miniature raised beds, and the fact that tyres are black helps absorb heat from the sun, giving the strawberry plants that bit of extra warmth. Young bare-rooted plants (known as runners) are best planted in August and September to give them plenty of time to establish before fruiting the following season. They can also be transplanted in March or April, but if this is the case they should be prevented from cropping for a full twelve months by removing any flowers that form. As with other fruit, container-grown specimens can be planted at more or less any time of year. If growing in conventional sized car tyres, allow two plants in each one, and no more. Otherwise, plant them about 18" apart, and aim to settle the runners with the crown of the plant level with the soil surface once firmed down; any lower and you risk the plant rotting over winter; any higher and it will dry out and may die.

Strawberry plants growing in old tyres.

• **Care:** Keep the young plants weed free, and a bit of feed in the early spring to give them a boost won't go amiss, but don't overdo it. Ours get a top dressing of wood ash. When the plants flower, apply a good mulch around them. Traditionally straw is used for this (unsurprisingly), but black plastic also works well. The purpose of the mulch is to keep the developing fruit off the ground, protecting them from mud and wet. Make sure the plants don't go short of water while the fruit is swelling, or they'll be small and wizened. However, don't over water them in pursuit of high yields as excessive irrigation (or rain) can ruin the flavour of the berries. Once fruiting is complete, take off all the

A straw mulch protects the ripening fruit.

leaves at about three inches above the crown, and clear away the old mulch. Also remove any runners not needed as new plants (see propagation, overleaf).

• **Pruning:** None required.

• **Harvesting:** Pick when the fruit is plump and well coloured. If birds and slugs are a nuisance, you might need to gather them when they're slightly unripe, but you can net the plants if you feel so inclined. We've never bothered with this – the blackbirds are usually too busy stealing redcurrants to bother with strawberries. Try to harvest them as quickly as they ripen, and eat or use straight away, if you can. For the most intense flavour experience, eat them straight from the plant. If you have to keep them at all, put them in the fridge, where they'll be ok for a couple of days, but allow them to come back up to room temperature before use, as cold seems to inhibit the flavour. Don't bother freezing them. Strawberries can be used in jams and preserves, and homemade strawberry ice cream is wonderful, but the best way to enjoy strawberries is straight from the garden, first thing in the morning, with home-made yoghurt or thick fresh cream, and the merest sprinkling of demerara sugar.

• **Propagating:** Strawberries aren't long lived, and each plant will generally give only three good crops. After that the amount of fruit produced declines rapidly, so grub them up and replace. One of the beauties of strawberries (in common with many other types of soft fruit) is that once you've acquired your original stock of plants there should be little need to ever buy more. Unless you're unlucky enough to have a pig problem, as we did, or a case of disease, you should be able to grow your own replacements. Each year, after fruiting has finished, the plants obligingly throw out a multitude of runners. At the end of each of these, a little plantlet will form. If you pin the end of the runner under some compost in an 3" pot (we find fencing staples excellent for this), it will put down roots, and, given a bit of time, you'll be able to separate the runner from the parent. These new plants are then used to replace the oldest, although not on the same piece of ground.

Propagating strawberry plants by potting runners.

Strawberry pests and diseases

Probably the commonest problem with strawberries is botrytis, also known as grey mould, and you'll almost certainly encounter it at some point. It's easily identified as its common name is self-explanatory. Once a berry has this on it, there's nothing you can do except chuck it to the chickens or pigs (who'll love it), but pick it you must, otherwise it'll spread mould spores onto any undamaged fruit. Prevention is the answer to the problem, so make sure that ripe fruit is regularly harvested, remove any damaged fruit and dead leaves, and keep the berries clean by using a good mulch.

Strawberry mildew is another fairly common ailment, characterized by dark patches on the upper surface of the leaves, which subsequently curl to reveal grey, mouldy patches on the underside. Berries fail to reach their full size, and may be shriveled and dull in appearance. In some cases the crop will still be useable, if only for cooking, but where the attack is severe it'll only be fit for pig food. Picking off affected leaves at an early stage may help to control the extent of the mildew, but if a plant is really badly affected, it's probably best to grub it out and start again.

Birds and slugs can be major pests, competing for your fruit as it ripens. The only real way to keep birds off (apart from distracting their attention by providing a redcurrant bush nearby) is to net the strawberry plants. Bear in mind, though, that this will make picking the fruit quite awkward, and it'll be more difficult to monitor potential disease threats.

Slugs are the bane of most gardeners' lives, and they love strawberries as much as we all do. They can be controlled around strawberries in the usual ways, although we avoid using slug pellets in the vicinity of ripening fruit.

Top Fruit

Top fruit is defined as that which grows on trees, such as apples, plums and pears, rather than on bushes or canes (e.g. berries and currants). All are deciduous, and potentially long-lived.

The planting of fruit trees is not something to be undertaken lightly, as it involves a considerable investment of time, space and money. Young trees aren't cheap to purchase, and the ground you set aside for your orchard will be occupied for an extended period. It certainly wouldn't be worth trying to grow top fruit on short-term rented land.

However, if your circumstances permit the planting of an orchard, the long term benefit you can expect from these trees makes it well worth the effort. Properly cared for they have the potential to outlive you, and could produce a vast quantity of fruit over their lifetimes. In recent years a great deal of work has been done to develop strains and varieties that will begin cropping within a few years of planting, so the payback time has been reduced considerably.

We've planted a fair number of trees – maybe not enough to be described as an orchard, but that's how we like to think of it – a mixture of apples, pears and plums, giving a range of different fruits over a long harvest period. Initially, we visited a local nursery with the idea that locally-grown trees would already be acclimatised to our situation, and therefore more likely to survive. However, we discovered that most nurseries buy in their trees from specialist fruit growers situated much further south. In the end we bought our trees directly from the growers, cutting out the middle man, and found that this gave us a wider range to choose from. We made our selection based on hardiness, yield, flavour, resistance to disease, and pollination group.

Rootstocks

In general, top fruit doesn't do well on its own roots, and may take as long as 15 years to start cropping. In order to circumvent this difficulty, the different varieties are usually grafted, or budded, onto what are known as rootstocks. This is the part (usually only the roots and the bottom 10"-12" of the trunk) that controls the eventual height and vigour of the mature tree, but not the attributes of the fruit. Professional fruit tree nurseries may have varieties available on more than one rootstock, so you can choose the combination most appropriate to your needs and location.

It's hard to beat the spectacle created by an orchard of full standard apple trees in flower, but you would need a lot of land, you may have to wait a long time before getting a decent harvest, and you'd have to consider how to pick the fruit from the uppermost branches. But having said that, a standard tree may produce a massive crop (possibly as much as 300lb in a season), and, well cared for, it could live for 100 years. At the other extreme, in a limited space, a tree on dwarfing rootstock could be grown in a pot, as it would be unlikely to exceed 4' to 5' in height, yielding around 20lb of fruit per year by the time it's five years old. However, the life expectancy of a tree on dwarfing rootstock is considerably reduced.

Consider your location when deciding which rootstock your trees should be grafted onto. We live in a fairly windy spot and, although we're not short of space for our orchard, there's not enough room for full standards. We wanted smaller, easier to manage trees, but felt that whatever we chose would probably be dwarfed to some extent by the weather anyway. In the end we decided upon a hardy semi-vigorous stock (often used in commercial orchards) known as MM106 for our apples, and St. Julien A for the plum family, which has resulted in mature trees of about 10′ to 12′ in height.

For further information regarding rootstocks see table 4, page 445.

Varieties

There are literally hundreds of varieties to choose from, particularly in the case of apple trees. Most can be classified as either 'eaters' or 'cookers', and this may well influence your choice. Our preference was for cooking apples. There are some that are described as dual-purpose, but often this results in a fruit that is not quite right for either job, although the magnificent Blenheim Orange (an apple, not an orange!) comes pretty close. Think about fruiting and harvesting times, whether or not the apples are suitable for storage, or if they need to be used fresh. Can they be frozen, or are they good for making preserves? Or perhaps your aim is to make cider – or perry – in which case there are specific varieties that will do this

job to perfection. Remember large trees on vigorous rootstocks may produce huge quantities of fruit, and there's a limit to the quantity you can eat fresh off the tree.

On a small plot, 'family' trees may provide a practical solution. These are plants with more than one variety grafted onto a single rootstock, meaning that you get several different types of apple from a single stem. (It's worth pointing out that family trees are all within species, so you won't find one that'll provide you with both apples and plums!) The varieties chosen for grafting onto the single rootstock will be capable of pollinating one another, so you won't need to worry about that. If you only have room for one type of tree from each species, and family trees don't appeal, make sure you choose self-fertile varieties. As the term suggests, these are able to set fruit with the pollen from their own flowers.

Pollination groups

In order to obtain decent yields, your fruit trees need to be within reasonable proximity of appropriate pollinators. As mentioned above there are some self-fertile trees, but even these will produce heavier crops if they're within reach of a suitable pollinator. Generally, trees are categorised into one of three flowering groups (called, quite simply, 1, 2, and 3). This indicates how early in the year that particular variety will flower. Ideally you should have all your trees of the same species in one flowering group. You might get away with having a combination of 1s and 2s, or 2s and 3s, but certainly not 1s and 3s. An alternative, for apples, is to plant

An apple tree in flower needs to be reasonably close to an appropriate pollinator.

a crab apple somewhere nearby, as these do an excellent job of pollination, and produce a crop of their own for making jelly or wine. There are also a few apple cultivars that need to be fertilised with pollen from two different varieties in order to set fruit. Known as 'triploids', Bramley's Seedling and Blenheim Orange both fall into this category. In general, triploids tend to produce large fruit, can often survive under difficult conditions, have good disease resistance, and are likely to grow into large and vigorous trees. They won't act as pollinators for other apple varieties though, so allow for that when planning your orchard.

Where to buy

In recent years it's become much easier to buy fruit trees. Many mail-order seed companies now supply top fruit, and this is a convenient way to buy as you can do it all at the same time as ordering your vegetable seeds. However, the range is often fairly limited in terms of varieties, and usually there are no options regarding the rootstock, the age of the tree, or its form (see right). Local nurseries are worth a look, but again, choice tends to be very limited. I've even seen fruit trees offered for sale in the local supermarket, but personally wouldn't consider buying one as the conditions in which they've been transported and stored are likely to have been far from ideal. Also, unless you buy from a tree nursery, the plants are likely to be grown in pots. This does have one possible advantage in that you can (theoretically) plant the tree at any time of year, although I have to say that our only attempt at transplanting a pot-grown tree was a dismal failure. On balance, the preferred option would always be to buy from a fruit specialist. Although you may have to pay a bit more for your trees, you'll have a wide choice of variety, and some will also be able give you various options regarding the age of the trees, the rootstock they're grafted onto, and the form in which they're grown. These trees are usually sold bare-rooted, in the dormant winter period only. The age of the tree will be reflected in the price. We've bought trees of various ages in the past, with varying degrees of success: buy them too young and they won't be strong enough to grow on and make it through their first winter; too old, and they'll be excessively stressed by the move, and may never get over the shock. We've had most success, and better survival rates, with second year trees. The first year maidens we bought initially, seduced by the lower price, all perished in the first winter after planting.

Form

Fruit trees can be trained to grow in various shapes and forms. Trained trees may take more skill to maintain, but some styles can be particularly useful if you have restricted space or limited options regarding the site for your orchard. Apples and pears can both be trained as cordons, which are basically trees grown as a single stem where the fruit is borne on short side shoots. Cultivars that are particularly strong growers aren't suited to this type of training, and neither are those that bear fruit at the tips of their branches. If you're planning to plant a stone fruit (plum, peach, apricot etc.,) up against an existing wall, then fan training is probably the best option. The name is pretty self-explanatory, in that the tree is grown in a fan shape with the main branches trained in even arc above the top of the trunk. This requires some effort, but the result is well worthwhile, as it not only looks stunning, but achieves great results in terms of quality and yield. For wall-grown apples and pears, espalier growing is more successful. In this case, the trained tree has a central vertical stem, and from this pairs of branches extend horizontally on either side, forming tiers. These lateral branches produce short side shoots, and it is on these that the fruit is produced. Single-tiered espaliers, commonly known as 'step-over' trees, are sometimes used as productive border plants in large, formal vegetable gardens. If you're planning something similar you'll want plants on a very dwarfing M27 rootstock. It should be possible to train cordon apples horizontally to get the same effect.

There are also a number of different forms for free-standing orchard trees, the three main types being bush (where the length of the trunk is only about 3', suitable for garden situations where a semi-dwarfing rootstock is used, such as M26), half-standards (where the clean stem is around 4'- 5' in height, more suitable for small orchards; an appropriate rootstock would be MM106), and full standards, which are really only used in large traditional orchards, where the trunk of the tree may be 6' or more in length, and where a vigorous rootstock such as M25 is used. Free-standing trees will need the least attention in terms of pruning, so if you have the space, these are the ones to go for. It's also worth bearing in mind that, all other things being equal, you'll get far higher yields from bush, half-standard and standard trees than you will from restricted forms such as cordons, fans and espaliers.

Planting

If you've purchased bare-rooted trees, planting will take place during the dormant winter period, between early November and the end of February (or possibly into the middle of March in northern parts of the UK). On the whole, earlier in winter is better than later, as it gives longer for the roots to settle into position before growth gets started in spring.

TIP

You'll need to delay planting if the ground is frozen or particularly wet. If this is the case, leave the packaging around the roots of your new trees, and store them in a dry, cool but frost free place. They'll be fine like this for a week or two. A couple of hours before planting, stand the roots in a bucket of water to soak.

Plan in advance where each tree is to go, so you can get straight on with planting out as soon as they arrive. Make sure that you dig a really big hole that's wide enough to take the roots without having to squash them in. If the area is grassed, take the turf off and keep it to one side. As you remove the soil, place it in a tidy heap on a piece of tarpaulin or similar, as you'll need most of it to fill the hole in again. Unless the ground is very poor, it's best not to mix any fertiliser in with it; to do so may discourage the roots from spreading out beyond the improved area. A couple of handfuls of bonemeal will probably be sufficient, although some people also add peat. Fork over the earth at the bottom of the hole, and the turf you removed earlier can be broken up and dropped in. Next, position a stake to support the tree until it's settled – for the first few years at least. Stand the stake in the hole so that it rests against one side (because you want the tree in the middle), and knock at least a foot of it into the ground. Make sure you use a support that's been treated with a tree-friendly wood preservative (not creosote).

Place the tree carefully in the hole, ensuring that the soil mark on the stem is level with the top of the hole, and that the graft, where the rootstock and the tree were joined, is above the final soil level. Spread out the roots so that they're not tangled or congested in the bottom of the hole. If there's a particularly long root that won't fit, you can trim it back a bit. Have a helper holding the tree in the right position while you carefully backfill the hole using the soil you dug out in the first place. Firm it as you go, but don't over compact it. Once the hole is filled, pour a bucketful of water onto the soil. Tie the tree to the support stake, either using a proprietary tree tie, or by using an old pair of nylon tights. It needs to be something both soft and stretchy, with sufficient 'give' not to damage the trunk, but long-lasting enough to stay in place for a couple of years without disintegrating. It's also sensible to install a rabbit guard at this stage, but more substantial protection will be required in areas where deer are a nuisance.

It's a good idea to apply a mulch (e.g. well-rotted manure) to conserve moisture and suppress weeds until the tree is well-established and growing strongly.

TIP

Believe it or not, geese will strip the bark off young fruit trees, so if you're planning to keep poultry in your orchard, bear this in mind.

Apples

• **Site:** Avoid frost hollows as a freezing night in late April could decimate the blossom, resulting in virtually no crop. If you're in an area that experiences late frosts, choose varieties that are in flowering group 3 to minimise the risk of damage. Apple trees aren't generally fond of salt-laden coastal air, and they don't like shallow, alkaline soil very much either. Similarly, they won't do their best in areas where rainfall is very high, where light levels are low, that have poor drainage, or are at high altitude. Cookers are more tolerant of imperfect conditions, so bear this in mind if you're trying to establish an orchard on a challenging site.

• **Pruning:** Whole books have been written about pruning fruit trees by people who know far more about it than we do. However, basic pruning is a combination of a little knowledge and a lot of common sense. Standards, half-standards and bush type trees can all be pruned along the same lines, so, in the interests of simplicity they're what we'll consider here:

TIP

Remember that all pruning of top fruit (other than plums and gages) must be done when the tree is dormant, and cuts should be made just above a bud.

Lack of pruning results in an overcrowded tree and a very low yield of fruit.

Any shoots that have grown from below the graft should be removed.

Blossom on fruiting spurs.

If you've just planted a one year, unstopped maiden, in the first instance all you need do is cut the top off at the height you want the branches to form. (i.e. 2 to 3' for bush trees, 4 to 5' for half standards, and at least 6' for standards.) During the next growing season, the sapling will send out a number of leaders which will form the main framework of the tree, so, in the winter following planting, the aim of pruning is to develop an open structure that'll allow good air circulation and maximise the amount of light getting into the middle of the tree. You should have about 5 or 6 branches forming the main framework of the tree, so if there's any more than that the surplus can be removed. The ones to cut out are those that grow too close to others, or that clutter up the open shape you're trying to achieve. Also cut back shoots that have grown out of the trunk to one bud,

and anything that's sprouted from the rootstock (i.e. from below the graft) should come off completely. The leaders that you decide to leave should be shortened by about half, cutting back to just above a bud on the underside of the branch. This should cause them to grow in a direction that facilitates the development of the open shape you're trying to achieve.

In the second year things are a little more complicated as there are now laterals to deal with as well. These are smaller side branches that grow out from the leaders. As before, remove anything that's growing across the middle of the tree, and cut back the previous season's growth on the leaders by about half. The laterals should be pruned to five buds; it's these shoots that will gradually develop into fruiting spurs.

Any shoots coming out of the lower trunk now can be cut off flush.

Over the following two winters carry out more-or-less the same pruning regime, but cut back less

Pruning apple trees in winter.

as the tree's framework develops, until, in the fourth year, you probably won't need to shorten the leaders at all.

In subsequent years, the purpose of pruning switches to maintenance of the open shape, the removal of any dead or diseased material, and encouraging the growth of fruiting wood. At this stage it's useful to know if the varieties are spur-or tip-bearing. For spur bearers, trim back any laterals that are growing too long and extending beyond the end of the leader, and for tip bearers take a little off the leaders and leave the laterals alone.

Canker identification and treatment.

Apple Pests and Diseases

There are a multitude of problems that can inhibit or threaten to kill your apple trees, but here I'll just mention a few of the most common:

The main difficulty that we've experienced with our apple trees is canker. This is a potentially serious or even fatal problem that's more likely to occur on wetter soils – which is probably why we get it here. It can be quite hard to spot initially, especially if you're not specifically looking out for it. The disease manifests itself as areas of sunken bark which then crack and die. If the damaged area completely surrounds a particular branch, there's nothing you can do except chop it off below the infected part. If it encircles the entire trunk then the tree will be a goner. It can be controlled, but in our experience it's very difficult to eradicate, especially on larger trees, in which case not only is it more likely to go unnoticed for a while, it's also awkward to access all the damaged areas for treatment. To try to keep an infection under control, each winter you need to take a sharp knife to the tree concerned and ruthlessly cut out any affected wood. In the case of twiggy bits, it's probably best to take them off altogether, but on larger, structural branches, you need to pare away the shrunken bark. You'll discover that below the surface, the wood is discoloured to a dark brown, rather than the yellow / green it should be. All this stained material must also be removed, right back to clean, healthy tissue, and then the cut area should be sealed with proprietary wound paint. All the trimmings from the diseased tree are potentially infectious, so make sure you gather them up and burn them. Your secateurs and knife could also pass the infection to a healthy tree, so clean them thoroughly after use.

Scab is a fungal disease that affects the fruit crop, but shouldn't kill the tree. It usually becomes apparent in early summer when you'll start to see brown spots on the leaves. Untreated, the spots increase in size and join together to form large splotches. The infection will spread to the developing fruit, manifesting as brown, scabby patches on the skin. This in itself doesn't affect the interior of the apples, but, if the patches cause the skin to split, the fruit will be un-useable. You might be able to limit the spread of the fungus by removing any obviously affected shoots at an early stage, but in practice this is unlikely to be effective unless your trees are very small. In the past, trees would've been treated with Bordeaux mixture, but this is now no longer permitted.

Bitter Pit is another fruit fault that you might come across; it's a physiological problem rather than a disease, caused by a combination of calcium deficiency and water shortage. Affected apples display small shrunken areas on the surface of the fruit, and, if the skin is removed, it will be seen that the flesh underneath is also affected. Regular watering and mulching should help avoid recurrence.

TIP

To make a fruit picker, get a large tin can and cut a V-shaped notch in the rim. Tape this to one end of a long bamboo cane. Use it to gather fruit that's out of reach by lining it up and giving a sharp upwards push so that the V-notch severs the stalk and the fruit is contained within the tin.

Pears

• **Site:** Being closely related to apples, pears have many of the same requirements, but tend to be a little more sensitive. Although potentially long lived (up to 100 years), they're less tolerant of shade, and really don't like cold, blowy conditions, as the young leaves are inclined to become wind-burnt. They'll cope better than apples with wetter, heavier soils, but are not so happy where the soil is particularly dry, alkaline, or in the salt-laden atmosphere of coastal regions. Pears generally flower a fortnight or so before apples, so are more susceptible to frost damage.

Pear pests and diseases

Canker will affect pear trees too, so keep a close eye out for it and control in the same way as for apples. Pears can also suffer from a form of scab. It's caused by a different fungus than that which troubles apples, but the symptoms and treatments are virtually identical.

Pear midge attacks may cause fruitlets to become misshapen, which subsequently leads to the development of blackened areas, and then they'll drop off the tree in early summer. This midge lays its eggs on the blossom buds, and the larvae then develop inside the growing fruit, turning it brown and mushy. Once the immature pears fall, the larvae pupate, emerging as egg-laying adults the following spring. Prompt removal of affected fruit can help reduce the problem in subsequent seasons.

Pears infected with Stony Pit are hard and inedible, in some cases becoming so hard that you can't even cut them with a knife. This is caused by a virus, and in most cases the tree will need to be destroyed.

• **Pruning:** As for apples. Unless you have lots of space, grow as a bush or restricted form; standard and half standard pears have the potential to develop into very large trees.

Plums and gages

• **Site:** Plums and gages are more delicate than either of the two aforementioned species. They flower very early in the season, making them particularly susceptible to frost damage, which will seriously impact the crop. If your orchard is on sloping ground, put them at the top of the incline, above the apples and pears where it will be warmer. Plums can't tolerate having waterlogged roots, so must be grown in free-draining soil, but they don't like it dry either, so make sure that the ground contains a good amount of organic matter, which will assist both water retention and drainage.

• **Pruning:** Never prune plums and gages in winter; you should only ever cut them back when they're growing fast, ideally between late May and mid June. One of the major diseases of these plants gains access through pruning cuts that don't heal sufficiently quickly, and summer wounds heal much faster than those inflicted during the dormant period.

Plums don't need much cutting back if you're growing them as bushes or half standards, but you should still aim for the same basic framework of well-spaced leaders. Once well-established, bush and half standard plums and gages will need very little interference, bar the occasional removal of growths that are crowding the centre of the tree, or crossing and rubbing on other branches. They're well-suited to training as fans when grown on walls or fences, but aren't usually seen as espaliers or cordons.

The wood of these trees is rather brittle, and branches can be susceptible to breakage if carrying a particularly heavy load. To avoid structural damage, it's good practice to thin potentially heavy crops in early summer, before the plums swell too much. Yes, you'll get fewer fruits after doing this, but they'll be better for it, and you'll have prevented any injury to the tree. If you don't thin, and the crop is very large, it may be necessary to rig up supports for individual branches.

Plums pests and diseases

Wasps can cause damage to all your tree fruits, but those with soft skins, such as plums and gages, are most susceptible. The only way to deal with wasps is to locate their nest and destroy it. It's possible that they may be attracted in the first place by damaged windfall fruit, so keeping the orchard tidy should help.

Silver Leaf is the most serious disease of plums and gages, and the main reason why you should never winter prune these species. Symptoms begin with silvering of the leaves, followed by die back progressing along the branch. Diagnosis can be confirmed by removing the affected wood and inspecting the cross section – in cases of silver leaf, the central section of the wood will be stained a dark brown colour. Affected shoots must be removed as quickly as possible, at least 6" below the infected areas, and the wound covered with a proprietary pruning paint. Quick action may save the tree. Victoria plums are particularly susceptible to silver leaf, and we've lost two trees to the disease.

In cases of false silver leaf, the leaves also show signs of silvering, but it occurs all over the tree rather than travelling down an individual limb. Confirm by cutting an affected branch as outlined above, but in this case there will be no central staining in the cross section. It's usually caused by lack of nutrients and irregular availability of water, both of which are easily remedied.

Bacterial Canker is a fairly serious infection which primarily affects plums and gages, but can also cause problems on other stone fruits. Sunken, dead areas appear on the bark in the spring and early summer, and these areas may leak a sticky goo. Leaves develop small, round, brown spots, which later fall out, leaving small holes. The only option is to remove all the affected areas, taking care to dispose of them in such a way as to minimise the risk of infecting other trees, and remember to clean your secateurs carefully. Historically, copper based fungicides would have been used to treat this, but as most have now been withdrawn from sale the treatment regime suggested above is the only real option.

Cherry pests and diseases

The attention of the local bird population is likely to be your biggest problem. In the case of sweet cherries the entire crop will probably have been pinched before you are even close to getting a ripe one yourself, unless you net the whole tree. Sour cherries are less likely to be targeted to the same extent, and have the advantage that you can harvest them before they're fully ripe (i.e. before they become attractive to the birds).

Leaf Spot can be a potentially serious problem in cherries, with affected trees developing purplish brown spots on their leaves. Later the leaves yellow around the edges, and will then drop from the tree, spreading the fungal infection as they go. The best way to control this is to clear up as many of the infected, fallen leaves as possible, and consider applying a fungicide to the tree. Cherries can also be affected by bacterial canker (see left), which resembles leaf spot in the early stages.

Gummosis is a disorder that sometimes occurs following a period of freezing weather, in which the tree appears to bleed a sticky gum from cracks in the trunk or branches where the wood is healthy. This is not a disease in itself; rather, it's a symptom of the tree being under stress. There could be all sorts of reasons behind it, including incorrect pruning, physical damage, or an infection of some sort. In general, improving the health and vigour of the tree will rectify the problem. It can also occur on plums and gages, but less commonly.

Cherries

• **Site:** Ideally cherries like a deep, fertile, well-drained soil, and will turn their noses up at shallow, sandy or badly-drained ground. Sour cherries will tolerate some shade, but the sweet types will do much better in full sun. If your garden or orchard offers less than perfect conditions, you could consider growing them as fans against a wall. Sour cherries will do well enough even if the wall happens to be north facing. Sweet cherries can grow into very large trees, and you may have to wait a long time for any fruit, so opt for a dwarfing rootstock, or grow sour cherries which are naturally less vigorous.

• **Pruning:** Sour cherries can be grown as bushes in an orchard.

Fruit is borne on the previous season's growth, so the intention is to regularly remove fruited wood, allowing new branches to grow on. Aim to remove about one in four of the fruited branches, cutting back to a new shoot each time. August is probably the best time of year to do this.

Other fruits

In addition to the species outlined above, there's an ever increasing range of top fruit available to the home grower; peaches, nectarines, figs, kiwis and lemons, to name just a few. Lovely though it would be to have these, they can hardly be regarded as staples for those aiming towards self-sufficiency, and, as such, they fall outside the scope of this book. However, some years ago we had a small peach tree growing in a pot in the conservatory alongside a fig that we picked up at a farm sale for a fiver. They only lived for a short time before both were killed by infestations of red spider mite, but not before they had produced a handful of the most fantastic peaches and figs we've ever eaten. So feel free to have go, but don't expect these delicate crops to do much more that give you an occasional treat.

Small-Scale Cereal Production

Another writer said, fairly recently, that *"growing cereals on a small scale is novel and fun"*, and so it is – when the sun is shining and you've got a willing band of volunteers to help with the harvest. But, if you depend upon it, a lot of the novelty and fun disappears, particularly when it's blowing a gale, pouring with rain, and all the volunteers have got fed up and gone home. Generally speaking, it's not worth trying to grow wheat for flour unless you're in an arable area, or you simply won't achieve the necessary yield and quality. Even then you have to ask yourself whether the resulting crop is actually of higher value than the grass (or vegetables) you could have grown instead (and more easily). The same goes for malting barley – we have malted our own home-grown barley, but the resulting beverage, whilst

recognisable as beer, was not good, and certainly didn't justify the input. Growing malting-quality barley is a skilled job, and not suited to all areas of the UK. If you want to grow cereals then it's best to aim to produce feed-quality crops – oats in the wetter western regions, and barley elsewhere – and let your animals turn them into meat, milk and eggs. These crops can be undersown with grass, and, if the weather's dodgy at harvest time, the whole lot can be wrapped up as wholecrop silage. That's better by far than having a field tied up for a whole season, then seeing a year's worth of bread destroyed in a week of rain.

In the kitchen, Dot uses approximately 300kg of high quality flour per year, which we buy in bulk. 15 years ago this cost about fifty quid. Now we're paying £225 for the same amount,

but, despite the price increase, there's simply no way that we can compete with this, and the half-acre of land that would have been taken up by trying (and probably failing) to produce it ourselves is more profitably used for something else.

CEREALS FOR FEED

There are a surprising number of small- and medium-scale livestock keepers who grow a modest acreage of cereals every year for their animals. We've done it ourselves, and would do so again – if there was a suitable field on our current holding. Given the shocking rises in the price of purchased feed recently, the number of grassland farmers who also grow their own cereals may well increase. For the smallholder this could involve anything from a few rows of mixed grains (known as 'dredge corn') harvested by hand to feed the poultry, to several acres of cereals to supplement the diets of sheep, cattle, pigs and goats. And, of course, it's not just the grain that's valuable – straw, too, can be an expensive input if you're not in an arable area, so what little you obtain as a by-product of your small-scale cereal growing is well worth having, whether for feed or bedding.

As I mentioned before, the two cereal crops of most interest to the smallholder are oats and barley. The threshed grains can be fed whole to all classes of stock (although it's perhaps better to roll or crush them slightly for pigs), and the leafy parts of both oat and barley straw make reasonable fodder. If the crop is harvested in the traditional manner, using a scythe or reaper-binder, then it can be fed to livestock on the sheaf –

they'll eat the grain and pick out any palatable bits from the straw, and the remainder can be thrown under them for bedding. We've fed barley to our goats and pigs in this way, and oats to cattle and poultry – a sheaf of oats hung up in the hen house in the winter keeps the birds occupied for ages. Assuming that all your sheaves are more or less uniform in size, rationing is straightforward. In the case of our goats, we simply replaced their evening concentrates with a sheaf of barley per animal, thus halving the feed bill.

Both oats and barley can be 'undersown' with grass and clover. This has the advantage that, after harvesting the cereal crop, the field is immediately returned to pasture without delay. In the case of barley, the grass seed mixture is broadcast into the established crop when the plants are 3"- 4" high and then lightly harrowed. Quite apart from anything else, the barley seedlings benefit from being knocked about a bit at this stage. Oat seedlings, on the other hand, are not quite so robust, so the grass seed should be broadcast immediately after sowing the cereal. Where grass is grown in conjunction with the cereal crop then the resulting straw is clearly going to contain a lot of lush stuff. Therefore it'll need to be tedded (as for hay) before baling, or it could be baled green and wrapped as for silage.

Oats

Oats will thrive where other cereal crops might fail. They'll grow on a wide range of soils, even under slightly acid conditions. Oats favour a moist climate – hence their popularity in the north and west of the country – and require less sunshine to ripen than other

Oats.

cereals. Where oats follow grass in the rotation there can be some difficulty in consolidating the newly-ploughed field enough to retain sufficient moisture, in which case the crop will suffer. In most respects, the smallholder would be best to sow oats after roots such as swedes or turnips that have been grazed off by sheep. In this case the land will need very little in the way of preparation, and it probably won't be necessary to spread any additional manure or lime either.

Barley

Like oats, barley can be grown on a wide range of soil types, but it is susceptible to acidity, so lime will almost certainly be required. Its place in the smallholder's rotation is probably after roots, as described above, although on good land where the root crop has been grazed *in situ* the soil may actually be too rich. In this case, oats should be grown in the first year, followed by barley undersown with grass. Where barley follows grass in the rotation then, provided it ripens and is harvested early enough, a crop of fast-growing brassicas such as rape or turnips can be sown directly into the stubble.

Rolled and whole barley grains.

TIP

If you've got a few fields suitable for cereal growing (or can subdivide a larger one), an appropriate 4-year rotation on a livestock holding might be:

1. Pasture (grazing / mowing);
2. Barley followed by rape / turnips;
3. Oats undersown with grass and clover;
4. Pasture (grazing / mowing)

SOIL PREPARATION AND SOWING

In all likelihood you'll need to plough the field for cereals, although that's not to say that you might not get away with a simple surface cultivation (e.g. rotavating), particularly after recently grazed roots. If you want to try rotavating after grass then you'll most certainly have to spray off the sward first. Ploughing, on the other hand, will bury the old vegetation, so the chemical treatment probably won't be necessary, except perhaps where weeds such as thistles and docks are well-established.

Vintage ploughing, as a craft, is alive and well.

Ploughing and drilling

Ploughing a field is an art form in itself, and not the sort of thing you can learn from a book! You really need to find an experienced ploughman who'll help you get the implement set up correctly, and start you off in the right direction. This is particularly relevant if you're using older 'vintage' type equipment, as is the case for many smallholders. Vintage ploughing, as a craft, is alive and well, and there's no shortage of expertise for you to tap into.

Ploughs vary in design, although all have multiples of three main components: shares, mouldboards and coulters. The mouldboards are the wing-shaped curved metal plates which fold each slice of soil over, thus forming the furrows. At the tip of each mouldboard is a share which makes a horizontal cut through the soil. This is the part of the plough that suffers the most wear in abrasive soils and may need to be replaced from time to time. The mouldboard and share together make up what's called the plough body. Coulters are usually free-spinning sharp-edged metal discs, although some older ploughs may have knife coulters. The discs are mounted on legs which hold them just above, and slightly to one side (the unploughed side) of the shares. Their purpose is to make a vertical cut in the soil for each furrow. The position of the coulters is adjustable, but they should never be set so low that the vertical and horizontal cuts meet – a 'hinge' of uncut soil is required to ensure that each furrow turns over neatly. When ploughing-in old grassland, the coulters should be moved forward to run slightly ahead of, rather than directly above, the shares. Sometimes each disc coulter is augmented by a skim coulter: this skims a small strip off the top edge of each slice of soil as it is lifted and turned, ensuring that no unburied vegetation remains poking up between the furrows.

Different styles of plough can be categorised by the shape of their mouldboards, the number of furrows they'll turn in each pass, and whether or not they're reversible:

• **Mouldboard shape:** At one end of the scale is the 'lea' (or 'ley') style – very long and narrow, which cuts a furrow wider than it is deep, and presses each slice of soil neatly against the last at an angle of about 45° in an unbroken line. At the other extreme is the 'digger' mouldboard – short and broad which will, if required, plough a furrow that is deeper than its width, leaving the turned soil in a fairly broken state. Somewhere between these two lie the 'general purpose' and the 'semi-digger', either of which would be suitable for use on the smallholding.

• **Number of furrows:** A plough is made up of a number of units, each consisting of a plough body and coulter(s), mounted onto a beam or frame in a staggered line. Apart from the foremost one (which turns a furrow to lie against the last furrow of the previous pass), each mouldboard lays its slice of soil onto that left by the plough body travelling in front, and to one side of it in the formation. Thus several furrows are produced in each pass. Older implements, such as those drawn by horses, or the early tractor-drawn models, may have only a single plough body, whereas the modern ploughs used in large-scale agriculture may turn a dozen or more furrows at a time. The number of furrows needs to be matched to the size and power of the tractor – too few and you're wasting time and fuel running up and down the field; too many and you'll wrench the guts out of your machine. A two-furrow plough would be appropriate for use with most of the types of tractor commonly found on smallholdings, which tend to be in the range of 20-60hp. Small single furrow ploughs are available for use with compact tractors, 2-wheeled garden tractors, and even quad bikes.

• **Reversibility:** The reversible plough is, in effect, two ploughs, with one being mounted upside down above the other. When the right handed set of plough bodies is in work the left handed set is raised, and vice-versa. At the end of each pass, the plough is lifted from the ground and the whole thing rotated through 180°. It's then possible to plough back down the field alongside the previous pass, with all the furrows lying over the same way. Quite apart from the time (and fuel) saved by doing away with unnecessary travel on the headlands, the reversible plough makes it feasible to work the field in successive narrow strips, which might be a useful consideration for the smallholder dividing up a field for a range of different crops. However, the reversible plough is quite a bit heavier than its fixed counterpart, which is something to bear in mind if your tractor is a particularly small one. My parents had a 2-furrow semi-digger reversible plough on their smallholding, and I wish to goodness I'd brought it from there when they retired.

If using a non-reversible model you need to plough up one side of the area being worked, and back down the other, turning all the furrows towards the centre. To do this, the field needs to be divided into 'lands', with a land being a strip of a width that can reasonably be ploughed by this round-and-round method, before the amount of travel required on the headlands becomes excessive. The lands need to be measured and set out quite carefully to ensure that you won't be leaving yourself with a lot of half-furrows to plough. The usual method of marking the extent of the lands is to plough very shallow furrows, just to score the surface

and give lines to work to. The headlands should be marked out in the same way.

The first pass with a fixed-furrow plough runs down the centre of the land. At the end of the field the tractor makes a turn to the right, and the next pass produces a furrow leaning in towards the first, so their tops rest together. Thus a small ridge is formed, with a narrow unploughed strip buried beneath it. (A cross-section of the furrows at this point would look something like a capital A). Continue in the same fashion, travelling up one side and down the other, of an ever-widening strip of ploughed ground, until the whole of that land is completed. Repeat on the next land, and so on. With a reversible plough there's no need to set out lands, but you should still mark the headlands in the same way – this gives you clearly defined points at which to drop the plough into work and to lift it out again at the beginning and end of each pass. The headlands should be ploughed last, but if you're cropping the field in strips you might wish to leave them unploughed for access.

Ploughing has a threefold purpose: it buries surface trash, exposes the soil to frost action and produces a state of readiness for further cultivations. However, amid concerns about soil erosion, nutrient leaching and the increasing cost of diesel fuel, minimum tillage ('min-till') methods of seed bed preparation have become more popular in some farming systems.

Following ploughing, you'll need to work the land down into a plantable state using a rotavator, or by repeated passes with harrows. Any lime required can be

incorporated at this stage.

Seed is generally drilled in neat straight lines nowadays, but you can just as easily broadcast it with a fertiliser spreader or by hand, or use a seed fiddle. The period for planting spring cereals runs from early February right up until early May, depending on locality. However, there's no point in sowing into cold soil, so it's generally best to wait at least until late March / early April. On the other hand, crops that are established earlier (i.e. if conditions allow) are less prone to attack by insect pests.

TIP

Always use treated seed, particularly if corn follows grass in your rotation. Cereals are grasses too, so the insect pests that inhabit pasture in big numbers (particularly wireworms and leather jackets) are going to have a field day with your emerging crop, unless it's got some protection. I made the mistake, once, of sowing untreated barley – the germination rate was fantastic, but not a single seedling got beyond about 2" high. Luckily it was sufficiently early in the year for the field to be replanted.

Drilling requires 80-100kg of seed per acre, and you'll have to up this by about 50% if broadcasting. As soon as the seed has been distributed you need to bury it by going over the field with a chain harrow (which will more or less pull it into rows, too), and then roll to consolidate.

Assuming that you don't want to have to spray your crop during the growing period, weed control

123

In predominantly livestock rearing areas smaller, older machines have survived.

English (curved) and Austrian (straight) style scythes.

depends on good germination and establishment, in the hope that the cereal plants will out-compete and smother the unwanted vegetation. Therefore take care over the cultivation processes, and don't stint on the seed.

All being well, once the seed is in you should be able to shut the gate on the field and leave it to get on with it.

HARVESTING

Somewhat ironically, it's actually harder to get someone in to harvest your grain if you live in a predominantly arable growing area. The machines used by commercial cereal growers and contractors these days are just so huge that cutting a smallholder's meagre acreage would be a rank impossibility. Big machines need big fields, and that's that. However, in the mainly livestock rearing regions, where only a limited area of cereals is grown, the smaller, older machines have survived. Therefore, if you've got a couple or three acres of combinable crops, and neighbouring farmers

are growing similarly small areas, then you might be able to get it harvested properly. Otherwise you'll just have to do it yourself. When we lived on Bardsey, someone unearthed an old reaper-binder (dating back to the early 1900s, or thereabouts) on which we flapped and clanked our way around the field, leaving a trail of more-or-less neatly tied sheaves. If you can find one then by all means have a go, but it'll probably drive you mad. It's reputed that the chap who invented the knotting mechanism later committed suicide because he couldn't figure out why it worked! Smaller areas we cut successfully with a scythe, and once, in desperation, I mowed our whole field of ripe barley with the hay cutter, forked it all into trailers and carried it in and stacked it loose. It was fine. And, if you don't mind a lot of noise while you work, a strimmer with a brush-cutter blade attachment does a very neat job of cutting a cereal crop.

A combine harvester will not only cut your crop, it'll thresh it too. Then all you need to do is transfer the grain from the tank on the machine to a suitable storage bin

Sharpening a scythe

To sharpen your scythe you stand it upside down, with the top of the 'snath' (handle) resting on the ground. The heel of the scythe will now be somewhere around shoulder height, with the blade passing left to right in front of you. The top of the blade (now the underside, because you're holding it upside down) should be sharpened first, as this is the face that has the bevel. The bottom of the blade is basically flat so the main purpose of using the stone on this face is to remove the burr created while sharpening the bevelled edge. Initial sharpening is carried out using a fairly coarse stone, with a much finer one kept for re-sharpening during work.

As repeated sharpenings take the edge back into thicker steel, it may be necessary to 'peen' the blade from time to time. This involves hammering out the edge of the blade against a small anvil to reduce its thickness.

In north and western parts of the country it can be very difficult – if not impossible – to harvest grain at a sufficiently low moisture content to ensure that it'll store without deterioration. Larger farms may have drying facilities, but, in the absence of that, the usual practice is to treat the grain with propionic acid ('Propcorn') to inhibit the growth of moulds and fungi. On very small holdings, sheaves may be spread out on racks in an outhouse, or hung up from the rafters to dry. Another option is to cut the crop while it's still moist and ensile it, although you'd probably need to be doing an acre or more for it to be worthwhile getting someone in to bale and wrap it for you.

Stooking sheaves of barley cut with a scythe.

The lost art of scything

The traditional English scythe is fairly heavy and cumber-some, so enthusiasts in this lost art tend to use Austrian scythes nowadays. The Austrian scythe has a straight snath (unlike the traditional English model with its graceful curve) and moveable handles that can be adjusted to suit the individual.

The angle of the blade also needs to be adjusted, to suit the crop: horizontal with the ground for mowing grass, but at an increased angle for cutting cereals.

The blade cuts with a slicing action as a result of being swung in an arc around the scyther's body, which is achieved by swivelling at the waist. To keep the blade at the correct level, bend your knees as required. Move forward with each stroke taken, and gradually advance down the field, leaving a swath of mown corn (or grass) on your left.

and bale the straw. But the grain must be dead ripe, your fields need to be reasonably large and easily navigable and, above all, you need to find someone who's willing to bring his machine and do it for you. At the other extreme, cutting with a scythe will simply leave the crop in mown swathes for you to tie into sheaves, put into stooks and finally carry home and stack.

The pattern to follow when cutting a field of corn is just as I've described for mowing hay (see page 146). If the crop contains a lot of grass (e.g. if it was undersown) then it'd be an arduous task indeed to cut it by hand, and it probably wouldn't be suited to this method of harvest anyway. (See wholecrop, overleaf). However, assuming that you've grown a relatively clean crop of cereals, there's no earthly reason why the scythe shouldn't be a perfectly adequate means for tackling a small area. An accomplished man may manage to mow as much as a couple of acres in a day (although an acre would be a more realistic target), with helpers in the field to bind and stook.

Oats are generally mown when the stems are still fairly green, but barley needs to be completely ripe, with all colour gone out of the straw. Provided that the scythe is swung rhythmically, and systematic progress is made, the cut crop should be left in fairly neat lines with the stalks all facing the same way. Sometimes a hoop is fitted to the scythe to gather the crop into bundles for tying, otherwise it's the job of the helpers to collect it together in armfuls. In fact, a good armful is about right for each sheaf. Traditionally the bundles were tied into sheaves using a twisted band of straw, which we found easy enough with pliable oats, but near impossible with the shorter, more brittle barley. Therefore, we pre-cut a whole lot of short lengths of baler twine and tucked them in our belts ready for use.

• **Stooking:** Once tied, the sheaves are put into stooks: first one pair of sheaves are stood up in an inverted V with their heads together and their butt ends pressed firmly onto the ground, then another pair are leant against them, and another pair on the other side, and so on, thus making a short, tent-shaped tunnel. This should run north to south to get the maximum benefit of both wind and sun. Usually five pairs of sheaves go to make up a stook, although the number varies between regions, and between crops.

Given that barley is harvested in a state of full ripeness, one could argue that stooking is scarcely necessary for this crop – just get it in and get it safe! Traditionally harvested oats, on the other hand, will need to remain in stooks in

The straw is a useful by-product of small scale cereal growing.

the field for at least 10 days after cutting, and possibly more than a fortnight. Not until all the stem and leafy material is fully dry must sheaves of oats be carted and stacked.

• **Stacking:** The traditional stack, either square or round, depending on locality, was built outdoors and thatched to protect it from the weather. However, if you've got sufficient outbuildings on your smallholding then I strongly suggest that you stack it under cover, just as you would do with hay. To my mind, the risk associated with storing the crop outdoors, even with thatch on the top, is just too great. And besides, if you're intending to feed it 'on the sheaf' as we have done, then you'll be using just a small amount each day, and you can't do that with an outdoor stack because once you start pulling sheaves out the weather will get in. The outdoor stack is only any good if you're intending to thresh it out, in which case the whole lot is dealt with in one day.

Building a weatherproof stack is a highly skilled operation, but, if stacking under cover, then provided that it's done tidily, the crop will be ok.

• **Threshing and winnowing:** Perhaps it's the threshing and the winnowing that's supposed to be novel and fun; it certainly isn't necessary for livestock feeding purposes, but you might want to have ago at it anyway!

If you take a look at a range of traditional farm buildings you'll often find one shed, built side-on to the prevailing wind, with a pair of doors directly opposite each other. Closer examination might even reveal the remnants of a wooden floor situated in line between the two. This would once have been the threshing floor. On a really blustery day, the sheaves would be bashed about with flails on the wooden floor to remove the grain from the straw, and the wind blowing in through one door and out of the other would carry all the chaff to one side (known as 'winnowing'). The separated grain was then shovelled up into sacks or bins, and the straw carried out again to be re-stacked. On a smaller scale, we have thrashed out grain by beating the crop, a handful at a time, against a panel of 1" squared weldmesh propped up at an angle over a sheet of tarpaulin. Again, this wants to be done in a windy location.

Wholecrop silage

If you're serious about growing cereals to feed to ruminant livestock then, despite everything I've written above about stooking, stacking and threshing and so on, I think wholecrop silage is the way to go, in big round bales. This will provide a complete winter diet for even highly productive animals such as lactating cows and in-lamb ewes, with the minimum of hassle.

The crop, undersown with grass and clover, is mown just before it ripens when the grain is still soft and slightly juicy. An ordinary hay cutter is fine for the job. Before baling it can be left in the swathe for a day or two to wilt, but shouldn't be tedded for fear of knocking off the grains. The bales should be double-wrapped, otherwise the straw, being so much stiffer than the more usual grass silage, could cause punctures that would lead to spoilage of the crop.

One of the downsides of big-baled wholecrop is that it's almost irresistible to rats, mice and squirrels. Therefore it's common practice to build rodent bait stations into the stack. If you're not keen on using poison then a well-maintained string of traps around the perimeter of the storage area is a must. The stack is also prone to attack from above, so netting against birds might be a wise precaution.

Forage Crops for Livestock

Capable, in some cases, of producing in excess of 60 tonnes of edible material per hectare (24 tonnes to the acre), forage crops are well worth considering, even on a small scale. Some – such as swedes or mangels (or mangolds) – tie up the land for a full season, but others are ready for feeding just 10 weeks after sowing. These fast growing crops are particularly valuable as they can be sown after taking hay, silage or cereals off the field, effectively giving you two crops from the same piece of land in the same season. This is known as a 'catch crop'.

A rotational system which involved a different field on the smallholding being planted with roots or brassicas each year, before being put back to grass (which could be sown at the same time as the forage crop) would lift the output of a livestock enterprise no end, and benefit the soil too.

Forage crops can be grazed *in situ* by folding sheep (or even cattle) over the field behind electric fencing, or, in the case of the larger roots, they can be harvested and stored for use right through the winter. Swedes, in particular, are a valuable feed in spring, just before the grass growth gets going. The commonest use of grazed forage crops is for fattening lambs, mostly during the autumn and early winter period. Quite apart from anything else, this gets lambs off the pasture, which at that time is needed for tupping the ewes. A good crop of brassicas might provide as much as 5,000 'lamb grazing days' per hectare,

(or nearly double this, in the case of swedes). In simple terms, this means that you ought to be able to fatten about 90 lambs per hectare (or 36 lambs per acre) over a 9 week period. The best way of doing this is to strip graze, by moving an electric fence a bit further down the field each day. Although it makes a little more work, this gives far better utilisation of the crop than simply opening up the field and letting them graze where they please. Ideally the lambs should have a 'run back' area onto pasture (the headland of the field will do) where they're provided with a rack of hay or good quality barley straw. Grazing forage crops *in situ* in a controlled fashion with sheep is the traditional way of improving soil fertility on light land, and results in far higher yields from whatever follows, whether it be cereals or grass. This is what earned sheep the nickname of 'golden hoof', and, at one time, flocks may have been kept on arable farms primarily for this beneficial effect.

Sowing

If planting a forage crop directly after taking hay or silage off the field, then you might be able to get away with only the barest minimum of cultivations – simply criss-cross the field with a spiked harrow, broadcast the seed, and roll. However, be aware that the preceding crop will have pulled a fair amount of nutrients from the soil, so you might want to incorporate some manure before sowing. Also, if the aftermath re-growth is strong it might out-compete your emerging seedlings, leaving you no better off than you were before. Therefore it's probably best to

Rotavating old grassland prior to sowing a forage crop.

spray off the existing sward (using glyphosate), spread the manure, and then run over the field with a rotavator. There's no need for a deep cultivation – just enough to break up the turf layer and mix in the muck. Then broadcast and roll, as before. Other options include direct drilling or slot seeding, where a single pass with a specialist piece of machinery opens small slots in the ground, deposits the seed therein, and rolls them shut. But that's a job for a contractor.

Some forage crops – such as fodder beet and mangels – require closer management, so, on a small scale, I reckon that they're best grown on a vacant plot in the garden, and attended to regularly along with the vegetables.

Commonly grown forage crops

• **Kale:** A member of the cabbage family, which provides particularly good food for milking cows during the first half of the winter. It can be strip grazed *in situ* or cut and carried as required. For housed cattle, a daily ration of kale will provide a welcome change from a dry hay diet. It'll also keep good colour in the milk, so even your winter butter will be yellow. There are also shorter stemmed varieties of kale that are more suitable for fattening lambs. Broadcast seed at a rate of 3kg to the acre (use about half this amount if drilling) at any time from April (e.g. after grazing with ewes and lambs) through to mid July (e.g. after mowing for hay or silage). The feeding period usually runs from November through to January.

TIP

As with members of the cabbage family that are planted in the vegetable garden, the land used to grow forage brassicas needs to be less acidic, with a pH of up to 7.5. Therefore it will probably be necessary to spread a bit of lime when carrying out the pre-sowing cultivation.

• **Stubble Turnip:** Often sown directly after harvesting a cereal crop (hence the name), turnips can just as easily be used to follow hay or silage. The sowing period runs from May through to mid July. Later (August) plantings may be considered in the south. Broadcast seed at a rate of 3kg per acre (2kg if drilling), and the crop should be ready for feeding from 12 weeks after sowing – or even as little as 10 weeks in a good year. Turnips are usually fed *in situ* behind electric fence. A heavy ewe will consume about 12kg of turnips per day, so, given that the crop may yield as much as 40 tonnes to the hectare, even a relatively small area, if it's utilised properly, has the potential to provide plenty of feed for your sheep.

Swedes grown for livestock feed are equally useful in the kitchen.

• **Swede:** Although in many respects similar to turnips, swedes have a higher dry matter and metabolisable energy content, and are therefore more nutritious. However, they can be more difficult to establish, and take longer to reach maturity. They may be grazed *in situ*, lifted and fed as required, or harvested and stored in a clamp for later use. Seed rate is 2kg to the acre if broadcast, or 1kg per acre for drilling, and sowing can take place from mid April through to mid June. As I mentioned before, swedes are a particularly useful feed for ewes with lambs in spring. If the sheep don't have access to the crop to help themselves, whole swedes can simply be tipped in a line on the field where the flock is grazing, or they can be chopped / sliced and added to the daily ration.

Incidentally, the varieties of swede and turnip grown for fodder are equally suited to culinary use, so, if you've grown a nice clean crop, lift the choicest of them for your own consumption.

• **Forage rape:** Another brassica, forage rape is best described as a turnip without the bulb. In many respects, rape is the more suitable crop for marginal land

Store lambs grazing a mix of forage rape and stubble turnips.

TIP

To avoid the risk of poisoning, sheep should always be introduced gradually to rape and other brassica crops. Some breeds of sheep – texels and their crosses in particular – are more susceptible to the effects of over-consumption, which may include anaemia, goitre and photo-sensitivity.

smallholdings, due to its ability to thrive on poorer soils and in exposed locations (which is probably why it's so popular here in Wales). Manure should be spread and incorporated before sowing, with the seed being broadcast at a rate of 4kg to the acre (2.5kg to the acre if drilled).

Often, however, it's sown with a ryegrass and clover seed mixture, in which case less than ¼ of the amount of rape may be needed. It can be sown at any time from May until late August (although that's pushing it a bit), so is an ideal crop to follow hay or silage. It's ready to feed from about 13 weeks after sowing. Sowing rape and grass / clover together, and then grazing off the rape *in situ* is a really good way of rejuvenating worn-out hay fields – the subsequent crop of grass will be a big improvement on what was there before.

• **Fodder beet:** This crop has the potential to produce exceptionally high yields, but the young plants aren't particularly competitive, and good weed control is essential. This is why I suggest that a spare plot in the vegetable garden is the place to grow fodder beet on a small scale – it's easy to keep an eye on it there, and hoe between the rows as required. Sow sparingly in rows 24" apart and 1½"- 2" deep in early April, and thin the crop down to one plant every 9" or so after 4-6 weeks, giving approximately 10 plants per m². (If growing on a field scale, you'll need about 100,000 seeds per hectare / 40,000 seeds per acre.)

Fodder beets continue to grow well into the autumn, so shouldn't be harvested until at least the end of October. The roots are generally clamped for storage and can be fed right through the winter, and even into the spring. The high energy content of fodder beets makes them a useful alternative to cereals in home-mixed rations for all types of livestock, including pigs.

• **Mangel:** The mangel is, in respect of its cultivation, essentially the same as the fodder beet. However, it's not at all frost hardy, so will need to be harvested before this becomes a risk. Before feeding, the roots require a period of maturation, so mangels lifted at the beginning of October wouldn't be suitable for use until after Christmas. Mangels aren't such good food for sheep as either swedes or turnips, but are ideal for feeding to dairy cows and goats as there's no risk of 'milk taint' as there may be with brassicas. The low DM content makes them unsuitable for pigs.

Root clamp

A clamp is a traditional way of storing root vegetables (including potatoes), particularly those which aren't frost hardy so cannot be left in the ground until required.

On free-draining ground the crop was often piled up in a shallow trench, but on heavier ground you're more likely to have to build it on a small mound, and open some drainage channels all the way around. You heap up your roots on a layer of straw, keeping the pile in a nice even ridge shape. Cover the whole lot with another layer of straw and then a layer of earth, to a depth of about 9". Leave some tufts of straw poking out the top to act as 'chimneys', allowing the crop to breathe.

A simpler way is to place 3 heston bales of straw in the form of an open-ended rectangle to make the back and sides of your clamp. Pile up the crop so that it slopes down to the front then cover with straw and earth as before.

If you've got space in an outbuilding you could just pile the roots on the floor and cover with straw or dry bracken, then lay an old carpet or something like that on top. We used to store mangels like this for our goats and they kept very well indeed.

Grassland Management

To the farmer or smallholder, grass is a crop. It's an easy crop to grow, but a very difficult crop to grow well. In many cases grassland is rather taken for granted, but when you consider that well managed grazing provides food for livestock at less than 20% of the cost of purchased concentrates, you'll realise it's worth putting a bit of effort into. Really, when we say 'grass', what we're referring to is the whole sward, consisting of a variety of grass species, clovers and broad leaved weeds, some of which are useful, many others less so, and a few of which are a downright

nuisance. More than 50 plant species may combine in varying proportions to form the diversity of habitats that we collectively refer to as pasture. A few of the more significant species are detailed below:

• **Ryegrass:** There are two basic types of ryegrass – perennial and Italian. Italian ryegrass probably has no place on the average smallholding – it's fast growing and high yielding, but requires high inputs of artificial fertilisers in order to achieve its potential. It has a low level of persistency (1-2 years) so is used in seed mixtures

for heavy cropping short term leys. Perennial ryegrass, on the other hand, forms the mainstay of most long term leys, and, in conjunction with white clover, should be the dominant species found in improved permanent pasture.

• **Annual meadow grass:** Annual meadow grass thrives in areas damaged by poaching, such as in gateways or where feed troughs have been sited. After resting a field for a while, this species will be seen to be growing thick and strong on the previously damaged area, giving the misleading impression that there's plenty of fresh grazing. Annual meadow grass is, in fact, a low-yielding, un-palatable weed species, and of no real value to livestock at all.

• **Cocksfoot:** This large, coarse grass is a component of more traditional seed mixtures. It thrives under lax grazing or conservation regimes. It has very good drought resistance, so is useful on thin soils.

• **Timothy:** This is another component of traditional leys, but is used less often in seed mixtures nowadays as it cannot compete with the more productive ryegrass. It is winter hardy, has a moderately high yield potential, and is very palatable to grazing livestock. Timothy thrives on heavy soils or in high rainfall areas.

• **Fescues:** These are hill and upland grasses of moderate to low productivity. Red fescue is a valuable species under poor conditions, and is often included in seed mixtures on hill farms. Sheep's fescue is less useful. Both species would be considered undesirable in a lowland sward. Meadow fescue combines well with timothy and white clover to give a seed mixture suitable for non- intensive livestock holdings.

• **Mat grass:** This is another upland grass, commonly found together with fescues on peaty soils. It is low yielding and not particularly palatable to stock, but its presence indicates good potential for improvement.

• **Purple moor grass (or flying bent):** Yet another upland species, common on deep, wet peat. It has a low level of digestibility, and is palatable only when very young. It is really only grazeable for 2-3 months of the year (June, July and August).

• **Tufted hair grass:** A weed species of poor pastures in both lowland and upland situations. Tufted hair grass thrives on heavy or badly drained soils, and is unpalatable to grazing livestock.

• **Yorkshire fog:** This is a common component of underutilised lowland swards. It will tolerate low fertility and low pH, and is typically found in pastures cut late for hay. Yorkshire fog produces a relatively high yield, but has low palatability.

• **Creeping / common bent:** These are low yielding grasses of both upland and lowland environments. Bents tolerate low fertility, and are quite valuable in hill swards in conjunction with fescue. However, a high proportion of bent is a common cause of sward degeneration.

• **Sweet vernal:** This is a common species found in poorer swards. It is drought resistant and tolerates low fertility. Sweet vernal is what gives traditional hay from old fashioned meadows its beautiful aroma, however, it has a high

proportion of stem to leaf and is unpalatable to stock. Clearly, the sweetest smelling hay is not necessarily the best thing to feed to your animals.

• **Meadow foxtail:** An early growing grass of lowland pastures, meadow foxtail is palatable, nutritious and fairly high yielding, making it a valuable part of a traditional hay meadow sward. Unfortunately it is a difficult species to establish.

• **Crested dogstail:** This is a valuable species of less intensively managed swards, and is commonly found in sheep pastures. It is fairly hardy, but not particularly competitive, so will grow well late in the season when the growth rates of more dominant species slow down.

• **Rough stalked meadow grass:** This palatable species is commonly found in fertile lowland swards in conjunction with perennial ryegrass (with which it may easily be confused). It produces moderate yields early in the season, but may suffer from moisture stress later on in the year.

• **Smooth stalked meadow grass:** This meadow grass is not as productive as the rough-stalked variety, but has good drought tolerance, so is suited to light land. It provides early spring growth, and produces a leafy aftermath following topping or mowing. It's quite a useful species for sowing in poultry runs.

• **Clover:** Both red and white clover, in common with other leguminous plants, have the ability to 'fix' nitrogen from the atmosphere – a dense clover sward may contribute the equivalent of up to 250kg N / ha. This is why

A mixture of grass species makes up the sward.

ryegrass and clover work so well together. Red clover isn't very persistent (up to 3 years) so is best suited to short or medium term leys. Its high protein content makes it ideal for fattening lambs, or for conserving as hay or silage. Don't graze with ewes for 6 weeks before or after tupping due to negative affects on fertility. White clover is of more interest to the smallholder – it will occur naturally in many swards, and should be encouraged to become well established.

• **Broad-leaved 'weeds':** Deep-rooted herbs such as plantain and yarrow provide essential trace elements for grazing stock. Chickweed can be a nuisance during the establishment of new leys as it quickly colonises areas of bare soil – control is difficult without also damaging clover.

Pineapple weed (a member of the chamomile family, I think) will appear together with annual meadow grass in gateways and other damaged areas – if you allow your house cow, goats or dairy sheep to eat it, their milk will taste dreadful for a few days. Dandelions, daisies and buttercups have no agronomic value, but together with many other wildflower species such as knapweed and cat's ear they present an uplifting splash of colour in any traditional meadow, as do vetches and tares.

Thistles, nettles and docks are a real pest and will considerably decrease the productivity of grassland. Ragwort is a poisonous weed that you are legally obliged to control. It's rife on many smallholdings due to poor land management and overgrazing with horses. It is also worth mentioning here bracken (an invasive fern) and soft rush (common on overgrazed, poorly-drained, acid soils). Both of these species are capable of rapidly dominating large tracts of grassland, almost to the exclusion of all other species, rendering the area more or less non-productive. Their only saving grace is that they can be cut and carried for use as animal bedding.

SWARD TYPES

Grassland isn't the original ecosystem of any part of the British Isles. At one time, woodland of varying types would have covered the lower lying areas, becoming scrub at higher altitudes, and moorland above 2,000 feet. This means that the grasslands of today are a rather unstable habitat, and any change of management will quickly be reflected by a change in sward composition.

Upland: Moor and mountain

These are the most natural of our grassland habitats, but at

best can only be described as semi-natural. Generations of management, such as the burning of heather on the grouse moors and extensive grazing by sheep, have suppressed many indigenous species and encouraged others to dominate. The soil will be acidic – many of the species present, including the heather, rely upon a type of root fungus for their nutrition, which cannot thrive under alkaline conditions. The predominant grass species are likely to be bent and fescue on the better areas, with flying bent, mat grass, mountain heath grass and wavy hair grass elsewhere. Particularly poorly-drained areas and bogs will be colonised by cotton sedge. Bracken will often be found encroaching into the better, well-drained areas. This type of grassland is only likely to be significant on smallholdings that enjoy common or mountain grazing rights, and, although the stock carrying capacity is very low, I cannot really advocate carrying out major improvements on such pasture, as moorland has become something of an endangered habitat. However, there may be small, localised areas on the smallholding where the types of grasses described above are found to be dominant due to factors such as acidity and poor drainage, and where some reasonably gentle improvement can be carried out:

Firstly, open out some ditches or land drains. If bracken is a problem then turn in your pigs without rings in their snouts – while engaged in rootling for buried delicacies they'll bring the rhizomes of the bracken plants to the surface, where they'll die (the rhizome requires anaerobic conditions in order to survive). Electric fencing should be used to concentrate the pig's attention onto a small area

at a time, and to prevent them gaining access to your newly dug ditches. Use your poultry to scratch out all the dead grass and moss. Run over the land a couple of times with a spiked harrow, spread a bit of lime and then broadcast your new seed mixture (the sweepings off the hayshed floor will probably do here). A few passes with the chain harrows (or a rake on smaller areas) should suffice to ensure that the seed is buried. Squash it all down a bit with a roller and hope for the best. The result will be what is known as a partial re-seed, i.e. you haven't completely killed off the existing species before sowing the new. By good grazing management you can ensure that the more desirable species will thrive. At best, the sward composition will now be something like this: bent, fescue, perennial ryegrass, cocksfoot and the meadow grasses – rough stalked, smooth stalked and annual. If you're lucky, some white clover will also be present.

Low quality permanent pastures

This is the type of sward that will probably be encountered when taking over a grassland smallholding – unimproved (or semi-improved) permanent grassland, either currently or previously employed for the continuous grazing of cattle and sheep, with perhaps an occasional cut of poor quality hay being taken. Fields may have been ploughed only once or twice within living memory, or not at all. These swards are likely to be dominated by bent grasses and fescues, together with both rough- and smooth-stalked meadow grasses. Other species of low productivity such as Yorkshire fog, creeping soft grass, downy oat, meadow barley, soft brome and wavy hair grass will be seen in varying proportions. Grasses of higher agronomic value (perennial ryegrass, cocksfoot, timothy, meadow fescue and meadow foxtail) are likely to be present in small quantities – it is the density of these species that determines the overall quality of the sward. White clover is unlikely to be found in any significant quantity. Poorly-drained areas will be indicated by clumps of rushes.

TIP

When taking on a new piece of ground, don't be too disheartened by the sight of a mass of thistles. Remember the story of the blind farmer who went out one day in his pony and trap to 'view' a piece of land that was for sale. Upon arrival he asked his boy, who had accompanied him, to tie the pony to a thistle. "I'm sorry, sir" replied the boy, "I can't do that. There's no thistle big enough!" "Then we'd best go home again!" said the blind man. A strong crop of weeds will be indicative of good fertile soil, albeit under rather poor management.

The smallholder has two courses of action open to him when faced with this type of sward – cultivate and begin again (with either a partial or full re-seed), or improve (and subsequently maintain) the sward composition through grazing management.

High quality permanent pastures

Consisting almost entirely of perennial ryegrass and wild white clover, these traditional fattening pastures are maintained in a highly productive state through careful grazing management, and are capable of carrying high densities of grazing livestock without resorting to artificial fertilisers. Historically, probably the most famous example of this type of grassland was found in the Romney Marsh area of Kent, from whence comes the Romney Marsh breed of sheep. At one time this was said to be the most densely stocked sheep pasture in the world, with set stocking rates of up to 12 ewes (+ lambs) per acre. Heavy grazing during the summer months ensures that the clover is kept free of competition from the ryegrass, with occasional rest periods in spring, autumn and winter, as appropriate to each species, allowing both the clover and the ryegrass to make up growth. It should be possible to take a good crop of hay off such land from time to time, but not too often from the same area or the sward composition will alter. Most of these traditional pastures were lost during the ploughing campaign of the Second World War, and many more have subsequently been ploughed and re-seeded with fast growing, heavy-cropping short term leys for silage making. It must be noted that the types of high-quality and low-quality permanent pastures outlined here are extremes within their categories. Many intermediates will be found, and management should be varied accordingly. In addition, there are other very specific types of pasture that I've not mentioned such as

chalk downland, wetlands and watermeadows, each forming its own distinctive habitat.

Leys

It is likely that, with the exception of any out-lying inaccessible fields, steep slopes or very poor pieces of land, most of the grassland on the smallholding will be managed as either a long or short term ley. The dividing line between the two seems somewhat blurred, so we also have 'one year' and 'medium term' leys. At what point does a long term ley cease to be classified as such, and become permanent pasture? Your guess is as good as mine. Basically, a ley is a temporary pasture – a field is put under grass for a number of years, grazed and mown accordingly, then ploughed under and the land used for another type of crop (or re-seeded with grass). A ley forms an integral part of many traditional rotational systems of land management.

Short term leys: The short term ley of one or two years is a particularly useful part of traditional arable rotations, such as the famous Norfolk Four Course (wheat – roots – barley – grass). As such, it'll be of interest to smallholders who wish to grow small areas of cereals and root crops in addition to grass in order to be self-sufficient in livestock feeds. The barley in the rotation can be undersown with the grass mixture, thus acting as a nurse crop, protecting the grass seed during germination. Once the barley is harvested the grass will soon grow up through the stubble. For a one year ley – primarily for hay or silage – commercially available seed mixtures usually consist of Italian rye grass and red clover, however, as we've already seen, Italian ryegrass may not be an ideal species under more traditional management systems. Having said that, it has the potential to outyield all other varieties when cut for hay or silage in its first year, so perhaps it should be given consideration in situations where only a limited area of the smallholding is suitable for mowing.

Medium term leys: A medium term ley is likely to be intended for 3-4 years of use. Seed mixtures may contain both perennial and Italian ryegrasses. Management of this type of sward will be as for the short term ley in the first two years. By the third year the Italian ryegrass will have come to the end of its useful span, making way for the more persistent perennial. During years 3 and 4 a more 'intensive' grazing regime can be employed – probably mixed rotational grazing with cattle and sheep – with definite grazing and resting periods. At the end of year four it is time to plough in the grass to make way for the following crop. By this stage quite a few weed species will have crept into the sward. Perhaps the livestock used for the last grazing period of the season should be your pigs – they'll grub up the weeds and carry out a fair proportion of the cultivation required.

Long term leys: The long term ley is land put under grass for a period of 5-10 years, but don't be surprised if, after ten years, you start calling it permanent pasture. The simplest form of long term ley is a basic perennial ryegrass / white clover mixture, with several different strains of the grass and clover included, to give as wide a range of heading dates as possible. For a longer term ley that may

well end up as 'semi- permanent' it is important to include a few of the more persistent grass species such as timothy, cocksfoot and crested dogstail, which will enable the sward to withstand the various regimes of mowing and hard grazing to which it will be subjected. Seed mixtures can be tailored to suit specific conditions, and traditional herb species, old-fashioned grasses and wild flowers can be incorporated.

GRASSLAND RE-CREATION

So far we've worked on the assumption that the smallholding will consist of existing grassland, of one type or another, that will be managed for mowing and grazing in a traditional rotational fashion. Established swards will contain a diversity of grass species that can be augmented by sown varieties. Occasional ploughing of worn out leys may turn up a long forgotten seed bank of wildflowers. Plants found in field margins, hedge bottoms and rough corners will contribute to the general bio-diversity of the holding, and the overall result will be an attractive, ever-changing patchwork of habitats.

But what if there is no grass on the holding? As I mentioned earlier, many 'new' smallholdings are formed from small pockets of former arable land, and, after many years of intensive monoculture, this type of land will be more or less devoid of naturally occurring grassland vegetation. Simply leaving it alone and expecting re-generation to occur is not really an option, since the only colonisers (other than arable weed species) will be wind blown – witness the ragwort infested mess known as

'set-aside'. Don't despair though: grass seed mixtures are available specifically for arable reversion, containing all the traditional hay meadow grass species, together with wild flowers, clovers and vetches. Independent advice (i.e. not sponsored by one of the agri-chemical giants) is readily available, and mixes can be tailored to ensure that varieties suitable to the locality, soil type and proposed management regime are included. This type of re-seed, used in conjunction with long and short term leys on other areas of the holding can, with correct management, transform a former arable desert into a wildlife-rich, diverse ecosystem that is also capable of putting food on your plate.

PASTURE RESTORATION

More often than not, smallholdings change hands in a run-down state, and the newcomer will be faced with the task of rejuvenating worn out pasture. In most cases this will consist of previously improved (but now sadly neglected) permanent pasture, which has become dominated by weed species of little agricultural value. Overgrazing by unsuitable classes of livestock (equines, mostly) will have reduced the environmental value of the habitat too. Following a period without livestock (i.e. after the previous owners have removed their stock, but before you've introduced your own), this type of sward will be characterised by clumps of couch and other course grasses, growing through a dense mat of flattened and decaying vegetation. Thistles, docks and ragwort will be widespread, and patches of nettles abound. It's enough to make your

Neglected pasture, characterised by clumps of couch and other course grasses, growing through a dense mat of flattened and decaying vegetation.

heart sink, particularly if the word 'organic' appears in the strategy for future management of your holding.

There are a number of different options that can be considered when carrying out grassland improvements, but in the long run it generally pays to be pretty heavy handed early on, even if this means resorting to the use of some chemical treatments and artificial fertilisers in the first year or so. This shouldn't jeopardise any long term ambition to manage the land organically. Whatever your principles, there's no point starting off with your hands tied – get the land and pasture in good shape first and then concentrate on the long term view. Remember, you don't become a martyr until you're dead!

A word about fertiliser

Unfortunately it's not possible to devise a fully sustainable self-contained management system for the smallholding: No matter

how careful you are to spread manure, compost your waste and rotate your crops, you'll find there's an overall deficit of nutrients, particularly phosphates. From time to time you'll need to import fertility in one form or another. The alternative is to witness a progressive decline in the productivity of your holding and the health of your stock. You might get away with it for 20 years or so, lulled into a false sense of security by an initial increase in output following generous use of FYM (farm yard manure) on land previously not managed in that way.

Now, before you all start jumping about and yelling that farmers managed perfectly well before the advent of artificial fertilisers, so why can't we do it now?, let me remind you of the millions of tonnes of guano imported from the islands of the South Pacific during the 19th century, and the contents of the 'night soil' cart, and the Thames sailing barges carrying stable litter from the

hundreds of working horses in the capital to farms on the east coast, and the dung from city dairy cows, many thousands of which were housed in cellars and basements up and down the land. (During the 1850s, one dairy in Glasgow housed 1,700 cattle, hand-milked three times a day by a regular army of dairymaids!). Also waste fish from the docks, and blood-and-bone meal from the abattoirs and knackers yards, and seaweed spread on the land, and manure from pigs fed on waste food from the cities (waste food that now goes to landfill I suppose, now swill-feeding is banned), and industrial waste such as basic slag. These were all bought-in fertilisers, most of which are no longer available for a range of political, environmental, human health and economical reasons. And if we turn the clock back even further to before the enclosures of the 18th century, to a time when a large portion of the British countryside was open common and deciduous woodlands, peasants had rights of venville and pannage. Livestock grazing the moors and commons (venville) and pigs foraging for acorns and beech mast in the woods (pannage) during the day time would be penned up at night on the smallholding in order that their dung could be collected for use on the land – a very convenient way of importing fertiliser from the surrounding countryside. The modern smallholder will also need to import some fertility. This could be in a variety of forms such as by buying in hay rather than making it on the holding, but if you have to resort to a bit of artificial fertiliser from time to time, then so be it – as the late John Seymour said on the same subject, *"A man can't really hoist himself up by his own boot-laces, nor can a farm".*

SOME OPTIONS FOR PASTURE IMPROVEMENT

The appropriate course of action will depend upon a number of physical factors (e.g. accessibility, aspect, altitude, drainage, etc.), soil type (structure and analysis), and the degree of degradation of the existing sward. The intended use of the land (e.g. grazing / hay making / amenity / wildlife conservation) and any long term management ideals must also be considered, particularly when choosing seed mixtures.

Physical factors are largely fixed. Although drainage can be installed, and access improved, at the end of the day a field that's too steep to plough will always be too steep. An indication of soil type / structure / analysis can, to a certain extent, be gained by studying the plant species present, although it may not be a good idea to rely too heavily on this method of evaluation, as this brief extract from *Hovel in the Hills* by Elizabeth West shows –

"We have learned to keep an open mind on the theory that plants can be used as soil indicators. I can show you a patch of ground here where bird's-foot trefoil, clover, moss, sow-thistle, chickweed, groundsel, bracken, goosefoot, buttercup, foxglove, self-heal, rush, daisy, sheep's sorrel, yellow rocket and knapweed all grow together. According to our various reference books, this indicates that we have rich, very acid, gravelly, calcareous, well-drained, poor, wet, sterile, loamy, undrained, fertile, dry, sour, markedly alkaline, marshy clay soil."

The simplest option is probably to buy a basic soil testing kit from your local garden centre, and, if you do nothing else, at least check the pH, which should ideally be about 6.0.

The quality of the existing sward is also determined by examining the species present, and in what proportions. Remember to take into account the amount of bare ground. In some cases a reasonable density (more than 40%) of desirable grasses and clovers will be found – these can be encouraged to proliferate through careful grazing management. At the other end of the scale there may be very few species of agricultural or environmental importance in the existing sward, in which case it's best to plough up the whole lot and begin again.

Total re-seed
(Usually spring or early autumn).

The idea of ploughing up an established piece of grassland can seem a rather drastic step to take, particularly if you're new to this way of life. Really, though, it's the best way to get your smallholding livestock venture off to a flying start.

As the name implies, a total re-seed means you start from scratch, usually by first spraying off the existing sward with glyphosate ('Round-up'). Glyphosate is a broad spectrum systemic herbicide that is transported throughout the plant, ensuring that no part survives. It is de-activated in contact with soil. There is no persistent or residual effect, so a new crop can be sown almost immediately. Of course, it's possible to re-seed without killing off the old sward, but establishment of the new grassland will be hampered by competition from the existing weed species, resulting in a rather short-lived improvement.

Probably, the decision as to whether or not to use a spray will depend upon the density of species such as docks and couch in the old pasture – carrying out cultivations without first killing them off will simply cause these species to multiply as each chopped up piece of root will form a new plant. Personally, I would view this type of treatment as a one-off occurrence in order to tackle a badly neglected field, returning to more traditional management methods thereafter.

Method:

1. Graze down the old sward really hard. You'll need high stocking rates for this to be effective. A lot of animals for a few days will do a better job than a few animals over a longer period. Cattle are useful if there's a dense mat of vegetation that needs breaking up. You could ask a neighbouring larger farmer if he'd like to turn in a lot of bullocks for a week or so. If you've only got a small number of animals to work with then divide the field up into more manageable sections. Failing this, get a contractor in to marmalise the whole lot with a flail mower.

2. Kill off the redundant sward by spraying with glyphosate as soon as it shows signs that it is beginning to recover from step 1. (Systemic herbicides are more effective on rapidly growing vegetation).

3. Spread manure if required. If you are new to smallholding, you probably won't have

Spreading manure on grassland is an essential aspect of smallholding management.

accumulated much muck, in which case some artificial fertiliser can be applied later (see point 10, right).

4. As regards cultivation, if you've sprayed off the old pasture, then heavy discing, or repeated harrowing, may be sufficient to break up the surface. However, if you've decided not to use chemicals, you'll need to plough the field in order to bury the existing vegetation, where hopefully it'll die and rot down. You'll also need to rotavate after ploughing, in order to produce some sort of seed bed.
(NB: When re-seeding very small areas, your pigs can be usefully employed carrying out steps 1, 2, 3 and 4 in their own fashion).

5. Broadcast the new seed mixture. A fertiliser spreader can be used for this (but not on a windy day). A ground-wheel drive spinner is ideal, as it can be towed behind a car or quad-bike, or you can get a little distributer that mounts on the rear rack of an ATV.

6. Spread lime if required.

7. Chain harrow.

8. Roll.

TIP

Grass seed is fairly fine and free flowing. If you're not careful, you'll find you've spread the whole lot in one pass, leaving nothing for the rest of the field. The trick is to thoroughly mix the seed with sand before you start. This gives you a greater volume to work with, making it a simple matter to ensure even distribution across the whole area.

Groundwheel driven fertiliser spreader / seed broadcaster, ideal for towing behind a quad or small tractor.

Spraying off the old sward.

9. The new sward should be very lightly grazed by sheep as soon as ground conditions and growth stage allow. This may be within a few weeks in the case of a spring re-seed, or perhaps not until the following spring if the re-seeding was carried out in the autumn. Nipping off the young plants encourages them to 'tiller' out from the base, resulting in a denser sward.

10. Fertiliser should be applied after this initial light grazing. The amount required will be dependent on the intended use – if a high-yielding ley has been sown, it is quite reasonable to expect to be able to take a crop of hay or silage in the first year, in which case fairly high fertiliser inputs will be needed. If, on the other hand, you've used a more traditional seed mixture, use less fertiliser for a rotational grazing regime. Hay can be cut in the second year when the sward has become well established.

A newly established re-seed.

Partial re-seed

(Usually spring after grazing with ewes and lambs, or late summer after mowing for hay or silage).

Partially re-seeding basically consists of giving a 'face lift' to a tired pasture. It's a less drastic procedure than completely re-seeding, and so may be more attractive to the smallholder,

Using a 'nurse' crop

A nurse crop is sown at the same time as the grass in order to protect the developing sward. It is, in fact, doubtful if any 'nursing' actually takes place (there is more likely to be competition between species), but it's a useful way of getting two crops off one piece of land. A spring re-seed may be sown together with a cereal crop (usually barley, sometimes oats, but never wheat), with the grass growing up through the stubble for autumn grazing as soon as the corn is harvested. In the case of a late summer re-seed, for example after hay making, forage rape can be included in the seed mixture. This is probably most appropriate for the smallholder. Rape can be grazed from about 10 weeks after sowing, and is useful for fattening store lambs through the autumn and winter. Its rapid growth will protect the recently ploughed field against soil erosion, and the dung from the folded sheep will be thoroughly trodden in, providing nutrients for the emerging grass. Once the rape has been eaten off, the new sward will grow on to give a useful bite in the spring. (See also pages 128 - 129).

particularly if the existing sward is reasonably bio-diverse (but not too weedy). Considerable increases in yield can be achieved, although the improvement will be short lived unless management is amended in accordance with the new composition of the sward. On a commercial scale, partial re-seeding is carried out by 'slot seeding'. This involves the use of a pretty complex seed drill that cuts narrow slots in the ground at approximately 9" intervals. The

Chain harrowing grassland stimulates growth and helps to disperse mole hills and dung pats.

machine deposits grass seeds, fertiliser granules and slug pellets into each of the slots, before pressing them shut. It then applies a small amount of herbicide along the top of each slot in order to reduce competition from existing species. On smaller holdings the process can be carried out more simply (albeit with more passes) as follows:

Method (for spring sowing):

1. Check pH during the preceding autumn and apply lime if required.

2. Graze down the existing sward. Assuming that the old pasture is in reasonable condition (if it isn't, you should be considering a total re-seed) then normal hard grazing by ewes and lambs in late March / early April will suffice.

3. After removing the stock (say mid April), make passes in two directions with spiked harrows in order to open up a criss-cross pattern of scratches.

4. Broadcast grass seed mixture.

5. Chain harrow.

6. Roll.

7. Re-introduce sheep to the field and continue to graze until the new plants are seen to be emerging.

8. Remove the sheep (probably the beginning of May) and apply fertiliser according to intended usage. Subsequent management should be tailored to favour the newly introduced species, otherwise you'll soon be back to square one again.

Partial re-seeding can also be carried out in late summer on fields recently cut for hay or silage. In this case, forage rape is often included in the seed mixture for autumn grazing.

ROUTINE GRASSLAND MANAGEMENT

It's worth remembering that good grassland management and good livestock husbandry go hand in hand. There are a surprising number of parallels, too: just as we need to ensure that our animals are kept free of pests and diseases, and receive an adequate level of nutrition for good health and growth, so must we apply these same principals to our grassland – it's a living thing, after all.

There are a number of routine procedures involved in grassland management which should help maintain the pasture in a healthy, productive state, and prevent sward degeneration:

Re-seeding: I've already talked about re-seeding as a method for creating new grassland, or for replacing neglected pastures, but there may well be areas of the holding where regular re-seeding is part of the routine husbandry. A temporary grassland or 'ley' forms an integral part of most traditional rotational systems of land management, with fields being under grass for only a few years before being ploughed up to make way for the next crop in the sequence. The burden of disease and the drain of nutrients are considerably less under a rotational system than where land is continuously cropped or grazed in the same fashion year on year. And I'm not just talking about whole fields here. It's quite a good idea to put a spare plot in the vegetable garden down to grass from time to time, and fold over it with poultry for a year or two.

You'll also need to periodically re-seed any poached areas in fields, for example around gateways or where feed troughs have been sited.

Fertilising: When we talk about fertilisers we include farm yard manure (FYM). Generally speaking, I don't think that smallholders make enough use of manure. The first muck heap is usually a source of great enthusiasm, particularly where previous experience has been limited to the constrained environment of a suburban back garden, but, as the amount of livestock on the holding increases, so too does amount of manure produced. Enthusiasm wanes as muck handling becomes a chore, which always seems to get put off for another day. I've seen vast accumulated muck heaps on smallholdings, perhaps ⅓ of an acre in extent (yet scarcely more than a wheelbarrow high), just sitting there in the rain as all the

Habitat creation

If you're struggling to balance the need for a productive holding with a desire for wildlife conservation, consider the following:

Hay cut from the 'headlands' (round the edges) of a field is typically harder to make and of poorer quality. When choosing your new seed mixtures, why not sow a traditional, old-fashioned wildflower mix for the first pass right round the headland, with conventional higher yielding species being sown on the remainder of the field? This will give you the best of both worlds – an attractive wildlife habitat on the poorer area and a good crop on the better land. (Remember not to spread manure or fertiliser right up to the field margin). At hay making time use the rough headland bales to form a sacrifice layer at the bottom of the stack, and the following year they can be broken up and spread on the land, putting the wildflower seeds back where they belong.

essential nutrients leach away down the nearest land drain. What a waste! True enough, you'll need some sort of smallish muck heap to supply well-rotted manure for the vegetable garden (we carry about 5 tonnes of rotted muck into our garden each year, putting the whole lot on one plot. Each of the five plots gets mucked once in five years), but the remainder should be spread straight on the land, whenever weather conditions allow, where it'll do a lot of good. Perhaps it's not so much a lack of enthusiasm that causes the backlog, but a lack of suitable equipment to take the backache out of the job – I believe that a muckspreader is one of the essential bits of kit that every livestock keeping smallholder should have. And if you don't own a tractor, don't worry – there are several small muckspreaders available that can be towed behind a 4x4 or ATV.

It's fairly common practice on mixed farms nowadays to have samples of manure and slurry analysed in order to determine its fertilising value. This allows it to be applied accurately in accordance with the requirements of the growing crop, and if there's a shortfall of nutrients, then (and only then) the deficit is made up with artificial fertilisers. It strikes me that this is a very sensible compromise.

Manure is usually spread on grazing land during the spring and autumn at rates of up to 15 tonnes / acre. Be aware, when applying manure to fields that are soon to be grazed, that the dung from pigs fed on proprietary feeds will contain high levels of copper, which is toxic to sheep. It's also a good idea to identify areas of the holding where ground conditions will allow some spreading to be carried out during the winter, in order to limit the amount of muck that needs to be stored (an inappropriately sited muck heap can lead to prosecution and hefty fines). Fields that are due to be ploughed up in the spring are good candidates for winter spreading, as it doesn't matter about churning up the surface. If hay or silage fields are to be mucked this must be carried out early in the year (or in the preceding autumn), in order that all the manure has had time to break down and disappear from the surface before mowing, otherwise you'll end up incorporating lumps of dung in the crop, with possible health consequences for the stock that eat it. Muck can be spread fairly liberally onto the stubble of a mown field as soon as the bales are shifted, but not if you're aiming to take a second cut – the 6-8 week interval between 1st and 2nd cut isn't long enough for manure to break down. Slurry would be ok in this situation, or an artificial fertiliser (probably straight nitrogen).

Artificial fertilisers can be used 'little and often' on grazing land, from spring (for early bite) through to late summer (for the autumn flush). There's nothing to be gained by very early applications – wait until soil temperature starts to rise. On mowing land, apply an appropriate amount when closing the fields off in April. The main thing is not to use too much – artificial fertilisers are just basic plant food (nitrogen, phosphate and potash) and, as with animals, overfeeding is wasteful. A bit of light drizzle after spreading is ideal as it will gently dissolve the prills and put the nutrients where they're needed. Heavy rain will simply wash it all away, and in very dry weather it'll just sit on the surface and scorch the plants.

Grasslands that are rich in clover will not require applications of nitrogen, which is why clover is such an important part of organic farming systems – the clover itself may contribute the equivalent of up to 250kg N/ha. However, the sward will need to be managed in a way that encourages the clover to proliferate, and it might be necessary to supply other essential nutrients – phosphates, in particular.

From time to time a top dressing of lime may be required in order to keep soil pH between 6.0-6.5. We've found that applying calcified seaweed to fields that have been mucked helps to maintain the right balance.

Harrowing: It's a good thing to harrow grassland in May or thereabouts. Harrowing will disperse mole hills, rake out dead grass and moss, and let some air and light into the base of the sward, to the benefit of the finer grasses and clovers. Also, in response to the bruising effect, the higher value grasses will grow more vigorously, producing a denser, heavier yielding crop. Harrowing should be carried out again after grazing with cattle or horses, as this will spread out dung pats and prevent the formation of sour areas. The ubiquitous chain harrow is ideal in most situations, but where there's a lot of dead material, or where a bit more aeration is required, use a spiked harrow or a spring tined grass harrow. Chain harrows can also be used to good advantage on fields recently spread with manure in order to break up lumps, distribute the muck more evenly, and generally work it down into the surface. This is particularly useful where muck has been spread by hand, for example by forking it off

a slow-moving trailer. In fact, you can attach the harrow to the back of the trailer and chuck the muck off in its path.

Rolling: The rolling of hay or silage fields using a heavy ballast roller is usually carried out towards the middle of the growing period. It may seem rather harsh, this business of squashing down all that lovely long grass, but don't worry – it'll soon spring back up, thicker and stronger than before. In addition to its stimulating effect, rolling will squash mole hills, level wheel ruts, and bury any small stones that may inadvertently have been distributed when muck spreading, removing these obstructions from the path of the mower. Quite apart from preventing damage to machinery, this reduces the risk of soil contamination to the crop, which could lead to cases of listeria in your livestock.

Make your own roller using a 45 gallon oil drum filled with concrete. Remember to put a piece of pipe through the middle of the drum before pouring the concrete in.

Topping: Topping is one of the most satisfying aspects of grassland management – it keeps weeds in check, reduces the incidence of lameness and orf in sheep, and gives straggly summer pastures a real boost. Basically, plants have two types of growth – vegetative and reproductive. Grasses, however, don't need reproductive growth (seed heads) in order to reproduce – they are able to multiply by vegetative means. It's this dense vegetative growth that we, as farmers and smallholders, need to encourage on our grazing land. Reproductive growth is wasteful,

Listeriosis

A bacterial infection
• Usually associated with big bale silage, although clamp silage, haylage, big bale hay and conventional hay bales have also been identified as sources of outbreaks.
• Generally introduced into silage via contaminated soil.
• Affected animals usually die, despite treatment.
• The disease is also transmissible to humans.
• Avoid soil contamination by chain harrowing pastures to disperse molehills, rolling to flatten ruts, and by not setting the mower too low.
• Repair damage to wrapped bales immediately to ensure good fermentation and preservation.

Topping stemmy pasture in mid-summer to control weeds and encouage new grass growth.

Gorse and heather habitats benefit from occasional burning.

unpalatable to stock, and results in sward degeneration. For the most part of the grazing season the livestock themselves keep grass growth within reasonable bounds, by constantly nipping off excessive vegetation, which encourages further dense growth. But there comes a time in the summer when the grass just shoots away, throwing up seed heads all over the place, and this is when it needs topping to bring it back under control, otherwise both the sward, and the livestock that depend upon it, will suffer. Topping is a particularly important part of organic grassland management regimes.

Topping simply consists of cutting off all the unnecessary seed heads (thereby stimulating vigorous vegetative growth), and, by timing it right, it also plays an important part in weed control, particularly thistles which, unlike

grasses, don't like being cut down – by allowing them to produce flowers (but not set seed) before cutting, the plants are eventually exhausted and die, but timing is crucial; remember the old adage: *"Cut a thistle in May and it's back next day, cut a thistle in June and expect more soon, cut a thistle in July and then it'll surely die!"* Having said that, thistles seem to have been setting seed much earlier in the last few years, so it's also worth remembering that *"one year's seeding makes seven years weeding"*. Top a bit sooner than is customary, if you think it's necessary.

One type of weed that should never be topped is ragwort. This poisonous plant becomes more palatable to stock (and more toxic) when cut and dried. Nor should ragwort be allowed to set seed. Mature ragwort plants should be pulled up and burnt as soon as the clusters of yellow flowers betray their presence. Better still, nip it in the bud, quite literally, by grazing.

The topper itself is like a rather crude, heavy duty mower. In fact, an old mower set to cut high (8" or so) will do just as well.

Burning: Where gorse is encroaching on pasture it should be burnt off in a seven year rotation, so divide the area into

seven blocks and burn one section each year. The fresh young growth can provide an important winter feedstuff, particularly when other herbage is covered in snow. Some animals are particularly well adapted to this diet – New Forest ponies, for example, grow thick bristly moustaches in winter to protect their sensitive lips from the prickles. In some areas young gorse used to be harvested and put through a chaff cutter for inclusion in livestock rations.

Gorse can be burnt between October and March without the need to apply for a permit, although the local fire department should be advised of your activities.

Heather habitats will also benefit from a similar regime.

Mole control: The traditional mole catcher would once have been a familiar rural figure, and probably a bit of a rogue and a poacher too! However, the increasing use of poisons – strychnine in particular – put the whole business into the hands of 'pest control operatives' with the necessary qualifications to allow them to use these lethal chemicals. The old boy doing the rounds in his moleskin weskit faded into country lore.

The traditional art of mole trapping has made a comeback in recent years.

Now, thank goodness, the situation has completely reversed following a ban on the use of strychnine. And not a moment before time, either. The old art of mole trapping has been revived, and if you've got the knack it makes a nice little sideline. I know of several smallholders who offer a mole trapping service to local farmers, and at £10 per mole caught they're doing very nicely out of it.

Mole traps, which come in a variety of designs, are fairly cheap to purchase. This is just as well, as you do need quite a few to be effective. The claw type trap is probably the most popular. Traps should not be set in the mole hills themselves, but in the tunnels that run between them. These can be found by prodding the ground around each pile of earth with a thin metal spike – it will suddenly go in with very little resistance when you encounter a run. After using a trowel or narrow bladed spade to dig out a small section of turf, it's a good idea to use an old spoon, bent at the right angle, to smooth the sides and base of the tunnel before setting the trap. Once the trap is in place, replace the turf to block out any light and mark the place with something obvious like a little flag on a stick. Rather than dotting your traps around the holding it's best to concentrate your efforts on one place at a time by setting a dozen or more traps in close proximity to one another, then moving them all to another place in a week or so. Once you think you've caught all the moles in a specific area, rake out the mole hills so you'll then be able to spot any new burrowing activity.

GRAZING AS A MANAGEMENT TOOL

Grazing management is very much a two way thing – we manage the grassland in order to maintain and improve our livestock, and we manage our livestock in order to maintain and improve our grassland.

Weed control

Ragwort: Many smallholdings, particularly those that have been over grazed with horses, are badly infested by ragwort. That was the situation here at Ty'n y Mynydd when we moved in, yet within a very few years we'd totally eliminated it from our land without resorting to any chemical treatments. Although we pulled up quite a lot, the demise was largely achieved through grazing management.

Mature ragwort plants aren't palatable to stock unless cut and dried, for example by accidental inclusion in hay. However, in spring the tender young shoots (which are not nearly so toxic) will be consumed readily by sheep, and, if they are repeatedly nipped off, the root reserves will be exhausted. The secret is to graze hard with sheep during the whole of April, and when I say hard, I mean really hard – the poor things need to be more or less licking bare earth! But it's worth it in the long run. Provided that you remain vigilant about pulling up any ragwort that occurs in inaccessible places, you'll find that just two seasons of this regime will be the end of it, and you'll be able to bale future crops of hay with confidence.

Ragwort - a common poisonous weed.

Thistles: Thistles thrive under low nitrogen input, extensive systems. As we've already seen, thistles can be controlled by cutting, but they can also be discouraged by good grazing management. Cattle are more effective at reducing thistle numbers than sheep. (An Irishman once told me that all you had to do was to sprinkle a bit of salt on each thistle, whereupon the cows would eat the lot!). Avoid over grazing in winter and early spring, and avoid under grazing in summer. But above all, don't let them set seed. And the same goes for docks, too – if organic options are preferred,

White clover is a valuable part of the sward due to its ability to 'fix' nitrogen from the atmosphere.

it's even worthwhile hand-weeding standing crops of hay.

Encouraging clover

Contrary to popular belief, clover is not directly killed off by applications of artificial fertiliser, but, as it's not very competitive, it is rapidly ousted by the more dominant nitrogen-loving grass species, if the management regime favours them. In order to avoid having to apply chemical nitrogen we need clover, which fixes nitrogen from the atmosphere… which encourages the high-yielding grasses… which shade out the clover… and so we're back to square one again. This is where good grazing management comes into the equation.

A suitable grazing pattern to encourage the spread of white clover in a sward would be as follows:
• Soil pH should be in the range of 6.0-6.5.
• Soil potash and phosphate indexes should be around 2.
• Eat the pasture down with sheep

during November.
• Graze heavily in March and April (clover is very tolerant of heavy stocking rates).
• Heavy grazing after April will have a negative effect on clover, as it favours the more dominant ryegrasses.
• Graze rotationally throughout the summer, with well defined rest periods of 3–4 weeks, followed by fairly rapid defoliation. (Interestingly, this regime seems to be completely at odds with that required for thistle control. It seems that you just can't have it both ways!)

We've found that the greatest natural proliferation of white clover has occurred in the field where we strip graze our cows. The field is grazed by sheep from early March to Mid April. We then apply a light top dressing of artificial fertiliser (100kg / acre of 20:10:10) and rest the field for a few weeks before putting the cows in at the beginning of May. In some years we omit the fertiliser and apply calcified seaweed instead – this depends upon the amount of manure the field has received, which in turn

depended on ground conditions in the preceding autumn. The cows are strip grazed behind a single strand of electric fence, which is moved forward by about a yard a day. Ideally they graze under the wire, so don't trample or dung on any of the crop. After a while we introduce a back fence behind the cows to allow re-growth on the grazed area. Any thistles occurring behind the back fence are topped, and dung pats are spread. By the time the cows reach the bottom of the field there's sufficient new growth back where they started from, so the sequence begins again. In good grass growing years we've moved the cows back to the top of the field before reaching the end, and made hay from the surplus. The cows are housed at the beginning of November, whereupon we put sheep in the field to tidy up, before spreading manure. The field is then rested over the winter.

In this way our one-and-a-half acre field provides all the grazing required for 3 milking cows, and sometimes a portion of their winter fodder too. We have all the milk and other dairy products we require, including cream, butter, cheese, ice cream and yoghurt. The remainder of the milk is used to rear around 12 calves / year, the sale of which gives us some cash income. Any surplus milk helps to fatten our pigs. The dung from the calf pens and pigsties is spread on the field at the end of the grazing period, where it contributes to the next year's crop. Grazing for a small number of sheep is available at two key times of the year – lambing and tupping. This, I think, is getting fairly close to the type of intensive land use that old John Seymour was talking about.

143

Hay and Silage

In basic terms, the principal difference between hay and silage is that hay is preserved by drying, whereas in silage, preservation is by fermentation, followed, in effect, by pickling under anaerobic conditions. The natural juices within the crop are required to ensure that the process is a success. Therefore, a crop which has been fully dried for hay, and subsequently spoiled by rain, cannot be saved by baling and wrapping as silage.

The belief that hay making is somehow more 'old fashioned' and so better suited to smaller, more traditionally run holdings, together with a romantic image of hay time and harvests, seems to form a stumbling block preventing many smallholders from considering silage as an alternative. Well, maybe summers were hotter and drier years ago – certainly there is nothing romantic about hay making on this (western) side of

the UK.

Besides, the process of ensiling crops for winter fodder may not be as modern as you think – the ancient Egyptians were apparently very good at it, and even preserved whole cereal crops by this method, something considered very up-to-date these days. However, this old-fangled technology did not catch on in the UK until MAFF's *'Make Silage, Make Sure'* campaign during the years of the Second World War, and even then it was really only the farms of the wetter western regions that took to it.

As the science behind the processes (and the problems) of silage making were researched, and people's knowledge of the nutritional requirements of ruminant animals increased, so more stock farmers dropped hay making from their annual routine, until today the majority of conserved forage in the UK is ensiled. Initially this would have been in clamps, silos or pits,

but the introduction of baling and bagging (and more recently wrapping) has made silage an extremely convenient process for smaller acreages. Indeed, I know of a number of smallholders with 10 acres or less who wouldn't dream of returning to the 'good old days' of hay making.

With regard to the rationing of conserved forages, silage is far superior to hay, not only nutritionally (see table 3, page 445), but is on the whole more palatable to stock. However, there are other factors to be taken into account when deciding which type of feed is most appropriate for your specific circumstances.

There is no doubt that the portability of individual small bales is a valid consideration – the ability to lift a single bale onto your back and carry it to the hay racks is very handy. However, as numbers of stock increase to say, more than 40 sheep, or 2 cows with calves, the enthusiasm for small bales begins to pall – there seems to be a constant trudging to and fro, often across muddy fields, to keep up with the apparently insatiable demands of hungry animals. Big bale silage suddenly becomes more attractive, with several days' worth of fodder being shifted in just a few minutes.

This may be of importance to part-time farmers / smallholders who perhaps are not at home much during the week. What time they do have is best spent in observation of their stock, and routine tasks should be streamlined to allow this.

Where stock is fed indoors there is little to choose between hay and silage, and a decision may be based purely on the number

Milk taint

A concern when using silage, most usually expressed by goat keepers, is that of 'milk taint', i.e. the flavour of the feed having an adverse affect on the taste of the milk. This is not an issue with the type of high dry matter crop that I am talking about, although problems may occur if very wet, poorer quality silage is fed. Goats, being fussy eaters, would probably turn their noses up at that sort of food anyway. Wherever animals are kept for their milk, a change from hay feeding to good, palatable silage is likely to be followed by an increase in yield.

of mouths to be fed. Probably it's not worth opening a big bale for less than 20 sheep / 2 cows / 8-10 goats. If properly handled, a bale of high DM silage, once started, will keep for a surprisingly long time – we've had a bale open for as long as a month, feeding a bit off the outside layer each day, with very little evidence of deterioration.

When stock are allowed free access to feed, or are in any other way fed on an ad lib basis, then big bales are undoubtedly more convenient, but where animals are individually housed, numbers are small, or access is restricted, then conventional hay bales are probably more practical.

Hay and silage making

If you're planning to have a go at making your own hay then livestock need to be excluded from the fields no later than early May. This is also a good time to spread

some fertiliser, if required – we use approximately 100kg per acre of a compound fertiliser such as 20.10.10 or 25.5.5 on our mowing fields. Plants need these essential nutrients for healthy growth, so any deficiencies in the soil must be made up by the use of artificial fertiliser or farmyard manure if there's to be any hope of obtaining a decent crop. However, May is a bit too late in the year to apply muck to land that'll be mown in the same summer – the dung won't have time to break down properly, and you risk incorporating it into your crop. It would be better to wait until the hay is off the field, then immediately spread manure onto the stubble. This should give a nice bite of grass for autumn grazing, and a much improved hay crop in the following year.

TIP

If possible, where animals are housed on a deep litter basis, refrain from mucking out your outbuildings until you're actually ready to spread, because muck stored outdoors will lose nutrients through leaching, which, quite apart from the fact that it's wasteful, could land you in trouble if effluent from the muck heap finds its way into land drains and watercourses.

While the grass is still short, take the opportunity to walk the fields and mark any hazards (such as rocky projections or boggy areas) that may not be noticeable when the crop is fully grown. Also look out for, and remove, any stones or branches that might be lying about, having fallen from the boundary wall or hedge. Likewise, keep an eye open for trailing or broken wire from fences – if cut into short pieces by the mower and

incorporated into bales of hay or silage, these represent a serious risk to livestock, and cattle in particular.

If moles are a problem in the field then I'm afraid they'll need to be dealt with (see pages 141 - 142), although I always feel rather mean about this as they're such appealing little creatures. However, it's a case of needs must. Mole hills in the crop will damage your machinery, and stones flung out by the mower could be the cause of injury to yourself or a bystander – I once had the back window of a tractor smashed while I was driving it as a result of encountering a mole hill when mowing hay. Also, the incorporation of soil in the finished crop can result in fatal outbreaks of listeriosis in the animals it's fed to (see page 141).

Going over the ground with a chain harrow will disperse any existing mole hills and also break up any dung pats left behind by the previous occupants of the field, and then you simply close the gate and wait for midsummer.

However, don't turn your back on it completely: remain vigilant for ragwort growing amongst the crop, and hand weed it as soon as it's seen. You should also spot treat any areas that are dominated by nettles, thistles or docks. In addition, the field might need to be rolled. This is usually done at around the middle of the growing period, and is particularly important on fields that have recently been reseeded, due to the inevitable presence of small stones on the surface.

Machinery

Theoretically, you can make hay without using any tractor-mounted machinery. In fact, we have made perfectly reasonable hay off our rather unkempt lawn using a brush cutter for mowing (a scythe would have been equally suitable) and pitchfork for turning, then carried it in and stacked it loose. On any larger area this is hardly a realistic option. In the predominantly grassland areas of the country there's no shortage of contractors – both large concerns, and those who specialise in smaller acreages – so don't despair if you aren't fully kitted out with your own equipment. If, however, you live in an arable area, it may be harder to find a local contractor with grassland machinery. If you do decide to employ a contractor then contact him early in the year to discuss your requirements, rather than leaving everything to the last minute. Certainly you must speak to him before you cut your crop.

It's becoming increasingly difficult to find contractors with conventional balers, so if small bale hay is your aim, you will probably have to own this piece of equipment yourself, baling being the most time-sensitive part of the whole process. You may pick one up at a farm sale for a reasonable price. Our own, a vintage Jones mark IV, cost us £80, and we've spent about the same again on parts. You should get something far more up to date for under £500.

Believe it or not, the large machinery required for silage making is generally more manoeuverable than an old conventional baler, so if your access is tricky, or your field entrances narrow, this is something to bear in mind.

Mowing and tedding requirements are about the same for both hay and silage, although for silage it is preferable (but not essential) to use a mower with a conditioner as this results in better wilting of the crop. Even under ideal weather conditions hay will need tedding a few times to get it perfectly dry, whereas silage can be baled straight from the swath left by the mower, and will only need tedding if it is a very heavy crop, or if it gets wetted by rain. You'll need a trailer – preferably a large flatbed – to get your hay in off the field, and some willing helpers for loading and stacking. To move big bales, a simple spike on the back of your tractor will suffice, although if your tractor is a small one, put some weights on the front to keep the wheels in contact with the ground – a bale of silage may weigh more than $\frac{1}{3}$ of a tonne.

Mowing

Whether making hay or silage, the optimum stage of growth for cutting is generally when the grass is just beginning to come into flower, but before it has had a chance to be pollinated and set seed. If the crop is mown earlier than this (for example, where it's intended to take two cuts of silage off the same field in the same season) the nutritional quality may be higher (due to the greater proportion of young leafy material), but the yield will be low. Crops mown after the optimum growth stage may have a greater bulk, but the nutritional content will be significantly reduced. The majority of grass growth occurs during the months of May and June, with improved pastures usually reaching a mowable stage during the second half of the latter month. More traditional swards,

managed under a lower input regime, might not be ready until some time in early July. Where two cuts are being taken, the first would have to be during the first half of June (ideally in the first week), with the second some 6-8 weeks later. From about the middle of August hay making becomes increasingly difficult, due to reducing day length and heavy dews, although I've known hay to be made right through September, and even at the beginning of October. I doubt that the quality was up to much, though.

As I mentioned earlier, hay can be cut using a scythe or a brushcutter, although this only really applies to small areas. It can be quite useful to make some rough hay in out-of-the-way places such as the orchard, or the lawn when it gets too long, and mowing by hand is just the thing in these confined spaces. However, if you're seriously intending to make all of the hay (or silage) that you need then this is going to require a greater degree of mechanisation.

Most of the mowers that are of suitable dimensions for smaller scale producer are 'power take-off' (PTO) driven, and mount on the 3-point linkage of the tractor, with the cutter bar offset horizontally to the right when in work. For transport, the cutter bar either raises to a vertical position, or swings out behind in line with the tractor.

The older 'finger bar' models that have a reciprocating blade can still occasionally be found at farm dispersal sales, and would be suitable for use on the back of a very small tractor such as a grey Fergie. My parents always used a finger bar mower on their Fordson Major, but it was painfully

Small and inaccessible areas can be mown for hay using a scythe or brushcutter.

Start mowing around mid-day, when all the dew has dried off.

slow, and prone to blockages and breakages. More up-to-date mowers have small blades mounted on a number of revolving drums or discs.

The actual process of mowing a field takes place in three stages:

1. Once the dew has all dried off (say, about mid-day), start from the outside edge of the field and cut 6-8 passes (depending on the width of your mower) all the way around in a clockwise direction.

2. The area in the middle of the field is mown next, by making repeated passes up one side of the uncut area and down the other, again going around the field in a clockwise direction. Lift the mower out of work to turn around at the end of each run. In very large fields, divide the area to be cut in step 2 into two (or more) narrower rectangles by mowing a swath down the middle.

3. Lastly, mow the headland (i.e. the part of the field that you were driving on when you made the first pass in step 1). To do this you'll need to cut around the perimeter of the field in an anti-clockwise direction. The reason for leaving this pass until last is because it's where you run the greatest risk of breakages due to the possibility of encountering unseen obstacles such as fallen branches or loose stones from the field boundary.

Of course, the steps given above are based on the assumption that you're working in a regular-shaped field. In reality you're probably not, but the same principles can be applied by mentally dividing the area into more manageable shapes, and mowing each in turn.

TIP

A fairly common practice is to mow just the edges of the field (i.e. carry out only steps 1 and 3) initially, and make this area into silage. About a week later, the remainder of the field is cut (as per step 2) and made into hay. There are two good reasons for this:

Firstly, the outer edges of the field, being closer to the hedgerow, will spend part of each day in the shade, so are better suited to silage than hay. Secondly, having cleared around the edges with the more manoeuvrable round baler, the process of making and baling the hay can proceed along much simpler lines, with only straight swaths to deal with, and plenty of room to turn on the headlands without driving across any of the crop

147

The tedder consists of a whole lot of tines mounted on a couple of spinning circular frames, driven by the PTO.

Tedding

There are various implements designed for the purpose of spreading and turning the crop, but the tedder has become the most commonly used. The tedder consists of a whole lot of tines mounted on a couple of spinning circular frames, driven by the PTO and mounted on the 3-point linkage. The angle of the tines can be changed to allow either spreading or rowing up to be carried out. Older machines were turners, rather than tedders, and worked on a raking principle. The really old ones were ground-wheel, not PTO driven. Very small areas can be turned by a gang of willing helpers wielding pitchforks and rakes.

Unless you're planning to bale silage straight from the swath, the first thing you need to do is get the newly mown grass spread out to dry. Thereafter, the number of times you run the tedder through it is going to depend on the drying

Small areas of mown grass can be turned and tossed about in the sun using pitchforks and rakes.

conditions. For high DM silage ('haylage') you might simply leave it spread out for a couple of days before rowing up and baling. Hay, however, is going to need a lot more work than that. Be warned, though, that the more times you ted the crop in an effort to get it dry, the more wastage and deterioration will occur – that cloud of dust you see behind you as you travel

down the rows is actually the most nutritious bits of your crop breaking off and blowing away in the wind. As much as ⅓ of the DM content of the crop could potentially be lost in this way. Under ideal conditions you might ted your hay just a couple of times over a 4–5 day drying period, but when the weather's less favourable you may be tossing the crop about two or three times a day, for a week or more.

TIP

If rain is forecast part way through the drying period, put the crop up into rows until the showers have passed. Don't spread it out again until the ground between the rows has dried off.

Baling silage is usually carried out by a contractor.

Baling

• For silage you're going to be dependent on a contractor to do the baling and wrapping, so to a large extent the timing of this stage of the process is in his hands. However, I like to get ours baled when the top of the crop almost looks like hay, but the bottom layer, in contact with the ground, still looks freshly mown. At this point I put it up into rows (if it's not already been done) and try to get the contractor onto the field as

Bales should be made into little stacks ready for collection.

The crop rowed up for baling.

Baling hay.

soon as possible. If it's a light crop (e.g. second cut) then you should merge two (or more) rows into one, which will make life easier for the chap doing the baling. Make sure you've got sufficient wrap, because it may be quite late in the day by the time they get to you (they work more or less around the clock at this time of year), so it mightn't be possible to obtain more if they run out. Generally, a roll of wrap will do about 30 bales, and you may get as many as eight bales to the acre. It all depends on the weight of the crop and the density of the bales. One big bale is roughly equivalent to 12 small ones.

• For hay the crop needs to be reduced to a moisture content of just 20-25% (and preferably less than this) before it can be considered fit for baling. Given that the moisture content of the grass at the time of mowing may have been in the region of 80%, this is by no means an easy task in a typical British summer.

Generally you can tell when it's ready to bale by the noise coming from the tedder – when it's really dry, the hay makes a continuous hissing sound as it's flicked back by the machine. Another test is to take a handful of the dry grass and twist it – if the stems crackle and break then it's probably dry enough, but if they simple bend then probably it isn't (although the feel and the sound of it will depend, to an extent, on the grass species present). Once you've decided that it's fit to bale you need to change the setting on the tedder and put the crop up into rows. Do this about lunchtime and leave it for a while, allowing the breeze to run through the fluffed-

up hay, driving out any lurking pockets of moisture. Aim to start baling at around 3 o'clock in the afternoon.

The first pass with the baler will be in an anti-clockwise direction around the edge of the field to pick up the outermost swath (although you might actually decide to leave this one and pick up the second swath, i.e. the first one that you mowed) instead, because the outermost swath is unlikely to be as dry as the rest of the field). For this pass you'll need to have someone walking along behind to shift the bales or they'll be in the way next time you come round. They should put them up into little stacks of five at the edge of the field ready for collection later. (They can also re-spread any bales that fail to tie, which is bound to happen from time to time, particularly at the start.) Having completed one circuit of the field you now turn around and commence baling in a clockwise direction, picking up all the swaths that were mown in step 1. Traveling in this direction, the bales should be dropped clear of the next pass, but on sloping fields they'll often roll. Either way, it's best to have a helper in the field, making small stacks as you go along. At the ends of the field the bales will need to be cleared away to give room for turning when

You should end up with at least 100 small bales of hay per acre.

Wrapped silage bales don't need to be stacked under cover, so should be considered where storage space is limited.

Unless by force of circumstance you have to store your hay on wet ground, don't build a stack up on pallets. To do so simply creates a luxury housing complex for all the rats in the neighbourhood, and lets too much air into the bottom of the pile.

All the bales making up the base layer (i.e. the ones in contact with the floor) should be placed on edge, with the bales in subsequent tiers laid flat.

Make the stack as tight as possible with no air gaps, particularly if it was baled a bit green and you're worried about heating. The last thing you want is a lot of fresh air drawing up through the stack as warm air exits at the top – that's the sort of scenario that could lead to spontaneous combustion. If the hay does get a bit hot then, provided that you've kept the airflow within the stack to a minimum, the worst that's likely to happen is that the top layer of bales will be soaked by condensing steam and subsequently go mouldy.

you're baling the long swaths, which is the next step. If you can rustle up enough helpers, and an extra tractor, then there's no need to wait until the baling is finished before starting to cart the crop back to the yard. You should hope to end up with at least 100 small bales per acre, although the density (and hence the weight) of bales can vary enormously.

Storage

If you're lucky enough to have plenty of outbuildings then the storage of small bale hay should present no problems. A designated hay barn is best, but failing that, the small size and compact nature of conventional bales enables good use to be made of any available space. A traditional hayloft over animal housing is far from ideal. This reduces essential ventilation for the livestock below, who furthermore will be living in an environment of dust and potentially harmful mould spores filtering down from above. An outdoor stack covered with tarpaulins is also unsatisfactory as high losses through weathering and condensation will occur.

Where storage space is at a premium then wrapped silage may be the answer. The layers of stretch film so essential to the ensilage process also provide a perfect weatherproof coating for each

TIP

To prevent deterioration of the crop it's vital that you check over your stack of big bales from time to time and stick repair patches over any holes that may have appeared in the wrap. Birds (particularly crows) are often the culprits, perching on the topmost bales and spiking them with their beaks and claws. Some people net their stacks to prevent this kind of damage, but a cheaper solution is to place a few old car tyres on top of the bales. Most birds will choose to land on the highest point of the stack, so by creating a new high point – the tyres – you've provided them with an alternative perch.

bale. Store outdoors either as a single layer or stacked, depending on the capabilities of your tractor. Any damage to the wrap must be repaired promptly to prevent deterioration of the crop which, if well looked after, can be carried over from one season to the next, although that is about the limit. Hay, by contrast, can be kept in store for a number of years and remain perfectly usable.

Probably the single most off-putting aspect of silage making is the wrap itself, or rather, the disposal of used wrap. The UK agricultural industry (and if you have a holding number that includes you) produces in the region of 500,000 tonnes of non-natural waste per annum, and most of this is silage wrap. Traditionally these waste products have been disposed of by burning or burying on farm, or, on smaller holdings, by putting them in the dustbin along with domestic

Round bales of hay make poor use of storage space.

rubbish. However, these practices have been banned since 2006, and agricultural waste plastics must now be disposed of at a licensed site. There are several companies which recycle agricultural waste plastics (which incidentally includes the polypropylene twine used on small bales, which also can't be burned, buried or chucked in the bin) into a number of useful products, and hopefully the idea will catch on.

Whilst it is right and proper that we should take these environmental concerns seriously

and aim to keep our holdings as 'green' as we practically can, I feel that the issue should be given some perspective: the 500,000 tonnes per year of agricultural waste pales into insignificance when compared to the fact that the great British public produces some three million tonnes of refuse over the Christmas period alone!

ADDITIONAL CONSIDERATIONS

Cost

• Based on an estimated 12 small bales to each big bale, contractors charges per unit of feed will be about the same for each, although the purchasing of wrap will add an additional cost to silage making. Given that the wrap also provides winter storage this may be considered a worthwhile expense.

• If you buy in forage (or if it's your intention to sell any surplus) then be aware that the price (per unit of feed) of small bale hay is almost double that of big bale silage.

Other types of bale

• Round bale hay makes poor use of storage space

• Small bale silage is expensive to make and awkward to handle.

• Heston bales have not generally found favour on smallholdings, although they may be worth considering if you buy in hay or straw, as the price per tonne is a lot less than conventional bales. Personally, whenever I buy in straw, or occasionally hay, I always get hestons because I find them so convenient to move about with the front end loader of the tractor.

Sisal twine

Sisal twine can be used with some older conventional balers. Being a natural product it does not present any disposal problems.

Weather

• The shorter weather window required for silage making allows greater flexibility in the timing of the harvest. This may be an important consideration if you work part-time on your holding, or if you intend to take two crops in one season.

• Be guided by what has become the normal practice in your area. If you live in the drier south east, hay making should present no problems, however, in wetter regions silage may be the most practical option.

Lie of the land

Think carefully when choosing which fields to set aside for mowing. Consider factors such as ease of access for machinery, shape (not too many awkward corners), whether they get enough sunshine (e.g. not overshadowed by large trees), slope, proximity to buildings for storage of the crop, and also whether the grass species present are likely to give sufficient yield to make it worth all the hassle.

There is more than a bit of truth in the old saying that *"to buy hay is to buy land"*, because if you buy in your winter fodder, you'll be buying in fertility. Up to 50% of the nitrogen used to grow a crop of grass can be returned to the pasture in the form of manure. Therefore, someone else's fertilizer applications will greatly benefit your soil after the crop has been processed through your livestock.

The converse also applies – think twice before selling off any of your home-grown hay or silage.

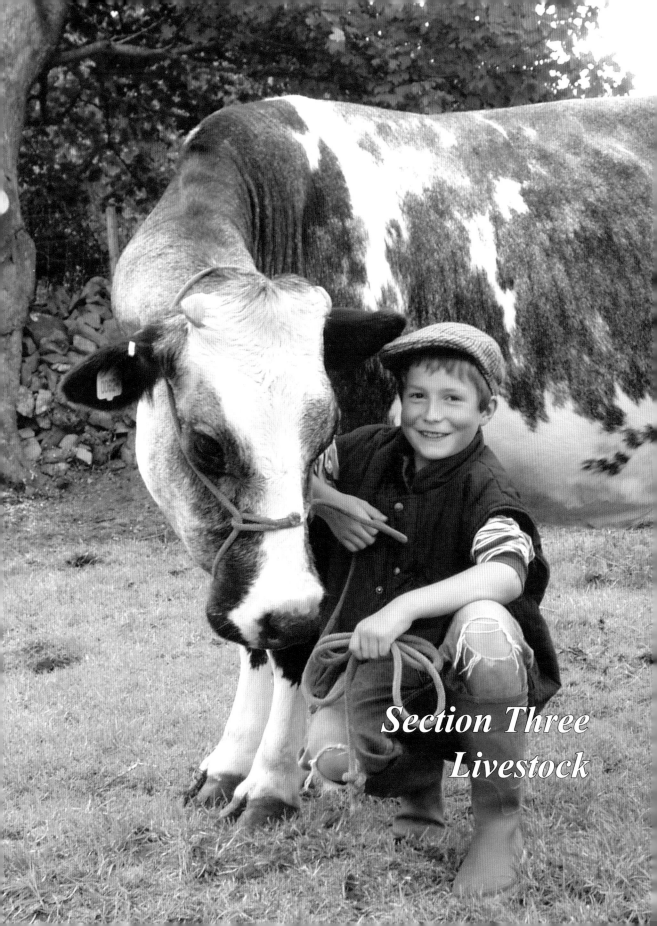

Section Three
Livestock

An Introduction to Livestock Management

"I am firmly of the opinion that there is no place for the vegetarian within the ranks of the true self-supporter in Great Britain"
Tim Tyne

Are there to be animals on the holding, or not? If you seriously intend to have a go at living the sort of low cash income lifestyle that we're advocating here, then you'll have to aim for a pretty high level of self-sufficiency, and that means animals. There simply isn't a place for vegetarianism on the average marginal land smallholding – I doubt you could come anywhere near to producing enough soya or other plant protein to replace the output of a couple of cows on rough pasture, or a pig reared on garden waste. Even if your 'smallholding' comprises little

more than a patio garden, a few hutches of rabbits can take you a long way down the road to self-sufficiency. (In fact raising rabbits for the table makes an excellent project for younger family members. It is important, I feel, for children to understand the origins of what they eat, and to play a part in food production on the holding). As a vegetarian, however, you'd need to crop every inch of your land, so there'd be no room for animals – neither pets nor wildlife; you'd have to kill them off or starve yourself. John Seymour once said *"The vegetarian cannot share his holding with other large mammals. I don't think I have the right to be so exclusive,"* and he was quite right. People are an integral part of the whole global ecosystem and, although we as individuals can do little to halt the inexorable trail of environmental

destruction that will ultimately bring about the end of civilisation as we know it, we can at least ensure that our holdings form small oases of symbiosis within the general chaos, where humans, plants and animals support one another in a natural and balanced fashion. Of course, this doesn't mean you can just turn everything over to Mother Nature and go back to living like cavemen, and neither is it a cosy 'live and let live' situation – there are tough decisions to be made if the balance is to be maintained, but the overall effect is a good one.

Good stockmen are born, not made.

Stockmanship

There is a saying that *"good stockmen are born, not made"*, which is probably true, but this doesn't mean that you need to have been bred in a farming family – quite the contrary, in many cases. Some people may work with livestock all their lives and never really develop the natural touch. Others, from a diverse range of backgrounds, take to it immediately, appearing to have inherited the correct attitude from some distant ancestor. If you're the sort of person who, when following a footpath through a field of cattle, seems to always end up with the cows inquisitively crowding round you and blocking your way, then you'll possibly make a very good stockman. If, however, you're the sort of person who worries about being in that predicament, then perhaps you won't. A bit of self-evaluation never did anyone any harm – it really is worth asking yourself whether you're genuinely cut

out for livestock keeping before going any further. Unfortunately, it's not sufficient that you simply love your animals – you need to really understand them, both as individuals and as part of a group, be able to empathise without being overly sentimental, and to be aware of their many subtle psychological requirements in addition to possessing a knowledge of their physical needs.

Having previously kept other types of animals such as poultry or rabbits is a help, as you'll be well aware of the responsibility entailed, but there is a big step from keeping small pets in hutches or runs to keeping larger animals in open fields, particularly if said animals can run faster than you and jump over fences. If your only animal experience has been with the more boisterous kinds of pet dog, you may find it difficult, initially, to tone down your behaviour and learn to approach sheep or goats without upsetting them. Horse keepers will, of course, already have experience of managing larger animals, but again, a considerable change of mindset may be required before handling farm livestock. Horses are generally dealt with on an individual basis, with the animal either tied up or with you sitting on its back, whereas sheep problems, for example, are flock problems, no matter how small the flock, and even if only one animal in the flock needs attention.

It's interesting to note that people who are very shy, or who were bullied as children, or who have learning difficulties, or who have suffered some traumatic experience, often make the best livestock handlers. They fully understand the animals' fears. It seems to work both ways.

Stocking rates / density

Stocking rates are generally calculated using Livestock Units (LSUs), with different classes of stock being given standard values according to their feed requirements (see table 5, page 445). This is a useful system as it enables you to calculate requirements for grazed and conserved forage for each of the different categories of animal on the farm. Having said that, you'll often see stocking rates and densities given as so many animals per acre or per hectare, which is fine. You should be reasonably conversant with both methods. The overall stocking rate refers to the whole of the area of land used for grazing livestock, including land closed off in summer for the production of hay or silage for use on the farm, whereas stocking density refers to the number of LSUs (or animals) per acre on a specific area during the grazing period. Thus you'll have a summer stocking density, when grass is growing fast but available acreage is reduced (due to a portion having been kept for mowing), and a winter stocking density, when more fields may be available for grazing, but the grass isn't growing.

High stocking rates on a big scale don't make sense these days, either ethically or economically. The smallholder, however, faces something of a dilemma – serious small-scale operations need to be fairly intensive in order to survive, and others become intensive through mismanagement (e.g. retaining too many animals on the available area, for 'sentimental' reasons), yet morally and financially the high level of inputs required may be difficult to justify. The net result, unfortunately, tends to be a steady decline in animal health and welfare. The saying *"stock-and-a-half is half-a-stock"* is very, very true indeed. Overstocking and non-productive livestock units are two of the commonest factors that lead to the downfall of many budding small-scale livestock enterprises.

Non-productive livestock units

Ask yourself whether you really need to keep a horse, and the answer will probably be no. Ask the same question about pot-bellied pigs, or llamas, and you'll get the same answer, unless of course it is your intention to breed these animals for sale to other people who don't really need them. Non-productive livestock are one of the biggest drains on the resources and finances of potentially productive smallholdings. The problem doesn't end with species / breed selection, either: some time ago I visited a smallholding to look over the sheep flock. *"200% lambing this year,"* I was told, and I have to say that when I saw 20 ewes in a field with 40 lambs between them I was pretty impressed. After a while I noticed that an adjoining field also held about 20 ewes, this time without lambs. *"What about that lot?"* I asked. *"Oh,"* replied the owner, *"They're the old girls; we don't breed from them anymore."* So in fact, for their crop of 40 lambs, they were feeding a flock of 40 ewes, and their lambing percentage, in truth, was far less impressive.

Now, we all have one or two old favourites amongst our flocks that are kept on well beyond their useful sell-by date, but there are limits. A productive and profitable smallholding really cannot carry so

many passengers, and neither can a geriatric population be considered 'balanced'. As I mentioned earlier, there are difficult decisions to make, but if you really are aiming for an economically and environmentally sustainable holding, you'll have to make those decisions.

Overstocking

Consider the following: "A smallholder decides to keep a few sheep and, finding that he does rather well out of them, decides to keep a few more. Once again he has a good year, his freezer packs of lamb finding a ready market amongst friends and family, so again he increases his flock. This pattern of behaviour continues for a year or two more, until one season our smallholder finds that the profits from his sheep enterprise are way below the expected level – non-existent, to be precise. He blames the weather, the sheep, market prices – everything, in fact, except himself and, on doing a few sums, comes to the conclusion that if he'd had just a few more lambs to sell he would at least have broken even. Once again the flock is increased, and the following year is a total disaster…"

If you see reflections of your own situation in this scenario don't worry, I can wryly assure you that you're not alone. It's not difficult to identify the point at which things went wrong – your bank balance can tell you that; the difficulty lies in admitting to yourself that you got it wrong, and taking the necessary steps to cut the flock back down to its optimum size. And of course, this doesn't only apply to sheep. It would be better, I think, to be slightly understocked, and make

any surplus grass into hay or rent it out to a neighbour, than to be faced with the embarrassment of having to sell off a load of painfully thin animals simply because you went over the top. Fewer animals of higher quality will generally give better returns, particularly now that there are no headage-based subsidies to be claimed.

It is clear then that having some idea of the potential stock carrying capacity of your grassland (table 2, page 445), together with the requirements of the stock you intend to keep, and having a preferred management plan in place before embarking on a potentially expensive project, will greatly increase your chances of success. Quite considerable variations in stock-carrying capacity can be seen between different sward types, and, on larger holdings, it's unlikely that all the available land will fall within one category.

In the light of all this, I would suggest that a reasonable starting point for the average smallholding would be an overall stocking rate of 0.24-0.32 LSUs per acre without using any fertiliser. Fertiliser applications totaling around 120kg N / ha (50kg N / acre), or the equivalent contribution from white clover in well-managed swards and farm yard manure (FYM), could see the figure rise to 0.48 LSUs per acre and / or enable some fields to be closed off for the production of hay or silage.

Optimising output

If the preferred option is to keep fertiliser applications to a bare minimum, or to not use any at all, there are a few strategies that can help optimise output:

• **Mixed grazing:** Stocking density

Mixed grazing with cattle and sheep can lead to an increase in overall output.

can be increased by as much as 10% by grazing sheep and cattle together, without additional inputs, and without any detrimental effect on the performance of either species. In fact, individual animal performance (e.g. daily liveweight gain) is seen to increase by up to 6% in the case of cattle, and 10% in sheep, with an increase of up to 40% in the proportion of the lamb crop that are sold fat off their dams. The optimum ratio for efficient land use is probably in the region of 1 suckler cow and calf to each 6 ewes with lambs, although, in our experience, having fewer sheep in the mix (eg. 3 sheep per cow) results in much heavier lambs at weaning.

• **Strict rotational grazing:** While rotational (or 'paddock') grazing systems are generally impractical on extensive farms, they do lend themselves to the more intensive land use requirements of the smallholding as a means of maintaining higher stocking rates. Generally applied to sheep, the area available should be divided into 6 or more roughly equal paddocks, around which the flock is moved in a fairly strict rotation. The process of rapid defoliation followed by periods of rest is inclined to encourage the spread of white clover, so rotational grazing ought to result in an overall improvement in sward composition. You should aim to have the sheep grazing on sward heights in the range 4-8cm, with 6cm being the optimum. As soon as sward height falls below 4cm it's time to move the flock into the next paddock. When grass growth is exceeding the rate of consumption, take a couple of fields out of the rotation for the making of hay or silage, or introduce a few cattle to eat off the 'stemmy' stuff. Another option would be for cattle to precede sheep in the rotation. Geese could follow the sheep.

The establishment of a permanent paddock grazing system can be expensive, due to the amount of fencing involved, and the fact that each enclosure will need a water supply. However, on a small scale, the whole thing can be set up fairly cheaply using electric fencing.

• **Strip grazing:** This usually applies to cattle (see page 189)

• **Forward creep grazing:** (see page 214)

• **Extended rest period:** Where grazing is limited, there's a lot to be said for housing livestock for an extended period during the winter – there's not much nutrition to be had from grazed grass during the winter anyway. Fields that are badly poached seldom recover in time to give an early bite, and sacrifice areas may need to be re-seeded. Where there's sufficient acreage for the winter stocking density to be kept low, or where annual spring re-seeding of a portion of the available land is part of the usual pattern of management, then it would be normal practice to house a sheep flock for only a few weeks around lambing time. On smaller holdings, however, it may be beneficial to house a March lambing flock as early as December. This fits in well with organic systems of grassland improvement, as white clover needs to be eaten off in November and March, and rested in between. Cattle are better off indoors for the whole of the winter period, both for their own sakes and for the sake of the land, and for ease of management.

Livestock Housing

Anyone who keeps livestock – no matter how small their flock or herd – is going to need some sort of accommodation for them. Even when they're kept on a wholly grass-based system, out of doors all year round, provision for housing will need to be made, if only to provide a sheltered place to temporarily pen up a poorly individual. Where breeding animals are kept, or milking cows or goats, then the need becomes more pressing. Although it's quite possible to satisfy these requirements using small-scale temporary structures such as field shelters or pig arks, and while it is true to say that many types of domestic animal can spend most (if not all) of their lives outside, I would advise most smallholders to think more seriously about winter housing for their stock, despite the current move towards low-input outdoor management systems.

For part-time smallholders the advantages are clear: if you have to be away at work all day then it's quite likely that, during the shortest months of the year, you'll leave

before it gets light in the morning and not return until after nightfall. Under these circumstances it simply isn't possible to adequately care for animals outdoors. You're kidding yourself if you think you can do it.

However, having them all housed, with lighting available at the flick of a switch, makes tending to your livestock through even the worst of the winter weather a pleasure rather than a chore. (And, if I were a sheep or a pig, I'm sure I'd rather be lying on a dry straw bed with a roof over my head than standing about in the mud and the rain.)

Another big advantage is that it gives the land a rest. The stocking densities on many smallholdings are rather high – far higher, in fact, than on many commercial farms, where a larger acreage can be utilised. Combine this with a general lack of experience in grazing management, together with a marked reluctance to plough up and re-seed old pastures or to use artificial fertilisers, and you can see why the grassland

TIP

A cautionary word of advice – sort out the housing arrangements before buying any animals. This may seem like stating the obvious, but it isn't unheard of for people to arrive home after a day away at a show or sale ("We're only going for a look ...") with new purchases mooing, baaing or grunting their displeasure from within the trailer, without a thought having been given to housing requirements. There generally follows a frantic scurrying about (often in the dark), gathering up old pallets and lashing them up with baler twine to form some temporary accommodation.

Unfortunately, and in spite of the best of intentions, these temporary arrangements often become semi-permanent – there are many smallholdings (and some larger farms too) which seem to be entirely held together with pallets and string. While this type of stop-gap measure is perfectly acceptable to both owner and animal in the short term, it will not be long before levels of stockmanship and animal welfare begin to suffer. Let's face it, if entering a pen means untying yards of string and moving heavy pallets, then in all likelihood mucking out and other routine tasks will not be carried out as often or as thoroughly as they should be.

on smallholdings is so often in decline. Taking the animals off the land in the winter may go some way towards maintaining the productivity of the holding (and the health and welfare of its livestock), without resorting to drastic measures. Furthermore, having all the animals penned up in one place is going to provide you with a fantastic load of manure to spread on the fields or use in the garden. If you buy in straw to bed them on, and possibly hay and feed, then you'll also be buying in the fertility that you need to keep your land in good heart. Of course, it's perfectly feasible to achieve all this by good grazing management alone (and many people do achieve it very successfully), but, on very small holdings, with only a limited number of tiny fields, there often isn't the scope. If you're going to have to carry feed to your animals in winter anyway, then you might as well do it in comfort. The low-input outdoor systems that we hear so much about these days are far better suited to large-scale farming operations.

Small "bonding" pens should be provided for newly lambed ewes.

Livestock housing requirements

In many respects the recommended minimum space allowances and other criteria specified for each species are largely academic, as what may be suitable for some breeds and management systems may not be appropriate for others. However, the basic data does at least give us a good starting point. In addition to this, there are a number of practical issues relating to the routine care of housed stock which may need to be addressed at the design stage, and of course there are factors affecting welfare that must be considered.

(NB: The following dimensions are for guidance purposes only, and don't necessarily correspond exactly with the minimum legal requirements. In many cases I've given a more generous allowance than that specified by law. However, most published guidelines refer only to modern housing solutions, so I've had to use my own judgement and experience when referring to more traditional husbandry methods.)

Sheep

Generally speaking, in the UK sheep are housed only for the lambing period, if at all. However, on smaller acreages, there's a lot to be said for extending the housed period. In the case of early lambing flocks, this may mean keeping them in after lambing, and possibly fattening the lambs indoors. In later lambing flocks ewes may be housed some considerable time before any lambs are due. Either way, it gets them off the land and makes management easier for part-time shepherds. Although the rights and wrongs of winter housing are hotly debated, the concept isn't new – in mediaeval times a far higher proportion of the national flock was housed during the winter than is currently the norm. At other times of year sheep may be housed for the purpose of fattening, or for preparation for shows and sales.

Basic requirements (assuming straw-bedded pens):

Floor space:
Small ewes: 1.1m²
Medium-sized ewes: 1.2m²
Large ewes: 1.4m²
Horned ewes: allow an extra 0.1m² per ewe
Shorn ewes: reduce area by 0.25m² per ewe
Ewes with lambs: allow an extra 0.5m² per ewe
Store lambs: 0.9m²

Trough length:
Small ewes: 400mm
Medium and horned: 450mm
Large ewes: 500mm
Shorn ewes: reduce length by 75mm per ewe
Store lambs: 300mm

Space will also be required for individual 'bonding' pens at lambing time. Each pen should be approximately 1.35-1.5m², and, for housed sheep, a minimum of one pen to each 6-8 ewes should be provided, increasing to as many as 1:3 in synchronised flocks.

Cattle

Cattle are usually housed for the whole of the winter period, i.e. from the 1st of November to the1st of May, although again there are differences of opinion here. Beef cattle, particularly native breeds, can be successfully out-wintered (as can dry dairy cows and heifers), but they'll poach up the ground something terrible. Likewise, in the dairy industry, there's a move towards extending the grazing season in order to keep winter costs to a minimum and to get as much milk as possible from grass.

However, as with sheep, I think there's a strong argument in favour of small-scale producers housing their cattle for the duration, particularly where only a small number of fields are available for grazing purposes.

The traditional method of housing adult cattle is to tie them in stalls, and, for the smallholder, this method still has a lot going for it. Alternatives are cubicles (like stalls, but with the cows free to come and go), as used on most commercial farms nowadays, or loose housing in strawed yards. Loose housing is the preferred option for youngstock.

Basic requirements:

Cubicles:
Small breeds (e.g, Jersey):
1.98m long x 1.06m wide
Medium breeds (e.g. Ayrshire):
2.13m long x 1.12m wide
Large breeds (e.g. Friesian)
2.28m long x 1.17m wide

For very large modern dairy breeds such as the Holstein, cubicles may need to be increased to as much as 2.5m long x 1.2m wide.

CUBICLES

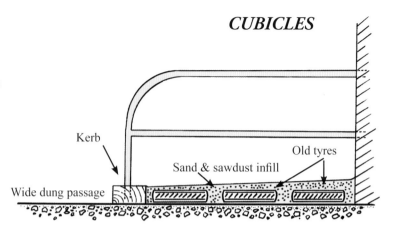

Kerb

Old tyres

Sand & sawdust infill

Wide dung passage

COW STALLS

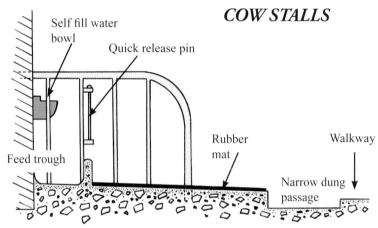

Self fill water bowl

Quick release pin

Feed trough

Rubber mat

Walkway

Narrow dung passage

Cow stalls

Stalls:
Small breeds:
1.37m long x 1.0m wide
Medium breeds:
1.52m long x 1.06m wide
Large breeds:
1.67m long x 1.14m wide

An additional 0.6m is required in front of stalls to allow for trough space.

Individual calf pens:
Calves under 4 weeks old: 1.12m²
Calves 4-8 weeks old: 1.8 m²

Group calf pens:
Calves under 8 weeks old:
1.1 m² per calf
Calves 8-12 weeks old - 1.5 m² per calf

Any building used to house calves should have a minimum air space of 5m³ per calf.

Individual pens are ideal for housing calves up to about 8 weeks old.

Calf pens and the law

These are the minimum standards that should be adhered to:

• The width of an individual calf pen should be at least equal to the height of the calf at the withers (measured when standing).

• The length of the pen should be equal to, or greater than, 1.1 x the length of the calf, measured from the tip of the nose to the base of the tail.

• Calves must be able to have direct visual and physical contact with calves in adjacent pens, except where sick animals are isolated for veterinary reasons.

• Calves older than 8 weeks should not be confined to individual pens except under veterinary advice.

Straw yards (lying area only):
Store cattle:
2.8-3.2m² per head
Finishing cattle:
3.2-3.8m² per head

Calf hutches

Calf rearing is an ideal enterprise for the more serious smallholder, but it's now recognised that traditional farm buildings are not particularly well suited due to poor ventilation and the difficulty of cleansing and disinfecting stone, brick or timber between batches. Small-scale producers are unlikely to be able to justify the cost of a permanent purpose-built shed, so calf hutches provide an excellent solution. Similar in appearance to the plastic pig arks (but usually white in colour, to avoid overheating), each hutch is appropriately sized to hold one calf. Adjustable ventilation ensures good airflow, and integral bucket holders, accessible from the outside, make for easy routine management. Larger hutches are available for group rearing. When the calves outgrow their accommodation the hutches can be thoroughly cleaned and moved to a fresh piece of ground, ensuring that there's no risk of disease carry over from one batch to the next. This method of calf rearing has been proven to give lower mortality rates, due to reduced incidence of pneumonia and scours.

Adult cows:
3.25-4.0m² per head (depending on breed, and whether or not they are suckling calves)

A feeding / loafing area will also be required, which, depending on the specific feeding method chosen, may double the overall space requirement per animal.

Loose boxes (suitable for calving):
Small breeds: 9m²
Medium breeds: 10.5m²
Large breeds: 12m²

Trough length:
Self-feed silage etc.:
150-250mm per head, depending on breed, age and size.

Restricted feeding:
600-750mm per cow, depending on breed.
450-650mm per head for store and finishing cattle, depending on age and size.
(NB. Horned cattle will require a greater trough length)

Goat keepers often subdivide the available area using permanent wooden partitions.

Goats

Goat keepers are funny people. I know – I've been one! They invariably sub-divide the available building space, using permanent wooden partitions, into a multitude of small pens, which, together with the inevitable restriction of access and narrow doorways, makes for just about the worst housing solution possible. Why this has become the accepted norm

I don't know. Goats can be housed more simply in groups, just like sheep, or, where it's desirable to keep them in individual pens, these should be capable of being disassembled to facilitate easy mucking out. Goats are generally housed throughout the winter, and at night and in wet weather during the summer. This means that they're actually indoors for an awful lot of the time, so anything that simplifies management is worth considering.

Basic requirements:

Individual pens:
Adult females, small breeds: 2m²
Adult females, large breeds: 3m²
Youngstock: 1.2-2.0m²
Adult males: 4.0m²

Group housing:
Adult females: 1.6m² per head
Youngstock: 1.0m² per head

Trough length (for groups):
Adult females: 400mm per head
Youngstock: 300mm per head

Pigs

Pigs, like goats, are going to need some sort of housing all year round. In the summer a simple ark may suffice, but something more substantial will be needed for the winter months. On many smallholdings, pigs are only temporarily in residence, with a batch of weaners being bought-in each spring, and slaughtered in the autumn. In this case it should be possible to make use of accommodation that has an alternative use at other times.

However, where pigs are kept all year, and possibly bred from, I think that some purpose-built

In our own pigsties, half of each pen is a bedded sleeping area, and the other half is for feeding and dunging.

housing is advisable, augmented by arks for use by certain groups (e.g. dry sows) during the summer. Simplicity of management is key because, even if you only keep 2 or 3 sows, you could, if you take all progeny through to slaughter weight, find yourself with as many as 50 pigs at times. Traditional pigsties are not always the most practical solution, but we can utilise concepts of traditional husbandry in the design of a more up-to-date building. Pigs are, by nature, very clean animals, and will use one particular area of their sty as a toilet. The layout of the building should encourage this behaviour in a way that facilitates easy mucking out and reduces wastage of bedding materials.

Although good ventilation is essential in all livestock buildings, pigs do like to be a bit warmer than other farm animals. Therefore, a building that is perhaps a little too stuffy for calves or sheep could be successfully used for pigs. If there's a choice of sties available, the boar should be given the warmest – he carries less fat than sows and growing pigs, and, as he'll be spending most of his time alone, he can't snuggle up to other pigs for warmth.

Basic requirements for indoor pigs:

Adult pigs:
Dry sows (group housing): 3.2m² per head
Boar pen: 9.0m²

Farrowing pens:
Six week weaning: 7.0m²
Ten week weaning: 9.0m²

Group pens:
Weaners 6-9 weeks old: 0.23m² per head
Weaners 9-12 weeks old: 0.3m² per head
Porkers: 0.4m² per head
Baconers: 0.57m² per head
Gilts: 0.65m² per head

Trough length:
Weaners 6-9 weeks old: 200mm per head
Weaners 9-12 weeks old: 250mm per head
Porkers: 300mm per head
Large pigs: 350mm per head

These figures are based on the minimum space requirements, as specified by British certification bodies. However, I suspect that most smallholders would wish to provide their pigs with a bit more space than that. Having said that, there's nothing to be gained by being over generous with the space allowance, as management is more difficult, and animals may become more easily stressed in accommodation that's too roomy.

My own recommendation for keeping pigs indoors is to have pens of approximately 9m², of which half is a bedded sleeping area, and half is a yard area for feeding and dunging. It should be possible to contain the pigs in either one half or the other while mucking out etc. These pens would be more than adequate for 1 boar

Pig arks

The traditional corrugated iron semi-circular pig ark is an extremely simple structure that doesn't have any of the 'mod cons' seen in the plastic versions. Following the recent rise in the popularity of small-scale pig keeping there's lots of companies selling traditional pig arks, but at over £300 for a basic 8' x 4' model, they're not cheap. There's not a huge difference in price between the traditional arks and the plastic ones, although of course you can't make any savings by building the plastic ones yourself. They may not look very pretty, but the plastic arks have the advantage of being rot and rust proof, and many are double walled for insulation, with provision for adjustable ventilation. They can also be thoroughly cleaned and disinfected between occupants. Conversely, the traditional metal arks are freezing cold in winter, like ovens in summer, and will eventually fall apart (particularly if you have a boar pig as large and destructive as ours!).

or 2 dry sows, or 1 sow with litter (provided there is provision for a creep area), or 8-10 growers, or up to 6 fattening pigs taken to pork weight.

Outdoor pigs

Where pigs are kept outdoors they'll need a basic shelter and sleeping place. The traditional semi-circular ark remains a firm favourite with both small and large-scale pig keepers, and is available in various sizes for different purposes. Suggested dimensions are as follows:

1.83 x 1.22m
2 weaners up to pork weight

2.44 x 1.83m
2-3 dry sows or 6-8 porkers

2.44 x 2.44m
4 dry sows or 1 sow and litter, or 10-15 porkers

2.44 x 3.05m
6 dry sows or 15-20 porkers

2.44 x 3.66m
8 dry sows or 20-25 porkers

A basic hen house can easily be built from reclaimed materials.

Poultry

Building a basic hen house is often the first DIY project undertaken by novice smallholders, and quite rightly so: the idea that anyone would consider buying such a simple item ready-made is anathema to me, and totally contrary to the ethos of self-sufficiency. The economics just don't make sense – a serviceable poultry house, every bit as good as any you could buy, can be built (using reclaimed materials) for a few quid, yet there are companies out there who sell them for hundreds of pounds!

Just as with other types of livestock, there are differences in housing requirements between breeds (with some being so much larger than others), and between management systems.

Hens that are truly free-range will spend very little time in their house (so less house space is required per hen), whereas birds whose wanderlust is curbed by an attached run will utilise the indoor space a lot more freely.

The needs of waterfowl also differ from those of other poultry. In addition to the basic floor space requirement we also need to consider perch space (if necessary), nest box allowance, ease of cleaning, portability, and protection from predators.

Basic requirements (chickens):

Layers kept indoors (e.g. deep litter): $0.5m^2$ of floor space per bird.

Bantams kept in house and covered run (i.e. not 'free range'):

House (with perches and nest boxes):
$0.16m^2$ per bird.
Attached run:
$0.23 m^2$ per bird.

Layers kept in house and covered run (i.e. not 'free range'):
House (with perches and nest boxes): 0.24m² per bird.
Attached run: 0.33m² per bird.

House (with perches and nest boxes) for 'free range' layers:
0.2m² per bird.

Grass run for 'free range' layers:
4m² per bird.

Trough length:
100mm per bird.

Perch space:
200mm per bird.

Perch height:
Heavy breed layers: 500mm
Light breed layers: 600mm
(Very heavy breeds such as the Brahma and Cochin should have low perches, set no higher than the height of the bird's back,)

Nest boxes (for laying): Minimum 2 boxes per 6 hens.
Dimensions:
350mm deep x 230mm wide x 260mm high

Nest boxes (for hatching):
450 x 450mm floor space

Traditional 'broody coop':
600 x 600mm floor space x 750mm high at the front, sloping down to 450mm at the back

Perches must be positioned above the height of any nest boxes, otherwise the birds will simply roost on the edges of the boxes, filling them up with droppings. The incorrect siting of perches is one of the commonest faults in purchased hen houses.

Meat chickens can be reared indoors, on a deep litter basis.

Meat chickens:

The minimum requirement for meat chickens is usually specified in kg per m², which isn't much help for the smaller producer who just wants to fatten a few birds for domestic consumption using existing facilities. However, if you have a rough idea of what your birds weigh at different ages it will enable you to calculate how much you'll need to expand their allocated space as they grow. Bear in mind that a day-old chick (the age at which you'll be buying them in) weighs next to nothing, whereas at 10 weeks of age they'll probably be around 5kg. Occasionally we've allowed them grow on longer than this, and have had whoppers weighing up to 11kg liveweight.

Meat chickens housed on a deep litter basis:
33kg per m² of useable area

Ducks

Permanent run:
2.5m² per bird where alternate runs are used
4.0m² per bird where only one run is provided

(Smaller portable runs are perfectly ok, provided that they're moved very frequently, as ducks do make a terrible mess if kept intensively

on the same piece of ground for any length of time.)

House:
0.19m² of floor space per bird

Perches and nest boxes:
Not required

Ponds:
Where domestic ducks are given access to a pond, no more than 4 ducks should be kept for each m² of water. The number of ducks / m² could be doubled if it's fast flowing water.

Small portable runs are fine for ducks, provided that they're moved frequently.

Geese

Similar accommodation to ducks, but larger.
House:
0.7m² per bird

Perches and nest boxes:
Not required

Permanent run:
10 birds per acre

Geese are grazing birds, so it would be better to rotate them with your other livestock, in which case higher stocking rates could be maintained. Use electric fence to contain them within temporary paddocks.

Turkeys are often kept in open-fronted pole barns.

Turkeys

Turkeys are often kept in open-fronted pole barns. They like to perch high up, but often modern breeds are too heavy to fly properly. Therefore perches should be arranged as ladder-like structures.

Breeding birds:
House:
0.5m² per bird
Permanent run:
17m² per bird

Fattening birds:
House (pole barn style):
410cm² per kg
Permanent run:
10m² per bird

All the dimensions given here for poultry housing are merely guidelines, useful as a starting point if you're intending to build your own hen house.

There are no hard-and-fast rules (unless you're marketing eggs as having been produced in a certain way, for example 'free range', in which case you must comply with the minimum legal requirements of that system), so use your judgement to adjust the figures according to the size and nature of your chosen breeds.

Some of the more ornamental types of fowl – such as those with feathered legs or extremely long tails – may have additional requirements, and so too might birds being kept for exhibitor rather than utility.

The basic rabbit hutch is a design that everyone's familiar with.

Rabbits

The basic rabbit hutch needs no introduction, as it's a design that everyone's familiar with – typically a box-like structure divided into two compartments. One of these (the larger) has a mesh front, and forms the 'living room', where the rabbits take their exercise and eat their food. The smaller compartment, fully closed in and connected to the main area by a pop-hole, is the rabbit's 'bedroom', and is where the doe will make her nest and give birth to her young. However, there's a world of difference between a rabbit living in a properly constructed hutch of the correct dimensions, and one condemned to live out its days in a converted tea chest with a bit of wire netting tacked over the front!

That's not to say a hutch needs to be expensive; recycled timber such as pallet wood is as good a source of building materials as any other – but it does need to be strong, secure, and big enough.

A large doe rabbit will need a hutch with a little over 12 square feet of floor space in order to be able to live comfortably with her litter until weaning, and she must be able to sit up without her ears touching the ceiling. This means that a 2' high hutch measuring 5' long by 2'6" wide will be ample. Somewhere between ⅔ and ¾ of the length should make up the living quarters, with the remainder being boxed in to form the nest area. A shelf should be provided to enable the doe to escape from her litter for a bit of peace and quiet from time to time. The size of the mesh on the main part of the front of the hutch should not exceed 1" squares, with weldmesh being used in preference to chicken wire.

The same size of hutch will also be adequate to house a buck rabbit, or up to six youngsters from weaning through to slaughter.

It's quite a good idea to make a sliding door to close the pop-hole between the two sections of the hutch, enabling the occupants to be shut into one side or the other while routine jobs such as mucking out are undertaken. If the hutch has a lifting lid it's helpful if this can be raised in two parts for the same reason.

Outdoor hutches will need to be built of tongue and grooved timber, and have a sloping top waterproofed with roofing felt or some similar material. A hutch that's to be located under a lean-to or in an outhouse can be of simpler construction. All hutches should be raised at least a foot off the ground, either by building them with legs, by making a separate stand for each hutch, or by placing each hutch on a few concrete blocks.

Cattle

"The cow should be absolutely central to the economy of a smallholding" John Seymour.

So you want to produce your own milk and assume that goats must be the answer… well, think again. Have you considered keeping a cow (or two)? Seventeen years ago we made the decision to switch over from goats to cattle, and have never regretted the move. Having been goat keepers for many years, you'll appreciate that at the time it wasn't an easy choice to make. However, within less than a week of buying our first cow and calf, all the goats were either sold or in the freezer. That was about how long it took us to realise that the cow is cheaper to keep, easier to handle and more gentle than the majority of goats, and can be of real economic benefit to the smallholder. We now have four crossbred cows, capable of rearing between them more than 16 calves per year, in addition to providing us with milk, cream, ice-cream, yoghurt, some butter, and

occasionally cheese. This is from grazed grass, home-grown hay and silage, and the barest minimum of bought in concentrates. Calves may be sold at weaning or at any time up to 20 months of age, depending on the availability of grazing and conserved forage. In addition to the income generated by the sale of calves, we value the dairy produce for home consumption at around £50 / month, although this is of course a non-cash receipt.

Pay a visit to your local livestock market and see what types of cattle are selling regularly for good prices. Unfortunately you aren't likely to see a Gloucester, Longhorn, Dexter or any other of our picturesque older breeds. Why? Quite simply because their lack of commercial qualities has caused these breeds to fall by the wayside. If you intend to keep cattle purely as a hobby, and can afford to indulge your whim, then by all means choose a rarer breed – traditional breeds are an important

part of our heritage and must be retained. If, however, you want your smallholding to keep you and not the other way around, then a commercial type animal should be chosen. The exception to this is where you intend to exploit a niche market for your products, although I suggest you make absolutely sure of your customers before buying stock.

In the past it would have been appropriate to have recommended one of the 'dual-purpose' breeds, but over the years, as farms have become more specialised, and with dairy farmers chasing ever higher yields, the traditional multi-purpose animal has been ousted by the Friesian and the Holstein. The old milking strains of dual-purpose cattle have been lost, and breeds such as the Welsh Black, British White and Red Poll are now bred solely as beef producers. Although individual animals of a milky type can be found within these breeds, on the whole they are unlikely to give a high enough level of production to be really viable on a small scale. Other pure beef breeds such as the Hereford, Aberdeen Angus and Charolais may also be disregarded as milkers, as these will produce sufficient only for one good calf. At the other end of the spectrum are the pure dairy breeds. These are capable of giving a huge quantity of milk daily – probably more than the average smallholder could cope with – and will require a proportionately high level of nutrition. High yields put considerable strain on the cow's body systems, resulting in increased susceptibility to metabolic disorders such as staggers (magnesium deficiency) and milk fever (calcium deficiency).

Therefore, it's clear that what's

required is a 'middle of the road' type of animal, something akin to the old dual-purpose breeds. Thankfully nothing could be simpler to produce; every dairy cow must be bred from annually in order that her output can be maintained. As only a limited number of pure bred heifer calves are required each year for herd replacements, the vast majority of Britain's dairy cows are bred to a beef bull. The resulting offspring are usually sold off the mother at a few days old and, if female, are often reared on for entry into suckler herds. The combined qualities of their sire and dam make these crossbred cows very similar in type and temperament to the old multi-purpose breeds, and when they themselves are bred from, using a beef breed bull, the resulting three-quarter bred beef calves produce really high quality carcasses.

Dairy Shorthorn.

Rosie, a British Blue x Jersey, our finest ever housecow.

Without doubt the finest type of house cow we've come across is a British Blue x Jersey. Both parent breeds have a reputation for good temperament, which seems to come through strongly, resulting in the gentlest of all animals. Combine also the commercial qualities of the British Blue as a beef producer, with the

milkiness, easy calving ability, and relatively small size of the Jersey and you have, I think, the ideal smallholder's cow. During a lactation of 42 weeks our first cow of this type provided us with all the milk we needed for our own use, and reared 7 calves at minimal expense. Needless to say, following this experience, most of our subsequent cows have been BB x Jersey.

If, despite all this advice to the contrary you still feel that a pure bred animal of one of the more traditional breeds is the thing for you then the traditional Dairy Shorthorn would probably fit the bill admirably, as would the Irish Moiled.

Don't be misled into the assumption that the small size of a breed makes for easier handling. How often do we hear of a great cart horse being described as a 'gentle giant' whilst the little Shetland pony is frequently called a 'cheeky sod'? The same applies to other classes of domestic stock – sheep, cattle and goats. Having said that, smaller breeds of cattle do eat less, so are cheaper

to keep, and may be more suited to a smaller acreage. If size is an issue then the Jersey is an obvious choice – we have had one pure Jersey cow, and she was a tiny little thing. However, we put her to a British Blue bull in order to breed a crossbred heifer to replace her.

Dairy Shorthorn

• Hardy and long-lived.
• Milks well off grass.
• Good temperament and attractive appearance.
• Retains many of the original 'dual purpose' characteristics.

I'm convinced that the traditional Dairy Shorthorn is one of the few pure breeds of native cattle ideally suited to a productive smallholding. As ever, though, the devil is in the detail – most of today's Dairy Shorthorns are what is known as 'blended', in that there's been an introduction of red cattle genetics from other dairy breeds, such as the red-and-white Holstein, the Danish Red and the Dutch Meusse Rhine-Issel, in

Irish Moiled.

Jersey

order to improve their commercial viability. Of course, this may be a good thing in so far as it's enabled the breed to survive in an increasingly competitive market, but it does mean that some so-called 'pedigree' Dairy Shorthorns may be only 30% pure, and finding one of the old-fashioned traditional types is not an easy task.

Irish Moiled

• The only surviving breed of livestock native to Northern Ireland.
• Numbers fell to critically low levels 40 years ago.
• Naturally polled (hornless).
• Thrives on poor quality forage.
• Suitable for beef production or small-scale dairying.

Originally a dairy / dual purpose breed, the moiley fell out of favour when agriculture became more specialised, until, by the early 1970s, only about 30 animals remained. However, a group of dedicated breeders, encouraged by the RBST, have brought the Irish

Moiled cattle back from the brink of extinction. Given the level of interest nowadays in lower input farming systems I believe that this is a breed that could potentially have a very bright future ahead of it. By no means least amongst the breed's attributes is its attractive appearance. The basic body colour is a rich red, with a characteristic white stripe ('finching') running along the length of the back. The undersides are also white. The amount of red in the coat is actually quite variable, with some animals being predominantly white, and others being speckled or roan. However, the nose and ears are always red.

Jersey

• Often recommended as the ideal house cow.
• Easy calving, so can be safely crossed with a beef bull.
• Very docile.
• High quality milk.
• Low value calves, so it's difficult to cover the cost of home milk production.

This Channel Island breed is the quintessential smallholder's house cow, as recommended by Seymour (and others) during the self-sufficiency heydays of the late 1970s and early 1980s, but, to be honest, we've only ever kept one pure-bred Jersey. Over the years we've had a number of Jersey crosses which have satisfied our requirements very well, but we didn't find the pure Jersey quite so well-suited to small-scale farming as those earlier writers would have us believe.

Getting Started

If you're new to cattle keeping, you may wish to start by rearing a calf. In this way you build up confidence with her as she grows, and by the time she herself calves at around two years of age, and it's time to milk her, you'll be so familiar with one another that there are unlikely to be any tantrums. By far the easiest way to get a calf is to go directly to a local dairy farm and ask if they have any available, and if not when will they, or do they know of anyone who has? A Hereford x Friesian or an Aberdeen Angus x Friesian would make a perfect house cow, although any beef / dairy cross can be considered (with the exception perhaps of the Limousin x Friesian – these can be rather flighty). Buy two. Keep the one with which you form the closest bond, and hopefully the sale of the other, when weaned, will cover the costs of purchasing and rearing them both. However, two years is a long time to wait before getting any milk. If you want to 'hit the ground running' by purchasing an adult cow, or perhaps an in-calf heifer, then probably the simplest way to find yourself a suitable animal is to put the matter in the hands of a reputable livestock dealer. Having made contact with such an individual, probably through the recommendation of another farmer or smallholder, give him a precise description of what it is you're after. Over the next few weeks he'll probably try to sell you all sorts of animals that are nearly what you're looking for (remember, he is also acting on behalf of the seller, so will do his best to bring about a deal), but stick to your guns and eventually you'll get exactly what you want. Sometimes the dealer will have bought the animal and moved it to his own premises for you to view her there. If she's not quite what you had in mind, don't feel obliged to buy her – he probably has another half dozen or so potential purchasers lined up. Sometimes the dealer is content to simply act as an agent between yourself and the vendor on the understanding that he will be given the job of transporting your purchase, and paid accordingly. This situation is preferable, as it enables you to view the cow on farm, talk to the owner, and find out a bit more of her history. Even so, it can help to take with you a down-to-earth, stony-hearted, feet-in-the-mud friend to prevent you making purchases on impulse. If you have reservations about livestock dealers you could try classified advertisements, but look out:

Beware the single minded devotee of a particular, probably obscure, breed of cattle (or any other kind of livestock, come to that). You'll be swamped by their enthusiasm as they extol the virtues of their chosen type, and in no uncertain terms they'll convince you that these – and only these – provide the perfect answer to the smallholder's dilemma as to what is the best cow for all management systems. As it happens they have quite a few for sale, a small starter herd in fact, just the thing to get you going. By now of course, alarm bells should be ringing in your mind. Why have they so much unsold stock? And why is there no stream of eager purchasers beating a path to the door? Buy them at your peril. A year or two down the line will see you in the same position, with a now increased herd of cattle of a breed that no one seems to want. You place an ad in the classifieds and sit with fingers crossed, hoping that some innocent newcomer to cattle keeping will buy the lot from you… as a starter herd perhaps.

Whereas a dealer will not be at all perturbed if you don't buy what he has on offer – he has, after all, a large network of regular buyers – the private advertiser will be keen to sell, and can be very persuasive. Your stony-hearted companion may prove invaluable.

In addition to basic information relating to age and breed, find out when the cow calved, and whether or not the calf is included in the sale, or would that be subject to a separate negotiation? Or perhaps the seller intends to keep the calf for himself? Maybe she's in-calf, in which case when is she due, and by what breed of bull? If she was served by artificial insemination you should be shown the slip of paper recording the A.I. man's visit – check that the details match the cows tag number. Is she confirmed in-calf (i.e. been pregnancy tested), or simply believed to be in-calf (in which case you could offer such-and-such a price subject to the outcome of a pregnancy diagnosis, although you'll have to pay for the vet). Has she been milked before, in which case is she used to hand-or machine-milking? Or perhaps she's always suckled her calves – has she been

taught to accept other calves for double- or multi-suckling? Is she trained to a halter, and will she tie up quietly in a stall? It may be that she's a heifer calving for the first time, in which case some of these will be unknown quantities. If a younger animal is being considered – a 'bulling heifer' not yet in-calf – has she been observed to be coming on heat regularly? Is all the paperwork in order? Each animal must have an official passport or identification document that matches the number on both of the tags in its ears – this is a legal requirement, and without it your cow will be worthless. It's also a condition, in some areas, that any cattle being moved between holdings must have been tested clear for Bovine TB within the last 60 days (known as a 'pre-movement' test). Your regional Animal Health office, or any local cattle farmer, vet or livestock auctioneer will be able to tell you what the requirements are in your area.

General common sense and good stockmanship will tell you whether or not the cow is healthy. Choose a leaner animal in preference to one that is over fat – cows that put

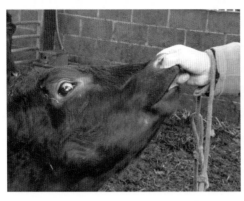

How do you get a halter on a cow, if you don't have a crush?

Well, I simply walk up to our cows in the field, with the halter in my hand, and put it on. A bucket of nuts is a useful bribe if the animal is being awkward.

If you do need to get a halter on an uncooperative beast, loop the part that will encircle the animal's nose over your right wrist then grasp its nostrils with the fingers and thumb of your right hand. You could do this when it puts its head in the feed bucket, or temporarily trap the animal behind a gate. If using a gate, it must be properly hung, and have a pin to stop it being lifted off its hinges. The effect of gripping a cow's nostrils is similar to that of applying a twitch to a horse – the release of endorphins has an immobilising effect (but you do have to grip pretty hard!). Once you've got a good hold, it's a simple matter to use your other hand to transfer the loop from your wrist to the cow's nose, and to place the other loop of the halter over the back of its head, behind the ears. The halter should tighten under the animal's jaw, and you should always lead from the left hand side. Never wrap the end of the rope around your hand – a friend of mine lost some fingers like that once. I like to use a long lead rope (6' or more), as it allows me to close gates after leading an animal through without letting go or having to turn the animal around. A long lead rope also makes halter training less stressful, as you can use 'join-up' style techniques, rather than the 'fight and fright' methods more commonly employed.

The sale of quality young cattle covers the cost of all our dairy products, and provides a modest profit.

all their feed on their own backs are not renowned for milkiness. Look for a feminine conformation, not too beefy and with a good wide pelvis for easy calving. The udder should be nicely attached, high up at the back and well forward at the front, giving a balanced appearance. Avoid a great pendulous udder – the cow

has either been worked too hard or is older than you are being led to believe. Check the udder thoroughly for lumps or swellings – if she tries to kick your head off while you're doing this then she probably isn't the cow for you!

HOUSING

One of the beauties of keeping cows is that for a large part of the year their housing requirements are virtually nil. In fact, if your land can take the strain, cattle may live entirely out of doors (although this option is not generally suitable for the smallholding, particularly where milk production is one of the aims). For the winter period, during which you'll probably wish to house your stock, you'll be relieved to hear that their accommodation requirements are fairly basic, and despite the large size of the animals, can take up a surprisingly small amount of space. For the other half of the year buildings can be put to

alternative use. In our case calf rearing, fattening pigs and lambing all take place in buildings that are also used to house cattle.

Loose housing

The term loose housing could be applied to anything from a small loose box or stable, up to large covered yards for groups of animals, the word 'loose' implying that the cattle are not restrained or restricted in any way, and are free to move about the yard as they please. Although the unrestricted nature of this type of housing clearly has its attractions on welfare grounds, one major disadvantage has probably by now occurred to you – if the cattle are free to move about the yard as they please, then they're also free to shit where they please. Keeping them clean is going to present some problems.

Main: *Cattle yards can be constructed entirely from gates.*
Inset: *A linchpin prevents animals from lifting gates off their hinges.*

Cattle yard construction

Usually you'll find yourself wanting to adapt an existing building, for example by setting up some pens within a pole barn. By far the quickest, simplest and most practical option is to do this entirely using gates – galvanised metal gates represent good value for money, and are extremely versatile. Attach hinges to every available upright in your shed, and if necessary, install some intermediate posts, preferably removable ones that fit into sockets in the floor. While you're at it, put two sets of hinges at each point, one pair set at a height such that the hung gate will clear the floor by about four inches, and the

other pair eight inches higher. The upper hinges should be used when housing cattle, but it's a simple matter to drop the gates down to the lower setting for other classes of stock such as sheep or pigs. Thus, when you arrive home late at night with some impromptu purchase to add to the menagerie (come on, we've all done it!) it is a simple matter of re-hanging a few gates to provide suitable accommodation. And it will look professional too. At the end of the winter remove the whole lot to give one clear area for easy mucking out. Drill a ¼″ diameter hole through the top hinge of each pair to take a linchpin. Forget bent nails or reversing the top hinge (the former is shoddy, the latter too permanent) – this method is perfectly stock-proof, yet still

gives you the flexibility to re-hang gates as required. In fact I suggest you go round and do this with your field gates as well. All stock, from sheep to shires, seem adept at lifting gates off hinges, and there is nothing quite like the sound of a gate crashing to the ground to have you bolt upright at 3am. You wouldn't be the first person spotted rounding up errant livestock clad in nothing but wellington boots and a head torch...

The usual practice is to split the area into two with a low kerb of some sort (old railway sleepers or some other heavy timber will do the trick), with half being a strawed lying area and the other half kept clear. Feeding takes place in the non-bedded part which can be regularly scraped out. The lie-back area is generally topped up with straw as required on a deep litter basis.

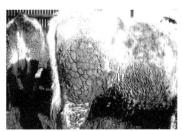

Sometimes it can be difficult to tell where the muck ends and the animal begins.

The major drawback to trying to keep stock clean under this type of regime is what I call the 'wattle and daub' effect – the gradual build up of layers of dung and bedding material adhering to the belly and flanks of the cattle, until by the end of the winter it can be difficult to see where the muck ends and the animal begins. This looks unsightly, and, while it presents no problems to store cattle (they will lose that crust when they shed their winter coat

Contented cows in stalls

after turnout in the spring, and soon look sleek and glossy again), clearly the production of clean milk from cows in this state is a total impossibility. Furthermore, any cattle intended for slaughter would be rejected by the abattoir unless trimmed. Clipping the belly of a bolshie bullock is not a job for the faint hearted, and some nasty injuries to operators have occurred. It can be seen, therefore, that unless you have the time to spend on twice (or maybe thrice) daily cleaning out, regular grooming, and can afford to be pretty lavish with straw, then loose housing may not be the most suitable option.

Stalls

This is the most traditional method of housing milk-producing cattle. Look at any old illustrations detailing agricultural practices of times gone by, right back to the early domestication of livestock, and you will see cows kept in this way. The principal difference between this and other systems is that the animals are restrained – tethered, in effect – by a neck chain or yoke, a situation which the modern way of thinking may

deem unacceptable. It's interesting to note that the individuals most vociferous in their protestations against keeping cattle tied in stalls are usually those who claim to be in favour of a return to more traditional farming practices! I must ask you to put aside (for the time being, at least) any anthropomorphic reservations and consider some of the points which may make this old-fashioned method of housing relevant to the smallholder of today:

Strengths:

• **Individual attention:** Modern farming methods seem to require that animals be kept in more or less homogeneous groups for ease of management. The fact that stalled cattle require attention on an individual basis is why they are no longer found on commercial farms. However, for the smallholder individuality is the name of the game, particularly where two or more cows are kept to ensure a year-round milk supply. Stalls facilitate this type of approach.

• **Quick and easy to keep clean:** I have just timed myself carrying out the morning routine of cleaning

and feeding four stall-housed dry cows (i.e. not in milk) – 7 minutes. That includes mucking out, taking a full wheelbarrow to the muck heap, fetching hay and feed from separate buildings, and serving out the required ration to each cow. The same routine is repeated in the evening. It's certainly an attractive system for anyone who has to feed their stock in a hurry before departing for a day at work. The design and layout is also such that animals do not become encrusted with dung, and nice clean udders = nice clean milk.

• **Minimal space requirement:** A worthwhile consideration where it's intended to house cattle in existing traditional outbuildings. The lying area per cow may be as little as 5' 6" by 3' 6", with additional area needed for feed troughs and dung passage. Many older farm buildings were originally designed to accommodate this layout.

• **Ease of handling:** There is no doubt that cows kept in this way become extremely gentle and tame as a result of their close contact with the people who tend them. It makes things very simple when the vet or DEFRA inspectors call to check tags or carry out testing if all your cows are tied up in a neat line, and are quite used to being handled – far better than trying to catch flighty youngsters in an open yard, or force frightened animals into a crush.

• **Reduced bedding costs:** As cows can't dung on the lying area, any bedding material stays clean for a long time. Straw can be used, although cattle are inclined to kick it out from under themselves and end up lying on the floor. Fine sawdust is good, but may block drains. We have fitted rubber matting, which is excellent, and incurs no expense beyond the initial outlay.

Weaknesses

• **Permanent fixtures:** It's difficult to put the building to other uses at different times of year.

• **Difficult to spot cows 'bulling':** The fact that they are tethered prevents cows from exhibiting the usual display of lesbian behaviour that is generally the stockman's first indication that an animal is on heat and ready to be mated.

• **Alternative accommodation will be required for calving:** In practice this is a good idea anyway, whatever housing system is chosen.

• **If using reclaimed or existing fittings:** Not all older stalls were fitted with a quick release mechanism. This is an important feature allowing an animal in trouble to be released quickly and easily without fumbling about trying to undo the chain.

• **Possible objections on welfare grounds:** These are in part overcome by releasing cows twice daily to suckle calves or be milked, and to take some exercise at the same time. I make no apologies for housing some of my cattle in this rather outdated way, and rather than succumb to prejudicial views, I prefer to let my cows 'tell' me what they think of it. They are always glad to come in in the autumn when the weather begins to turn, and stand patiently in their accustomed places for me to fasten the neck ties. Resigned to their fate or content with their lot? With shelter, fresh water, good food and a clean dry bed to lie upon, I am inclined to believe it is the latter.

Certainly when it is blowing a gale outside, with sleet in the wind, they look very content tucked up in their stalls, patiently chewing the cud.

Cubicles

Cubicle housing is an attempt to combine the best qualities of the other two systems I have discussed, and is probably the most common form of cattle housing seen on commercial farms today. Although superficially similar in appearance and layout to stalls, cubicles do differ in their dimensions and, as the cattle are not tethered to them, do not need to be of such heavy construction. Like stalls, they are usually made of tubular steel, though a home-made timber alternative will suffice.

The required floor layout for cubicle housing can be simply and cheaply installed by forming a suitable kerb (perhaps old sleepers again) and filling in behind it with old car tyres topped with a sand / sawdust mixture. This forms a comfortable, well-insulated lying area. For the cubicles themselves either construct in timber, as mentioned above, or pick up second hand metal ones at a farm sale – they crop up quite often.

Home-made cubicles.

TIP

When housing male cattle in cubicles, for example fattening bullocks, the lying area should be concreted, with a good slope front to back. Due to the anatomy of the male animal, the sand / sawdust bed suggested for cows would quickly become puddled with urine.

In use, cows have free access to a yard or passageway for feeding and return to their cubicles to lie down, the design of which is such that the animal can only enter forward, so dung is always deposited in the passageway with the lying area remaining clean. Not so clean as stalls though, as muck will be carried in on hooves. The dung passage must be regularly cleaned, either by using a manual scraper or a tractor mounted implement. (I have seen scraper attachments for 2-wheeled 'garden tractors' which look like a wonderful idea). Bedding requirements are the same as I have outlined for stalls.   The biggest drawback to this system (and it is a big one, though it may not appear so on the face of things) is that the constant passing and re-passing of cattle up and down the passage way will churn up accumulated dung and urine into that delightful semi-liquid substance known as slurry. Most smallholders are not geared up to handle this stuff, and would not want to anyway. The problem can be minimised to a certain extent by feeding a drier diet, such as hay in place of silage.

Each of these systems has its faults and merits and, in practice, after weighing up the pros and cons of the alternatives I've discussed, you'll probably find that a combination of two or more types of accommodation is likely to be required for even a small-scale cattle enterprise in order to cater for different age groups or classes of stock. To summarise, I'll give a brief outline of our own cattle housing arrangements:

• Adult cows – stalls

• Young calves – individual pens

• Weaned calves and 1st winter stores – group pens (in effect small-scale loose housing). The same pens double up as calving boxes

• 2nd winter stores – loose housed (straw yards)

Using the cattle crush when dosing young cattle.

Cattle crush

The cattle crush is a piece of equipment we don't need to use very often. Our store cattle, having all been hand reared as calves, are sufficiently docile that we can generally walk up to them in the field to apply a pour-on or read ear tags, or, failing that, we can just run them into a pen in the shed and handle them there. The adult cows are, of course, very docile, all halter trained, and used to being tied in stalls, so no handling issues there either.

Having said that, we are legally required to have safe handling facilities to enable officials to carry out inspections of individual animals, and for the vet to do routine TB tests and suchlike, so a crush is an essential bit of kit that every responsible cattle-keeping smallholder should have. We've also been glad of it when faced with the task of castrating a group of larger cattle, and it's been useful on our livestock handling courses as participants are able to carry out tasks such as ear tagging and dosing without the anxiety of

having to tackle an unrestrained animal. Added to this is the fact that cattle going to slaughter may need to have their bellies and tails clipped, which would be downright foolhardy to attempt to carry out without the secure restraint afforded by the crush.

Like most of our equipment, we bought this crush second hand at an auction of farm machinery held at our local livestock market. It failed to meet its reserve price, so I negotiated with the vendor and bought it at the end of the sale for £120. It's not a sophisticated item – it doesn't include weigh cells, belly straps, leg slings, an automatic yoke, or any of the other refinements typically found on more up-to-date models – but it does have opening panels for easy access to the part of the animal we need to get to, and it can be lifted and carried on the 3-point linkage of the tractor.

In use we keep the crush attached to the tractor for stability. This gives us the versatility to locate a

temporary cattle handling system anywhere, safely. Generally we set everything up in the shed, using one of the yards as a holding pen. As all the yards in the shed are created from gates it's a simple matter to change the layout to incorporate the crush at the apex of a lead-in funnel or short race. One day, when I get around to it, I'll weld some gate hinges to the crush itself.

Cattle entering from the open end are prevented from backing out by a short bar (a small piece of scaffold pole) that is slid across behind them. Angled 'teeth' enable the bar to be moved forward bit by bit as the animal is coaxed on. When he's far enough in a lever is pulled to close the yoke. Once the animal is properly restrained, the front of the crush can be opened, giving access to the head, and a side panel at the front can also be opened, giving plenty of room for an assistant to help hold the head steady while I apply ear tags or whatever. There's also a sliding section that gives access to the neck area for TB testing. It is important to make use of these access panels, rather than simply reaching through the bars, to avoid the risk of a hand getting squashed between the animal and the side of the crush. To release the animal it's a simple matter of opening the yoke and letting him walk out the front.

When carrying out tasks such as castrating, which involve working at the back end of the bullock that's restrained, it's important to close off the lead-in to the crush to prevent the next animal in the queue from running into the back of you. Although cattle are very gentle creatures on the whole, it's not a good idea to take chances in an enclosed space – the unfamiliar experience can result in irrational behaviour, and if a nervous animal thinks that the only way out is to go over you, then that's the way he's going to go.

THE NEED TO BREED

Eventually the time will come (although it may seem a long time coming, if you started out by buying calves) when you need to breed from your cow, for until she gives birth to a calf she will not produce any milk. Furthermore, she will need to be bred from annually thereafter in order to maintain a reasonable level of production. Cattle do not have the same useful feature as goats of being able to 'milk through' from one year to the next without producing offspring – many milking goats are only bred from in alternate years, and I know of a few which seem to continue milking indefinitely. I describe this as a useful feature, and so it is in goats, where the kids are often

Summer Mastitis

This is a horrible condition of the udder tending to affect dry cows during August – just the time when our autumn calver wouldn't be in milk. A cow that has had summer mastitis once seems to get it again each subsequent year, until eventually she loses the ability to produce milk in first one quarter of the udder, then another, and so on, until in the end she needs to be culled. Flies contribute to the spread of the infection – it's common to see clusters of black flies on the teats of grazing cows – so ensure that some sort of fly repellent or insecticide is applied during late summer, either a natural product such as citronella, or one of the proprietary pour-ons that are available to treat and prevent a whole range of internal and external parasites. You may also wish to use an intra-mammary antibiotic as an additional precaution.

surplus to requirements. With our house cow, however, we rely on the annual sale of weaned calves or store cattle to pay the bills, thereby ensuring that all our milk and dairy produce has effectively cost us nothing. We are glad, then, of the annual calf, and must do all we can to ensure that it is a good one.

Heifers will begin 'bulling' (or coming on heat) at a remarkably young age, but clearly must not be bred from until well-grown. Usual practice would be to serve them at no less than 15-18 months of age, to calve down at over 2 years. Older cows will come on heat approximately 7 weeks after calving, and every 21 days thereafter, until mated. Cattle aren't seasonal breeders and can reproduce at any time of year. Often, however, sexual activity will be suppressed during the housed winter period, and cows will not be seen bulling until turnout at the end of April. We have been caught out by this, fondly believing our cows to be in-calf as we had observed no sign of heat all winter, only for the whole lot to fire up into rampant sexuality in the spring. They were clearly enjoying themselves, but we lost 6 months of production.

If a continuous supply of milk is required for the house, it'll be necessary to keep two cows, usually a spring calver (April / May) and an autumn calver (September / October). We followed this system to begin with, but found that our autumn calving cow was constantly troubled by summer mastitis (or 'August bag') We now aim to have all our cows calving in the spring, with both 'early' spring (Feb / March) and 'late' spring (May) calving cows ensuring we get milk all year round, with none of them dry during the peak risk period.

Spotting the signs

Unless your cows are running with a bull, it is going to be up to you to spot them bulling so that service can be arranged. Where several animals are grazing together it's not too difficult to identify an individual cow on heat, as she will be mounting the other cattle in her desperation. If two or more cows are bulling at the same time things can get quite steamy, and they'll come in for the evening milking looking ragged and sweaty with their rumps rubbed raw. Don't expect much milk on a day like

Bulling heifers dispaying typical behaviour.

this! Spotting them bulling does, of course, depend on you being able to see them easily, so if you can graze them close to the house rather than in some distant corner of the holding, so much the better.

Where only one cow is kept heat detection can be tricky, and it's necessary to look for more subtle signs. At grass the lone cow on heat will usually take herself off to the highest part of the field to get a view of the surrounding countryside, clearly hoping to spot some fellow beast. There may be a lot of bellowing going on, calling then listening for a reply from the distance. If your immediate neighbour keeps cattle you can expect your cow to spend the day up against the fence – I hope it's a strong one! Look for the telltale string of clear viscous mucus from the vulva, but this isn't always very easy to spot. You're more likely to see the straw coloured, slightly bloody, tacky mucus that occurs 2-3 days after a cow has been on heat, and, although this means you've missed your chance, you can at least work out when the next heat will be due. Look for behavioural changes at milking time, accompanied by a slight drop in yield. Our first cow used to demonstrate her frustration by kicking over the milking bucket,

and usually me and the stool as well, the one and only time she would do such a thing. As I picked myself and my utensils up from the floor, a quick glance under her tail would tell me what I needed to know.

Artificial insemination

The use of artificial insemination (AI) has a number of advantages, in addition to the obvious one that it eliminates the need to keep a bull. It enables you to make use of the very best bulls of your chosen type (all the mainstream breeds are available, and also a number of minority and specialist breeds), and as each bull will have been rigorously tested and evaluated before inclusion in the AI stud, a large amount of accurate data is available to enable you to make a well-informed choice based on factors such as calving ease, pedigree, growth rates, gestation length etc. The disadvantage of AI is that it relies wholly on your ability to detect oestrus, something that a bull can do so much more accurately. Provided you spot your cow bulling first thing in the morning, a phone call to your local Genus branch will result in a visit from a technician that same day (although you must phone before 10.30am in our area). Failing that, a visit can be arranged for the next day, by which time your cow will have gone off the boil, but AI should still be effective. If you need the AI man to call at a specific time of day this can often be arranged, but remember they have a busy schedule covering a large geographical area. If you're likely to be out when he calls, leave the cow tied in her stall, identified by means of some coloured tape around her tail. All being well, you're looking at

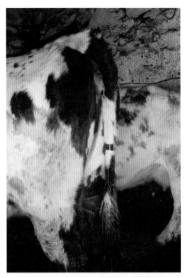

Temporary identification by means of colured tape around a cow's tail.

Artificial insemination.

spending around £35 to get your cow in-calf. However, if repeat matings are required due to your inability to accurately detect oestrus, then it's going to start getting expensive.

Natural service

Provided that you're not too fussy as to the breed of the sire, it's still possible, even in this highly regulated day and age, for a cow to 'go astray' and end up spending the night with a neighbour's bull. Ensure that your neighbour is a willing partner to this crime, as you might need some help in the morning – if the cow is really enjoying herself then catching her for milking may be a devil of a job.

In the case of a heifer, you could arrange for her to visit someone else's bull for six weeks or so, long enough to have spanned two or more heat cycles, although this is hardly a practical option for the house cow in milk. This leaves you with two alternatives – buy or borrow a bull. Buying a bull is not likely to be a viable proposition for only a couple of cows, but possibly a local group of smallholders could justify a jointly owned animal. He would need to be based with whoever has the most experience and / or the most appropriate facilities, with each member of the group paying an annual 'stud fee' (based on the size of their herd, perhaps) to cover the costs of his keep.

Bull breed choices

If you've opted for pedigree cattle then you have already made your choice in this respect. If you're lucky your chosen breed may be available by AI. If not, and you don't fancy owning a bull, then I hope you've chosen a breed that is popular in your locality, as it's not really feasible to be traipsing your milking cow half way across the country for service. Also be aware that the pedigree circuit can be rather 'cliquey', with prices maintained at unrealistically high levels by breeders buying and selling amongst one another. As a newcomer you will be expected to buy your way in at these prices, but there is no guarantee that you will receive similarly high prices when you have stock to sell – you may have to work a long apprenticeship under the wing of an established breeder. Good quality commercial crossbreds, on the other hand, can generally be relied upon to fetch good commercial prices, time after time, which is probably the preferred option for an efficient and profitable smallholding.

Ease of calving and the temperament of the offspring are two important considerations when choosing a bull breed. If using AI bulls, it'll be possible to use their calving ease data to make comparisons between breeds and between individuals within a breed. Temperament is largely judged by reputation – for example, the offspring of both British Blues and Herefords are known for their docility, whereas Limousin crosses can be flighty. Having said that, much so called 'temperament' is down to handling. If you approach cattle in a nervous and jumpy fashion, they will respond in a like manner. Our children are able to handle all our cattle with the same confidence we do ourselves, even the Limousin crosses, and we have encountered no problems.

If your calf is intended for home consumption then simply choose the easiest calving bull available, probably the Aberdeen Angus. A friend of ours uses the AA (by AI) on his little Dexter cows with every success, the resulting calves being single suckled to provide beef for his own freezer. An added attraction is that the calves by the AA are naturally polled, so do not need dehorning.

If your cow is one of the 'coloured' dairy breeds, (i.e. red, or red and white, rather than black and white) such as the Jersey, Ayrshire or Shorthorn, then I would recommend the use of a British Blue bull – the calves will tend to take after their father and be more saleable as a result. Don't be dissuaded by difficult calving horror stories – they are about 25 years out of date. The modern BB ranks as an easy-calving breed, with incidence of awkward calvings as low as 0.6% by some bulls – that's less than recorded in some of the traditional native breeds.

For a Frieisan cow, use either a Limousin or a Hereford bull, as the female offspring are in demand as suckler cows, giving you another potential market for your calves. Make your decision based on whichever cross is the most popular in your area.

On crossbred cows I would generally use a Limousin, being easy calving and producing very popular store cattle, though you may be put off it by its reputation for being a bit on the lively side.

If you intend to hire or buy a bull then both the Hereford and the Charollais have an excellent reputation for good behaviour. The Hereford is the easier calving of the two, but the Charollais will produce more saleable offspring. Take your pick!

Pregnancy

Once your cow is in-calf (it's worth having a vet to P.D. her after 8 weeks) you have a wait of about 285 days, but there's no need for mollycoddling. A cow in milk need not be dried off until about 6 weeks before her next calf is due. In the case of a first calving heifer, it's worth spending plenty of time over the last few weeks getting her used to having her udder stroked and washed in preparation for the time when you'll begin to milk her. Some feed may be given in late pregnancy, depending on the body condition of the animal and the time of year, but do not 'steam up' too much or you'll only end up with a big calf and problems. It's a good idea to introduce the cow to the milking area before she calves, perhaps by giving her daily feed allowance there, and if you intend to use a milking machine, let her get used to the sound of it, and not just the engine running but all the other rattling of buckets and various noises that tend to accompany milking time.

Drying off

In a natural situation where a cow suckles her own calf, the cow's yield drops as the calf's demand for milk reduces. In order to dry off a milking cow you need to mimic this falling demand situation. Late in her lactation yield will already have fallen quite considerably. The next step is to reduce her concentrate feed a bit, and stop stripping her out after each milking. As the daily yield falls still further you can move to once-a-day milking (and, if it's your custom to feed concentrates at milking time, this further reduces her feed intake). When the amount of milk you're getting makes it hardly worth the bother, you can cut down to milking only on alternate days, then stop altogether. The whole process may take 3 weeks. After the final milking it's best to squirt an antibiotic 'dry cow' tube

A 'dry cow' tube should be squirted into each teat at the end of a cow's lactation.

into each teat. This will clear up any latent infection (which may otherwise get worse, unnoticed, during the dry period) and seal the teats against ingress of any harmful bacteria that could initiate fresh infection. Do make sure that the milk withhold period for the product you're using is shorter than the length of time remaining until she is due to calve.

Finally the day will come when you notice that your cow has 'dropped her bones', a term used to describe the slackening of the pelvic ligaments preparatory to the birth of the calf, indicated by the appearance of a large hollow either side of the root of the tail. In all likelihood her udder will be looking very distended and uncomfortable at this stage, and may even be dribbling colostrum onto the floor. She'll begin to talk to her unborn calf, turning her head and softly mooing at her flanks – not long to go now! If you haven't already done so, move her to the calving area, either a sheltered paddock or a clean, airy loose box. If calving outdoors it's as well to have a place ready inside just in case problems occur or the weather turns.

Calving

When your cow is in labour it's quite natural that you will feel anxious – after all, there is no animal quite like a much-loved house cow for becoming one of the family. You may find it hard to resist the urge to hold her hoof, mop her brow, or offer her occasional sips of iced water. If she has anything like the temperament of ours she'll probably revel in all the attention, but on the whole they'd rather be left alone to get on with it. Be re-assured by the fact that the cow knows an awful lot more about calving than either you or I, and above all, remember the golden rule (applicable to the supervision of any birthing animal) of 'maximum observation, minimum interference'.

Some cows will calve incredibly quickly – in minutes, in fact. This is usually the case with our British Blue / Jersey crosses. On more than one occasion, having noticed the first signs of labour, I've popped into the house for my camera, only to find on my return that it was all over. While this is clearly an ideal situation, in many cases calving will be a more drawn out affair, and it may (quite safely) be as much as five hours from the time that the water bag emerges, or you first notice the calf's hooves peeping through, to when the calf finally enters the world. Any longer than this, though, and some assistance may be necessary. Fortunately, mal-presentations are not common, and all but the simplest are best dealt with by the vet. In all likelihood the calf will be correctly presented and just need a bit of a pull. The same rule that applies to assisted lambings also applies to calving – firm but gentle – although the degree of 'firmness' required

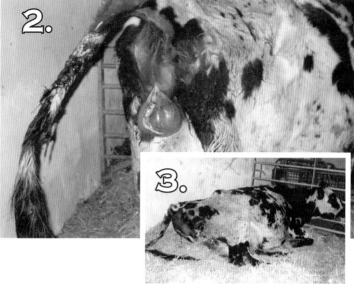

is proportional to the size and strength of the animal. There is an implement known as a 'calving jack' that's popularly used as an aid, although personally I find them rather awkward things. My preferred method, when assistance is required, is to use a simple but hefty block and tackle, with one block attached to a suitable low down anchoring point, and the other hooked to ropes on the calf's front legs. It's possible, using one hand, to keep up a steady traction, taking up the slack every time the cow strains, leaving the other hand free to guide the calf's head through, clear the mucus from his nose, and support his body as it slips out. The fact that I can manage this on my own makes it a less stressful experience for the cow than if there were a whole crowd of helpers busying around pulling on ropes. Usually it is just me, the cow and the calf in the middle of the night. No people. No fuss. Lovely.

Calving the cow step-by-step

Generally speaking, cows are pretty trouble-free when it comes to giving birth, which is just as well really, because you can't simply tip them over on their sides and sort out any problems in the same way as you would with sheep. Sometimes, though, a cow giving birth to a very large calf will need a helping hand, even if the presentation is normal. This is something that any reasonably experienced smallholder should be able to deal with themselves.

1. Although cows are, in most respects, better off calving outdoors, they don't always choose the most sensible places, and nor is the weather always good. The two main advantages to outdoor calving are that it's generally more hygienic, and, being on soft turf, there's less risk of the cow being unable to get up easily after the delivery. This might sound a minor point, but believe me it's no joke having a cow that's down and unable to rise. The disadvantages

of outdoor calving become apparent the moment darkness descends and it starts to rain…

2. Even if you do decide you'd rather let your cattle calve outdoors, it's essential that you've got somewhere undercover to house one if required. We have a number of pens measuring about 7' x 14', which make ideal maternity accommodation for our small cows. We try to ensure that a pen is ready for use well in advance of when it's required, but we don't move the cow into it until she actually starts to give birth, as indicated here by the presence of the waterbag.

3. As you can see, this pen has been recently mucked out and washed down, and is bedded with clean straw only. However, in the light of my own experience, this isn't something I'd now recommend. Fresh straw on a clean floor is easily pushed aside, and the concrete underneath becomes slippery with the fluids of birth. If a newly-calved cow slips and injures herself when she attempts to get to her feet, she might never

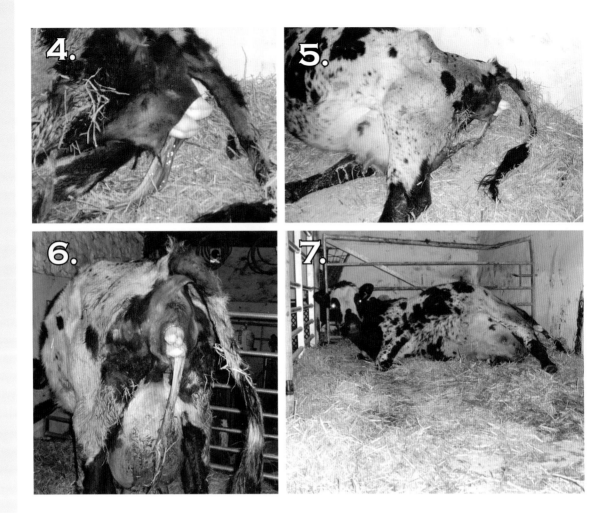

get up at all. Now I'd rather have deep litter in the pen, topped with a sprinkling of hydrated lime and a layer of clean straw.

4. Once the waterbag has broken, the cow begins to strain in earnest, and the tips of the calf's front hooves soon come into sight. Initially they'll disappear from view between contractions, but as each subsequent heave pushes the calf a little further, you'll also be able to see the tip of his tongue, closely followed by the end of his nose.

5. If you look carefully at this picture you can see colostrum squirting out of the cow's full udder and running over her leg

onto the floor. If – as seen here – the floor is clean and likely to become slippery, it's a good idea to throw down a few shovelfuls of sand for extra grip.

6. During the course of her labour, the cow will change position fairly frequently, alternating between lying and standing for periods of time. She'll continue to strain in the standing position. I can see here that the calf is correctly presented, but judging by the size of the hooves it's clearly a big one, and I'm beginning to think that some assistance might be necessary. However, as with all animals, it's a mistake to intervene too soon, so I'll leave her a while longer yet...

7. Five hours later, and the calf still hasn't put in an appearance. Furthermore, the cow is looking like she's fed up with the whole business. Time for me to lend a hand…

8. I attach a short loop of rope to the calf's front legs, just above the first joint, and onto that I hook one end of a block-and-tackle. The other block, with the free end leading off it, is attached to one of the gateposts.

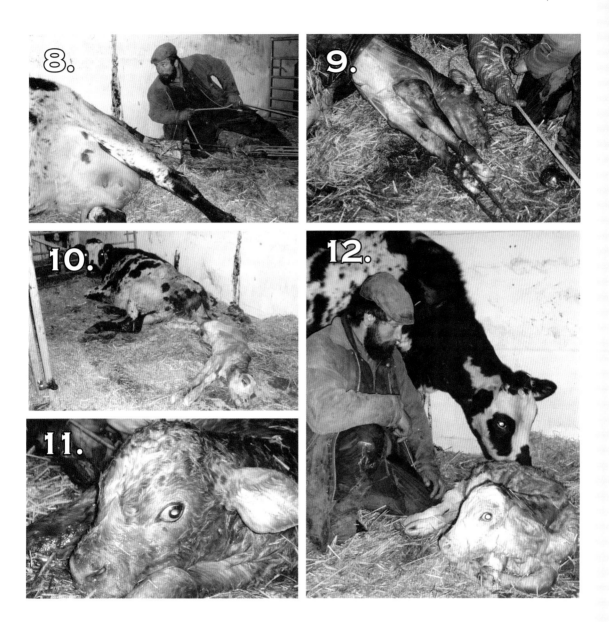

9. By maintaining a steady traction on the rope I gradually ease the calf into the world, in time with the cow's contractions.

10. For the first few moments after the birth the calf appears quite lifeless, but I've seen his tongue twitching and his eyelid flicker, so I know all is well.

11. Sure enough, the calf is soon taking stock of his surroundings, shaking his head and spluttering to clear the mucus from his nose and mouth.

12. The cow is quickly on her feet and nuzzling at her newborn. She then begins to systematically lick him all over. Stimulated by this rough massage, the calf's breathing becomes more regular and he starts making attempts to stand up.

Before leaving them I spray the calf's navel with iodine or something similar. I then just pop in from time to time to make sure all is well, and also to keep an eye out for the 'cleansing', i.e. the afterbirth. Usually this follows shortly after the calf, but sometimes it may take a couple of days. If, after 3 days, it still hasn't been expelled then the cow will need antibiotic cover and possibly veterinary treatment.

What is a freemartin?

Freemartins occur when twin calves are born, one of each sex. The female is the freemartin, and is generally sterile. This is brought about by the fact that the developing embryos sharing the uterus also share placental membranes (from about the 40th day of gestation). The unborn male produces hormones in its testes that circulate via the shared placenta and enter the bloodstream of the female calf, suppressing the development of her reproductive system. Outwardly, a heifer born as a freemartin appears normal, so it's important when selling cattle (except if selling direct to slaughter) to declare any that may be unsuitable for breeding. The twin-born bull calf may also have reduced fertility, but this is not an issue as the majority of male calves are castrated anyway. Incidence of twins in cattle is low (only around half a percent), although some herds do experience a much higher proportion of multiple births.

Calf rearing

Apart from applying some suitable spray to the calf's navel and ensuring that he suckles regularly (colostrum is critical, so do get the calf up and suckling as soon as possible after birth) and is passing dung, you need do nothing more for the first four days, beyond what is dictated by common sense and good husbandry, such as keeping the cow's udder clean, checking regularly for signs of mastitis or oedema, and generally keeping

Single suckling.

A double suckled cow can sometimes be turned out with two calves, just like twins.

the pair under close observation for any indication of ill health or post natal complications. Let the calf enjoy the undivided attention of his mother for these few days, ensuring the best possible start in life.

Now you could, of course, simply turn cow and calf out to grass at this point, and rear some good quality beef in as healthy and natural a fashion as possible. However, at a time when many commercial suckler herds are struggling to break even without production subsidies, despite economies of scale, it's unlikely that single suckling will be economical on a small scale, where input costs are often proportionately higher. Traditionally small farms and smallholdings would have practiced double- or multi-suckling, buying in additional calves to rear under each cow. We've done this with some of ours, and it works very well. The fact that a smallholding cow will be docile and well-handled is a great help when persuading her to accept extra calves. Usually we bring cows in to suckle the calves twice a day, but in some cases it's possible to turn the cow out with two, just like twins. A maternally-minded milky cow can rear a succession of calves throughout her lactation, and it's

not uncommon to hear of cows that have reared 4, 6, or even 8 calves in a season.

Really though, what we're talking about here is the keeping of a house cow for domestic milk production, in which case neither single-, double-, nor multi-suckling will be appropriate. Therefore it's necessary to harden our hearts and separate cow and calf after four days if we are to have any of the milk for ourselves.

A simple option, and one that is most suited to a beginner or part-timer, is to separate the cow and calf during the day, either by turning the cow out to graze (if it's summertime), or by having separate indoor pens (in the winter). Milk the cow in the evening and then reunite the pair for the night. There are a couple of disadvantages to this system though: firstly, the cow will become cunning, and, knowing that she's about to get her calf back, will refuse to let any milk down until she sees him. You can squeeze away at her teats all you like but she won't give you a drop until she has reassured herself that her baby is fine! She may take this one stage further by holding back the milk until she actually has the calf with her. This can make milking very complicated as you will constantly have to fend off a boisterous and hungry calf. Some people claim to be able to milk one side of the cow while the calf sucks the other. Well, yes, it can be done, but having the calf slobbering and dribbling into the bucket is hardly conducive to clean milk production.

The second disadvantage is that milk production is largely a matter of supply and demand. As the calf grows and takes in more solid feed, his demand for milk will gradually tail off, so the cow will respond by producing less. This means less milk in your bucket at the end of each day, and a fairly short lactation.

It's most appropriate, if you want to get the best from your cow, to separate her from the calf completely and rear the calf yourself. We always part ours early in the morning of day 5, and so far none has objected strongly to this. Regular milking begins on the evening of the fifth day after calving, and continues twice daily thereafter. Following this regime you'll find that, even after taking out what's required for domestic consumption and to feed the cow's own calf, there's plenty of milk left over, so you buy in a few extra calves to rear alongside the homebred one. And, when its time to wean these, the cow will still be churning out a fair amount of milk, so you buy in another batch of calves or some weaner pigs to slurp up the surplus, by which time your second cow will be about due to calve, so you start all over again.

Buying calves

This isn't difficult if you live in a dairy farming area, as many of the calves born in commercial dairy herds are surplus to requirements, and are sold off at a few days

Young calves can often be purchased directly from dairy farms, where they may be surplus to requirements.

old. Certainly it's preferable to buy directly from a farm rather than through a market. It's worth checking round prior to the time that you will need to buy in, to find out who has cows due to calve about the same time as your own. This also gives you an opportunity to see the sort of health status maintained on the farms – you may wish to cross one or two off your list of potential sources.

To prevent a cow from kicking, tie a length of rope tightly around her middle, just in front of her udder.

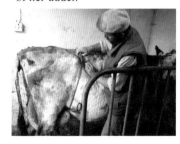

It may not be possible for you to source calves locally. Some livestock dealers specialise in calf procurement, and will have contacts further afield. They can

generally be relied upon to find what you're looking for. Specify whether you need a calf to go under a cow (for multi-suckling), or whether it is to be bucket reared (this is important – once a calf has learnt to drink from a bucket it can be impossible to get it to suck from a cow). If you're buying several at once, ask for a matching group in terms of breed and sex. This is a help when it comes to selling them on later as stores. Expect to pay more for a bull calf. Be wary of anything that seems cheap, and avoid animals that are 'free to a good home' as they tend to cost more in the long run. See that the calf's navel has been sprayed and is dry – there must be no swelling, moistness or unpleasant smell in the region of the 'belly button'. Run your hand over the leg joints to check for signs of heat or swelling. Look for any evidence of ringworm (circular crusty lesions, usually on the face and neck) – once you bring something like that onto your farm you may be stuck with it annually thereafter.

Laboured breathing and / or coughing may be indicative of pneumonia. Pneumonia and scours (diahorrhea) are probably the biggest threats to the health and wellbeing of your calves. Don't buy a calf with a mucky bottom. Lice can be a problem, particularly on winter-born calves, so give each new arrival a dusting with louse powder. Be aware that not only can bought-in calves introduce disease to your home-bred stock, there could be problems present on your farm to which your own animals have a degree of resistance to which bought in calves may well succumb. Observe reasonable bio-security precautions and keep calves from different sources separate initially (impossible if double- or multi-suckling).

Ringworm

Ringworm is a fungal infection that chiefly affects housed young cattle. It's most severe in animals in poor condition. Usually it's seen on the head, particularly around the eyes, but can affect other parts of the body. It can also infect humans and other animals. Older cattle that may already have been exposed to the disease are generally resistant to further attacks, but can become carriers. The fungus can survive for long periods in the environment, particularly in the fabric of traditional farm buildings and in the bark of some species of tree, only to re-emerge with each successive batch of calves.

One crude (but effective) traditional remedy is to apply creosote to the affected areas. Another treatment involves pasting the lesions with live yoghurt – apparently the fungus shifts its attention to the yoghurt, which then dries into a crust and drops off. Personally, I think that the best course of action is to isolate the affected animal (or group) and spray the bare patches with Bactakil. Generally, once the cattle are turned out in the spring, the problem will clear up on its own.

Observe reasonable bio-security precautions, and house calves in individual pens initially

Good ventilation in the calf shed is essential. House calves in individual pens, preferably solid sided, which should be thoroughly cleaned and disinfected between occupants.

Make sure that any calves you buy in are correctly ear-tagged and accompanied by the appropriate paperwork.

Feeding

You'll need to allow one gallon of milk per calf per day, although in practice you dilute it slightly, so 3-3½ gallons of surplus milk will feed four calves. The rate of dilution is not an exact science, but a 3:1 ratio of milk to water seems about right. Dilute at 2:1 for the first couple of feeds until the calves have settled down to the new regime. Diluted milk forms softer curds in the stomach of the calf and results in fewer occurrences of scours. If you do observe a calf with a bit of a 'runny tummy', immediately reduce the amount of milk in the mixture to 50% or less and administer a Kaolin / Sulpha type medication (to be kept in stock at all times). Don't wait to see if it's a bit better in the morning – it won't be.

Initially divide the calf's daily

ration into four equal feeds, spread fairly evenly across the 24 hour period (although there's no need to get up in the night). By the end of week one it should be given as 3 feeds, and after a fortnight 2 equal feeds of 4 pints each (3-3½ pints of milk topped up with water), which will fit in nicely with the morning / evening livestock routine on the holding.

Don't feed bought-in calves on the day they arrive. They'll be quite stressed enough, and a bellyful of milk won't help matters at all. Provide a bucket of fresh water with perhaps a spoonful of glucose powder added, and some clean straw to nibble at, then leave them alone in peace and quiet to get used to their new surroundings.

To begin with the milk should be given warm – the addition of hot water for dilution will help to offset some of the cooling that will have occurred since the milk came out of the cow – but as the calves get older, cold milk will be fine. To teach a young calf to take milk from a bucket, back him into the corner of his pen and stand astride him. Holding the bucket in one hand, dip the fingers of the other hand in the milk and insert them into the calf's mouth (clean hands please!). He will begin to suck them, whereupon you gradually draw his head down into the bucket. The aim is to get your hand into the milk while the calf is still sucking your fingers – it'll take several attempts as the calf will be used to having to look upwards for his food, not down. Hold the bucket pretty firmly or he'll bunt it out of your hand. Most calves get the hang of it pretty quickly, so before long there'll be no need to

Holding the bucket in one hand, dip the fingers of the other hand in the milk and insert them into the calf's mouth

Once the calf is sucking your fingers, gradually draw his head down into the bucket.

have made your own, then choose a coarser bale. Hay-fed calves always seem to develop a rather pot-bellied look, though.

It goes without saying that fresh water should always be available, and fresh bedding put down regularly.

TIP

'Contract rearing' (i.e. rearing calves for someone else) may be a viable smallholding enterprise. You don't own the calves (so have no capital outlay for the purchase of each batch) and are paid on a per head basis. Certain production targets are set, for example daily liveweight gain, and there may be bonus payments over and above the minimum rate where performance exceeds the target. Similarly, deductions will be made if the target is not met, and clearly you wouldn't be paid for any animals that die.

Smallholdings are often created following the breaking up of a much larger farm, and as a result frequently have a disproportionately high number of buildings in relation to acreage. This means that an indoor project such as calf rearing can be established with the minimum of start up costs, and without impacting on other activities.

However, the role of the calf rearer is a specialist one, and strict attention must be paid to stockmanship, hygiene and bio-security in order for the project to be a success. There simply isn't room for cutting corners.

restrain him, though sometimes it may be necessary to continue to let the calf suck your fingers for the first week or so. All buckets used for milk, feed and water must be kept scrupulously clean.

Start offering some pelleted calf feed from the very beginning, just a little at a time, removing any uneaten and replacing it twice daily. Allow one bag (25kg) of

really good quality starter pellets per calf, before changing to a standard ruminant feed. Provide a rack full of good clean barley straw too. Straw is preferable to hay at this stage, as its fibrous nature stimulates good rumen function – the development of an efficient digestive system at an early age will stand calves in good stead for the rest of their lives. If you prefer to feed hay, perhaps because you

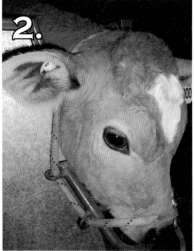
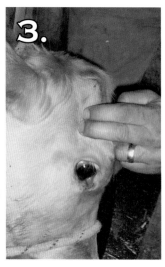

DEHORNING AND CASTRATION

These are both relatively simple procedures that you're able to carry out yourself, following appropriate training. I learnt the necessary skills while at agricultural college, but you may find that LANTRA will be able to organise tuition for a group of smallholders, or perhaps an experienced cattle keeper or your vet could give a demonstration.

Calves should be dehorned using a heated dehorning iron when the horn buds are no more than 5mm high. If you have a calf crate for restraint, it simplifies things no end, otherwise you'll need an assistant to hold them. Probably the trickiest part of the whole job is injecting the local anaesthetic at the correct point to numb the hornbuds. Whether or not anaesthetic should be used at all is something of a moot point – those in favour claim quite simply that to carry out such a procedure without it is little short of barbaric. The argument against anaesthetic is that calves seem to recover more quickly, with less bleeding, when it

isn't used. Get plenty of experience before forming your own opinion.

A dehorning iron is quite an expensive bit of kit, and they don't crop up second hand very often. We were able to justify the purchase of ours (about £85 at the time) by carrying out dehorning for other farmers. Alternatively, it's the sort of piece of kit that could be owned collectively by a regional smallholding group, and made available to members as required. Electric dehorners can still be bought quite cheaply, as can those that attach by rubber hose to a large gas bottle, but they lack the portability of the refillable lighter gas or small canister models. Expect to pay £150-200 for a good one of these nowadays.

Removing the horns of older cattle is not a pleasant task, and should be avoided.

Calf Dehorning step-by-step

Although cattle (particularly native breeds) do look pretty impressive with a fine spread of horns, there are a number of reasons – not least your own safety – why it's most sensible to dehorn them.

1. Tools of the trade (left to right): Dehorning iron; scissors; small syringe with short, fine needle (21 gauge x ⅝"); local anaesthetic. Light the dehorning iron before catching the calf, so it's got plenty of time to warm up.

2. A purpose-made crate or yoke to hold the calf makes the whole process a one-man job. However, you can manage just as well without the crate if you have a helper to restrain the animal.

3. Firstly, identify the correct location for injection of the local anaesthetic. The nerve lies in a small channel that can be felt running from just below the horn bud to the corner of the eye.

4. The injection site is at the mid point of this channel.

5. The anaesthetic that I'm using here is Lignocaine and Adrenaline, with a dose rate of 3ml per horn bud.

6. The needle should go in to its full length. If it doesn't then you've clearly missed that narrow channel in the bone. During the process of administering the injection, the needle should be partially withdrawn, moved slightly and re-inserted a couple of times, just to ensure that the area is properly infiltrated.

7. Clip away the hair from around the horn buds while waiting for the anaesthetic to take effect.

8. Check that the iron is hot enough (by pressing it on a piece of scrap wood), then apply it fairly lightly over the horn bud.

9. After a couple of seconds, remove the iron and have a look at the horn bud to make sure that you're burning in the right place.

10. Assuming all is well, reapply the iron with considerable pressure this time and a screwing motion. After a short while you'll hear a slight pop and feel a change in resistance – this indicates that the burn is now deep enough.

11. If you lift the iron off at this point you'll see that the scorched horn bud is surrounded by a white line of bone (just visible at the lower edge in this photo). If the white line doesn't extend all the way around the horn bud then briefly reapply the iron as appropriate.

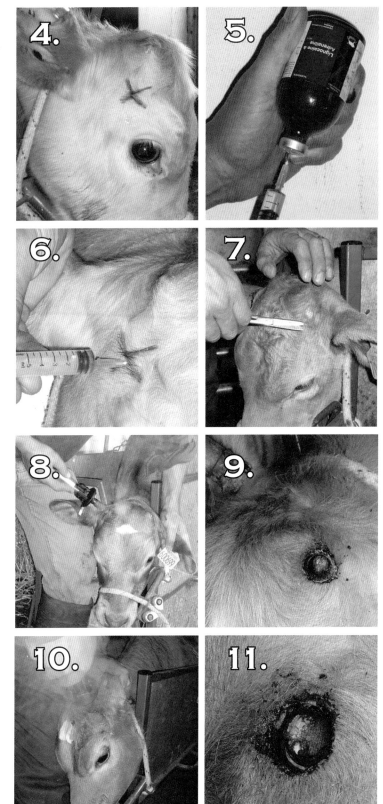

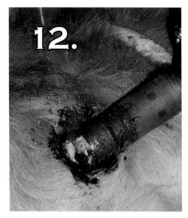

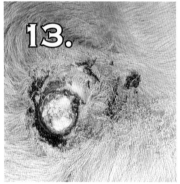

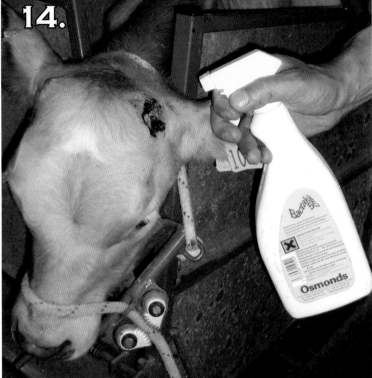

12. Now it's time to undermine the horn bud by applying the iron at an angle and gradually working all the way around, pushing in under the bud until it comes free and drops off.

13. The end result should be a neat, round, shallow hole with a base of clean white bone. No blood or mess!

14. A squirt of an appropriate antiseptic spray completes the job. The whole operation takes only a few minutes, from start to finish.

Castration

There are three options for castration – surgical, bloodless and rubber rings. Surgical and bloodless castration have the advantage that they can be carried out on older animals – bull calves

left entire up to the age of 7 months or so will develop a better conformation. Having said that, the rubber ring method (applied in the first few days) is simplicity itself.

Bought-in calves may already be over the age for legal rubber ringing – avoid this problem by buying in heifer calves only.

After 8 weeks or so, re-house calves in group pens, with milk fed in a communal trough. Individual pens can now be dismantled, thoroughly cleansed, and rested. Weaning takes place from around 12 weeks and, assuming that your cow is still milking well, you can go out and source another batch. It's not difficult to rear seven or more calves per cow per year like this, although four would probably be a reasonable target for the smallholder, in addition to having a good supply of milk for the house.

Transfer calves to group pens at around 8 weeks of age.

GRAZING AND FEEDING

Grass in summer, hay in winter. It really can be that simple, although clearly the more you want to get out of your stock, the more you will need to put in. The science behind the correct formulation of rations for ruminants is complex and fascinating, and is not only relevant to the managers of high-yielding Holstein herds chasing every last pennyworth of milk. Anyone aiming to achieve that little bit of extra performance from their animals would be well-advised to read around the subject, even if only to get a better understanding of the analysis given on bags of proprietary feedstuffs. For many of us though, running fairly low-key enterprises, a bit of general knowledge and a few rules of thumb will usually suffice to ensure that our animals are well fed and healthy.

Grazed grass

Thankfully cattle at grass aren't particularly difficult to keep within bounds – certainly they seem less inclined to go walkabout than either sheep or goats. A traditional cut-and-laid thorn hedge makes a fine boundary, and a better one if reinforced with two or three strands of well-tensioned barbed wire, as cattle are rather inclined to lean on things, and will eventually push through a weak point in a hedge. If you also graze sheep then you'll probably want a stock fence alongside your hedges anyway. Dry stone walls are good if well-looked after, but even here you may wish to add a strand of wire to prevent sheep and ramblers from scrambling over and dislodging the top course of stone. Once the copings have fallen, the whole integrity of the wall seems to suffer, and large (cattle-sized) gaps will soon appear. The life expectancy of any field boundary can be considerably extended by a simple single strand of electric fence wire run around the inside. Cattle are particularly sensitive to this type of fencing, and the addition of that single strand will be sufficient to stop them rubbing themselves on the principal boundary, and eventually slackening the wire,

Strip grazing using an electric fence. The cattle graze under the wire, so do not waste grass by trampling or dunging on it.

loosening posts, toppling stones etc. At times a single strand of electric fence is all that separates our cattle from our silage or hay crop, and occasionally we will even graze cows on a fallow plot in the vegetable garden, with only one wire between them and our precious cabbages.

Strip grazing with electric fence is undoubtedly the most effective way to utilise a small area for adult cattle. A single wire 28" - 30" above ground is moved forward on a daily basis to provide regular fresh grazing, in a way which allows for a degree of rationing. Ideally the cattle feed under the fence, so cannot trample or dung on any of the uneaten grass, and wastage is minimised. After a week or more a second fence, known as a back fence, is introduced. As the first fence is moved on in front of the cattle, so the back fence is moved on behind them, allowing re-growth on the

grazed area. Some fertiliser can be applied behind the back fence, if required. A small corral (which can also be of electric fence) is handy to close the cows into while you move the wire (there is no need to turn it off – just wear gloves), or if you have an assistant, one of you can be moving the fence whilst the other does the milking.

It may be that the grass in your field grows more quickly than your cows can eat it. In this case, when hay time comes around, you simply move the cows back to the beginning of the field (where it will have re-grown nicely behind the back fence) and mow the uneaten part for hay. On a field of just 1½ acres managed in this way we have kept one cow, produced all the milk we required, reared a couple of calves, and taken enough hay to keep that cow through the following winter (the calves were sold as weanlings). Usually, though, we strip graze 3 or 4 cows on that field and cut most of our hay elsewhere. Although strip grazing will, in all likelihood, prove to be the best grazing system for your milking cow(s), it may be appropriate to manage other ages / classes of stock differently – cows with calves at heel, for example. We tend to graze these rotationally, moving them into a fresh paddock every month or so, and following on behind with sheep. We also use this group of cattle to eat off the rough headlands and awkward corners in the mowing fields after taking our crop of hay or silage. Store cattle, on the other hand, are 'set stocked' throughout the grazing season – we use a field for the summer that we know is just enough to keep our bunch of stores from turnout at the beginning of May until early September, when we move them closer to home.

For the sake of simplicity, on a small scale it is probably preferable to rear calves indoors and sell them between weaning and one year of age. In this way you have only one category of stock – the milking cows – to provide grazing for.

Out-wintering

In the case of out-wintered cattle it is not so much a question of what to feed them, but where. Many farms have a small rough patch – a little piece of poor stony ground, perhaps with scrub providing

Outwintered cattle will cause a lot of damage to your grassland.

shelter, or in the lee of an adjacent wood, which traditionally has been used as a sacrifice area for out-wintering. Unfortunately the worthy environmentalists who now dictate what we can (or more commonly, what we can't) do on our holdings have decided that these areas are far too sensitive to suffer the trampling of hooves every winter. Now if you wish to keep cattle outdoors through the winter then it will probably have to be in the middle of your best hayfield. The chances of getting a decent crop the following year are considerably reduced without a fair amount of remedial work – the field may need ploughing and re-seeding to rectify all the damage caused by poaching. (Minimise damage during the winter by moving feeding points regularly.) Unless you have a couple of 'improved' fields and can use them and re-seed in alternate years, then you'd be better off bringing your cattle in. It is not a bad thing to give the land a rest during the winter anyway, and keep your fields in good condition ready for turnout in the spring.

Conserved Forage

Except under exceptional circumstances (e.g. summer drought) cattle will only need supplementary forages during the winter months. For the rest of the year requirements can be fully met by grazed grass. The winter, believe it or not, lasts for 180 days. Ok, so that's a bit of a generalisation as it will vary from year to year and from place to place, but you can generally reckon on having your cattle housed from 1st November until 1st May. In fact it makes management much easier if you stick to set dates for housing and turnout as it takes a lot of the guesswork out of things, enables more accurate planning of feed and building requirements, and eliminates the annual autumnal family argument over whether the cattle should be in yet.

Knowing exactly when cattle will come in, and exactly how much they'll eat, enables optimum use to be made of available space – I know that if I stack 240 of my hay bales in the area that I use for individual pens at lambing time,

Good quality barley straw provides a realistic alternative to hay or silage for store cattle, particularly if you live in a predominantly arable area where it can often be purchased cheaply off the field. (If you have your own baler you may be able to get it for next to nothing). Straw has a low nutritional value (although tends to be more consistent in analysis than either hay or silage), so a fairly high protein supplement will need to be provided. This should also contain an appropriate mineral blend, and maybe urea to aid in the digestion of cellulose.

One winter, as an experiment, we fed straw to a group of stores for a couple of months. We were pleased to find that not only did they do well and look healthy, they stayed much cleaner, and bedding costs were considerably reduced. In some subsequent years we have fed straw to all the young cattle, right through the housed period. Although transport costs mean straw is relatively expensive in this neck of the woods, land is expensive too, and we feel that straw feeding may provide a viable alternative to paying a high rent for silage / haymaking field.s

and start using them on the 1st of November, then the four cows will eat the last bale on the 28th of February. I can then get on with sorting everything out before lambing begins in mid March. Careful planning in this way has avoided the need to build a designated hay store.

This barrier, through which the cattle put their heads to feed, is simply an adapted gate.

We always budget for a 200 day winter. This allows us to start feeding a week or so prior to housing, and gives us a bit of fodder in hand should bad weather delay turnout in the spring. A cow will need half a bale of hay per day (small cows eat a bit less, obviously) split into two feeds, so allow 100 bales per cow per year. You'll have to use your own judgement a bit, as variation in weight between bales, even from the same machine, can be considerable. (I have just weighed a couple and was slightly startled to find one almost twice the weight of the other. Same baler, different field) If your bales weigh much less than, say 25kg, you'll need to add a bit to each cow's ration, either an extra slice of hay, a forkful of silage, or some kale or roots. If they're heavier, then half a bale will probably feed a cow and her calf.

We feed small bale hay to our adult cattle simply because rationing is so much easier. With four cows in individual stalls in the cow shed it's a simple matter

of splitting a bale between them in the morning, and the same again in the evening. If using silage, base your calculations on the assumption that 10 cows will eat one bale in 2 days. Big bale silage really comes into its own when cattle are housed in groups, with each bale containing enough fodder for maybe several days at a time. Ring feeders are usually used for feeding big bales to cattle out of doors, and could also be used for housed stock, but it is much more convenient to construct some form of feed barrier. Our first was a rather basic affair consisting of some heavy timbers and a couple of scaffold poles fixed across a gap in the partition that divided our old shed in two. On one side we stacked our hay and on the other we kept our cows, so it was a simple matter to toss a bale down from the stack to land in front of the barrier, through which the cattle put their heads to feed. In our new building we use two barriers forming a 7'6" wide feed passage – it is just wide enough to drive in with the tractor and drop off a couple of big bales.

Other feeds

If you've got the land to do it, why not grow a few other crops to feed your cows? With a bit of luck, and provided you're not bent on achieving a high milk output, it should be possible to significantly reduce the amount of purchased feed required, or maybe do away with it altogether, resulting in a truly self-sufficient system. Root crops would be a good thing to start with – mangels will give a heavy yield per acre (try Edwin Tucker and Son for seed), but swedes have a higher feed value. Mangels are frost-susceptible and should be harvested early and stored in a clamp. Swedes, on the other hand, can be lifted as required right into the New Year. Or try fodder beet, which falls somewhere between the two. Roots should be chopped for feeding. Unfortunately the old cast iron root-choppers, which would once have been two-a-penny at any farm clearance sale, have mostly been snapped up to decorate patios and pub forecourts. The best small scale alternative is to place the roots, a few at a time, in a heavy wooden box and chop them up with a sharpened spade. Cabbages and marrowstem kale can be served in a like fashion.

Cereals aren't easy to grow on the smallholding, partly due to the machinery required, but whole crop silage might be worth a go. The crop – usually barley, often undersown with grass – is harvested before it is fully ripe using an ordinary mower, then baled and wrapped. The resultant silage is more or less a complete diet. Or grow a small patch of oats to be cut by hand and stooked in the traditional manner – if you could harvest 100 sheaves per cow kept, you'd be well on the way to self-sufficiency.

Stock can feed from both sides, the passageway also acting to separate two different age groups. The barriers themselves are hung like gates (they are in fact 16' gates adapted for the purpose) so can be easily relocated should we wish to change the layout of the cattle yards in order to accommodate more (or less) animals.

Concentrates

Forage rations, as I've described above, should be sufficient to provide for maintenance and up to one gallon of milk per day, so my earlier comment *"grass in summer, hay in winter"* wasn't so far fetched after all – dry cows, single sucklers and store cattle shouldn't require any extra feed. It is only the milking portion of the herd that will require concentrates in addition to the grass-based part of the diet, about 3½ lb per day for each gallon of milk produced over and above the first one (i.e. a cow giving 4 gallons per day needs forage + 10½ lb of concentrates). Having said that, in the summer, when the grass is really lush, you could get away with feeding a lot less – currently we're only feeding 6½ lb per cow, and the yield from the best milker is in the region of 5 gallons per day (having eased back from 6 gallons at peak).

We use a general purpose ruminant feed for our cows which has the advantage that it can also fed it to sheep, so at times we can justify buying it by the tonne and make a considerable saving over the small bag price. We have, once or twice, forked out for a specialist dairy cow ration but, to be honest, we didn't really notice any improvement in either the yield or the condition of the cow, so we went back to the basic grub.

Unfortunately, the price of feed has shot up in recent years, and the concentrate we use now works out at about 23p per kg. Therefore, at peak yield, we may be spending as much as £1 per day on feed. However, for this we are going to get 4 gallons of milk, which is more than enough to supply our domestic needs, rear a few calves, and probably fatten a couple of pigs too. To achieve a similar level of production from goats would probably entail keeping at least three in milk, each of which would consume approximately 2kg of concentrates per day, and goat food is pretty dear – currently in the region of 65p per kilo. If you do the sums you'll find that the feed costs incurred in the production of a pint of goat's milk may be almost 4 times what a pint of milk costs from our house cow, and you'll understand one of the reasons why we changed from one to the other!

Vet and med strategy

Ideally you'll have a 'herd health plan' (or a whole farm health plan, if you also keep other livestock) worked out in conjunction with your vet. It's inevitable that a written document of this nature will shortly become a compulsory prerequisite to the keeping of any farm animal, so you might as well jump the gun and speak to your vet about it now. In the meantime, a brief summary of our own vet and med strategy will help to give you a general idea of what is involved.

• A few days before turnout in the spring all adult cows, particularly

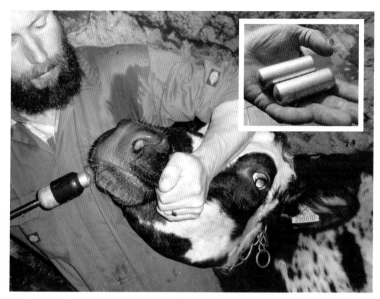

Main and inset: *Magnesium boluses should be administered a few days before turnout.*

those in milk, are given a couple of magnesium boluses. Lush spring grass is notoriously low in this essential element, and 'staggers' is a problem we can well do without.

• Three weeks after turnout, store cattle are dosed against roundworm and lungworm. We use a pour-on product, and as our animals are very tame we can walk amongst them and apply it in the field. Adult cattle are generally resistant to worms and do not require treatment.

• The stores are dosed again at 8-10 week intervals throughout the grazing season, with the last application being no more than 5 weeks before housing.

• Another pour-on product is applied to the adult cows to control nuisance flies which contribute to the spread of summer mastitis.

• The autumn flush of grass can be another risk period for staggers, so we provide high magnesium licks in September.

Pour-on products are a convenient way of treating internal and external parasites.

• Cows being dried off at the end of their lactation receive intra-mammary dry cow tubes to treat any existing problems, and to seal the teats against infection during the dry period.

• Youngsters are vaccinated against pneumonia at housing. Calves receive a primary course of two injections, and second winter cattle get a single booster dose.

• Stores are dosed mid winter for

liverfluke. Sometimes they've also needed a fluke dose in late summer / early autumn. In very flukey years cows may need a dose too.

• All cattle are regularly dusted with louse powder during the housed period.

Hoof care

In suckler herds (i.e. where the cows rear their own calves), lameness is very rarely an issue, except perhaps where some other problem, such as previous injury or poor conformation, is affecting locomotion. Regular hoof trimming generally isn't required. Likewise, traditional breed dairy cows seldom experience foot problems. It's in the high-yielding dairy cow that foot problems are a real cause for concern. Due to the vast size of the modern cow's udder she can no longer carry her hind legs in line with her pelvis, but must swing them unnaturally wide at each step. This results in uneven wear to the hooves, and undue strain on joints. Lameness is one of the commonest reasons why dairy cows are culled from commercial herds. Routine hoof care is usually carried out by contractors who have specially equipped mobile cattle crushes, and who will be fully trained in the use of the most up-to-date tools and techniques.

Sheep

"Almost wherever I have lived, if I could have had one domestic animal, I would have chosen sheep." John Seymour

By virtue of its versatility, the sheep is probably the ultimate self-supporters' animal. You can eat them, milk them, and make clothing from their wool and skin. Given the right conditions, they're capable of doing all this with surprisingly few inputs. What more could you ask for? Not surprisingly, sheep are often the first 'full size' livestock that the smallholder with grazing land acquires, and on many smallholdings the sheep flock is also the largest enterprise – the one that's expected to generate a bit of profit and help to pay the bills.

MANAGEMENT SYSTEMS

Different management systems have developed according to geographical constraints, and to suit different marketing opportunities, and breeds of sheep have evolved to suit just about

every permutation of these factors. However, for the self-supporter, for whom the ultimate goal is to put home-produced food on the table as economically as possible, the simplest solutions are often the most appropriate.

As a starting point, before making any choices as to breed or husbandry, you must ask yourself why you want to keep sheep (e.g. what is the intended end product, and is the flock expected to make a profit, or would breaking even be sufficient?), and also consider how the flock will fit in with the other enterprises on the holding in terms of availability of grazing at key times of year, housing requirements, winter forage, and so on. Having first answered these questions, it's not too difficult to decide upon an appropriate management system and then, finally, choose a breed or type that will suit your purposes. This is infinitely more sensible than choosing a breed simply because you like the look of it.

Conventional spring lambing: Despite the obvious attraction of alternative husbandry systems,

most small-scale sheep keepers opt for a conventional spring lambing approach, with the flock giving birth at some point during the period from February to April. Although this is considered to be the 'normal' regime, it's worth bearing in mind that it can place a considerable strain on your reserves of feed and forage, as ewes will be entering their period of peak nutritional demand (i.e. late gestation) at a time when grass growth and quality are at their lowest. However, early spring-born lambs ought to be able to be fattened off grass (either grazed or via their mothers' milk) without supplementary feeding, so what you lose at one end of the year you may well gain at the other.

Some considerable ewe feeding costs can be eliminated by pushing the spring lambing period back to late May, but lambs born at this time may not be sufficiently well grown for slaughter before grass growth declines in late autumn, meaning that they'll need some additional feed for fattening. A May lambing system might be suitable for the smallholder who's aiming to produce mutton (i.e. sheep to be killed at 2-3 years of age, or maybe even older) for home consumption, using extensively managed grassland.

'Easy care' systems: Although there's a composite breed called the easy-care, the term is also used to describe a low-input system of sheep keeping, with the barest minimum of intervention.

Breeds that naturally shed their fleeces (or in some cases produce no fleece at all) are often chosen for this, as many of the costs and inconveniences associated with flock husbandry (e.g. dagging, fly strike, shearing, death of 'cast'

TIP

Sheep can be, and are, kept just about anywhere in the world, from arid desert zones to tundra regions. Somewhere between these two extremes lies the UK – blessed with just about the best sheep farming environment on earth. Furthermore, almost any type of sheep can be kept almost anywhere in the UK, provided that the husbandry and management regimes adopted are appropriate to the chosen breed. You'll often hear it said that traditional breeds from different regions of the UK are specifically adapted to the geography of the area from which they originate, but much of the adaptation has its roots in the prevailing husbandry methods of the locality. So, for example, in the hill and upland regions, where constant close shepherding and supplementary feeding has historically not been possible, we find thrifty breeds that are capable of looking after themselves to a large extent. However, these hill ewes are equally suited to low-input 'easy-care' style farming systems in the lowlands. Similarly, many of the down breeds of sheep can be successfully kept at high altitudes, under adverse climatic conditions, provided that the level of shepherding is consistent with their requirements.

ewes, etc.) are wool related. To establish an easy care flock it's necessary to be extremely rigorous about culling animals that give any trouble whatsoever, which would include even minor lambing difficulties, dirty bottoms, poor-shaped udders, etc. For small-scale sheep keepers, who tend to have a more personalised relationship with the individuals within their flocks, this can be a rather difficult bullet to bite.

However, the end result will be a much healthier flock, with less dependence on the syringe and the dosing gun, making this a good option on organic holdings. Easy care systems might also be suitable for part-time smallholders who have only a limited amount of time to devote to shepherding, but on no account should the term 'easy care' be used as an excuse for poor management or neglect.

Early lambing: Managing the flock for early lambing (which, for our purposes here, may be taken to also include frequent and out of season breeding systems) is ideal

for the smallholder who wants to add value to the end product, or who wishes to provide regular customers with a year-round supply of meat of a consistent standard. Early lambing systems are also an attractive option where the availability of summer grazing is the limiting factor to the size of the flock: housing the flock and lambing in December enables lambs to be fattened indoors and sold for peak prices at 10-12 weeks of age, meaning that only the ewes need to be provided with pasture over the summer. Admittedly this is a high input / high output system, but it is well suited to small-scale production using docile traditional down breeds.

Controlled breeding by the use of 'sponges'

While I can appreciate that some small flock owners might have reservations about using hormone treatments in order to manipulate the breeding cycle of their animals – it does sound a bit 'commercial' – I can assure you that the pros far outweigh the cons. Sponging is, in fact, a common practice not only in big commercial flocks, but on smallholdings too, although the reasons why it's carried out may differ. In big flocks it's a financial decision, based on the expected higher value of earlier born (or out-of-season) lambs, but for many smallholders, who may only be able to manage their flock on a part-time basis due to the commitment of regular employment, the use of sponges can dramatically simplify the management of the flock at lambing time, and result in a big improvement in animal welfare, simply because planning ahead becomes so much easier.

Having the whole lambing period condensed into a very few days should make it possible to book the necessary time off work well in advance, in order to be able to give your ewes the care and attention they deserve.

Fleece and fibre production: It wouldn't make sense for the self-supporter to keep such multipurpose animals as sheep purely for their fleeces, except perhaps under circumstances where a breeding flock is out of the question due to other commitments. Fleeces have a very low value, and are considered to be a by-product of the industry nowadays. However, if you've got the skill required to turn raw wool into yarn or garments (see pages 408 - 414) then considerable value can be added. The heaviest and best quality fleeces will always come from wethers (castrated males), so wool processing fits in quite nicely with the production of mutton, where a rolling population of wethers will be kept to supply meat for the freezer.

Milk production: Where the scale of a smallholder's activity doesn't permit the keeping of a cow then sheep provide a viable alternative to goats as producers of dairy products for domestic consumption. Personally, I'd like to see a lot more small-scale sheep keepers making use of their animals in this way.

Store lamb finishing: If all you want to do is put meat in the freezer then there's no need to keep a breeding flock at all. You can simply buy in commercial store lambs in late summer / early autumn for fattening. Purchase more than you actually need for home consumption, and hopefully the sale of the surplus (particularly if sold directly to the end user, rather than to a butcher, abattoir or through a market) will cover the cost of the whole lot. All livestock markets hold regular sales of store lambs from about late July onwards, so there shouldn't be any difficulty in sourcing what you want. Crossbred lambs by a terminal sire will be available first, and will cost more, but will fatten readily and give you a heavier carcass. Pure hill lambs come onto the market in the autumn, and will be much cheaper to buy. However, they may take longer to finish, will only produce small carcasses, and can be devils to keep within

bounds. Whichever you choose, remember that female lambs will finish more quickly, and may go over-fat if kept too long. Entire males may be difficult to fatten in late autumn, particularly if there are any ewes nearby. Mixed sex groups are best avoided, for obvious reasons. Wethers (castrated males) are a good bet, but not so many people cut their lambs nowadays, so you might have difficulty finding a suitable batch.

TIP

Commercially, most male lambs are left entire nowadays, as the modern taste is for a smaller carcass, meaning that the animals will be slaughtered before they reach sexual maturity. However, on a smallholding where traditional slower growing breeds may be kept for longer before slaughter, and where lack of space may make it difficult to segregate the sexes later in the year, it's generally better to castrate them.

BREEDS

The British Isles are home to a bewildering number of sheep breeds, both native and imported, together with any number of recognised crosses and composites. With over 80 different types to choose from, the wannabe flock owner is somewhat spoilt for choice. Breed societies' propaganda only adds to the confusion, as they all sound so convincing.

However, given that what we're talking about here is economically sustainable small-scale production, coupled with ease of handling and management, I think we can

narrow the field down to just six breeds from which the self-supporter should make his choice: Poll Dorset, Southdown, Ryeland, Llanwenog, Lleyn and Easycare. All of these breeds are suitable for crossing with a terminal sire (preferably a Charollais for ease of lambing) for prime lamb production, or can be bred pure.

Poll Dorset

The Poll Dorset can be used for very early lambing, producing a high value product for sale when prices peak at Easter, or for ensuring continuity of supply to satisfy private customers' requirements through frequent or 'out-of-season' lambing systems.

Southdown

The Southdown and the Ryeland are particularly well suited to fairly 'intensively managed' conventional spring lambing systems, or for moderately early lambing. Both of these breeds are very docile, and take readily to housing, handling and feeding, making them ideal for small-scale production.

Ryeland

Llanwenog

The Lleyn and the Llanwenog are true grassland breeds, most suited to lower-input systems. Their lambs may not grow so fast, or be ready for slaughter so soon, as those of the aforementioned breeds, but the costs incurred in producing them won't be so high. They'd be a good choice for the smallholder with a larger area of poorer land at his disposal, perhaps with inaccessible or rough fields that aren't really any good for anything other than 'extensive' grazing with sheep.

Lleyn

Of the five breeds already mentioned, the Southdown or the Ryeland will be of most interest to spinners and weavers, as they produce some of the finest fleeces of all the UK breeds, and both have recognised colour variants. On the other hand, the Easycare is a wool shedding composite breed that doesn't really produce a fleece at all, so is ideal where meat production is the sole aim. Both the Lleyn and the Poll Dorset have, at times past, been used as dairy animals, so we've got milk production covered in this list too. However, for economical dairying you'd really want to cross these breeds with a Friesland ram and keep the female offspring. Sheep milk production is discussed in more detail on pages 266 - 267.

GETTING STARTED

As with any livestock enterprise, the establishment of a new sheep flock is not something to be undertaken lightly. However, it's a sad fact that many people do embark on livestock keeping projects without really having given the matter full consideration, expecting that they'll pick up the necessary skills as they go along, which perhaps isn't very fair on the animals in question. The fact that sheep have a reputation for being able to largely look after themselves means that they're often the first animals on the holding to be neglected if things begin to get out of hand. A bit of forward planning could avoid potential welfare issues, and also considerably ease the workload of the amateur shepherd, making sheep keeping what it should be: rewarding and enjoyable.

Planning ahead

When you purchase other animals, such as pigs, goats or poultry, the chances are that you'll be housing them, or, in the case of poultry, restricting them to a small run, at least until they've had a chance to settle down and get used to you, and you to them. Sheep, on the other hand, are primarily a grazing species, so, as soon as you've given your new flock all the necessary health checks, you'll be turning them into an appropriate field. You're then immediately faced with two major concerns: firstly, will they stay where you've put them? And secondly, will you be able to catch them again when required? These worries (and many others) are largely alleviated by ensuring that you've planned ahead and made suitable preparations for your new venture:

• **Handling:** The ease with which you are able to move animals around the holding makes a big difference to the practicalities of running a small-scale sheep enterprise. Having all your land in one block, with centrally-sited handling facilities and / or buildings is the ideal scenario. If your farm is fragmented, with perhaps fields belonging to other landowners lying between fields of your own, or if it's bisected by public roads, then gathering the flock for routine tasks can become a major undertaking. Also, it becomes harder to regulate grazing pressure, as you can't simply open a gate to allow the flock access to two (or more) fields. Sheep kept on land away from the main holding are all too easily neglected when you're busy with other tasks, such as haymaking (which you'll inevitably carry out on the fields closest to home, in order to cut down on haulage costs), or if you have off-farm employment that results in you being away during daylight hours in winter. Under these circumstances you may not spot minor problems in time to prevent them becoming major ones. If you're intending to run a sheep enterprise across a scattered holding then remember to cost in extra equipment that you may need, such as a large livestock trailer and plenty of hurdles, or even a mobile handling system.

Also bear in mind that collecting all your sheep together for specific tasks at pre-set times (for example when a contractor has been booked for shearing or pregnancy scanning) is going to take a lot longer where the flock is split between several sites. You'll need to allow for this. Even if you only keep a very few sheep, if they're located away from your main holding or divided between locations, it'll require fairly careful planning to ensure that they are all in the most appropriate place at key times of year, particularly if you have other commitments, or if you keep other classes of livestock that are also dependant on the available grazing.

• **Fencing:** When we moved to Ty'n-y-Mynydd all the fencing on the farm was in an appalling state of repair. Now, nearly 20 years later, although some of it has been replaced, a lot of it is even worse. The thing is we keep sheep in order to make a living, so the flock has to generate sufficient revenue to provide us with an income before we can consider putting any funds aside for fencing work. Sheep farming hasn't been particularly profitable recently, so we've struggled along by patching up the existing boundaries. We've also wasted an awful lot of time fetching stray sheep. With the

wisdom of hindsight, my advice to anyone considering starting with sheep would be to sort the boundaries out first, even if it means dipping into your capital reserves. If your land is in a single block then you should at least ring-fence it before you buy any animals. Sub-divisions can then be repaired or installed as required, perhaps using electrified netting. (See pages 48 - 52 for information on installing and maintaining field boundaries.)

• **Housing:** It is of course possible (and perfectly acceptable) to keep sheep outdoors all year round. However, there are times when (as much for your own convenience as anything) it is a good idea to bring them in. In particular, on smaller holdings, housing the flock during part of the winter gives the land a much needed rest. Many smallholdings already have traditional outbuildings, but often these aren't really suitable for housing livestock (particularly sheep, which require plenty of ventilation). You'll need to consider an alternative. Building a new shed isn't always as costly as you might think, but if your smallholding is situated within a National Park or some similarly designated area, you may not be allowed to put up such a structure. For very small flocks you could consider using a mobile field shelter (which shouldn't require planning permission) or, on a larger scale, a polytunnel makes excellent temporary sheep housing. Temporary buildings should also be considered if you are a tenant grazier.

See pages 38 - 45 and 159 for detailed guidance on livestock housing requirements.

Equipment

Although much of the kit you'll need can be sourced as and when required, the following list contains a few fundamental items of equipment that I feel ought to be acquired before the new flock arrives on the holding. It'll make a big difference if you've got the essentials in place before you begin. Unfortunately, welfare and management standards on many smallholdings leave a lot to be desired, simply because the owners are ill-equipped for tackling even the most basic husbandry tasks.

Hurdles, hayracks and troughs

Hurdles: Hurdles are small, lightweight portable gates used to construct temporary pens for the containment of the flock, in order that routine activities (such as foot trimming) can be carried out. Generally they are around 6' long by 3' high, although various other sizes are available. Taller hurdles may be useful if you'll also be using them to pen goats, but, on the whole, the extra height is more of a hindrance than a help. You could, of course, make your own hurdles from sawn timber, or from naturally occurring materials, but in the first instance I'd strongly recommend the purchase of a few galvanised metal hurdles, just to get you started. Even if you'll only be keeping half-a-dozen sheep, 6-8 hurdles are the minimum requirement. In use, the cheaper types of metal hurdle are generally fastened to one another using simple loops at the top and bottom, but these rather unsatisfactory links always need to be reinforced with a couple of bits of string in order to prevent them coming apart at critical moments. Preferable by far (if slightly more expensive) are those that are joined together by means of a coupling rod. There's no need to buy particularly heavy-duty hurdles – lighter weight ones are infinitely more portable. Home-made hurdles are the sort of thing you can add to your inventory a few at a time, and can be tailor-made to suit the specific requirements of the job (e.g. individual lambing pens). Timber hurdles tend to be heavier and more cumbersome than their galvanised metal counterparts, so are more suited to applications where versatility is less of an issue.

Foot clippers: There are a range of different designs of hoof shear on the market, although, as is so often the case, the simplest are the best. CK manufacture a very good pair of all-metal foot clippers, available with either a plain or serrated blade. The serrated blade is preferable. The first pair I bought lasted more than 20 years, which represents pretty good value, I reckon. Light weight, plastic-handled clippers may be easier for shepherds with smaller hands, but they're not strongly made and don't last long.

Foot spray: Commonly known as 'purple spray', a general purpose foot care and cleansing spray can be used not only in the treatment and prevention of various hoof conditions, but for other minor cuts and abrasions too. I'd recommend that all new sheep arriving on the holding have their feet checked,

trimmed if necessary, and given a good squirt of spray before they even set foot on the grazing land. A 500ml can of purple spray is sufficient for quite a lot of hooves. Antibiotic sprays are available from your vet for the treatment of more serious complaints.

Dagging shears: Initially you'll need a small pair (3½" blades), simply for keeping the sheep's back ends clean and tidy (see page 220). If you decide to hand shear your sheep then you'll also need to buy a larger pair of shears (see pages 216 - 218)

Marker spray: As you get to know your sheep as individuals the need for marking will reduce, but, to begin with, you'll have a job to tell them all apart. Therefore, when carrying out initial healthcare tasks such as foot trimming and quarantine dosing, make sure you mark each sheep treated, in order that none are missed. A small, discreet spot will suffice. If you've purchased a mixed flock, with perhaps some ewes in-lamb (i.e. pregnant), it's a good idea to mark the different management categories in accordance with the information you've received from the vendor. By the time the marks fade you'll be able to recognise each animal anyway. It's also sensible to put some sort of flock mark on each sheep (ours all have a neat 3½" high blue 'T' stamped on one shoulder) in order that both you and your neighbours are able to quickly identify any escapees.

Marker sprays aren't cheap, so for small temporary marks a crayon is a more affordable option.

Hayracks or ring feeders: Given that the majority of sheep change hands in the autumn, it stands to reason that one of the earliest

A hayrack on wheels can easily be moved between fields.

requirements of the new flock is going to be supplementary feeding. Hayracks aren't difficult to construct from timber, but, as I mentioned earlier, heavy wooden articles may not be very portable. On the other hand, a galvanised metal hayrack on wheels can easily be moved with the flock from field to field, as you rotate your grazing. You might as well buy a big one (2.5 to 3 metres long), as the smaller models, sold as being suitable for smallholdings, are actually more expensive. Ring feeders (that can take a whole round bale of hay or silage) are a good choice if you want to keep your options open regarding the way in which you'll be feeding conserved forage. They're much cheaper, too. Second-hand hayracks and ring feeders crop up fairly often at farm dispersal sales.

You'll also need a few individual sized hayracks, in case you need to pen up a single sheep for any reason.

Feed troughs: Regardless of management requirements, you'll probably want to offer your new sheep a little bit of feed on a regular basis, in order that they come to know you. Feed troughs are one thing I'd definitely recommend that you make yourself, as purchased ones are rather expensive for what they are,

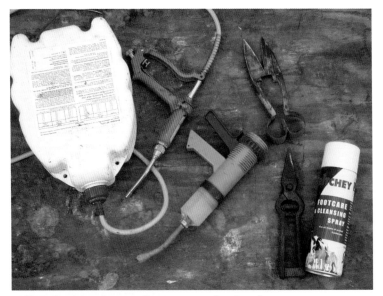

Some basic equipment: *Dosing guns, dagging shears, hoof clippers and foot spray.*

and are no less awkward to carry than their timber equivalent.

Dosing gun: All sheep coming onto the holding should be quarantine dosed on arrival, using two types of anthelmintic, in order to reduce the chances of introducing resistant parasites. Thereafter, you may not need to dose adult sheep against worms again (although this depends upon individual circumstances and the type of management regime you've adopted), but you probably will need to periodically dose against liver fluke. For large numbers of sheep it's best to have an automatic dosing gun which connects via a length of tubing to a pack of drench that can either be hung on a hurdle or worn like a rucksack. For smaller flocks it's possible to buy a single-dose drenching gun, which you refill from a suitable container between animals. Different sized nozzles are available for treating ewes and lambs. Never be tempted to administer oral medication to sheep using an ordinary syringe.

Syringes and needles: Regardless of what your sheep are kept for, they should be vaccinated against clostridial diseases (see page 226-227). An initial course of 2 injections is required (the first being given as soon as the sheep arrive on the holding, and the second 4-6 weeks later), with an annual booster thereafter (4-6 weeks pre-lambing, in the case of breeding sheep). You may also choose to use an injectable product as part of your quarantine dosing strategy, particularly as this will also control scab. Automatic syringes that have a mounting to hold a bottle of vaccine are very useful, and some even sterilise the needle between animals, but you'll need an assortment of ordinary syringes and needles for other purposes as well. Individual disposable syringes and needles can be purchased from your vet for a matter of pence, or you could buy a dedicated 'sheep pack', containing a selection of syringes and needles in a range of suitable sizes and gauges from an agricultural supplier. You should

also have a 'sharps' disposal bin, although any small tub with a lid will do, provided it's clearly labelled.

Raddle harness and crayon: As I've already mentioned, most sheep change hands in the autumn. Therefore, one of the first things in your flock diary is going to be tupping – the joining of the ram with the ewes for mating. To make management easier, it's normal practice to fit the ram with a raddle harness which holds a crayon in place on his chest. This then marks each ewe that he serves, enabling you to monitor his activity and to calculate when your lambs will be due.

Regular weighing is an important part of routine management.

Weigh crate: Regular weighing of growing livestock should be part of every stockman's regime, but most particularly in the case of anyone new to stock rearing. Without the benchmark of experience, the beginner has no other way of knowing whether his animals are thriving or not. On many occasions I've seen very poor examples of animal husbandry on smallholdings, where the owner was blissfully unaware that anything was amiss. Regular monitoring of weights, and comparing the results with target figures, would have identified the problem at a very early stage, enabling management practices to be amended before welfare became an issue.

Sourcing stock

It stands to reason that everyone who keeps sheep has to buy a few in at some point, even if only to get started in the first place. For many people, regular buying is the norm, perhaps because they've got a system that depends upon fattening batches of bought-in store lambs before selling them on. For others it's just a once a year occurrence, when ewes are purchased in order to replace any that have died or been culled from the flock over the past twelve months. In closed flocks (i.e. where all replacement females are home-bred) the only purchases will be rams, which, for small flocks, may mean as little as one every two to three years.

Here in the UK, most sales of breeding sheep take place in the autumn, although due to the diversity of breeds found in this country, and the corresponding diversity of management systems, the season actually extends from late summer right through to early November. Outside of this main period there are also sales of in-lamb ewes during the winter, and ewe and lamb couples in the spring (although these may be available any time from January to late May). Also, ewes suitable for early lambing may be sold in mid summer, in time for sponging to lamb at Christmas.

Unless you've opted for a specific breed not commonly found in your area, most requirements can be met through the local auction mart. The majority of livestock markets will hold weekly sales of store and breeding sheep throughout the autumn, where, depending on your locality, there'll be a whole range of commercial cross-bred and pure hill ewes on offer, and rams too. For most smallholders getting started with sheep, this is as good a place to begin as any. However, if you've chosen to keep a rare or traditional breed then you may have to travel further afield, to an official show and sale organised by the relevant society.

The more popular native breeds may hold several sales each year, in different regions, but in many cases there'll be just one, often held in the heartland of the breed's origins. In addition, there are a few multi-species rare breed sales organised by the RBST, and some livestock markets do organise their own collective rare breed or 'smallholder' events (although at these sales you're more likely to find unregistered stock, so, if you're looking for pedigree sheep, do check the details of the various lots before bidding).

At auction, rams and other male breeding livestock are customarily sold in guineas, a guinea being £1.05p. Don't forget to factor this into your budget or you could have a nasty shock when you go to pay for your purchase and find he's cost you a bit more than you thought he had.

If you're establishing a pedigree enterprise and prefer to buy 'off farm' rather than through the ring, avoid the temptation to source all your stock from one breeder, no matter how reputable he may be. It is better, I think, to shop around a bit to ensure a broad genetic base to your new flock.

One problem with buying sheep through a livestock market is that they may be sold in batches containing far more animals than you actually need. You could, of course, simply buy the whole lot and then re-enter the ones you don't want at the next weekly sale, but that's perhaps a bit risky. A better option would be to find a livestock dealer who's prepared to buy them all and then sell you the few that have caught your eye. The auctioneer will be able to recommend someone, so make sure you allow time to have a chat with him before the sale. However, you can expect to have to pay the dealer a little bit more than what they fetched in the ring – it is, after all, him that's taking the risk.

Older ewes, which are cheaper to buy than young ones, are generally the best option for beginners. They are far less likely to give you problems at lambing time, and may well have developed immunity to some of the health problems that beset younger sheep. Genuine 4-year-olds (e.g. draft ewes from a big hill flock) are always a good buy, but of course, once a sheep gets to four years old it is 'full mouthed', so it's no longer possible to accurately determine its age by examining its teeth.

Therefore you have to take the vendor's word for it. Really old sheep, or 'brokers' that have lost a few teeth, can be bought very cheaply, and with individual care and attention may give several more years of good service on a smallholding. The most expensive will be shearlings, ready to put to the ram for the first time. Two-shear ewes I would be very wary of – this is not an age at which people usually sell sheep, so it makes me think there may be some problem with them, such as a poor udder, which has resulted in them being culled early.

Grazing and feeding

A reasonable starting point for the average smallholding would be an overall stocking rate of 3-4 ewes per acre. Routine applications of manure or fertilizer could see the figure rise to 6 ewes per acre and / or enable some fields to be closed off for the production of hay or silage.

Generally, sheep will consume 1 to 1.5 kg of hay per day for a minimum of six weeks prior to lambing, although on a smallholding it may be better to start feeding a bit sooner than that, in order to give the land a rest. If your sheep are lambing fairly early in the spring (i.e. before late March) it might also be necessary to feed some hay after lambing. Probably you should expect to have a period of at least 10 weeks (maybe 12) each year when it'll be necessary to provide supplementary forage to all or part of the flock. As a rough guide, 30 ewes will eat more than one, but less than two small bales per day. When buying in, allow 3-4 bales per ewe per year.

Concentrate feeding usually begins about 6 weeks before lambing, with the amount being dependent on the size of the ewe, the number of lambs she's carrying, and when her lambs are due. For example, during the last two weeks of gestation a medium-sized ewe is going to need 0.45kg of feed per day if she's carrying a single lamb, or 0.6kg per day if she's expecting twins.

THE SHEPHERD'S CALENDAR

Although I've suggested a number of alternative management regimes, the majority of smallholders do adopt a conventional approach. Therefore, the seasonal husbandry requirements of the sheep flock, as given here, relate to a spring lambing system. For other systems the basic tasks are largely the same, although the timing of some will vary.

Autumn

The shepherding year traditionally begins in early autumn, when the flock is made ready for mating. All ewes should be treated for internal and external parasites, and given any trace element supplementation that they require, to ensure that they go to the ram in tip-top condition. Any lameness also needs to be dealt with. It goes without saying that the ram also needs to be in fit, healthy condition, so don't leave it till the last minute before giving him the once over. Ideally, he should be subjected to a full 'M.O.T' 8-10 weeks before his services are required. The exact date that you put the ram in with the ewes will depend upon when you want to

Tips for tighter tupping

• Sort ewes into groups according to body condition score as soon as the previous year's lambs are weaned. Any really thin ewes may need a bit of supplementary feeding, and very fat ewes will need to go on a diet.
• Move ewes onto better pasture a fortnight before introducing the rams.
• Treat as appropriate for internal and external parasites, and attend to any lameness.
• Administer trace element supplementation, and provide licks containing high levels of phosphorus.
• Run vasectomised 'teaser' rams with the ewes for 12-14 days before introducing the fertile tups.
• Always use raddle crayons on the rams, and change the colour after a fortnight.
• Act quickly to replace any ram that's not performing.
• Restrict the overall tupping period to a maximum of 5 weeks.
• Record not only the date that the ram went in, but also the date that you took him out, so you can calculate the full extent of the forthcoming lambing period.
• Keep ewes on good pasture (with supplementary blocks if necessary) for the first month after tupping (i.e. until at least a fortnight after the ram has been removed, by which time the majority of the flock will be more than a month into their pregnancies).
• Consider sponging ewes for greater control and synchronisation.

Use of a raddle harness enables tupping to be monitored, and the expected lambing date to be calculated.

start lambing, so work that out first then count back 147 days. This means that for a March lambing flock you'll be putting the ram in in October.

Good husbandry leading up to, and during, tupping will result in a much more compact mating period, which simplifies winter management of the flock and ultimately makes your life easier at lambing time.

Each oestrus cycle in the ewe lasts for 17 days, consisting of 1-2 days when she is 'on heat' or 'in season', and will allow the ram to mate her, followed by 15 days when she will not. If she isn't mated during the heat period (or if mating was unsuccessful), the ewe will continue to come on heat at 17 day intervals throughout the breeding season. This is known as repeating. If repeat matings also fail, then the ewe will remain barren. When a significant number of ewes are seen to be repeating then there is clearly a problem with the ram.

Winter

During the early part of the winter, once tupping is over and the ram has been removed, the flock's requirements are minimal. Give them a dose against liver fluke if necessary, then put them to graze on some of your poorer land, saving the best for later. Supplementary feeding shouldn't be necessary at this stage, although you might need to provide a bit of extra grub if there's snow on the ground.

TIP

The raddle marks on the ewes' backsides may fade away before the spring, so to avoid mix-ups later it's a good idea to re-mark the ewes now, using something more permanent.

Scanning: For a March lambing flock, pregnancy scanning can be carried out in early January. This is cheap (less than 50p per ewe around here, although small flock owners may have to pay a minimum callout fee), quick and painless, and is one of the

most useful aids to good flock management.

The scanning will determine the number of lambs each ewe is carrying, and identify any empties. This then enables you to manage the flock according to the ewes' nutritional requirements. Otherwise any feeding is simply guesswork, and just as likely to be wrong as right. Appropriate supplementation not only reduces the chances of metabolic disorders in late gestation (such as pregnancy toxaemia / twin lamb disease, which is usually fatal), but also cuts down the risk of difficult births and / or non-viable lambs.

One of the commonest causes of trouble during the birthing process comes from oversize single lambs born to ewes that received an inappropriately high level of feeding for the number of lambs they were carrying. Conversely, twin- or multiple-bearing ewes that are underfed may give birth to very small, weak lambs and produce only limited amounts of poor quality colostrum. The cost, in both time and effort, and money, of keeping these lambs alive and subsequently rearing them may be considerable, and all could have been avoided by the simple outlay of 50p per ewe. You'll also save a lot of bother by not having to feed or house the barreners.

Directly after scanning the flock can be split into groups according to the number of lambs each ewe is carrying. The singles still won't need any additional feed at this stage, but the twins will benefit from being moved to a better field, and they may need to be provided with blocks and / or a small quantity of nuts each day, if the weather's bad or you're particularly short of grass.

Sheep should be fed concentrates in troughs, not on the ground. Supplementary feeding may be required earlier than usual if there's snow on the ground.

Feeding: Concentrate feeding usually begins some 6 weeks before the first lambs are due, with hay or silage being offered a week or two earlier, depending on the weather. High nutrient density feed blocks are another way of supplementing in-lamb ewes, although regulating intake is difficult.

Hay or silage can be offered more-or-less ad lib, in racks or ring feeders, but concentrates should be rationed. If everything's going to plan then nothing could be simpler: having used the scanning results to sort the flock according the number of lambs carried, you can now use the raddle colours on the ewes' backsides to further sub-divide them into early and late lambers. Feed concentrates to each group in accordance with the recommendations given in table 7, page 446.

Vaccination: All in-lamb ewes will need their annual booster against clostridial diseases to be given 4-6 weeks prior to

lambing. This consists of an easily administered subcutaneous 2ml injection. Any previously unvaccinated sheep will need two injections, given 4-6 weeks apart, with the second jab being 4-6 weeks before lambing. The ram and any non-breeding sheep on the holding should be given a booster too. Clostridial vaccines can usually be purchased from an agricultural supplier, but in the case of very small flocks it might be possible to buy just the quantity you require, in a syringe, from your vet.

There are other vaccinations that your flock may need, but now is not the time to administer them.

Housing: Despite the recent trend towards low-input outdoor lambing systems, I think it's best for small flock owners to house their sheep for lambing. In fact, I'd suggest bringing them in fairly early – maybe as much as 4 weeks before they're due to give birth. It could be done in conjunction with gathering the flock for vaccinating.

When providing supplementary concentrate feed for sheep outdoors, always place it in troughs, not on the ground. As soon as they've finished eating, turn all the troughs over to keep them dry, prevent contamination, and eliminate the risk of a heavily pregnant ewe getting stuck on her back in one. If you roll the troughs over the same way every day then they'll gradually move along the field, so you won't end up with a badly poached area.

Don't feed sheep (or other animals) close to the field gateway or they'll always be hanging around the entrance, making access extremely difficult, particularly if you're carrying a heavy bag of feed or a bale of hay.

Quite apart from the fact that it must be much more comfortable for the sheep than standing about in the wind and the rain, it can remove a lot of the anxiety felt by novice shepherds – no longer do you have to trudge about the fields in the dark; there's no more worries about catching any ewe in need of assistance; routine tasks such as feeding and re-filing hayracks cease to be a battle against the elements and, above all, it makes it a pleasure to be with the sheep at any hour of the day or night.

Housing for sheep needn't be elaborate. A simple pole-barn built from reclaimed materials is ideal. However, at the design stage do give some thought to how you're going to muck it out (e.g. make the roof high enough to allow access with a tractor and loader), and what other uses the building may

Calcium deficiency and twin lamb disease

To the inexperienced eye, these two conditions are easily confused. Unless the early signs of pregnancy toxaemia (twin lamb disease – caused by an energy deficit in late pregnancy, and usually affecting ewes expecting multiple births) are spotted, which include excitability, 'star gazing', and a high stepping gait, then the chances are you'll simply be faced with an animal that's down and semi-comatose. The immediate course of action is to treat as for calcium deficiency, so administer 80ml of calcium borogluconate by subcutaneous injection. Divide the quantity between several sites. Ewes suffering from hypocalcaemia will respond very quickly to this treatment, and may well be up and about within 20 minutes. Twin lamb disease is more serious, so if there's no significant response to the aforementioned treatment then I'm afraid the outlook is poor. Affected ewes will require high energy drinks and careful nursing, but if they've reached the stage where they stop eating then the condition is usually fatal. Ewes that abort their lambs stand a better chance of survival, so you might consider asking your vet to induce labour in order to remove the foetal load.

Although there are alternatives, such as woodchips, rushes or bracken, straw is the most popular bedding material for use under housed sheep. However, while crisp yellow straw does make the pens look beautifully fresh and clean, the effect will be short lived. This type of straw is not very absorbent, so really isn't much use as animal bedding. What you really need is the grey, crumbly, broken straw of the sort that often comes from a badly weathered cereal crop. It may not look so attractive, but it'll keep your sheep much cleaner and drier, which, after all, is the aim of the exercise.

be put to at other times of year. Also remember to allow sufficient additional space for individual lambing pens.

Ideally you should bring the flock in on a bright and breezy day, when their fleeces are completely dry, and once they're in they should stay in until they've lambed. Provide fresh bedding regularly in the form of clean straw or dried rushes or bracken, and feed good quality hay or silage in addition to the required ration of concentrates.

Spring

With lambing time rapidly approaching, the ewes are seen to be 'bagging up' (i.e. their udders are filling with milk) – a sure sign that everything is proceeding according to plan. However, they're entering a critical period – the last few weeks of gestation – when feed intake alone may not be enough to meet the demands of their rapidly developing lambs, and they begin to mobilise their body reserves. It will help to stimulate appetite if you divide the daily ration into several smaller feeds, and you must remain vigilant for any signs

of pregnancy toxaemia (twin lamb disease) or hypocalcaemia (calcium deficiency). Keep stress to a minimum at all costs, so avoid unnecessary handling of the flock.

The presence of ketones produces a characteristic smell of pear drops on the breath of ewes suffering from pregnancy toxaemia.

The presence of ketones produces a characteristic smell of pear drops on the breath of ewes suffering from pregnancy toxaemia.

Ewes suffering from hypocalcaemia look like they've toppled over forwards, whereas those affected with pregnancy toxaemia appear to have slumped backwards.

Newly lambed ewes are confined in individual pens for a day or so.

Individual pens: At some point before the first lambs are due you need to set up individual pens, ready to accommodate newly-lambed ewes and their offspring. In the case of outdoor lambing flocks, if there's no suitable building nearby, then small huts may be built in the field using straw bales and other bits and pieces, with each hut being of a suitable size

Lambing time equipment check list

Together with time and patience, the following list of equipment should be enough to cover you in almost any eventuality:

• Disposable shoulder length obstetric gloves.
• Lubricating gel.
• Thermovite (a high energy colostrum-based paste).
• Bactakil (for spraying navels).
• Lambing aids (lambing ropes x 3, plus a 1 metre length of plastic coated clothes line, tied into a loop).
• Calcium borogluconate, penicillin, oxytetracycline and glucose solution.
• Appropriate syringes and needles.
• Prolapse restrainer.
• Dagging shears, hoof clippers and foot spray.
• Tailing rings and applicator (only required for certain breeds).
• Stomach tube, bottles and teats, powdered milk and colostrum, mixing jug and whisk.
• Heat lamp.
• Spray markers.
• Notebook and pencil.
• A copy of *The Sheep Book for Smallholders* (ISBN 978190487-1644).

Ewes housed for lambing.

to contain a ewe and her lambs for the first day or so after birth. Generally though, individual pens will be constructed under cover using either purchased or home-made hurdles. I'd recommend that you erect at least one pen for every 6 ewes due to lamb. Each pen should be about 1.4m², and needs to be equipped with a water bucket and hayrack. Pannier style hayracks are handy for this, as each one will service two adjacent pens. Between occupants, the bedding in each pen should be dusted with hydrated lime, and a fresh layer of straw put down.

Lambing: Sheep are generally quite capable of giving birth unaided – they've been doing it for thousands of years, and know much more about the job than you or I. Even if labour seems to be unduly prolonged, a bit more time and patience usually results in a natural delivery. Young ewes may quite normally take several hours to give birth, particularly if they're expecting a big single lamb. However, at times things do

Sheep are generally quite capable of giving birth unaided.

go wrong, and some intervention may be required. One of the most important things is for you to be aware of your own limitations – if something falls outside the scope of your capabilities then don't be afraid to admit it, and seek professional assistance. Don't go fumbling around inside the poor ewe for ages, expecting enlightenment, or you'll seriously compromise the chances of a successful outcome.

During a normal birth, after the water bag has broken, the first things to put in an appearance are the lamb's two front hooves, closely followed by the tip of his nose. Provided that this is what you can see then all is well, even if the delivery seems to be taking a long time. However, the absence of one or all of these things, or the appearance of hind feet or a tail at the vulva, are clear indications that there is a problem.

It's fairly easy to tell the difference between a lamb's front feet and its hind feet when they're visible at the vulva. In the case of front feet, the hoof tips point upwards, and on hind feet they point down. If you can't see the hooves, and you're trying to identify fore and hind limbs by touch inside the ewe, then just remember that in hind legs the first and second joints (the pastern and the hock) bend in opposite directions, and in the case of front legs the two joints (the fetlock and the knee) bend the same way.

Problem solving: Putting aside for a moment the possibility that you're faced with several lambs trying to exit at the same time (the scanning results will at least give you a clue here), there are two basic scenarios: either the lamb is coming forwards, or he's coming backwards. Then there are various permutations of these two situations, so, for example, he could be coming forwards but with his head turned back, or he could be backwards but with only one leg (or perhaps only his tail) presented.

Always use shoulder length obstetric gloves and plenty of lubricant, even for relatively minor internal examination

Your task is, firstly, to identify the parts of the lamb that are presented, and secondly to locate the 'missing' parts, and align them with those already present, in order that the delivery can proceed. You can't carry out any manipulation with the lamb in the birth canal, so it's necessary to push it right back into the uterus before attempting to correct the presentation. It helps if you first attach lambing ropes to those parts of the lamb that you've already managed to identify, just so that you don't lose track of them. Once the lamb has been returned to the relative comfort of the womb then, using your pre-placed lambing ropes for guidance, location of the missing parts should be fairly straightforward. Attach ropes to these, too, if necessary, and gently manoeuvre the lamb into the correct position. In the case of a forward presentation, once the lamb is lying correctly then, provided that the ewe isn't too exhausted, she'll probably push it out herself, with perhaps just a little bit of help from you. However, where the lamb is coming backwards it must be delivered hind feet first, and there is a need for some haste if the lamb is to be prevented from drowning in the birth fluids. Therefore it is up to you to draw the lamb out in one smooth, rapid movement.

Never attempt to turn around a lamb that's coming backwards; it must be delivered hind feet first.

Following a posterior delivery, some difficulty may be experienced in persuading the lamb to take his first breath, on account of the amount of fluid he'll inevitably have inhaled. You'll need to dangle him by the hind legs for a while, and maybe swing him about a bit, or you could also try poking a piece of straw up his nostrils or squirting cold water in his ear – these old tricks really do work!

Where a problem is caused by two (or more) lambs coming together, you'll be relieved to hear that the fear is always worse than the reality. Due to the small size of twins and triplets, multiple mix-ups are usually fairly easy to resolve, and, once the lambs are correctly positioned, the delivery is generally quick and uncomplicated.

Following any particularly complex assisted delivery, the ewe should be given an injection of long acting antibiotic, and possibly an anti-inflammatory / pain killer.

After the birth: First and foremost, you must just leave the new family undisturbed for a few minutes, to ensure that the ewe forms a strong bond with her offspring. Next, spray the lambs' navels with 'Bactakil' or iodine solution, and check that the ewe has sufficient colostrum (the first milk, rich in essential anti-bodies). Provide the lamb with an alternative, via stomach tube, if she hasn't. We also trim

Leave the new family undisturbed for a few minutes to ensure that the ewe forms a strong bond with her offspring.

away the wool from the ewe's tail at this stage, and clip her hooves, but you might prefer to leave these tasks until turnout in a day or two. The ewe and her lambs are then placed in one of the individual pens, where they remain under close observation for at least 24 hours. Then, provided all is well, they can be turned out to the field. If your chosen breed is one that customarily has its tail docked then now is the time to apply rubber rings to the lambs, and you should also give a combined fluke and worm drench to the ewe before she goes back to pasture. Spray matching numbers on the sides of the ewe and her offspring, so that you can easily pair them up on the field.

Stomach tubing step-by-step

1. Colostrum replacement powder, together with clean mixing utensils, should always be on hand at lambing time. It also helps to have a supply of hot water in the lambing area, or in an outhouse, so you can reconstitute the powder immediately it's required.

2. Read the mixing instructions carefully, and follow them to the letter. Not all brands are the same, so don't just assume you already know because of what you did last time. If in doubt, err on the side of caution, and mix it up a little bit 'runnier' than suggested. The label on the product pack should also include information on how much to feed, and how often.

3. Ensure that the colostrum is thoroughly mixed, with no powdery bits or lumps remaining, and is at the right temperature. The beauty of using powdered colostrum is that it's reliable, and always available when you need it. However, you could milk some off the ewe (if she's got enough), or keep frozen goat's colostrum in stock as an alternative. Only use cow's colostrum as a last resort, as occasionally it contains an anti-ovine factor, which, if present, will kill your lambs.

4. This may seem a trivial matter, but do ensure that you put the jug of colostrum in a safe place, easily to hand but where it can't be knocked over or trodden on by a flighty ewe. This is particularly pertinent if, in the absence of an alternative, you've painstakingly milked some off the ewe – it's precious stuff, and you can't afford to waste it. I like to use these jugs with open handles, because they can be securely hooked into the upright of a metal hurdle (or over the top rail of a wooden one), out of harm's way yet well within my reach.

5. With my left leg raised by placing my foot on one of the lower rails of the hurdle (or on a straw bale) I place the lamb across my thigh, holding him against my body with my left forearm, with his head cupped in my left hand.

6. Before inserting the tube I always lubricate the tip by dipping it in the jug of colostrum. It's important to note that any lamb that's too weak to hold up its head shouldn't be tubed (or bottle fed). Under these circumstances it's necessary to inject warmed glucose solution directly into the body cavity. It's well worth getting your vet to show you how to do this. Any hypothermic lamb which is more than 5 hours old **must** be provided with a source of energy (either by stomach tube or by intraperitoneal injection) before any attempt is made to restore its body temperature to the correct level (39-40°C). Failure to observe this simple rule will almost invariably result in a death.

7. I start by gently inserting the tube into the corner of the lamb's mouth, and over the back of its tongue. Notice that I've removed the plunger from the syringe part of the stomach tube. In fact, I've thrown it away. It's totally unnecessary, and shouldn't be used.

8. I steadily pass almost the whole length of the tube down the lamb's throat, until the end is correctly located in his stomach. If the tube should happen to go down 'the wrong way' (which is what most people worry about, and quite rightly so) then the lamb will show obvious signs of discomfort, so you will know to pull out the tube and start again. I have found that a tube length of about 14" is best. If it's any longer than this it becomes awkward to use, and inclined to kink.

9. When the tube is properly inserted, approximately 12"-13" will be inside the lamb. If it doesn't go in that far then it's not in the right place. (Although use

your judgement a bit here – clearly it's not going to go in quite so far in a really tiny lamb). The lamb actually looks quite comfortable, and may be chewing or trying to suck the pipe. Obviously don't proceed beyond this point until you're confident that everything is as it should be.

10. Now I change my grip on the lamb so that I can also hold the syringe part of the stomach tube with my left hand, and I begin to slowly pour the required amount of colostrum into the open end. It really isn't difficult.

11. Allow the colostrum to flow slowly down the tube, at its own speed. Don't be tempted to hurry it along by using the plunger. If it stops flowing just rotate the tube slightly, or withdraw it by half an inch or so.

12. When the full dose has been administered I always pinch the tube as I withdraw it, to ensure that any fluid remaining in the pipe doesn't cause the lamb to choke as I pull it out.

13. Well fed now, and warm, but not at all satisfied – this lamb can be immediately returned to his mother, where he'll continue his attempts to suckle.

Bottle feeding: Inevitably, in some years there'll be some lambs that need to be artificially reared. We use a powdered ewe milk replacer for this (which should always be mixed up slightly weaker than the instructions on the bag suggest), although goat's milk is ideal if you've got an adequate supply.

A moderate sized lamb is going to need in the region of 1 litre of milk in each 24 hour period. Initially, this should be divided equally into 6 evenly spaced feeds,

but the frequency of feeding can soon be reduced to four feeds of 250ml each. By the time lambs are a week old the total amount of milk fed may need to be increased to as much as 1.5 litres per day. At the earliest opportunity, reduce the level of inconvenience by getting lambs onto a cold ad-lib feeding system. This simply consists of a couple of teats mounted on a back plate, which is fixed to the side of the pen. A pipe, fitted with a non-return valve, runs from behind each teat into a lidded bucket, which you fill with a whole day's supply of milk. Lambs will naturally adopt a 'little and often' feeding routine, and are much healthier as a result. Offer high quality creep pellets from the very start, and provide either coarse hay or leafy barley straw to stimulate good rumen function. It goes without saying that fresh, clean water should be available at all times.

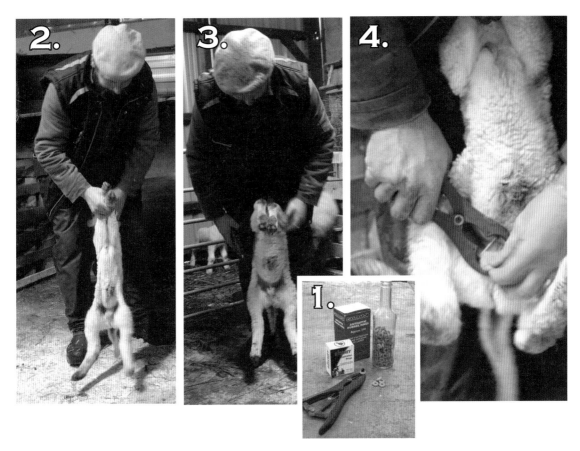

Wean artificially-reared lambs as soon as is practically possible. The first step in the weaning process is to further reduce the concentration of reconstituted milk, or, if whole goat's milk is being used, water it down quite considerably.

TIP

Whenever possible, a 'spare' lamb should be fostered onto another ewe, thus avoiding all the hassle and expense of artificial rearing. Initially, any spare lambs should be fed by stomach tube, in order that they don't get too attached to their two-legged 'parent'. Bottle feeding should be seen as a last resort, if suitable foster mothers aren't found within a day or two.

Tailing and castration

1. The equipment consists of 'elastrator' applicator pliers and rubber rings. After placing the ring on the pliers, give it a little twist, or it'll ping off when you squeeze the handles.

2. Traditional practice is to castrate lambs before docking the tails. Then, if for any reason castration isn't possible (e.g. if the testicles are undescended), the tail can be left as a visual reminder that the lamb still needs attention. This is far more reliable than either a paint mark or memory. I start by picking the lamb up by its forelegs and pushing its head back between my thighs.

3. With its head and neck high up between my legs, the lamb is held gently but firmly, with its body hanging down in front of my knees, belly outermost.

4. While using the applicator to place the ring around the lamb's scrotum I use my other hand to check that both testicles are present and correct. If they can't be felt then gently pushing in with the pliers will usually cause them to appear. Make sure they don't disappear again as the applicator is closed.

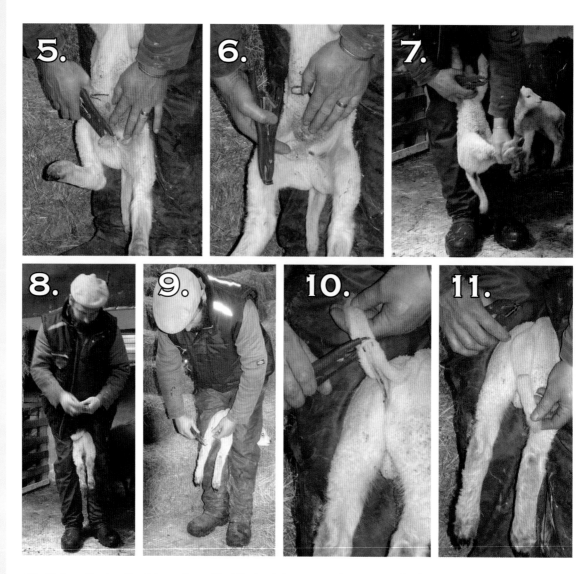

5. Before slipping the tightened ring off the applicator it's important to check that the rudimentary teats aren't trapped beneath it.

6. With this part of the job completed, we move on to the tail.

7. Reaching down, I take hold of the lamb's hind legs. Then, in one smooth sequence of movements, I let go with my thighs, swing the lamb forward, turn him over, and swing him back up between my legs.

8. The lamb is now gently gripped just in front of his hips by my legs (above my knees). He's 'right way up', and his tail is visible and accessible.

9. Using the applicator I place a ring on the tail at the point that experience tells me is right.

10. Before removing the ring from the pliers, a quick look under the tail confirms that it's positioned correctly – just where the area of bare skin ends and the wool begins.

11. Job done! The whole process is a 'one person' task, taking only a mater of moments from start to finish.

If castration has been carried out, don't be surprised if the lamb shows signs of discomfort for quarter of an hour or so. For this reason, avoid turning out ewes and lambs immediately after ringing, and be careful that one doesn't roll under a hurdle into the next pen.

Very short tail
docking – as seen on
this ewe – is illegal.
Sufficient tail must
be left to cover the
anus and vulva.

TIP

Very short tail
docking – as seen on
this ewe – is illegal.
Sufficient tail must
be left to cover the
anus and vulva.

TIP

Orf (contagious pustular
dermatitis) is transmissible to
humans, so take appropriate
precautions when handling
infected animals.

you're handling them, you can
take the opportunity to apply the
regulation eartags (see Statutory
Requirements, page 440)

Early summer

For the first 8 weeks or so, it's best
to graze ewes and lambs in small
groups, dotted around the holding.
Ideally, keep singles and twins
separate from one another, too.
During this period, remain vigilant
for any post-lambing problems that
might develop, and be prepared
to bring in anything that's not
thriving as it should. Early spring-
born lambs might benefit from
the introduction of a little creep
feed, and in some years it may be
necessary to provide additional
supplementary feeding for the
ewes as well. Either way, make
sure that they have access to feed
blocks containing high levels of
magnesium. Magnesium deficiency
tends to occur at times of rapid
grass growth, and ewes in milk are
particularly susceptible.

Keep an eye open for signs of
orf – a viral infection that causes
blisters and sores around the
mouths and hooves of animals that
haven't previously been exposed
to the disease. Treat the lesions
with topical sprays, and maybe
administer antibiotics in order to
keep secondary infection under
control: lambs that contract orf
early in life don't seem to suffer

as badly as those that get it later,
but the risk is that they'll spread
the infection to the ewe's udders,
leading to mastitis. If you regularly
experience problems associated
with orf in your flock, consider
vaccinating all lambs at around
3-4 weeks of age (see pages 226
- 227).

Another thing that may affect
young lambs in early summer
is coccidiosis. Most usually
associated with intensive livestock
husbandry, this disease (which
causes a nasty bloodstained
diarrhoea and ill thrift) can be a
problem on smallholdings due
to lack of alternative grazing –
repeatedly using the same fields,
year after year, to accommodate
ewes with young lambs, results
in a steady build-up of pasture
contamination. Where coccidiosis
is an issue, lambs can be a given
a drench that both treats and
prevents, or medicated feeds can
be provided.

By the time the lambs are eight
weeks old the main risk period is
over. At this point the flock can
be merged into larger groups, and
moved onto the land that you've
reserved for summer grazing.
First, though, the lambs should
be given a worm dose, and, while

Mid summer

During the mid summer grazing
period, management of the flock is
relatively uncomplicated. Lambs
may need to be dosed again against
internal parasites, particularly if
any are seen to be scouring, and
precautionary measures must be
taken against fly-strike – clip away
any soiled wool around the back
ends of the lambs, and apply a
preventative spray to the whole
lot. Failure to do this may result
in the blow-fly laying its eggs
on dirty areas of the fleece, and
the resultant maggots, when they
hatch, will quite literally eat your
lambs alive. Not nice.

Ewes in full fleece are also very
susceptible to fly-strike, but once
shorn they're relatively safe.
Unless you've opted for one of the
few wool-less breeds, shearing the
flock is the principal mid summer
husbandry task.

Clostridial vaccination of lambs:
Lambs born in late March / early
April should be given their first
clostridial injection when you
gather the flock for shearing,
followed by the second jab 4-6
weeks later. Early spring-born
lambs will need to be vaccinated
a little sooner, so you should be
aiming to give the second jab at
shearing time. All lambs should

be vaccinated, even those that will ultimately end up going for slaughter. Any female lambs that are retained for breeding should then receive a booster at the same time as giving the ewes their pre-lambing vaccination, and annually thereafter.

Late summer

As we move into late summer, the lambs' dependence on their mothers' milk diminishes, and it's time to wean them. In fact, if you've been creep feeding the lambs then you'll be able to wean them much earlier than this. Weaning simply involves separating the ewes from their lambs. Ideally you remove the ewes to somewhere out of earshot (if they're very milky you might need to house them for a while to dry off, otherwise just put them in a fairly bare paddock), leaving the lambs in the field to which they're already accustomed. Once they've settled down you can move the lambs to some really good pasture for fattening, such as the aftermaths from your hay or silage making. It's a good idea to handle and weigh the lambs at this point, as there may be some that are ready for slaughter already. Any lambs that aren't fit for sale now probably ought to have another worm dose, and also a trace element drench. Having sold the best, in order to pay the bills, the poorer animals are the ones to grow on slowly for home consumption, to kill as mutton when they're a couple of years old.

The ewes, once their milk has dried off, should be sorted into groups according to body condition. Some of the thinner ones may need a little extra feed to ensure that they regain sufficient

Selecting lambs for slaughter.

Forward creep grazing

Forward creep grazing fits in very well with a rotational system of grazing management. Basically, the lambs are allowed access to the next paddock in the cycle via a pop-hole or 'creep'. By this means, the lambs always get first choice of what's on offer. In early-lambing flocks this also provides an opportunity to push the lambs on a bit with some trough feed. Forward creep grazing is more difficult to manage later in the season, after shearing – by this time the lambs should be well grown, thus requiring a fair sized pop-hole, and newly-shorn ewes are adept at squeezing through small spaces, particularly when the grass really is greener on the other side.

condition by tupping time, and a few fat ewes might need to be thinned down a bit.

Selection of lambs for slaughter: Before you start, it's important that you're aware of the requirements of your customers – whether this be private sales to friends and family, or commercial sales to an abattoir – and that you appreciate the variation between different breeds and management systems. It also helps if you are used to handling your sheep on a regular basis, and, as mentioned before, I strongly recommend that you invest in a weigh crate.

As a general rule of thumb, the dressed carcass will weigh approximately 45% of the animal's live weight (although this can vary considerably between breeds and at different times of year). Therefore, if you know that your buyer is looking for carcass weights in the range 12-14kg (for example), you can start drawing lambs from about 27kg liveweight. We have found that this weight range suits direct marketing of whole boxed lamb to private customers. In the case of heavier breeds it may be more appropriate to market half lamb boxes, in which case aim for carcass weights of 18-22kg. For conventional sales (e.g. through a livestock market or direct to abattoir) it's probably best to draw lambs at 32kg liveweight and upwards, although there are variations in seasonal requirements, with smaller carcasses (8-11kg) in demand early on, for export, and much heavier (50kg liveweight) lambs selling better around Christmas and new year.

Only ever keep the very best home-bred sheep as flock replacements.

Once you've picked out a group of lambs within the right weight bracket you can go through them and choose the ones with the required degree of finish. The modern taste is for a lean carcass, and many beginners are surprised by how 'thin' a prime lamb feels. The correct method of selection is fairly similar to body condition scoring of ewes, although in addition to handling the lambs over the loin you'll also need to feel the dock and over the ribcage. All the individual bones of the loin will be discernable, although they'll feel smooth and rounded. The ribcage should have a firm covering of muscle, but no rolls of soft fat. The last place to flesh out on a fattening lamb is the dock (base of the tail), so here the individual vertebrae should be easily felt. If you cannot feel the gaps between these bones then the animal is too fat.

When you send lambs to the abattoir, each carcass will be classified according to its fat cover and conformation. It's very helpful to obtain a print-out of the grades of each batch, as it will give you a clearer idea of whether you're making an appropriate selection. If you sell through a live market you could ask the grader there to give you some guidance.

Selection of home-bred flock replacements: Having bred your own lambs, it's understandable that you might want to keep some on to increase the size of the flock, or to replace any ewes that have come to the end of their productive lives. However, on a very small acreage this may not be the most economical course of action; it might actually work out cheaper to buy in any additional animals that you require, in the form of mature ewes. One reason for this is that, in many cases it's not appropriate to put female lambs to the ram in their first autumn. Therefore, you'll have to keep these sheep for the best part of 2 years before seeing any kind of return on your investment. The question is, can you really afford to keep non-productive animals in your flock for that long?

TIP

Don't consider breeding from female lambs in their first year unless they've reached 60% of their expected adult weight by tupping time.

If you do decide to retain any home-bred sheep for breeding purposes, select only the very best, and don't keep more than you actually need. If you have a pedigree flock, and are a member of the relevant breed society, then now is the time to think about registering any lambs that you want to keep or sell as breeding stock, but again, only consider registering the very best, particularly in the case of males.

SHEPHERDING SKILLS

The keeping of sheep, more so than with other livestock, requires the small flock owner to acquire a whole range of husbandry skills in order to maintain his animals in good healthy condition. One of the attractions of shepherding is that all the various tasks are seasonally orientated, which means there's none of the monotony associated with, say, the daily routine of milking a cow or mucking out pigsties. However, this does mean that the trainee shepherd only gets a limited period each year in which to practice and become proficient.

Shearing

For all flock owners, (unless they've opted for one of the few wool-less breeds), shearing comes around once a year, as sure as night follows day. It's getting harder to find contractors willing to set up all their gear just to shear a handful of ewes, so the obvious answer is for smallholders to learn to shear

their own sheep, and, for very small flocks, what could be better than the traditional method of blade shearing?

As with all rural skills, there are regional variations in technique, but the conventional sequence of movements now used for machine shearing, which has become popular the world over, can easily be adapted for use by the hand shearer.

1. A clean surface to work on is essential (here I'm using a sheet of plywood), as is the correct footwear – slippers or moccasins, not workboots or wellies. The shears I'm using are straight single bows, with 6" blades. Well looked after, they'll last a long time – I've been using this pair for 25 years!

Having turned the sheep over properly I begin by shearing the brisket, followed by the belly and crutch. The belly wool is tossed aside, ready to be rolled into the centre of the fleece when the task is complete.

2. The sheep's right front leg slips back between my legs, and I use my knees and feet to turn her onto her right hip. Now I'm in position to shear her left hind leg. The whole of the leg, right up to (and if possible a little over) the backbone must be shorn at this stage.

3. After clearing the wool from the left hind leg, and before moving on to the next stage, I shear her tail.

4. Now I simultaneously step forward and lift the sheep up into a sitting position, which puts her in the right place for me to shear her neck. This is one area where my blade shearing technique differs considerably from the method I use when shearing by machine: with the machine I start the blow just above the brisket, and shear up the animal's neck, whereas when shearing by hand I start just under her jaw and work my way downwards, using a series of short blows running half way around her neck.

5. Having shorn the whole of the left side of her neck, I now move on to clear the wool from her left shoulder.

6. Using my left hand, I lift the ewe's left front leg, which has the effect of smoothing out the skin over and behind her shoulder – it's important to keep her skin as tight as possible over the area being shorn, in order to avoid cuts. As I finish shearing the shoulder, I begin to lower her down onto her side ready for the 'long blows'.

7. With the ewe lying on her right side, immobilised by my left foot under her right shoulder, I begin shearing her left side.

8. Starting from the forward edge of the area cleared when shearing the hind leg, each blow runs the whole length of the sheep, parallel with her backbone.

9. At the end of each long blow I lift her head slightly, and make a short blow around the right hand side of her neck. Once I've cleared all the wool from her left side I step over with my right leg, in preparation for shearing her right side. However, before I actually begin to lift her I make one final long blow, running up the other side of her backbone.

10. Now I lift the ewe's head up between my legs, and shear the remainder of the right side of her neck and her right shoulder.

11. Shuffling backwards as I work, which has the effect of gradually lifting the ewe back up into a sitting position, I continue clipping down the right side of her body.

12. Now it only remains to shear the right hind leg.

13. A few final snips and the job's done! The ewe can now stand up between my legs and run off behind me, leaving her neatly peeled fleece lying on the board.

It takes me about 5 minutes to shear a cooperative ewe by hand, which is pretty slow by professional standards. However, if you can do one in quarter of an hour you should be feeling fairly pleased with yourself – my early attempts took so long that I had to stop halfway to allow the ewe to stand up and suckle her lambs!

Hoof trimming

1. Having turned the ewe over correctly, she's now in the right position for me to check her feet and trim, if necessary. With the sheep sitting on her left hip, I'll trim the left hind foot first. Then I'll transfer her weight to her right hip and do the right hind foot, before moving on to do the front feet.

2. Use a proper pair of hoof shears, not a penknife, to remove any overgrown horn, and also to cut away any areas where the horn has separated from the hoof – if left untended, these separated areas will fill with soil and small stones, leading to lameness and, possibly, infection. Once the hoof becomes infected the problem simply escalates, and the lameness will become very severe indeed.

3. Neatly trimmed sheep's feet should be left with a small rim of horn standing proud of the sole, which takes the animal's weight. If you trim the outer horn down too short, the sole of the hoof (which is relatively soft) will become bruised on hard ground. In sheep, there's no need to cut or rasp the sole of the hoof at all.

4. A squirt of antiseptic spray completes the job.

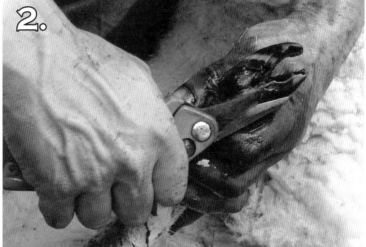

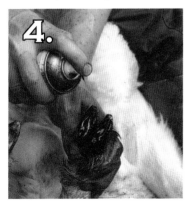

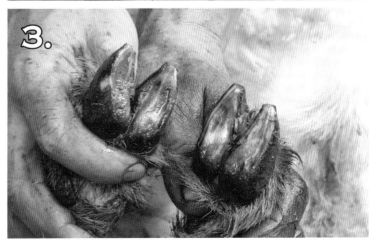

Dagging and crutching

The best shears for the job are very small (3½" blades), and have a double bow. Note carefully the way I'm holding them, with my thumb extended right along the back of the blade, almost to the tip. This grip doesn't stiffen my wrist at all, and provides the required level of dexterity.

Medium-sized ewes

1a. Medium-sized ewes (such as hill breeds), particularly those with long tails, are easier to crutch in a sitting position. It's important to master the correct method for turning sheep over, because getting it right involves no effort at all, and is far less stressful for the animal.

2a. Having turned the ewe over correctly, she's now sitting comfortably on her left hip.

3a. Notice that I've pulled the sheep's tail up over her right hip, and not up between her hind legs. This is extremely important. Pulling it up between her legs would make her udder and teats very vulnerable to accidental damage from the shears, would put me at risk of being kicked, and make it virtually impossible to clip the full length of her tail.
My left hand presses down on the ewe's hip (which keeps her hind leg extended out of the way) and also holds the tip of the tail, while my right hand, wielding the clippers, shears a succession of strips running the full length of the tail, starting at the tip and ending at the very base of the tail where it joins the body.

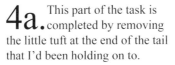

4a. This part of the task is completed by removing the little tuft at the end of the tail that I'd been holding on to.

5a. With the tail finished I can now turn my attention to the surrounding areas.

6a. My left hand is still pulling her tail over her hip, but I'm holding it much nearer the base now. This not only keeps it out of the way, but tilts the back end of the ewe up slightly, so I can see what I'm doing as I remove soiled wool from the crutch and the back of the thighs.

7a. Job done.

Small sheep and lambs

1b. Lambs, or sheep of small breeds, can be held in a standing position between the knees. When the animal is very dirty (as seen here) the process of clipping away the soiled wool is generally called dagging.

2b. As before, I shear the whole of the tail before moving on to the other soiled areas.

3b. By always following the same routine sequence of actions the job only takes a few moments.

4b. The lamb rejoins his flock mates, looking much more comfortable now.

Dagging and crutching Large sheep and rams

1c. Ewes of large breeds (particularly those with docked tails) and heavy rams can easily be restrained using an old fan belt looped over a rail of the gate.

2c. With his head run into the fan belt the sheep can't move forward, so it's a simple matter for me to hold him steady by pressing my knee into his flank, while I get on with the task in hand.

3c. Nice clean bottoms are what every shepherd likes to see.

2. A completely different scenario than that seen in the last illustration, this ewe is clearly suffering from liver fluke, as can be seen by the wasted appearance and the 'mealy' nose and ears. Adult sheep are generally fairly resistant to roundworm infection, so there's no need for this animal to be treated with a broad spectrum product – a fluke only drench will suffice.

Dosing

1. We're all familiar with the sight of dirty bummed lambs, but it would be wrong to automatically assume that the problem is worms. There are any number of other causes of scouring, such as coccidiosis, trace element deficiencies, or simply too much lush grass. It could even be a combination of these factors – for example, certain trace element deficiencies may reduce an animal's natural ability to combat parasites.

3. There are a bewildering number of products available, all carefully marketed to convince you that they're the answer to all your flock health problems. However, it's important that you choose with care. Don't just go by the brand name. Look at which 'group' it falls into, based on the

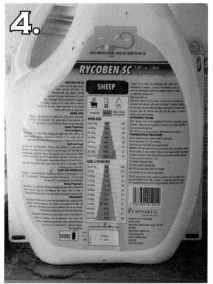

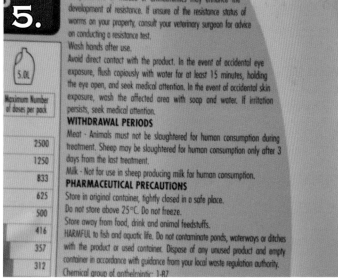

Maximum Number of doses per pack	
2500	
1250	
833	
625	
500	
416	
357	
312	

...frequent use or misuse of anthelmintics may enhance the development of resistance. If unsure of the resistance status of worms on your property, consult your veterinary surgeon for advice on conducting a resistance test.

Wash hands after use.

Avoid direct contact with the product. In the event of accidental eye exposure, flush copiously with water for at least 15 minutes, holding the eye open, and seek medical attention. In the event of accidental skin exposure, wash the affected area with soap and water. If irritation persists, seek medical attention.

WITHDRAWAL PERIODS

Meat - Animals must not be slaughtered for human consumption during treatment. Sheep may be slaughtered for human consumption only after 3 days from the last treatment.

Milk - Not for use in sheep producing milk for human consumption.

PHARMACEUTICAL PRECAUTIONS

Store in original container, tightly closed in a safe place.

Do not store above 25°C. Do not freeze.

Store away from food, drink and animal feedstuffs.

HARMFUL to fish and aquatic life. Do not contaminate ponds, waterways or ditches with the product or used container. Dispose of any unused product and empty container in accordance with guidance from your local waste regulation authority.

Chemical group of anthelmintic 1-BZ

active ingredient. There are 5 groups now available – white (BZ), yellow (LV), clear (ML), orange (AD) and purple (SI). The white drenches have been around for a long time, and are the cheapest, but due to overuse they're the ones that are now least effective (although they remain acceptable for treating nematodirus). The orange and purple groups are very new, so, in order to retain their efficacy for as long as possible, they should be used primarily for quarantine dosing.

4. Dosage rates will be given on the packet (sometimes in the form of a handy table, as shown here), based on the bodyweight of the animal(s) to be treated. Therefore, you need to be able to accurately estimate the weight of your sheep. Better still, actually weigh them. The dose rate should be set according to the heaviest animal in the group to be treated, not the average. I've noticed that a lot of smallholders are inclined to under estimate the weight of their sheep (and therefore under-dose), which is a sure-fire way of ending up with drug resistance problems.

5. Remember to read the small print. There will be a number of contra-indications and warnings (for example, some products shouldn't be used on ewes at tupping time or in early pregnancy, and most shouldn't be used on sheep producing milk for human consumption), and there'll also be a withdrawal period, before which no treated animals must be slaughtered and enter the food chain.

6. It's important that you use appropriate equipment for administration. The dosing gun on the left is connected to the product pack via a length of plastic pipe, and automatically refills between each use. The one on the right needs to be refilled manually between each dose, and is more suited to small flock owners who may only purchase small quantities of medicine at a time.

7. Always check the calibration of the dosing gun before you start by setting it at the appropriate rate and squirting it into a measuring cylinder, or the barrel of a syringe.

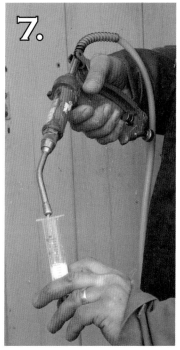

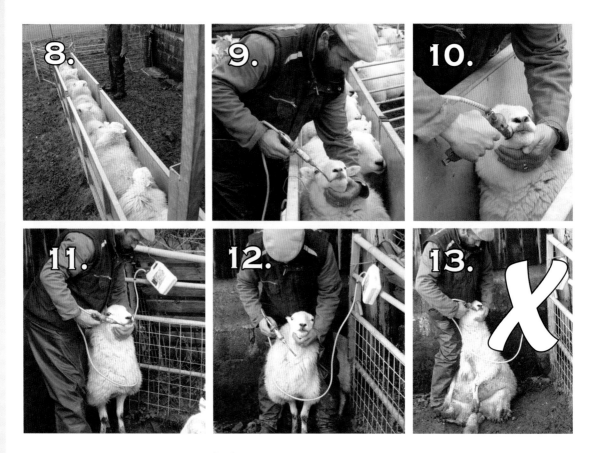

8. The best (and least stressful) way to contain animals for dosing is to have them all lined up in a race.

9. From the outside of the race I can work my way down the line of sheep, restraining each one with a hand under the chin as I administer the correct dose.

10. The nozzle of the dosing gun is entered at the corner of the mouth. It passes through the gap between the front and back teeth, and slides over the back of the tongue. Do be careful – injuries to the larynx can occur if you're rough, and may be fatal. Provided that the nozzle of the gun is correctly placed over the back of the animal's tongue, the whole dose will be swallowed immediately on administration.

11. If you haven't got a race, each individual sheep can be restrained by pressing her against a gate or hurdle with your knees while you administer the dose.

12. Another alternative, which may be preferable if your sheep are of a smallish breed, is to stand astride each one, as shown here.

13. Although it's tempting, when you've turned a ewe over to trim her feet, to do other jobs while she's securely restrained, you must *never* dose them when they're in a sitting position. Sheep weren't designed to swallow when upside down, and will inevitably choke.

14. Always make a small temporary mark on each sheep treated, just to be on the safe side. It's not unknown for breakouts to occur, and if they get mixed up again before you've finished dosing them all, you'll be jolly glad of that small mark. Remember to record the treatment in your farm medicine book too.

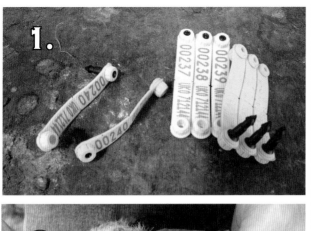

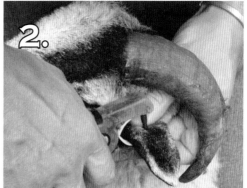

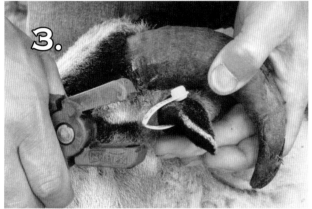

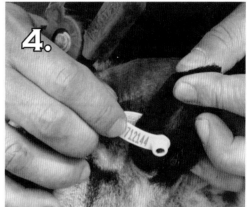

Ear tagging

1. The tags are made up of two halves – the 'male', which has a sharp pin, and the 'female', which has a hole. In some cases the two halves of the tag are joined to form a continuous 'one piece' tag (as shown here). For insertion, the tag is held in an applicator that resembles a pair of pliers.

2. The male part of the tag is inserted from the back of the ear. When the pliers are squeezed together, the sharp pin pierces the ear and locks into the hole in the female part of the tag. Care must be taken to avoid the blood vessels and lines of thicker gristle. It's easy enough to hold a lamb between your knees, leaving both your hands free to apply the tag, making this a simple 'one person' job.

3. The tag should be carefully released from the pliers – don't just pull the pliers away because you risk tearing the animal's ear if the tag is still gripped. When applying single piece 'loop'-style tags to young lambs, remember to allow space for the ear to grow.

4. Check that the tag can swivel freely in the ear, and that there isn't a piece of skin trapped in the closure. It's quite a good idea to spray the ear with a small amount of antiseptic such as Bactakil. One often sees sheep whose ears have become infected due to poor hygiene or incorrect tagging procedure, but if you take reasonable care then it won't happen.

5. Now repeat the procedure for the other ear, making sure that you've matched up the right pair of tags. If you carry out the statutory tagging sufficiently early enough in the year for you still to be able to identify which lambs came from which ewes, then you can use the official individual number for your own breeding records as well.

Vaccinating

1. The yellow vaccinator on the left of the picture can be connected to the product pack via a length of plastic piping, and is particularly useful in larger flocks. For small- and medium-sized flocks the green(ish) vaccinator in the foreground is most convenient. Here, the product pack attaches directly to the barrel of the syringe, so it is best used with the smaller 25 dose packs. For flock owners with only a very few sheep an ordinary syringe, together with either reusable or disposable needles, can be used (right of picture), but do ensure that a separate needle is used to withdraw the required dose from the pack between animals.

2. It's not practical (or economical) to use a fresh needle for every sheep. In order to maintain some semblance of asepsis there's a device called a 'sterimatic' that can be attached to most automatic vaccinating equipment. In use, the needle retracts through a small, disinfectant impregnated sponge between the administration of each dose.

3. Here you can see the needle protruding from the sterimatic device. This works very well when administering intramuscular vaccinations (such as toxovax), but is rather awkward to use when injecting subcutaneously, so I have to admit I don't often bother with it, and neither does anyone else I know.

4. Given that the clostridial booster is given at a time when the ewes are heavily pregnant, it's important that they're handled with care. It is best to run them single file into a race, rather than handle each one individually, or wade amongst them in a packed pen.

5. Provided that the race is properly filled, the ewes will generally stand quite calmly while you carry out the necessary tasks, keeping stress to a minimum.

6. Working from the outside of the race, I make my way down the line of ewes, vaccinating each in turn. The syringe refills automatically between each one. My preferred site is over the ribcage, just behind the shoulder, as I find that this involves less handling and restraint of the animal, and therefore less stress.

7. In one hand I hold the vaccinator, and with the other I part the wool down to a clear area of skin.

8. The clostridial vaccination is given subcutaneously, so it's a simple matter now to insert the needle under the skin and administer the correct (2ml) dose. It might be necessary to pinch up a fold of skin to inject into, but, if you do this, take care not to simply push the needle in one side and out the other, hence wasting the product (and leaving your sheep unprotected against a whole lot of nasty diseases.)

9. Temporarily mark each animal treated.

10. An alternative site that's often recommended for subcutaneous injection is high up on the side of the neck. The reason given for this is that, in the event of an injection site abscess forming, it would result in less carcass wastage. However, I don't find it very convenient as it's necessary to use one hand to hold the animal's head and the other to pinch up a fold of skin, which doesn't leave a hand free to give the injection.

11. Not all vaccinations are given by injection. The device shown here is used to vaccinate sheep and lambs against orf (contagious pustular dermatitis) via small scratches in the skin.

12. The correct site for orf vaccination is on the bare skin between the top of the foreleg and the chest wall (in what is effectively the animal's 'armpit'). A tiny droplet of the vaccine is held between the two sharp prongs of the applicator, which are then drawn firmly across the skin, forming a scratch about 2 inches long.

13. Examination of the site after about 10 days should show a raised scab, indicating that the vaccine has taken properly. As this is a live vaccine it's important that it's only used in flocks where orf is a problem, and care must be taken not to mix vaccinated and unvaccinated animals, as the scabs formed at the vaccination site could transmit the disease.

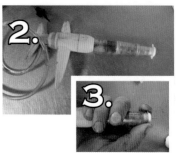

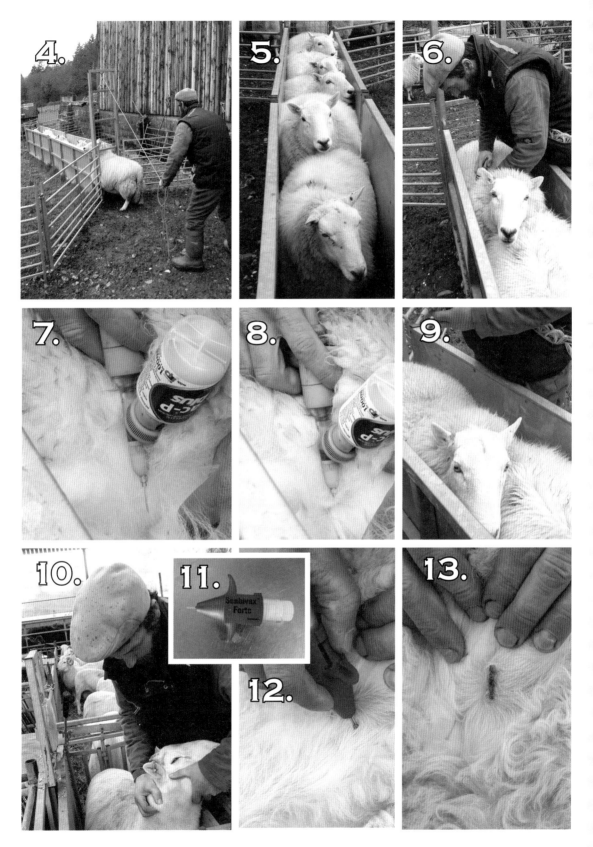

Pigs

"True, you can compost vegetable waste, but show me a better way of composting anything than putting it through the guts of a pig!"
John Seymour

Small-scale pig keeping has increased in popularity recently, and quite rightly so. They're relatively undemanding to care for, and have become far more accessible to beginners and hobbyists. For the more serious smallholder, with an eye on the bottom line, pigs are good for cash flow. The nature of the beast allows for a quick turnaround, so there is a comparatively short payback time on the money you've spent. True, if you're rearing pigs for home consumption then your repayment will be in kind, rather than in hard cash, but the amount that you save by not having to buy pork and bacon should exceed the outlay, and some revenue can be generated by selling bits off to friends and neighbours. Ideally, of course, the sale of any surplus should cover all of the expenditure, meaning that you get your own food for free.

Pigs can successfully be reared in a fairly restricted area, making them a viable option for even the smallest of holdings. They'll live out their lives quite contentedly indoors, so could theoretically be kept in a traditional sty at the bottom of a large garden. Some consideration would have to be given to any neighbours, as the squealing that they make when they know their grub is coming can be ear splitting at times, but they will stop as soon as they're fed. Even on a very small plot, the amount of manure produced by a couple of porkers can be fully utilised, and their clean habits mean that it's a simple matter to shovel up the dung daily and add it to the compost heap (although again, consider the impact this could have on any close neighbours).

If you have the space to keep pigs outdoors you can make use of their natural inclination to dig – they'll do a wonderful job in the garden, clearing scrubby bits of land and generally making themselves useful on any vacant plot, particularly where there are crop residues that need to be disposed of.

It's not all beer and skittles though – if it were, everyone would be keeping pigs. There are some downsides that need to be weighed up against the positives before taking the plunge. In all likelihood, the negatives will not stop you, but it's as well to know what you're letting yourself in for.

Firstly, you need to be aware that the retail price of pork is very low (currently about £5.50 per kilo for an average cut, as opposed to £8.00 for lamb or £11.00 for beef). Therefore, although the quick birth-to-slaughter interval is good for generating turnover, it's not so good for making a profit on a small scale. That's why commercial pig production tends to be carried out on large intensive farms – with each pig only generating a tiny margin, you need to sell an awful lot of pigs in a year to make a reasonable income. At today's prices, even the big producers are struggling to make ends meet. The small-scale producer cannot take advantage of volume sales.

Another downside (and one that exacerbates the negative effect caused by low pork prices) is the relatively high cost of bought-in pig feed. Pigs are not grazing animals, and will need a certain amount of supplementary feeding all year round. At current rates, compound feed for growing pigs, such as those you would be rearing for the freezer, may cost nearly £13 for a 25kg bag, as opposed to a general purpose ruminant feed (for cattle or sheep) at £5.95 – less than half the price!

These two points may rule out pig keeping as the principal enterprise on a viable smallholding, but shouldn't discourage you altogether – there's nothing quite like a pig for putting a large quantity of high quality meat in your freezer in a relatively short space of time.

GETTING STARTED

Buying in a couple of weaners (piglets that have been taken from their mother fairly recently, usually at 8-10 weeks old), with the intention of rearing them for domestic consumption, is undoubtedly the best way to begin. They're generally pretty trouble free, and, as they will probably be with you for only 3-4 months, they are not too much of a commitment.

Aim to purchase weaners in May or June. This way they can enjoy the summer months digging over a fallow plot in the garden, and be ready for killing just as the weather begins to turn chilly in late September. They will have a good

Electric fencing is a useful option for temporary containment - seen here around a plot in our vegetable garden.

life and, assuming that the weather is reasonably dry and warm, will efficiently convert their grub into meat without turning the whole of their allocated plot into a mud bath. However, once the weather begins to get colder and wetter in the autumn, pigs are definitely better off indoors, either dead and in the freezer, or, if you're running them on to heavier weights for bacon, in a suitable shed or sty.

Make sure you've got everything ready for your pigs before they arrive. Far too many newcomers to the smallholding way of life make livestock purchases on impulse, without having given proper thought to all that it entails. A very good way of making a temporary outdoor enclosure for small pigs is to simply join together 4 half-meshed galvanised metal gates in a square. 10' gates would do the job admirably, and when the pigs have gone they can be used for something else around the farm. 16' gates would be better still. This method of containing pigs is particularly suitable if ground clearing is part of your plan, as

Four half-meshed gates make a good enclosure for a couple of weaners.

they'll be much more effective at removing scrub and weeds if you limit them to a fairly small patch at a time. Once they've eaten everything, and dug and manured the soil to your satisfaction, it's a relatively simple job to drag the pen along to the next plot to be cleared.

Another option for temporary containment is to use three strands of electric fence. Pigs are quite sensitive to shocks, and generally respect an electric fence, and in truth there is not much to choose between the different types of fence unit available, although if you decide to use a battery

Pigs in winter

Personally, I wouldn't keep pigs outdoors in the winter. It's true that pigs are very happy outdoors during the summer, particularly if there's plenty of vegetation for them to root around in, and a nice wallow to cool off after a spell of sunbathing, but in the winter it's a different story: pigs are comfort-loving creatures, and don't appreciate plodding about in a quagmire in the wind and rain, when they could be snuggled up somewhere cosy. The idea that they need plenty of space is a complete fallacy – all that they really want to spend the winter doing is eating and sleeping, in maximum comfort and with minimum effort! Also, quite apart from welfare issues, it is very un-economical to keep pigs outdoors in winter, as approximately one third of their feed intake is used up in simply keeping warm. If it really isn't possible for you to bring your pigs indoors for the winter, the following suggestions might help to make their lives a little more comfortable:

· Make sure that the ark has its back to the prevailing wind, and stake it down securely so it doesn't blow away. (Don't laugh – I've seen it happen!)

· Reduce the size of the entrance to the ark and / or fit a curtain of rubber strips (of the sort that you see in the doorways of supermarket cold stores and the like).

· Ensure that the ark is situated on higher ground, so that surface water won't run in.

· Insulate the ark in some way. If it has a flat roof you could place a layer of straw bales on top. Another alternative is to fit a ceiling inside the ark (if space permits) using a sheet of plywood, and pack the space between it and the roof with loose straw. Traditional corrugated iron arks are difficult to insulate, but you might be able to cover them with loose straw, held in place with fence netting. Another alternative is to build a snug house out of big heston bales.

· Use simply masses of bedding in the ark. Also, heston bale sections can be laid (like giant carpet tiles) over very muddy areas outside.

· Divide the enclosure into two or more smaller paddocks, so that areas can be rested and allowed to dry out a bit if they get badly poached in wet weather.

· If your pig enclosure is a permanent fixture then consider installing a concreted area for feeding. This should be located in such a way as to be accessible from all the various sub-divisions of the field. The feeding area can also incorporate a handling / loading pen.

· Ensure that your pigs are free from all internal and external parasites at the start of the winter, and that they are in good body condition.

· Monitor body condition regularly, and adjust feed levels accordingly.

· Keep a close eye on the water supply in freezing weather.

powered unit, I can guarantee that the pigs will find out that the battery is flat before you do, by which time they'll have escaped and caused havoc in your vegetable garden! A mains powered energiser is definitely preferable. It's a good idea to teach pigs to respect an electric fence before letting them loose with only such a flimsy barrier between them and your precious vegetables.

TIP

In order to train pigs to respect an electric fence it's best to confine them to a loose box or some similar indoor accommodation initially, with a single strand of electrified wire run along one wall, a few inches away from it and about 8" off the floor. When you do eventually transfer them to an outdoor enclosure, watch them very closely for the first hour or so. Stand on the outside of the fence, armed with a stick, and give a sharp tap on the snout to any pig that approaches the wire. They very soon learn to approach the fence with caution.

Without this additional measure, pigs that are unused to electric fencing are likely to push their heads under the wire quite boldly, and then, on receiving a shock, jump forwards through it, rather than backwards. The efficacy of any electric fence is improved if there is a visual barrier (e.g. a hedge or stone wall) behind it.

Given that each batch of pigs won't be with you for very long, I wouldn't recommend going to all the trouble of erecting permanent stock fencing for them. It's expensive, it doesn't give you any flexibility in terms of moving the boundaries, and they'll eventually wreck it anyway.

If outdoors, your pigs will also need some sort of shelter – they really don't like the cold and wet. Weaners are very small and vulnerable, so they'll need quite a snug place to start with. Personally, even if it was the intention to rear them outdoors, I would keep them inside somewhere for a week or so until they settle down. Having said that, they are not too fussy about the form the shelter takes, provided that it's warm and dry. You could purchase a pig ark (either traditional style or modern, ready made or in kit form) from one of several companies now producing animal arks suitable for smallholdings, but this is a pretty expensive way of doing things.

The recommended floor area for a pair of porkers (which is what your weaners will become) is 8' x 4', and a ready made ark of that size is going to set you back £300-500 pounds. The sensible alternative is to build something yourself, equally suitable, for much less outlay. It's possible to purchase the semi-circular galvanised sheets traditionally used for pig arks for around £25 each, and they will cover an 8' x 4' area. All you need to do then is to make a wooden frame, and a front and back, using reclaimed timber. For summer only use, a floor isn't essential. In practice, you can use a much smaller shelter than the 'recommended' minimum, provided that there's room for the pigs to lie down comfortably out of the rain. In fine weather they'll often opt to sleep under the stars anyway. I also know of some smallholders who have constructed a pig house from straw bales, with a sheeted roof. This type of

housing has the advantage that it is warm and snug, so is a good option for young pigs. By the time the pigs are ready for the freezer, you may find that the walls a bit worse for wear, as the pigs will gradually destroy the bales, but it should see them through. Breeding pigs would require more substantial accommodation.

Having kept all ages of pigs, both inside and out, we now feel that it's best to only run dry sows (i.e. those not currently suckling piglets) outdoors. Young pigs always seem to do better indoors.

Nose rings

Our sows are used to dig over fallow plots in the vegetable garden, but if you don't want your pigs to dig, you'll have to ring them. Ringing pigs will more or less stop them from rooting up pasture, but they'll still be able to cause some limited damage. It will also help to prevent them from lifting gates off hinges and overturning troughs. There are two types available: the sow ring (like a bull ring, only smaller) which goes through the gristle between the nostrils, and smaller copper rings which are inserted along the top edge of the snout.
The latter are generally used for fattening pigs. Sow rings may be either self piercing, or may require a hole to be punched first. Personally, I have my doubts about

how effective the sow rings are, as one often sees them augmented with a number of the smaller rings. Also, should a sow catch the ring on anything and tear it out, it will make a frightful mess of her nose. The smaller rings are much cheaper, less damaging to the animal, and you can easily apply them yourself using a special pair of pliers.

Rings and pliers are available from many agricultural merchants and smallholder suppliers. It's common practice to insert four in each animal: two close together in the centre of the top edge of the snout, and another a bit further down on each side. If you want to put rings in a large pig you'll need to restrain her by putting a rope noose around the top jaw, and pulling it tight. It works on a similar principle to putting a twitch on a horse or holding a cow by the nostrils, and has an immobilising effect – she'll squeal like billy-oh, but stay still!

Buying weaners

Over the 30 years or so that I've been keeping pigs, the price of 'commercial' (i.e. non-pedigree) weaners has remained pretty constant at £25 to £35, which is quite extraordinary when you consider that the cost of pig food has increased threefold in that time! Sometimes the price has risen to as much as £40 / head, but it's just as often been possible to pick them up for as little as £10 to £15.

Generally speaking, you get what you pay for, but, having said that, you'll occasionally find some very good pigs at the lower end of the price range, simply because the breeder has to sell them at that point to make way for the next batch coming through his system. Conversely, many small-scale producers are rather inclined to over value their animals, so you may see some pretty poor specimens with unrealistically high price tags.

Pedigree registered weaners will obviously cost a bit more (maybe as much as £60 to £80 each), but this is only relevant if you're intending to raise one or two gilts as potential breeding animals. However many piglets you decide to buy (probably two for your first venture – one for home consumption as pork, and one to sell to family and friends, to cover the cost of rearing the pair. Or maybe 3, with the third one being run on to a heavier weight for bacon and ham.) Make sure that they're evenly matched in size, and are all of the same sex. It's often recommended that beginners start off by buying male piglets, thus removing the risk of you deciding to keep an unsuitable animal into adulthood, and embarking on a breeding programme too soon, simply because you have become rather attached to it. However, I should hope that any serious smallholder wouldn't be overly swayed by sentiment in these matters.

When buying weaners for fattening, factors such as the number of teats they've got and the size of the litter that they came from are totally irrelevant. What matters is health and conformation, so look out for piglets that are well grown for their age, with nice clean skins and silky hair. They should be long in the body, with well developed hindquarters and good posture. Avoid excessively hairy pigs, and any that have pimply or itchy looking skin, or

crusty ears. Healthy piglets are jaunty and inquisitive, so any animal that stands in a corner with a hunched back and a straight tail is clearly suspect. Look in the dung corner for signs of scouring (and don't buy any from that litter if you're in any doubt). Ask the vendor whether they've been wormed, and even if he says they have, do them again as soon as you get them home, just to be on the safe side.

Personally I would prefer to buy weaners for fattening from a small-to medium-sized commercial producer, e.g. the man with a dozen or so sows of a commercial breed. Large scale producers are generally reluctant to allow individual buyers onto their units for bio-security reasons, and, at the other end of the scale, inexperienced smallholders sometimes offer weaners for sale that are the product of indiscriminate matings between unsuitable animals of various obscure breeds – the resulting offspring are often multi-coloured, slow growing, hairy little things that aren't going to give you a very satisfactory return on your investment.

Although it's best to buy weaners directly from the farm where they were bred, they can generally be purchased more cheaply at an auction mart. However, the risks of bringing in health problems are clearly greater where livestock has passed through a market, particularly in the case of vulnerable young animals.

Buying in pedigree weaners as potential breeding animals is a different ball game altogether, and is discussed in more detail on page 237.

Weaner pigs can often be purchased cheaply at auction.

Feeding

Growing pigs don't need a vast amount to eat – a good rule of thumb is to allow 1lb of concentrate feed per day for each month of age, up to a maximum of 5lb per day, split between two feeds. Depending on the type of pigs you have, you might want to feed a bit less (or use a lower specification feed), as some of the more traditional breeds, particularly Gloucestershire Old Spots, are inclined to lay down vast amounts of fat. Unless you want several inches of lard on your chops, it's better to keep your pigs a little on the hungry side.

Of course, one of the beauties of the pig is its ability to turn waste vegetables, fruit and surplus milk into meat and manure, although it's important to remember that these bulky feeds can't be used to replace purchased meal on a pound-for-pound basis. We always keep a 'pig bucket' on the go, and put all the edible scraps in there – surplus milk, pea pods, cabbage leaves etc., – and when it's full we give it to the pigs, which they love. They don't mind in the least if the milk has gone a bit cheesy by the time they get it.

Whenever you transfer pigs to new quarters, always place some fresh dung in the corner of the sty that you want them to use as a latrine. If these are your first pigs arriving on the holding, look in the trailer for a bit of muck to use. If weaners are soiling their nest area, it 's usually because the area you've provided is too big, too cold, or too draughty. Use some straw bales to reduce the size of the sleeping place, gradually enlarging it as they grow. Older pigs that have got into the habit of dunging in their sleeping quarters can be dissuaded from doing so by hanging a low 'false ceiling' (e.g. a sheet of thick plywood) over the area where they sleep. It should be sufficiently low that they have to crawl under to go to bed (which they'll happily do). Pigs do like to stand up properly to dung and urinate, so they'll have to get out of bed in order to go to the toilet in comfort.

The contents of the bucket replace a proportion (but not all) of the concentrate ration at that particular meal time. Remember that you mustn't give the pigs meat of any kind (although they would gladly eat it, given the chance), and that any fruit and vegetable waste must be garden trimmings rather than household scraps – anything that's been in the kitchen is forbidden. That's the law, and I've done my duty by pointing it out to you. How you now choose to feed your pigs is your business…

Sensible use of the pig bucket is what will make one or two pigs profitable, in a situation where three or four (or more) would fail to generate a satisfactory return.

Provide outdoor pigs with a place to wallow in hot weather.

Traditionally, all edible domestic waste would have been recycled in this way.

It goes without saying that pigs must have free access to fresh water at all times, particularly if they're being fed on any kind of domestic waste food products, as they're highly susceptible to salt poisoning. Fixed troughs or nipple drinkers are fine for indoor use in purpose built accommodation, but for use in temporary outdoor enclosures it can be a bit difficult to find a suitable container that they won't constantly overturn. If you can get hold of them, the extremely heavy cast iron traditional pig troughs are great (they look a bit like Mexican hats), but they're now very popular as garden ornaments, so are usually snapped up for use as flower pots at ridiculously inflated prices. Otherwise use something that has a wide base and is quite shallow, such as a sawn-off barrel, which will be much more stable than a bucket.

Traditional cast-iron pig troughs look like Mexican hats.

In hot weather pigs will appreciate a mud wallow – if they can tip over the water trough they'll soon make their own. If not, a couple of bucketfuls of water chucked into a hollow in the ground will give them a good place to start. This is most important for pink pigs, which are susceptible to sunburn if they can't get a good covering of protective mud on themselves. If your pigs do well they could be ready for slaughter (pork weight) at as little as five months old (or maybe 6 months for traditional breeds). Given that they may have been up to 12 weeks old when you acquired them, you could be filling your freezer with home-produced meat within 10 weeks of buying your first pigs. As 'D-day' approaches, monitor the growth of your pigs regularly by measuring around the girth with a seamstress' tape. Measure all the way around the pig just behind the shoulder. As a rough guide, a pig with a girth measurement of 36" will weigh in the region of 140lb liveweight, and should yield about 100lb of pork (see table 8, page 446). A couple of pigs that size is probably enough for starters. See pages 276 - 278 for information on slaughter and butchery.

BREEDING

"Breeding sows are great favourites with Cottagers in general, but I have seldom known them to answer their purpose. Where there is an outlet, the sow will indeed keep herself by grazing in summer, with a little wash to help her out; and when her pigs come they are many in number, but they are a heavy expense."
William Cobbett

Having gained plenty of experience in pig keeping through buying in weaners for fattening, it's quite understandable that you might want to have a go at breeding your own. However, do make sure that you've done your homework with regard to the marketing of the progeny of your sows – our own experience suggests that breeding pigs is not the quickest road to riches. In fact, over the years I should say that this is the one enterprise that's more or less consistently lost us money. Interestingly, it seems that if we buy in weaners for fattening we can make it pay, and if we breed pigs for sale as weaners we can make it pay (just about), but

whenever we try to go the whole hog by doing both the breeding and the fattening, we are invariably out of pocket at the end of the year. On this basis, I would suggest that if you are keen to breed your own pigs, you should aim to sell all the offspring at weaning, with the exception of just the odd one or two that don't match the rest of the litter – these are the ones to run on for home consumption. Of course, this does all depend upon your proximity to a customer base. If you live reasonably close to a large centre of population (or if you don't mind spending several days a week manning a stall at a Farmers' Market), then direct sales of pork (and pork products) may well generate sufficient revenue to justify raising a greater proportion of your piglets through to slaughter. For sales of live pigs (pedigree or otherwise) to be successful, you really need to be in a well-connected location, as there's a limit as to how far off the beaten track prospective purchasers are prepared to travel – it's no good having top quality stock for sale if you can't persuade anyone to brave the wilderness. A smallholding close to a major motorway junction would be ideal in this respect, but hardly conducive to the type of quiet lifestyle that most of us want to be able to enjoy.

There are, of course, an increasing number of sales of rare, minority and traditional breeds of livestock taking place at auction centres across the country, which provide a very useful outlet for surplus pigs. However, you'll often find yourself keeping pigs on beyond their optimum age of sale in order to fit in with the market calendar, during which time they'll be steadily eating their way through any profit you might otherwise have made.

Breeds

I think, where pig breeding is concerned, and in particular when choosing a breed of sow, there's far more scope to let your head be ruled by your heart, and choose a breed simply because you like the look of it, than there is with other types of livestock. Let's face it: unlike sheep or cattle producers, the small-scale pig breeder is never going to be competing in the market place against the commercial boys. For the smallholder, the main emphasis of pig production will be on the supply of pork (and pork products) for family consumption. If it's decided to pursue a breeding program, then this is likely to be with the intention of supplying meat to a wider circle of acquaintances, or to exploit niche markets through direct sales, or maybe to sell weaners to other smallholders.

Well-to-do downshifters who can afford to keep livestock as an expensive hobby may choose to breed pedigree rare breed pigs and register them with the British Pig Association, but whether this would be a financially justifiable course of action for the genuine smallholder is debatable, due to the associated costs.

A lot depends upon whether pigs are to be the principal enterprise on the smallholding (i.e. the one that hopefully earns a bit of income), or solely for home consumption. Where pigs are the principal enterprise, breed can be an important aspect of marketing – for direct sales to discerning customers it may be appropriate to flag up a specific local or traditional breed.

For a more mainstream marketing strategy (e.g. via a high street butcher or direct to an abattoir), a conventional white breed (or cross) would be appropriate, due to the better meat / bone ratio, and the absence of coloured hairs (which are notoriously difficult to remove cleanly) and seedy cut. Either way, you could use management (free range / traditionally reared / organic etc.) as a marketing tool, rather than breed. If, on the other hand, you'll be rearing just a few pigs each year for your own freezer, then go for whatever you like the look of.

It's often said that the traditional breeds have a better flavour, but in reality this is due to the fact that they are usually reared in a more sympathetic fashion – a modern white pig tastes equally good if reared in the same way, and probably has a higher proportion of quality meat with less fat. Regardless of breed, we've found that the meat from free range pigs has a better flavour but a coarser texture, and costs more to produce. Many of the UK's older pig breeds evolved in the cramped (and often filthy) conditions of the traditional cottager's sty, and may not (as we fondly imagine) be ideally suited to a free range existence. Somewhat ironically, the recent upsurge of interest in commercial free range and 'traditional' production has led to the development of modern hybrid pigs specifically for outdoor systems.

It goes without saying that novelty breeds such as Kune-kunes and Pot-bellied pigs have no place on the viable smallholding.

• Gloucestershire Old Spots

The Old Spot is the breed most often associated with the backyard pig keeper. Known as the 'orchard pig', it was developed in the apple orchards of its county of origin. It's often said that apple sauce isn't required with Gloucester pork, due to the inherent fruity flavour of the meat itself. The Old Spot's inclination to graze, rather than dig, meant that the roots of the trees weren't damaged, as they may have been if subjected to the excavations of a more destructive breed.

The Gloucestershire is an attractive pig, being white with black spots and lop ears. Some of the older strains show a considerable number of black markings, of various sizes, giving a great deal of character – local folklore has it that the spots evolved from the bruises caused by falling apples. Sadly (I feel) the recent trend has been towards fewer spots, often resulting in an almost entirely white animal. The Old Spot is a breed with good length and depth, and extremely good hams. It's suitable for pork if butchered at a fairly young age, and individual animals showing the appropriate characteristics can be kept on for bacon. The sows produce average-sized litters, and make good mothers.

One drawback to the breed is that it is inclined to become coarse and overweight, particularly within the limited confines of a cottager's sty. This isn't a problem when taking pigs up to pork weight, but the quality of bacon and ham obtained from more mature animals may be reduced. In the case of breeding animals, it's worth considering that an overweight sow may be very difficult (if not impossible) to get in pig.

• Tamworth

Unmistakable in appearance, the Tamworth is our oldest breed of domesticated pig. With its ginger hair, exceptionally long, straight snout, and small, pricked ears, it's a very distinctive looking animal. The Tamworth will really thrive under rather rough-and-ready outdoor conditions, particularly in woodland. The coat colouring gives it excellent protection against sunburn, which can be a serious problem among white haired, fine skinned breeds such as the Middle White, or modern hybrids, when kept outside.

Tamworth sows are not particularly productive, producing on average 5-7 piglets per litter, and can be somewhat excitable mothers. Having said that, individuals of the breed are long lived, so a sow will make up for her small litters through additional years of production over and above what might be expected from other types. The Tamworth is primarily a bacon producer, having an exceptionally long, lean carcass. However, the young pigs are rather slow growing, with the result that the Tamworth is often crossed with other breeds to produce a more general-purpose weaner. At one time the Tamworth boar was commonly used on Berkshire sows, and it is thought that this is the cross that led to the development of the Oxford Sandy and Black breed. Tamworth sows have also been bred to wild boar to produce a reconstruction of the 'iron age' pig.

Being prick eared, the Tamworth (in common with other prick eared breeds) can be difficult to contain. Lop-eared pigs, on the other hand, tend to be less inclined to challenge their boundaries (probably on account of the fact that they can't really see where they're going), and may be kept at home with more simple fencing arrangements.

• Berkshire

The 'modern' Berkshire is a black pig with white points, although early examples of the breed came in a wide range of colours. The Berkshire has been steadily improved, and the colour standardised, over the past 200 years or so, and a breeder's association was formed in 1883, making this the oldest UK breed to have maintained proper pedigree records. It's a pretty pig, with small pricked, or semi-lop, ears and a short, up-turned snout – a legacy of the use of the now extinct Chinese Small White in the development of the breed. Berkshires are primarily pork producers, although the sows may be mated to boars of other breeds (such as the Tamworth and the Large White) to give general purpose offspring. They aren't particularly prolific, but the sows are good mothers, and the young pigs tend to be quick growing and economical feeders, resulting in efficient use of feedstuff throughout the rearing and fattening period.

• Oxford Sandy & Black

This is probably the least known of the minority pig breeds, though it surely deserves greater popularity. Thought to have originally developed from a cross between the old type of Berkshire and the Tamworth, the Sandy and Black is a medium-sized pig with a lustrous coat of gingery hair (anything from pale honey colour through to a rich, rusty red) dotted randomly with a good number of black patches and spots. This colouration is probably what gives it its alternative name of the 'plum pudding' pig, and it provides excellent protection against sunburn. It has pale points (feet, tail tip and snout), as has its ancestor, the Berkshire, and lop or semi-lop ears. Sows of the breed are fairly prolific, and motherliness and temperament are first-rate. The Sandy and Black is particularly good at utilising a poorer quality diet, and sows may be crossed with the Large White to produce fast-growing offspring with good feed conversion ratios and conformation. As a porker the pure Sandy and Black is excellent, but for bacon production the aforementioned crossbred is better, as it gives a slightly larger, leaner carcass.

I may be a bit biased, but, having kept a number of different breeds over the years, I've come firmly to the conclusion that the Oxford Sandy and Black is the perfect smallholder's pig, equally suited to free-range or sty housing.

• Saddleback

There are (or there were) two distinct forms of Saddleback, the Essex and the Wessex, both of which are a black bodied pig with a stripe of white running up one front leg, over the shoulders, and down the other side, forming a complete band around the animal. The difference between the two types is that while the 'saddle' of the Wessex type can be very narrow at the shoulder – so narrow that it may be barely visible – the saddle on the Essex pig must consist of a broad band, with both skin and hair being white. The Essex may also have white points. The conformation of the two types is almost identical. Indeed, so much alike are they that at various times in the history of the breed(s), the herd books of the two have been combined, resulting in the type known as the 'British' Saddleback. At one time Saddlebacks (of one sort or another) were numerically second only to the Large White as commercial animals, but they're now classified as a 'minority' breed, which means there may be as few as 500 pedigree saddleback sows in existence. How the mighty have fallen…

The Saddleback is an extremely prolific breed – a British Saddleback at one time held the world record of 31 live pigs in a litter! (The previous record holder was a Wessex type sow, with a litter of 30). However, despite the fact that the sows have good mothering ability, these large litters may prove something of an embarrassment to the small-scale producer, who is unlikely to have other sows farrowing at the same time to act as foster mothers for the surplus. Bear in mind that a sow can only really be expected to do a good job of rearing as many pigs as she has teats, so where excessive numbers are born, it's either going to result in a high mortality rate, undernourished / slow growing piglets, or time-consuming artificial rearing.

The pure Saddleback is a general-purpose animal, but it may be crossed with the Middle White to produce porkers, or, conversely, with the Large White to produce carcasses of a bacon type.

• Middle White

Of all the British breeds, the Middle White is the one which has been most influenced by the introduction of Chinese pigs during the late 18th century. Its snout appears to be flattened to such a degree that one would think it had recently suffered a nasty collision! It's a small breed, and rather short, producing specialist pork carcasses when killed at around 100lb liveweight, although even at this size it may be rather fat for modern tastes.

The Middle White sow is not particularly prolific, and, although the young pigs will fatten well, their early growth is inclined to be slow. It may be crossed with the Large White to produce a more general purpose litter.

The Middle White was very popular during the early 20th century, but is now classified by the RBST as 'vulnerable', which means that there may be as few as 200 registered breeding sows in existence.

• Large White

Although still to be seen in its original state in the hands of pedigree breeders, the Large White has had a huge influence on the British pig industry in its many hybrid forms. These may be true hybrids – the result of crossing the Large White with the Landrace and other long white breeds – or specialised pure strains selectively bred by one of the pig improvement companies who supply breeding stock to the wider industry. All of these pigs are white, with exceptional length of body and prick or semi-lop ears, the variation between the strains being their suitability to various management regimes, rather than their conformation or appearance. The Large White will primarily

be of interest to self-supporter as a 'terminal sire', i.e. the boar to mate to traditional breed sows to produce the slaughter generation of offspring. On a slightly larger scale, perhaps if pig keeping is to be the principal enterprise of the smallholding, producing either weaners or fat pigs for sale, consideration should be given to the various strains of Large White sows available. There are types available to suit most husbandry methods, including less intensive outdoor systems.

If it's likely that you'll be selling any of your output directly to an abattoir or butcher then white pigs will always be preferred, unless the buyer is someone who specialises in rare breed meats. If you'll be slaughtering any pigs at home, for your own consumption, then be aware that it's much easier to get the bristles off a white pig.

• Welsh

The Welsh is perhaps best described as a 'modern traditional' pig, and is therefore worthy of consideration by any producer who wants to do his bit for our native breed heritage, while keeping his eye firmly on the bottom line. The type developed many years ago in Cardiganshire, Pembrokeshire and Carmarthenshire, and became formally accepted as the indigenous Welsh breed when the Old Glamorgan Pig Society and the Welsh Pig Society merged under one title in 1922. The Welsh pig breeders of the time were clearly far-sighted, progressive men, and produced a type of pig that was well adapted to suit the rapidly changing tastes of the modern post war world

– this fact was recognised by a government committee in 1955, which recommended the Welsh as one of the three breeds on which the future of the UK pig industry should be based (the other two being the Landrace (which wasn't imported from Denmark, as many people believe, but from Sweden, and was actually called the Swedish Lantrass), and the Large White).

The Welsh is an exceptionally long, white pig, with lop ears and a fine head. Despite its claim to fame as one of the foundations of the modern British pig industry, it's now classified as 'at risk' by the RBST. However, the breed still has a loyal following in the heartland of its origins.

Selection of Breeding Stock

Having settled on a breed (or type) that takes your fancy, I'd advise buying 2 or 3 weaner gilts (young females). More care must be taken over the selection of this batch of pigs than will have been the case previously, when buying stock purely for fattening. In addition to the general indications of good health and conformation already mentioned, and the absence of any obvious defects such as under- or over-shot jaws or hernias, each animal must be examined with its potential breeding career in mind. Each gilt must possess *at least* 12 evenly spaced, well-developed teats, positioned as far forward as possible – the part of the udder towards the front end of the sow produces more milk than those teats tucked away between her hind legs. They should also be good examples of their breed as, you never know, one day you might want to produce a litter of

Only one sow?

Some people will say that it's unfair to keep a solitary sow, though I believe that if she's housed where she can keep an inquisitive eye on all that's going on around her, and where everyone who passes will stop to say a few words and scratch her back, she won't be lonesome. And besides, it's only going to be for the relatively short period between when her litter mates go to slaughter, and when she produces a litter of her own. From that point onwards there's always likely to be other pigs on the holding.

pure-bred offspring. If pedigree breeding is something you're considering then you'll also need to make sure that they've been registered with the BPA (or the relevant breed society, in the case of the British Lop), and have the appropriate eartags or tattoos. Initially, treat them just as you have been when rearing pigs for slaughter. Throughout the fattening period you'll have ample opportunity to study them and decide which of the three will make the best sow. Temperament will play a large part in the decision, and for a smallholder's pig I think it would be preferable to simply choose the friendliest. When the 'rejects' are slaughtered, the value of the pork produced ought to cover the cost of purchasing and rearing your sow.

Heat detection

Gilts can come into breeding condition from around five months of age (or even younger), although it's clearly inadvisable for them to be mated at this stage. In commercial herds gilts may be served at as young as 7 months of age, although I reckon 8 months should be the minimum. With traditional breeds, it may be necessary to wait until they're 9-11 months old, but leaving it too long can actually reduce the chances of success. Either way, growth and

Having a boar on the premises makes heat detection easy.

maturity are more important than age, so use bodyweight as a guide – gilts should weigh around 120kg at first mating.

Signs that a sow or gilt is 'on heat' or 'in season' (i.e. ready to be mated) include enlargement and reddening of the vulva (although the colour change can be difficult to spot in dark-skinned pigs), and general agitation. Behavioural changes are much more noticeable if there's a boar in the vicinity. Some sows are in season for only a very brief period, but in others the signs may be evident for several days before she'll actually stand to be served. To determine readiness for mating, apply firm pressure to the sow's back, whereupon she should stand rock steady, with perhaps an expectant smile on her face! From the time that she first stands in this way she'll remain in season for about 48 hours. However, ovulation (the optimum time for mating, when the 'eggs' are shed) occurs during the second

half of this 48 hour period, so it's important that you don't rush in and inseminate her as soon as she stands, as early matings are unlikely to be successful. Nor do you want to leave it too late, or you'll risk missing the season altogether. Therefore, the usual practice, whether using A.I. or natural service, is for the sow to be mated approximately 12 hours after standing oestrus is first detected, and again 12 hours later. Pigs aren't seasonal breeders so, unless mating is successful, they'll continue to come on heat at 21 day intervals throughout the year.

TIP

As a sow gets older, the number of piglets born in each litter will decline, and it is up to you to determine at what point the litter size is getting too small to be viable. The productive life of a sow in a commercial herd is usually fairly short – perhaps as little as 3-4 years – but on a smallholding she may be justifiably retained for much longer. In general terms, production falls fairly rapidly from about the sixth litter onwards, but some of the traditional breeds will typically produce smaller litters over a longer life. Regular breeding (i.e. 2 litters per sow per year) will help maintain fertility, so sows should be mated as soon as they come on heat after weaning (usually 4 days). Leaving a longer interval will increase the risk of the sow failing to conceive, and becoming a non-productive 'barrener'.

Artificial insemination

As in other species, the use of A.I. gives you access to the best sires in the breed, without the hassle and expense of owning a male or travelling long distances to visit a stud. There's also the advantage that A.I. in pigs is relatively easy to carry out yourself, which helps keeps the overall cost at an acceptable level. Semen can be ordered online for next day delivery, and for about £20 you'll get enough for 3 inseminations, together with the necessary catheters.

How it's done

The sow must first be encouraged to stand by applying pressure to her back. It helps to have someone positioned at her head to discourage her from moving forward. Skittish animals can be penned behind a gate, or in a farrowing crate if you have one.

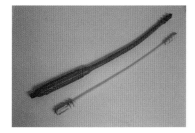

Two types of A.I. catheter.

The spiral end of the catheter should be lubricated with a few drops of semen, and gently inserted into the vulva. Take care to ensure that the tip is angled upwards to avoid the risk of it accidentally entering the bladder. When resistance is felt (after about a third to half the length of the catheter has been inserted), gently rotate it anti-clockwise until it locks into place – this engages the screw thread on the end of the catheter into the corresponding thread in the cervix of the sow. Strange as it may seem, this is exactly what happens during a natural mating, although quite how the boar manages to rotate his penis through several revolutions remains a mystery to me. (N.B. Some newer types of disposable catheters are not threaded at the tip, but have a soft foam plug that blocks the cervix. Therefore they don't need to be 'screwed in' in the same way.)

Connect the semen bottle to the catheter and hold it up to encourage it to flow. If, after 10 minutes or so, the semen still isn't flowing from the bottle, then it may be gently squeezed while the catheter is moved back and forward slightly. The catheter and the sow's tail should be held together in one hand, ensuring that if the sow moves forward, the catheter won't be dislodged at a critical stage in the proceedings.

When the catheter is removed (remember – clockwise to unscrew it) there should be very little leakage of semen from the sow. Make sure you write down the service date – it's easily forgotten if entrusted to memory, leading to obvious problems later – and remember to look out in 3 weeks time for any signs of her returning to heat.

If you've got a re-usable catheter, it should be thoroughly rinsed out with cold water after use, and then sterilised by boiling. On no account should soap or detergent be used. The catheter must be completely dry, both inside and out, before use, which means you really need two of them in order to carry out two inseminations 12 hours apart.

Natural service

Maiden gilts are notoriously difficult to get in-pig using A.I., and it seems to get more difficult with each missed opportunity. It would be best to use a boar for the first time, and return to A.I. thereafter. Either take the sow to visit someone else's boar, or buy in a young male pig and keep him just long enough to mate the sow before fattening him for the freezer, giving you a supply of pork to be getting on with while you wait for your home-bred pigs to be ready. We have done this on several occasions, and it works well.

It always used to be stated that at least 6 sows would be required in order to justify keeping a resident boar. Nowadays, however, movement restrictions make it much less convenient to take a sow away to be mated, as there is no longer an exemption to the 21 day standstill for breeding purposes. Increased awareness of bio-security has also made many breeders reluctant to take in visiting sows. In the light of this, and coupled with the fact that there are fewer small-scale producers who keep a boar these days anyway, I feel that 2-3 sows may be sufficient number to make it worthwhile having your own stud male. If there are a number of other small-scale pig producers in your area, you might be able to subsidise the cost of keeping a boar by making him available to others, although bear in mind what I said earlier about bio-security. Also, be aware that you'll need suitable accommodation to house visiting sows for 21 days, and, during that period you won't be able to move any pigs off your holding.

Natural service.

Always put the sow in with the boar, not the boar in with sow. In common with other nest-making animals, a sow is often defensive of her own territory, and may react badly to the introduction of a stranger. Conflict must be avoided, particularly when using a young boar for the first time. Besides, the boar will feel more confident about the whole business if he's on his home ground.

Don't even think about keeping a boar unless your level of skill in stockmanship is really up to it. The boar is a potentially dangerous animal, weighing perhaps half a tonne, and requiring careful handling. Don't take any chances!

Service routine

If your sows live outdoors you could simply run the boar out with them and let nature take its course. This is all very well, but it doesn't give you much control over the timing of events. More to the point, it doesn't give you much control over your boar, and should he decide to cut up rough you are going to have problems.

Remember, the boar is bigger, heavier and stronger than you are. Another potential problem associated with this rather easy-going system of pig keeping is that the boar may form a strong attachment to one particular sow, to the exclusion of all others. Having served her repeatedly for the duration of her heat period,

he'll be too exhausted to give any consideration to her herd mates.

In a truly free-range system, where matings are likely to take place unobserved, an experienced mature boar is a must – he should have proved his capabilities under more controlled conditions before being turned out to run with his sows. Young boars are notoriously inept lovers, and are just as likely to mount the head end of the sow as the rear. When they do eventually discover the right end, their aim tends to be pretty poor. Of course they will get the hang of it in the end, but the long delay and all the fooling about can be pretty frustrating for the sow, who will become restless and ultimately refuse to stand, meaning a missed opportunity, and a further 3 week wait for another attempt.

A compromise on the outdoor system would be to house the boar in a moveable fold unit within the paddock in which the sows reside. Any sow in season will naturally gravitate towards the pen containing the boar, and it should be a simple matter to let her in for supervised service.

Taken all round, I think it's best to keep the boar indoors, in purpose-built accommodation, and introduce the sow to him as and when required. Assuming that she is properly on heat (and the boar will be able to tell a lot better than you can), a certain amount of courtship will take place before the actual act of mating, although this shouldn't be prolonged. Once the sow is standing well, the boar will begin to paw at her with a foreleg, preparatory to jumping, so at this point he should be gently guided around to the sow's rear using a pig board (a 30" square piece of plywood is ideal). If the boar is particularly small (or the sow particularly large), you might need to align the pair of them in such a way that a step or slope in the floor of the sty gives him a bit of a leg-up. It's also a good idea to hold the sow's tail to one side as he mounts.

Once the boar is in position, you'll see that he's rapidly extending and retracting his penis, apparently thrusting every which way but the right one, so you'll have to guide him in the correct direction. Don't handle the penis itself, but, by parting the lips of the sow's vulva with one hand, and holding the sheath of the boar in the other, you

A board should be used when moving pigs, and in particular when handling a boar.

should be able to direct his next attempt into the correct orifice. He'll then thrust deeply, and his penis locks into the cervix of the sow. (If you're thinking that this all sounds like a lot of unnecessary palaver, just remember that repeated failures will result in an exhausted and disillusioned boar, a bad-tempered sow, and 3 weeks of lost production. However, once a young boar has got the hang of it, he can generally be relied upon to cover his sows unsupervised thereafter, so it's well worth giving him a bit of a helping hand at the outset).

Copulation may take some time. 20 minutes or so wouldn't be excessive. If the sow attempts to move forward she should be gently discouraged from doing so (use the board again) until the boar has had time to extricate himself. As soon as he's dismounted, the sow should be removed. Re-introduce her for a second mating after 12 hours or so, and remember to record the date.

The length of gestation is 114 days (or 3 months, 3 weeks and 3 days).

Feeding during pregnancy

There's no hard-and-fast rules governing the quantities of feed required by the in-pig sow. Common sense must prevail, with the regime being based on the body condition of the individual animal. In the case of a mature sow, it's likely that at the time of service she was a bit on the thin side, having just finished rearing her previous litter. It's not uncommon for a lean sow to gain 90-100lb in bodyweight during pregnancy, with the aim being to have her in tip-top condition by the time she farrows – you can rest assured she'll lose it all again once she's suckling a large and hungry litter! Sows are notorious for 'milking off their backs', and it's your job to ensure that these fluctuations in body condition remain within reasonable parameters.

The unborn litter doesn't begin to make any significant demands on the sow until around the seventh week of pregnancy, so during the early part of gestation she should gain body condition without high levels of feeding. After the seventh week the weight of the litter increases dramatically, and by full term the sow may be carrying around 30-40lb of piglets. In addition to the nutritional drain inflicted upon the sow, the rapidly developing litter takes up a considerable amount of space in her body cavity. Therefore, bulky feeds should be cut down during the latter stages of gestation. Raw potatoes in particular should be reduced at this stage, if not avoided altogether, as they may cause constipation if fed close to farrowing. Likewise, it's best not to feed apples during late pregnancy and early lactation, as they can cause acidity in the sow's milk, leading to digestive upsets in the young piglets.

Unless you can be sure that your home-produced feeds are sufficiently high in protein, it would be wise to use a proprietary sow ration for the last two weeks. However, if you've got plenty of surplus milk from your house cow, which you can mix with a bit of rolled barley, you should be able to keep the amount of expensive concentrates used to a minimum.

The feeding of a gilt during pregnancy will differ slightly from the requirements of a sow. Gilts won't be in poor condition through having just reared a litter, so there is no need to aim for a large increase in bodyweight during the first seven weeks. However, it must be remembered that the gilt is a young animal, and, as such, will still be growing – she's unlikely to reach her full adult size until after her first farrowing. Therefore the ration needs to be slightly higher in protein than would be necessary for a mature sow. On no account, however, should the sow or gilt be made over-fat; fatness results in increased embryonic losses, leading to very poor numbers of live pigs born per litter.

As a general guide, proprietary rations can be fed to sows and gilts at a level of about 1.5% of the animal's bodyweight. Therefore, a gilt may be needing around 4lb / day at service, rising to about 5½lb at farrowing. Provided that you've got a rough idea of the relative nutritional value of any additional feeds you may have at your disposal (e.g. milk, vegetable waste, barley, root crops etc.), you should be able to adjust the proportions accordingly to ensure that the diet remains reasonably well balanced. However, you can't simply replace sow nuts with other feeds on a 'pound for pound' basis.

Farrowing quarters

Although there's no reason at all why a sow shouldn't farrow outdoors in an ark or some similar temporary accommodation, it'll make your life a lot easier if you can move her into more convenient quarters. Not all sows make good mothers, and even the best of them are rather clumsy, so if you can be on hand to supervise the birthing process – and assist if necessary – you'll undoubtedly end up with more live piglets.

Observation is key, so, although a traditional style sty can easily be used to house a farrowing sow, you might find that trying to keep an eye on the proceedings in a typical low-roofed dark shed, with only a small 'pop-hole' for access, will be difficult. Also, every time you crawl in to take a look you'll be disturbing the sow, and, if she's at all fractious, putting yourself in a potentially dangerous position. It's better, therefore, to have a low-sided pen within a larger building, so you can observe the whole process over the wall, and only actually enter the pen if necessary.

You'll also need to create a safe area for the piglets. In its simplest form this could consist of a 'farrowing rail', a metal bar or piece of timber positioned approximately 8" from the wall, and 8" above the floor, which gives the young pigs somewhere to escape to as the sow lowers her bulk to the floor. However, the piglets will still tend to snuggle up to the sow for warmth, and so are at risk from smothering every time she moves. For total peace of

mind it's best to install a 'creep' area, with a heat lamp to draw the piglets away from the sow and into the safety of their own place. The creep needn't be a permanent fixture. I tend to use a short galvanised gate turned upside-down so that the wider gap is at the bottom, securely fixed across the most draught-free corner of the pen.

The heat lamp hangs behind this, where it's safe from damage by the sow. The piglets soon learn that it's nice and warm in the creep area, and quickly return there after suckling. However, it might be necessary to teach them where it is initially – I always put the newborn piglets into the creep area as soon as they've had their first drink from the sow. To begin with they just wander out again, but after a few attempts they begin to appreciate the benefits, and soon settle down to bask in the warmth of the lamp. From then on they're relatively safe.

Barley straw for bedding?

When a sow is in milk, or close to farrowing, her udder is very soft and delicate, and I have heard of cases where a sharp barley awn in the bedding has pierced the skin and worked its way in, causing abscesses and mastitis. Having said that, we nearly always bed our pigs on barley straw, and have even fed them barley on the sheaf, awns and all, and have seen no ill effects whatsoever. It might be the case that traditional breeds (particularly coloured ones), or sows that run outdoors, have thicker skins than their modern white counterparts.

Farrowing

Assuming that you've kept a record of when the sow was mated, move her into the farrowing pen a week or two before her litter is due, so she's got time to settle down. It's also a good idea to worm her at this point, and some people recommend washing the sow's tummy. As the due date approaches the sow will 'bag up', (i.e. udder development will take place), and you'll notice her whole body shape changing. Some pigs show signs a lot earlier than others, but by the final week all in-pig sows will look very deep-bodied. Behavioural changes will occur too, and the sow will spend a lot of time carrying mouthfuls of straw around, and worrying all her bedding into a big heap in the corner.

Provide sufficient bedding material to allow the sow to exhibit her natural nesting behaviour, but not so much that the piglets may be smothered.

How much straw to provide for a farrowing sow is always a dilemma – too much bedding results in smothered piglets, whereas too little doesn't enable the sow to exhibit her natural nesting behaviour, and won't provide much comfort or warmth. My own preference is to give the sow plenty of straw (about a wheelbarrowful) a few days before the piglets are due, so she's got a bit of time to chew it all up into a nice chaff-like consistency. She'll

If your piglets don't seem to be making use of the creep area then it's usually because it's too draughty, or you've got the lamp too high (about 18" is correct for newborn piglets). However, it may be that the pen you've provided for the sow to farrow in is simply too big, meaning that the piglets are tending to stay closer to the warmth of the sow, rather than cross a large open space in search of an alternative source of heat. Another possibility is that you may have provided too much bedding for the sow, enabling her to make a deep cosy bed that the piglets are reluctant to leave.

Once the piglets start using the creep you can adjust the height of the lamp according to their behaviour. If they lie piled up in a heap directly underneath the lamp then it's obviously a bit too high, whereas if they're sleeping around the perimeter of the area, leaving the centre clear, then the lamp is clearly too low.

eat a fair bit of it too, and some will become soiled and be mucked out, so by the time she actually begins to farrow the quantity has usually been reduced to a more manageable amount. On balance, less is best, so I will remove some if I think she's still got too much. I can always put it back in once the piglets are a few days old, and a bit stronger. In the creep area I generally use wood shavings or sawdust as bedding. One of our sows flat refuses to have any bedding at any time. It always makes me feel a bit guilty, seeing her lying there on bare concrete, but that's clearly the way she likes it, as, no matter how much (or how little) straw I give her, she always throws the whole lot out!

As the time of birth draws closer the skin of the sow's belly develops a silky sheen. As soon as I see this I begin to make frequent examinations of her teats, and from the time I can first draw a squirt

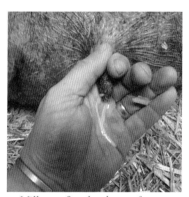

Milk can first be drawn from the teats about 7 hours before the birth.

of milk I know it'll be less than 7 hours until she farrows. Once she becomes 'recumbent' (a lovely word, which basically means she lies down and doesn't want to get up again) and begins talking to her unborn litter, parturition is imminent. Contractions will be seen as tremors passing through the whole sow, accompanied by momentary stiffening of the legs, and, sure enough, the little

Parturition is iminent when the sow becomes recumbent.

pigs will soon begin to leave the production line at a rate of about one every twenty minutes or so.

As soon as each piglet is born (which may be either head first or hind legs first) it'll give a convulsive shake to free itself from the enclosing membranes (particularly small or weak piglets might need a bit of help here), and immediately totter around to the milk bar. Initially it makes slow progress, due to being tethered to the sow by the umbilical cord, but this soon breaks. Sometimes a rather long length remains attached to the piglet, causing it some inconvenience, in which case it should be nipped off a little closer to the body by rubbing between finger and thumbnail. It's quite a good idea to spray a bit of bactakil (or similar antiseptic) on the navels of all the new born piglets while you're at it.

What can go wrong?

Thankfully, with pigs there are seldom any complications associated with farrowing. Occasionally, if there's been a particularly long interval after the delivery of the previous piglet, an examination may reveal an exceptionally large one jammed like a cork in a bottle, or maybe two piglets jostling for space trying to come out together. As with

Contented sow and litter.

TIP

In situations where it is inadvisable to enter the pen you can lean over with a stiff yard broom and gently 'sweep' the piglets into the safe area.

When you see the piglets nibbling at their mother's ration, start to offer them some feed of their own.

other livestock, you should always wear a shoulder-length obstetric glove and use plenty of lubricant when carrying out examinations or assisting delivery.

Due to the torpedo shape of young pigs you don't get the seemingly inexplicable jumble of limbs in need of manipulation, as you may find with sheep and goats. Generally all that's needed is to grasp the first pair of little legs you encounter and pull, gently but firmly.

Sometimes several piglets will be born in very quick succession, with the result that the first one is immediately smothered by the membranes and fluids that accompany those that follow. This is a prime example of why it's always a good idea to be on hand to observe the farrowing – it's a simple matter to extricate the one at the bottom of the heap and send him off in the right direction, but without your intervention he'd surely be a goner. Similarly, the last piglet(s) may be delivered

together with the afterbirth, and will need to be rescued. Incidentally, once farrowing is complete, sows will, if given the chance, eat all of the afterbirth. This is entirely natural behaviour, although in our experience it always makes them horribly sick, so we remove it from the pen.

From time to time one comes across a sow that's very restless during farrowing, especially in stormy weather. Usually this just consists of constantly standing up and lying down again, and frequent shifting of position, with the result that the young pigs get trampled or squashed. However, it might occasionally extend to attacks on the piglets (or even you!). Under these circumstances it's best to remove the piglets as soon as they're born and put them in a box under the heat lamp. They can all be returned to their mother once farrowing is complete and she has calmed down. If she's still being awkward then a gallon of homebrew will work wonders!

Feeding the sow and litter

Resist the temptation to immediately increase the sow's food ration straight after farrowing – you'll only make her ill. In fact, for the first couple of days it's best to cut the feed back to just under what she was getting before farrowing, and then gradually increase it to the required level over the next ten days or so. As a rough guide, she should be getting 4lb, plus an additional ½lb for each piglet she's rearing. Some additional feed can be provided for the piglets in the creep area from about 3 weeks old, or earlier if you've seen them nibbling at their mother's ration. I'd recommend buying one bag per litter of the best quality creep feed you can afford, in order to give the little pigs the best possible start in life. Begin by just sprinkling a handful of pellets on the floor, and gradually increase the amount when they're seen to be eating it.

Anaemia

Anaemia is a very common problem in piglets born indoors. Their red blood cell count falls quite rapidly after birth (particularly in individuals which bled excessively from the navel), and often drops temporarily below the optimum level. The sow's milk contains less than 7% of the piglets' iron requirements, so they need to obtain it from other sources. Outdoor litters will get what they need from the soil, but it is common practice in indoor commercial pig units to administer iron by injection.

Our own preferred method, when we have piglets born indoors, is to place a large lump of turf in the creep area for them to nibble at.
Signs of iron deficiency include a greyish yellow scour at about a week old. Generally, if you see this, placing a turf or a spadeful of earth in the creep will soon stop the problem.

If you've got plenty of spare milk from your house cow then some can be offered to the piglets in a shallow dish – they'll soon work out what they're supposed to do with it.

Keep a close eye on the sow's udder during the suckling period,

Tooth clipping

Clipping the 'tusk' teeth of newborn piglets is carried out to prevent the little pigs from damaging the sow's udder, and also to prevent them tearing each other's faces as they jostle for space at the 'milk bar'. The 8 teeth (two each side in both the top and bottom jaw) are cut off close to the gum using a small pair of side cutters, similar to those that are used to clip a dog's toenails. It used to be acceptable routine practice, but now the law states that it can only be carried out where a specific problem has been identified, (i.e. not as a purely preventative measure), and, in any case, before the pigs are one week old. The trouble is that problems do not usually manifest themselves until the litter is more than 7 days old, by which time it's too late (legally). Personally, I would always clip the teeth of larger litters (8+), where damage is almost inevitable, but leave smaller litters unclipped.

for any evidence of wounds caused by the piglets' teeth, and also look for injuries to the piglet's faces caused by fighting over teats. Although the piglets will recover quite quickly after weaning, damage to the sow's udder will have more long term consequences, possibly resulting in mastitis and loss of milk production in part of her udder. This may seriously compromise her ability to rear future litters, and could result in the animal having to be culled. To prevent this, consider clipping the teeth of newborn piglets.

Weaning

While I wouldn't advocate the sort of very early (3–4 weeks) weaning that's carried out on commercial farms these days, there's certainly

nothing to be gained by delaying weaning beyond the optimum time – leaving the piglets with the sow too long will only pull her down in condition, and besides, the sooner they're weaned, the sooner she'll be back in pig again, which is what you want.

Eight weeks is about right, in my opinion, although to a certain extent you'll have to be guided by the body condition of the sow – if she's looking really run down it might be best to get the piglets off her at 6-7 weeks. On the other hand, in slower growing traditional breeds such as Tamworths, weaning can reasonably be delayed until the little pigs are 10 weeks old, if the sow is coping well enough.

To reduce stress at weaning, always take the sow away and

A nice group of pigs, ready for slaughter.
Notice that the males haven't been castrated.

Boar taint

So called 'boar taint' is a funny thing. Some people (particularly from the older generation) insist that the meat from un-castrated male pigs is more or less inedible, while others cannot detect any discernible variation in flavour at all! I suspect there's more than a little prejudice involved, and that there's a bit of a psychological effect coming into play too – it's rather like people who insist that goat's milk tastes horrible, but, unless they're actually told that they're drinking goat's milk in their tea, they don't notice any difference.

I've slaughtered male pigs up to at least 15 months of age, and, even in young boars that have sired litters, we've not experienced the effects of boar taint. The only time we've noticed any adverse flavour in pork from a male animal was in the case of a much younger animal (20 weeks) that had been badly stressed when loading for transport to the abattoir.

In conclusion, therefore, I would say keep stress levels and journey times to an absolute minimum, and, for best results, slaughter your pigs at home, in the friendly environment that they are used to.

leave the piglets in their familiar surroundings. They shouldn't suffer any setback, particularly if you've got some surplus milk to mix with their feed. Weaning time is also a good opportunity to worm the whole litter.

The sow's ration should be cut back to the maintenance level, although don't restrict her fluid intake at all, even if her udder does look rather full and uncomfortable. In fact, a wet 'mash' is better for her than dry pellets at this stage. Within about 4 days of weaning she should be in season, and so the whole cycle begins again…

Castration

A lot of older books on pig keeping will state that it's necessary to castrate male weaners to avoid the risk of 'boar taint' spoiling the meat, and many give quite detailed instructions on how to do it. Due to the anatomy of the pig you can't use a simple method like rubber rings, as you could do with lambs, calves and goat kids, so surgical castration would be the only option. However, these days very few, if any, male pigs destined for slaughter will be castrated. There's simply no need. Your pigs (even those that you've run on for bacon) will be going to slaughter at a far younger age than would have been the case in the past, and boar taint isn't likely to be an issue at that stage.

Goats

"The household goat, with her modest housing requirements and lavish milk yield in relation to her small stature, and her ability to make use of weedy corners and all the extras from the vegetable garden, has proved herself invaluable to those attempting some measure of self-sufficiency."
David Mackenzie

"Goats are creatures I would never keep if I could possibly keep cows... I like goats one way only – and that is in curry."
John Seymour

Back in the early 1980s, when my family first took the plunge and embarked on a life of self-sufficiency, home dairying was the norm amongst self-supporters, and milking goats formed the mainstay of most peoples' smallholding activities. This is interesting when you consider that we all drew our inspiration from the example of John Seymour. For some reason, his championing of the house cow was the one thing all his disciples chose to ignore, and I can only assume that this was because, on the whole, people who were new to livestock keeping were rather frightened of cattle, and felt that

goats, due to their smaller size, would be a bit less daunting. Even Seymour, realising, perhaps, that a little more tact and diplomacy might sell more copies, moderated his tone slightly in later books, stating that *"for the self-supporting smallholder the goat can quite easily be the perfect dairy animal. For the person with only a garden the goat may be the only possible dairy animal"*.

Anyway, whatever the reasoning (and despite the fact that they had sufficient land and outbuildings to have kept a cow), goats were the first livestock to arrive on my parents' holding, and remained the principal source of dairy products for the family for almost 20 years. Dot and I continued to keep goats during the years we lived on Bardsey Island, and found that they suited our purposes very well. However, at that time there was no cost associated with our use of the land. Any hay and crops grown for our goats' consumption were effectively free, and we were able to sell sufficient milk on a daily basis to the other island residents to offset expenditure on the small amount of purchased feed that we used. Keeping our own billy wasn't a problem, and the kids (which always seemed to be born in threes), were easily slaughtered and butchered at home. Nevertheless, when we returned to the mainland, and had to make our chosen lifestyle pay its way, we found that goats no longer enabled us to achieve our objective, for the simple reason that, on a small scale, there was no way of generating sufficient cash income from them in order to cover the costs of milk production. Gone are the days when you could simply hang a "goats' milk for sale" sign on the farm gate, as my parents did, and the kids aren't

Main and inset: This little goat house is a converted poultry shed.

while you're carrying out tasks like mucking out, and if part of the yard can be roofed over, then so much the better. The outdoor area should have its own water trough, and also a high-level hayrack in which you can place tree prunings and so on for them to browse at.

Hayracks should preferably be covered.

worth anything either. In fact, home-produced goats' milk could easily end up costing you more than bought milk. The cow, on the other hand, produces a valuable calf of her own every year, and enough milk to raise several more, which means that recovering the cost of producing milk for home consumption is relatively straightforward. Having said all that, there's certainly a place for goats on very small holdings with limited resources, and, if our circumstances were to change, I'd have no hesitation in going back to them.

Of course it's possible to generate an income from 'commercial' goat keeping on a slightly larger scale, particularly if the milk is processed and sold in the form of cheese. However, going down this route does expose the smallholder to an additional raft of legislation, over and above that already inflicted upon livestock keepers.

Housing

Goats aren't hardy creatures, and will need access to some kind of housing all year round. In fact, throughout the course of a year they'll actually spend more time indoors than out. However, housing for a couple of goats need not be elaborate, and it's usually possible to adapt some existing outbuilding, or construct something yourself. Full details of the housing requirements for various ages and categories of goats are given on pages 161 - 162.

If your plans for domestic milk production are more ambitious than this, then probably you ought to be considering a cow. Where goats are the animal of choice due to lack of space (e.g. in the case of the back garden smallholder), a concreted yard area should be provided adjacent to the goat shed, where they can be allowed to exercise in fine weather, and also to get them out of the way

Within the indoor pen(s) you'll need to provide hay racks (preferably covered ones, as goats are inclined to stand up on their hind legs and pull all the hay out from the top of an open rack, and once it's been on the floor they won't touch it), troughs or buckets for feed, and a clean water supply. A lot of people hang the buckets outside the goat's pen, with pop-holes through which they put their heads to eat and drink, which seems to work well. If hay is to be fed in nets rather than racks, then these must be of a fairly small mesh, and shouldn't be used in pens containing young kids or horned goats. (Although, to be honest, we used home-made hay nets for all our goats (old and young, horned and otherwise) for years, and never experienced any trouble.)

Automatic self-fill water bowls in the goat house will save you an awful lot of time, and I'm always surprised that more people don't fit them.

Goats housed in dismantlable pens, for ease of mucking out. Notice the automatic self-fill water bowl mounted on the far wall.

Access to feed and water via a pop-hole.

Dairy goats at pasture.

TIP

It's not ideal for goats to share pasture with sheep, which is a pity as smallholders often want to keep both species. The reason for this is that adult goats don't develop a natural immunity to nematode infection in the same way that sheep do, and neither are the available treatments so effective in goats. Therefore, repeated dosing of goats may lead to the parasites developing resistance to the drug, making it impossible to control them in sheep, where they pose a very real risk to the health of young lambs at pasture.

Pasture

Goats are browsers by nature, so won't necessarily make optimum use of pasture – they much prefer the hedgerows surrounding a field. That's not to say they won't utilise grassland efficiently – they will, if you contain them securely. A series of electric fenced paddocks around which the goats can be moved in rotation is fine, but really is more suited to larger scale goat keeping enterprises. On the smallholding, it's the goat's ability to make use of the scrubby corners, where brambles and nettles tend to dominate, that makes all the difference. Therefore, it would be best to fence off some of the rough headlands for use by the goats, and retain the better pasture for other purposes, such as haymaking.

Goats will quickly wreck ordinary stock fencing, as they put their feet up on it to reach whatever's on the other side. Barbed wire along the top will help to a degree, but there's always the risk of a badly damaged udder if some bolder individual tries to make a break for it. A couple of strands of electric fence along the inside of the stock wire would be a better bet. Temporary enclosures can be made using electric flexinets, but, as with hay nets, they're not recommended for use with horned goats or young kids.

Tethering

When my family started keeping goats, tethering was a popular way of managing their access to grazing. You'd often see goats tethered on roadside verges, patches of wasteland, and even on village playing fields, and mail order smallholding supplies companies of the time always stocked chains and stakes, not only for goats but for pigs and cattle too. It's very much fallen out of vogue nowadays, but we found a combination of both paddock and tether based systems enabled us to make optimum use of the available land on our rather poorly-fenced smallholding.

If you do decide to tether your goats, chains must be at least 3 metres long (preferably 4 metres), and must have 2 swivels (one at each end), in addition to being able to rotate freely around the head of the ground stake. You also need to ensure that the area is free of obstructions on which the chain may become entangled, and not so close to walls, fences or steep banks that a goat may jump and hang herself. Water will need to be provided, but it's best to go and offer a drink several times a day, rather than leave a bucket where it'll inevitably get knocked over. Goats also require shelter, which can be quite difficult to arrange when they're tethered. Trees may give shade from direct sunshine, but if it starts to rain they need to be brought in.

Feeding

Anyone who tells you that goats will eat anything clearly doesn't know what they're talking about. The fact is they'll only ever eat the very best of anything, although it's true that their tastes are wide and varied. Unfortunately, this rather fussy attitude can result in quite a lot of wastage in the form of rejected hay or silage, and uneaten, trampled grazing.

On the whole I've found well-bred, high-yielding goats to be far more selective in what they eat than poorer quality 'scrub' goats. Therefore, in order to achieve the level of performance that they're capable of, you'll need to pander to their whims. The scrub goat, on the other hand, although she won't give anything like the quantity of milk, may actually prove to be

more economical on account of her simpler dietary requirements – if she provides enough milk for your daily needs at minimal cost, then what more do you want?

There's no getting away from the fact that bought-in concentrates formulated especially for goats are extremely expensive. With the aforementioned scrub animals you might get away with feeding a much cheaper 'general purpose' ruminant ration, but either way you're going to have to buy in some feed. We used to eke ours out using home-grown barley, although again, this mightn't be suitable for heavy milkers.

The lactating nanny is going to need something in the region of 1.5-2kg of concentrate feed per day (depending on yield), in addition to the forage-based part of her diet. Youngstock and goats not in milk will also need some hard feed daily. Not much, admittedly, but they'll always need a bit. (Store cattle and dry cows, on the other hand, will manage very well with just grass, silage or hay.)

Hay for goats needn't be of particularly good quality in the conventional sense, in that they're quite happy if a fair proportion of it is made up of thistles, nettles and docks, but it must be well made, and not at all dusty or mouldy. Weedy hay won't have such a high nutritional value as a predominantly grass and clover-based crop, which is therefore preferred for high yielders (although whether or not the goats prefer it is another matter). Soft, fine hay should be avoided. Silage ought to be high in dry matter (e.g. 'haylage'), have a sweet smell, and be free from moulds. On the whole, good quality high dry matter silage will result in higher

milk yields than hay. Conserved forages can be fed more or less ad-lib, with the hay racks being replenished at both ends of the day during the winter months. In the summer they'll need to be given hay in the evening, and also during the daytime if they're remaining indoors due to poor weather.

Given that goats spend quite a lot of time housed, and are wasteful eaters, you'll need to budget for an allowance of 14-16 conventional-sized bales of hay per goat per year.

TIP

You should always provide your goats with access to a mineral lick, but need to be aware that some products formulated for goats contain high levels of copper, and are therefore not suitable for sheep. If you do have sheep on your holding as well, it might be best to locate the goats' lick in their night quarters, rather than in the field.

One thing that goats really love is bundles of branches to nibble at – they'll strip the whole lot down to bare wood – so if they're confined to their shed at any time, for example when it's pouring with rain, go out and about with a pair of secateurs and prune back some of those overgrown hedgerows. For the back garden goat, this type of food can form a major part of the diet, and it's free, provided that you can find a suitable location (e.g. a patch of waste ground, common land, a verge alongside a quiet lane, etc.) where it's acceptable for you to forage. In our experience their favourite species are sycamore, ash, willow and elder (which is handy, because all of these will thrive on a 'cut-and-come-again' regime). They'll also enjoy holly, ivy (in moderation), brambles, and most other broad-leafed trees. Acorns are good – we used to gather them by the sackful and dry them out next to the Rayburn – but should only be fed in small quantities, or they'll cause constipation. Evergreens should be avoided (with the exception of those given above), as should ornamental plants and shrubs, but they'll gladly consume all prunings from your fruit trees and bushes, including raspberry canes. In fact, raspberry leaves are a very good thing to feed a goat just before she gives birth.

There's also an awful lot of goat food that can be gleaned from the vegetable garden. In fact, if you've got space, it would be worth growing some additional crops purely for fodder. All goats, without exception, are very partial to members of the cabbage family, but, like everything else, they should be fed in moderation as part of a balanced diet. Allowing goats to consume an excess of brassicas could result in anaemia and / or goitre. Also you may detect a 'cabbagey' taint in the milk, so it is best to feed brassicas only after milking, or reserve them for youngstock and dry nannies.

Onions and leeks also adversely affect the flavour of the milk, and so too might swedes. Regarding other vegetables, goats can safely eat pretty much what we eat from the garden, although, like us, they do have their preferences. Be aware that not all parts of all plants are edible – potato tops, for example, are poisonous to goats, but the tubers are fine. A couple of favourites with our goats were

Russian comfrey

The benefits of comfrey, both as a feedstuff and for medicinal purposes (another name for it is 'knitbone'), have long been recognised. With a crude protein content of around 16%, the plant compares favourably with other forage crops, and its 'cut-and-come-again' nature allows for relatively high yields to be obtained (around 2 tonnes of dry matter per hectare per month). In addition to being fed to livestock as a fresh crop, it has been successfully made into both hay and silage. *The Smallholder's Encyclopædia*, published in 1943, describes comfrey as *"a valuable fodder crop that should be much more extensively grown, in particular the Russian type if available."*

However, there's no getting away from the fact that comfrey contains toxic alkaloids, similar to those found in ragwort, which can cause serious liver and lung damage. These substances have an accumulative effect within the body, so it's likely that an animal would have to consume considerable quantities on a regular basis, over a long period of time, for there to be any adverse consequences. Therefore, it would stand to reason that shorter-lived species – such as rabbits, pigs and sheep – are less likely to develop ill effects than longer-living animals like horses and cattle. Goats would fall somewhere in the middle, I suppose. It's also likely that the degree of toxicity may vary according to the stage of growth of the plant, although even here no two authors seem able to agree, with some stating that the crop should be cut before it flowers, and others insisting that it must be allowed to flower before harvest.

There are many 'toxic' substances which may be beneficial in small doses, yet poisonous if consumed to excess (such as red wine or beer!), and comfrey is no different. With a few notable exceptions, most authors advise feeding comfrey with caution, on a 'little and often' basis. The exceptions are, on the one hand, those who won't touch it with a bargepole, and on the other hand those who swear by the stuff, shovelling it into their animals up to the maximum and claiming high levels of health, vigour and productivity as a result.

My parents always had a comfrey bed on their smallholding, and we do too. Although it has never been part of our animals' regular diet, it is always offered to anything that looks a bit off colour or has a jaded appetite, to good effect. Comfrey can also be used to make a fantastic liquid fertiliser for use in the garden, and, if you bury a few barrow loads of the fresh leaves in a hole in the ground, and plant pumpkins on the top, you'll grow whoppers!

pea haulms and maize stalks. Some were very keen on broad bean pods, but others wouldn't touch them. One crop we used to grow specifically for the goats was mangels. These we would lift and store in a clamp for winter use. To chop root crops for feeding, place them in a sturdy wooden box and attack with a spade.

251

General management

On a day-to-day basis, goats are far more demanding than either sheep or cattle, although much of the routine husbandry is more or less the same. The principal difference being that, because goats spend so much time indoors, there's a lot more fetching and carrying of feed, water and hay involved with goat keeping than there is with other ruminants. A typical goat keeper's day might be as follows:

- **7.00 am** – Give the first concentrate feed of the day. Where goats are housed in groups it might be necessary to separate them for feeding, as they're not particularly inclined to share.
- **8.00 am** – Milking. Any high yielders requiring extra concentrates can be given their additional ration now.
- **8.30 am** (or later, if milking takes longer) – On fine days in summer, turn the goats out to pasture after milking. Fresh water should be available in the field. Tethered goats will need to be offered water several times during the day. In winter, or in bad weather, the goats remain indoors, so re-fill hayracks and water buckets.
- **9.00 am** – Washing down the milking area, bottle feeding kids, etc.
- **1.00 pm** – Give a feed of branches, leafy vegetables or chopped roots to housed or yarded goats. Check on any goats at pasture. Tethered goats will need checking more frequently.
- **4.30 pm** (or maybe later in mid summer) – Measure out concentrate feed then allow the goats to return from pasture. Once they're used to the fact that their food will be ready and waiting for them then all you'll have to do is open the field gate (or unclip the tethers) and let them run.

- **5.00 pm** – If necessary, move tethers or electric fencing ready for the next day's grazing.
- **6.00 pm** – Evening milking – the same routine as the morning. Any particularly low yielders, or goats being dried off, won't need milking in the evening.
- **6.30 pm** (or later, if milking takes longer) – Re-fill hayracks and water buckets.
- **7.00 pm** – Washing down milking area, bottle feeding kids, etc.
- **9.00 pm** – Final check round, and top up water buckets if required.

This is, of course, just a very general guide, and the details will change according to individual circumstances and other variable factors. For example, when kids are very young they'll need four bottle feeds per day, gradually reducing to a more convenient two.

Also, should the weather turn wet after the goats have been put out to pasture, then they will need to be brought in again, unless provided with some kind of field shelter (which is quite difficult to arrange in the case of tethered animals). If they do get caught out in a heavy shower then it's advisable to dry them off with some old towels when you bring them in, as they're quite susceptible to chills.

Mucking out isn't a daily chore, as it is with housed cattle, because goats prefer to be kept on a 'deep litter' basis. They relish the warmth given off by the accumulated layers of decomposing dung and bedding, and are often credited with having invented the concept of underfloor heating. However, this does mean that the goat shed must be well ventilated to avoid a build up of foul air. Generally, mucking out is done twice a year, in the spring and in the autumn. I

have heard folk say they know it's time to muck out when the goats step over the gates of their pens.

The downside to the deep litter method is that, when mucking out time does come round, you're faced with a gargantuan task. Where more than just a couple of goats are kept I'd strongly advise that the shed in which they're housed is sufficiently roomy to allow access with a tractor and loader, and that all the pens and partitions can be dismantled.

Hoof clipping

Given the amount of time that the average goat spends indoors, it's understandable that they'll need their hooves trimmed fairly frequently – probably as often as every 4-6 weeks. The actual process of trimming a goat's feet is broadly similar to sheep, except that it's generally carried out with the animal standing up, as you would with a horse or pony. Use the same type of hoof clippers as used for sheep, not a penknife. Also, after cutting back the overgrown horn, a goat's feet should be rasped to get the whole of the bottom of the hoof level. A small surform is ideal for this, and can easily be bought at a hardware shop or builder's merchant.

Vet and med

Despite all their idiosyncrasies, goats are remarkably healthy animals, although they're not particularly stoical. Therefore, on the rare occasions when a goat does get sick, she tends to go downhill rather rapidly. It can also be pretty difficult to find a vet who really understands goats (they tend to just treat them like sheep), so, as with all animals, prevention is definitely better than cure.

A suitable health plan may include the following:

Clostridial vaccinations: Goats are not so badly affected as sheep, so the full '7-in-1' treatment isn't required. What's usually recommended is Lambivac, which protects goats against enterotoxaemia and tetanus.

They'll need an initial course of two injections (2ml, subcutaneous) given 4 weeks apart, followed by a single booster jab every six months (or more frequently if there's a history of these diseases within the herd).

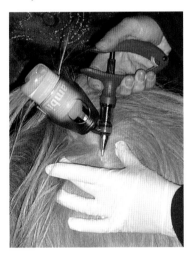

Adminsitering the clostridial vaccination.

Pasteurella vaccination: Ovipast is usually recommended for this. The regime is as for the clostridial vaccinations, except that a booster is only required annually.

Chorioptic mange: This affects the lower legs, and is often called 'heel mange'. It can be treated with Eprinex cattle pour-on.

Lice: These can be treated with Spot-on, as used for sheep, but we just used to dust our goats regularly with louse powder during the winter.

Internal parasites: It's best to use faecal egg counts to determine when worming should be carried out. There aren't any anthelmintic drenches licensed specifically for use in goats, making treatment rather difficult. This is why commercial dairy goat herds are often housed year round. Certain products commonly used in sheep can be prescribed for goats, using the 'cascade system', but higher dose rates may be needed, and lengthy milk withhold periods will apply.

Liver fluke: This is becoming more of a problem. Only one active ingredient (Albendazole) is licensed for use in animals that produce milk for human consumption. Other products may be used outside the lactating period.

Other health problems include:

Hypocalcaemia: Also known as calcium deficiency or milk fever, treatment is as for sheep, although an intravenous injection of calcium borogluconate will give far quicker results than one administered subcutaeneously.

Pregnancy toxaemia / acetonaemia: Like sheep, a goat that suffers from an energy deficit in late gestation is at risk from pregnancy toxaemia. Most likely to be affected are those that are overweight (because they were fed too much in early pregnancy, when they didn't really need it), or those carrying triplets or quads. Any goat that appears to lose its appetite

during the four weeks prior to kidding should be regularly dosed with propylene glycol. Pregnancy scanning can help avoid problems caused by inappropriate nutrition.

High-yielding goats are also at risk just after kidding, when the same condition is known as acetonaemia, characterised by the smell of pear drops on the animal's breath. In my limited experience this post-kidding form of the disease appears to occur more frequently, but the incidence probably varies hugely between different herds and management regimes. The outlook for an affected animal is pretty poor.

Coccidiosis: Apparently very common in housed kids, coccidiosis manifests itself as a particularly nasty diarrhoea, often bloodstained, and weight loss. It can be treated with Vecoxan, as used in lambs and calves.

Mastitis: Inflammation of the udder, characterised by heat, tenderness, enlargement or hardening of one or both 'quarters' (halves of the udder), accompanied by flakes, clots, or blood in the milk. Treatment is by antibiotics, but the disease may result in some permanent damage such as lumps in the udder and a reduced yield in future lactations.

Pay particular attention to hygiene at milking time, to reduce the risk of the problem spreading. Some goats seem to be particularly prone to mastitis, and it may reoccur year after year in these animals. They're best culled, as they provide a potential source of infection to the rest of the herd.

BREEDS AND BREEDING

The novice goat keeper isn't faced with the same bewildering range of breeds as the wannabe shepherd, so it ought to be much easier to make an appropriate choice of type.

There are, in fact, only around half-a-dozen recognised breeds of dairy goat in the UK, although there are also what's known as 'British' goats, which are basically crossbred animals produced from pedigree bloodlines, and named after the breed for which they show the greater likeness (e.g. any big white dairy goat, unless it's a registered pedigree Saanen, is likely to be described as a 'British Saanen'). An exception to this is the British Alpine – there is no equivalent type known simply as an 'Alpine'.

There are also a few non-dairy breeds such as the Pygmy, which need not even be considered by the self-supporter, and the Boer, which is ideal for crossing onto milking goats to produce kids for meat production.

Pedigree breeding isn't something we need to concern ourselves with here, as there's nothing to be gained by it unless you're particularly interested in that sort of thing, or want to exhibit your goats at shows. However, pedigree details backed up with milk yield records can be a big help in determining whether a particular animal (even a crossbred) is likely to suit your purposes, so it's always worth asking vendors for this information. At the end of the day, though, all that's really important is that your chosen animal gives a high yield in proportion to her bodyweight and appetite.

Dairy breeds

A high yielding dairy goat is capable of producing in excess of 300 gallons of milk during the course of a standard one season lactation, although 200 gallons might be a more realistic target for the smallholder.

For the self-supporting smallholder the goat may be the perfect dairy animal.

Saanen / British Saanen: A pure white goat of the classic 'dairy' type. The British Saanen is somewhat larger than the original Swiss breed. Milk yield is very good, and they're ideally suited to a more 'commercial' system of goat keeping. They won't do so well if they have to rough it.

Toggenburg / British Toggenburg: Rather more heavily built than the Saanens, Toggenburgs are better suited to extensive grazing systems. They're basically a brown or fawn coloured goat, with white facial markings and legs. Some individuals of the breed have fairly long hair. They're known for having a rather excitable temperament, and are renowned escapologists. I admit that they wouldn't be my first choice of breed, but they are economical feeders.

British Alpine: A large and graceful breed, showing the same markings as the Toggenburg, but having black, rather than brown as the base colour. They're good foragers, and will produce high yields, but do seem to require a lot of feeding.

Anglo Nubian: This easily recognised breed, with its big floppy ears and Roman nose, is less hardy than the other types found in the UK. It doesn't produce a particularly large amount of milk, but what it lacks in quantity it makes up for in quality, being extremely high in butterfat and other solids. Therefore, if cheese making is part of your plan, it would be worth having one or two Nubians in the herd. A cross between an Anglo Nubian and a British Alpine would make a very useful goat for the smallholder. However, some people don't like the appearance of Nubian crossbreds, due to their semi-pendulous ears.

English: Whether or not this low-yielding breed ought to be listed along with the dairy goats I'm not sure. It is, supposedly, our traditional native breed, and, as such, is much hardier than those already listed, and requires less supplementary feeding. In its pure state it's unlikely to produce enough milk to be worth keeping, but, when crossed with one of the higher yielding breeds mentioned above, the resultant offspring will be ideal for smallholders wanting to produce modest amounts of milk economically, from a slightly more 'rough-and-ready' low-input system.

Golden Guernsey: This pretty little golden-haired breed from the Channel Islands was at one time very rare. Coat colour (and length) is quite variable, ranging from a pale sandy colour, right through to a rich dark gold, with some individual animals having very long hair. Milk yield isn't high, but it's extremely creamy, as one would expect from a Channel Islands breed. The cream also seems to separate out more easily than is the case with other breeds, and often it's possible to simply lift it off the top of the milk after leaving it to settle for a while. An ideal breed for the smallholder who simply needs enough good quality milk to satisfy modest household requirements.

The first goats my parents had were Golden Guernseys, which were fine for domestic production, but they later added some British Alpines to the herd in order to increase the yield, thus giving a surplus of milk for sale. The goats we had on Bardsey were a right mixture, based largely on English and Toggenburg bloodlines, with a little bit of just about everything else thrown in for good measure. They were small and hardy, and didn't give much milk, but what little they did produce was produced cheaply, which is the main thing. Our billy (a majestic fellow, with immense horns and a sweeping beard) was of the British Saanen type, but, as his offspring were predominantly black with white markings, I suspect he was probably at least 50% Alpine.

Sourcing stock

There always seem to be plenty of goats available, and cheap, too, until you actually want one, of course. Then, all of a sudden, they become as rare as hen's teeth. Although I'm generally an advocate of livestock markets, I would strongly advise *against* buying goats in that way. You won't often find them in markets anyway, and when you do they're likely to be pretty poor specimens. Ideally, goats should be sourced from someone who's managing them in the way that you will want to, to ensure that you're getting something that's going to fit the bill. You could join a local smallholders' association or goat keepers' club in order to make contact with breeders in your area, but that wouldn't be my chosen course of action. Much simpler is to ask the staff in your local feed merchants – they'll know exactly who keeps what, and furthermore, you'll find out a bit about their reputation too.

Once you've made contact with someone who might have suitable stock for sale, you really need to visit them at milking time and see how things are done, how the goats behave, and what sort of conditions they're kept under, before proceeding with any transaction. And don't be led up the garden path over prices. Even the best goat in the world isn't worth very much, and realistic prices for non-pedigree animals are generally on a par with good quality commercial sheep. Therefore, £100-£150 ought to be enough for what you want. Understandably, a good nanny in milk is the hardest to find, although you may strike lucky and come across someone who's reducing the size of their herd. Failing that, a goatling, either in-kid or ready to be mated, would be a good bet. Another option would be to buy a couple of female kids and rear them on the bottle, but you've then got a long time to wait before seeing any return on your investment.

Personally I would try to buy two goats from the outset – a nanny in milk and an in-kid goatling, perhaps a mother and daughter.

And, if the vendor keeps his own billy, you could arrange to take the nanny back for mating when the time comes, as part of the deal. Look for animals that are sleek and glossy, have a graceful neck carriage, and well spaced hind legs. Avoid pendulous udders with outsize teats, although bear in mind that if you're hand-milking you do need the teats to be large enough to get hold of. Examine the animal for signs of dung staining around the tail, back of the udder and hind legs, which may indicate scouring caused be internal parasites (or worse), and check the coat for lice.

Ask the vendor about his herd health strategy, and to provide a list of all recently administered treatments.

Breeding

As with all mammals, a goat needs to be bred from in order to produce milk. Having said that, maiden milkers (i.e. where the animal comes into milk without having produced offspring, or without even having been mated) do seem to be more common in goats than in other species. In fact, my parents had one (a British Alpine) which never kidded throughout her long life, yet she remained in milk the whole while. However, this is the exception, rather than the rule. If a maiden goat should happen to 'bag up' then by all means milk her, if this becomes necessary, but attempts should still be made to get her mated.

In our temperate climate goats are – like most sheep – seasonal breeders. The period of sexual activity starts about September and runs through to March, with the nannies coming 'on heat' or 'in season' (oestrus) at 21 day intervals, until they're mated and become pregnant. Goats can be quite frantic when on heat, with constant high-pitched bleating (which drives you around the bend after a while) and much tail wagging. Other indications include enlargement and reddening of the vulva, together with some discharge, although the behavioural signs are much more noticeable. The period of time during which the goat will actually be receptive may be very short – as little as a few hours, in some cases – so don't leave it until the last minute before making the necessary arrangements to have her mated, or you'll almost certainly miss the moment.

Gestation takes around 150 days, which ensures that kids are born during warmer weather. Generally November seems to be the busiest month of the rut, although where several goats are kept it's advisable to have some mated at the beginning of the breeding season, and some at the end, to ensure a continuous supply of milk. However, it's not actually necessary for a goat to be bred from every year, as most have the capability to milk through two seasons. Therefore, the domestic scale producer could keep two goats and kid them in alternate years. This would be fine in a situation where the offspring are viewed as an inconvenient by-product of milk production (as they are by most goat keepers), but for the true self-supporter wishing to maximise the versatility of his goat herd, kids are a valued source of meat for the family, and one litter per year simply wouldn't be enough. On this basis I'd suggest that the smallholder keep three adult goats, with one being mated early, another being mated late, and the third one run on in milk

to breed the following year. With careful planning, this will ensure that there's a litter of kids born every six months or so, and that there's always at least two of the nannies in milk.

Keeping a stud male

Although A.I. is an option for goats, it hasn't reached the same levels of availability as it has in cattle. Therefore, natural mating remains the most practical method of getting your nannies in kid. However, given the reduced level of interest in home dairying amongst smallholders these days, billy goats are rather few and far between. This, together with an increased awareness of bio-security and the introduction of livestock movement restrictions, means that finding a suitable husband for your ladies is not the simple business it once was, making the idea of keeping one's own billy slightly more attractive.

Pros:

• Nannies will show stronger signs of oestrus if a male is kept on the same premises, resulting in fewer missed cycles.

• It gives you greater control over the timing of events, as you don't need to fit in with anybody else.

• Increased bio-security.

• No stud fees to pay.

• Potential to generate additional revenue by hosting visiting nannies (although this may negate the earlier point about bio-security).

Cons:

• In small herds, it may be difficult

to justify the cost of keeping a billy.

• Even if you take great care to change your overalls and wash your hands after handling the billy, his smell will eventually attach itself to you and to everything you come into contact with, to the extent that you may find that even your best friends begin to give you a wide berth. The ultimate catastrophe arises when the odour eventually contaminates your milk supply, resulting in an extreme occurrence of the infamous 'goaty' taste that so many people find off-putting.

• Additional secure and substantial accommodation will be required, at some distance from the main goat housing. Billy goats like nothing better, during periods of idleness, than to systematically destroy their quarters, and their determination to overcome all obstacles between themselves and a nanny in season is legendary. Our own billy, in his youth, jumped over the high half-door of his pen, breaking one of his forelegs as he did so. Evading capture, he crossed the yard at high speed on three legs, jumped another half door, and mated his own mother.

(Incidentally, I bandaged a couple of wooden splints to his leg before wrapping the whole thing up in layer upon layer of masking tape, which held it as firmly as any plaster cast. Within six weeks, the only sign that there'd ever been an injury was a small bald patch just behind his knee, where the end of one of the splints had rubbed.)

• His habit of urinating – with amazing accuracy – all over anyone who comes within range will not endear him to guests.

Our magnificent billy goat.

• With insufficient nannies to keep him fully occupied he may become aggressive and difficult to handle. This can be countered, to an extent, by ensuring that his accommodation is situated where he can keep an eye on what's going on around him, and that he gets plenty of exercise.

Which billy?

Of course, any old billy, provided he's man enough for the job, will do to get your nannies in kid, and, if milk production is your sole aim then that's all you need. A scrub male, cheap to buy and cheap to keep, will be fine. However, this does give you a rather limited outcome, and also makes it highly unlikely that anyone else would want to bring their nannies to you to be mated.

From time to time you might want to keep one of your female kids as a herd replacement, or possibly to sell as a breeding / milking goat, in which case far more care will need to be taken over the choice of sire. Under these circumstances I should say that it's worth making a bit of effort to locate a suitable top quality male standing at stud,

TIP

If you don't have a stud goat on the premises, you can persuade your nannies to show stronger signs of oestrus by the use of a 'billy rag'. Next time you visit somewhere where there's an adult male goat, take a small piece of cloth and rub it thoroughly over his urine-soaked beard, forelock and front legs. Keep the resulting 'billy rag' tightly sealed in a jam jar, where it'll retain its scent for many months (if not years). Now, when you're expecting one of your goats to come on heat, all you need to do is remove the rag from the jar and hang it up in the goat shed for a day or two, to be sure of spotting the signs in even the most reticent of females.

and transport your goat to him for service. I don't think that the small-scale producer could very well justify purchasing a billy of this calibre, given the limited benefit they'd get from it.

Considering that the majority of kids born in the smallholder's herd will be destined for the domestic deep freeze, it makes most sense, if a billy is to be kept, to have one of a specific meat breed (e.g. Boer), in order to maximise production from that aspect of the goat keeping enterprise. In contrast, kids sired by a 'dairy' type male are spindly little things that will take forever to fatten, so, given that you'll only rarely need to rear a replacement female, there's no earthly reason for making regular use of a dairy male.

Mating

Provided that the nanny is properly on heat, the actual act of mating is remarkably quick, and seldom fails to give a result. Even very young billies – as little as 3-4 months old – may be capable of effective service, which is something to bear in mind if you're rearing male and female kids together, or have left an entire billy kid to suckle his dam.

The problem for many goat keepers – most of whom do not

keep a male – lies in getting their nanny to the billy at the critical time. Usually, by the time the heat has been detected, a billy has been located, the necessary arrangements have been made, and the goat has been transported, she'll have gone off the boil It's very frustrating, for both the owners and the poor billy goat, to have a nanny who clamps her tail down firmly and refuses to play any part in the proceedings, when, only an hour or two beforehand, she'd been shouting her head off in desperation.

Another option is to find a stud owner who's able to board the nanny for you for a length of time that's guaranteed to include at least one heat period (preferably two). However, this does depend on someone being prepared to milk her while she's under their care, and of course you'll have to pay for her board and lodging. Really, though, once you've successfully observed your goat in season, you should be able to calculate when the next heat period is due, and make your plans in advance. Remember that the current 'six day standstill' legislation effectively means that you have to leave your nanny at the stud owner's premises for a week anyway, although how closely anyone adheres to that rule in situations like this I shouldn't like to comment upon.

Cloudburst

Phantom pregnancies, known as 'cloudbursts', seem to be more common in goats than in other species. The affected animal will give every indication of being in kid, even to the extent of developing a prominent bulge at the appropriate time. However, as the expected date for kidding passes with no offspring being born, the goat keeper will assume either that he counted the days incorrectly, or that the kids are simply overdue. Then, all of a sudden, after the barest minimum of preliminaries, the goat will expel a large quantity of clear, slightly gelatinous fluid. Often the only indications will be that the she has regained her former 'non-pregnant' figure, and the bedding in her pen is soaking wet. Some goats can then be milked as per normal, but others may fail to bag up properly during the latter stages of a phantom pregnancy, in which case they should be returned to the billy at the earliest convenience.

Pregnancy and kidding

In the early stages of pregnancy the goat doesn't need any special treatment, so just carry on as before. However, from about mid gestation her milk yield will begin to drop, which, if you had any doubt in the matter, is a sure indication that she's 'in kid'. The yield will continue to decrease through the second half of the pregnancy, until you reach the point when you need to dry her off completely, aiming for a six week break before the next kids are due.

Drying off is achieved by ceasing to strip out after each milking, eventually dropping to once-a-day milking, and then every other day, and so on, until you finally stop milking altogether. You need to cut the feed level down a bit as well, but obviously not too much or she may lose condition, which could have a knock-on effect on her health at kidding (and on the health of the kids), and on her next lactation. Occasionally one comes across a particularly high-yielding animal that simply won't dry off, in which case there's no option other than to continue milking her right up until the kids are due.

In late gestation the nanny goat develops a very prominent bulge, and it's quite easy to feel the movements of the kids within by running your hand over her flank, particularly just after she's had a long drink of cold water. With all that extra weight to carry around, nannies approaching full term are often inclined to just sit about, so a bit of gently enforced exercise might be required to keep them fit. As the time of birth draws near (i.e. within a day or so), the goat's body shape changes quite noticeably, with the bulge becoming far less apparent (due to the kids having shifted into a more central position, preparatory to the birth), and with the angle of the pelvis having become much flatter, often with noticeable hollows appearing on either side of the tail head. Behavioural changes will occur too, usually commencing with the goat 'stacking up' on a vast quantity of hay and other roughage, often eating quite frantically, as if afraid that she won't get another chance to feed for some time. The goat's udder will also be very full by this stage, and may be dribbling colostrum from the teats. In cases where the

Golden Geurnsey goat with new-born kid.

udder has become uncomfortably tight prior to kidding, it may be necessary to milk a bit off to ease the pressure.

Once labour begins, the goat will be observed pawing at the floor, repeatedly lying down and getting up again, and turning to her flank to 'talk' to her unborn offspring – exactly the same as is seen in cattle and sheep. Some goats like to have human company during the kidding process, whereas others prefer to be left alone – let yourself be guided by her behaviour: if she jumps up and calls after you when you leave the building then clearly she'd rather you stayed. I have to say that most of ours much preferred to be left alone, and the kids were usually born at night, unobserved. As the birth progresses, the water bag of the first kid will be seen, and, once this has been expelled, the goat will usually remain flat out on the floor (although some prefer to give birth in a standing position), straining hard until the kid puts in an appearance. The second kid follows in due course, and often a third. Some goats make a lot of noise during the birthing process, whereas others are more or less silent. The afterbirth(s) should be delivered shortly after the kids, but if not you'll need to provide antibiotic cover until the goat has properly cleansed. Just be aware that some antibiotics have a fairly long milk withhold time, so discuss suitable products with your vet.

Once the kids are born, some goat keepers (particularly those whose sole objective is milk production) take them away from their mother immediately, and they're often destroyed. However, as we always reared the kids, either for meat or as herd replacements, we preferred to leave ours with the nanny for 3 days, giving them the best possible start in life. Therefore, they should have their navels sprayed with Bactakil or some such product, and be left for the mother to lick clean, which she will do remarkably quickly. Once the kids are up on their feet and looking for the udder you might find it necessary to trim away the fringe of hair from long-coated breeds, making it easier for them to find the teats. – in due course this'll make milking easier for you, too. Weak kids can be fed colostrum via a stomach tube, as is commonly done with lambs. After kidding, I think it's a good idea to give the goat a high energy drink such as some glucose powder dissolved in warm water, and also to wash any blood and muck off her rear end and down the back of her udder – if left, it will go dry and crusty and could make her udder sore, possibly leading to mastitis.

What to do when things go wrong

In my experience, goats rarely have any difficulty in bringing forth their kids. In fact, in all the years that we kept goats I can only remember two occasions when any assistance was required, and never have we lost a kid as a result of an awkward or prolonged delivery. I'm sure that the slender shape of

the kids at birth has a lot to do with this, although all the same obstetric problems that are encountered in sheep could of course occur in goats.

As goats generally produce multiple litters, the size of the kids is relatively small – this means that you seldom encounter the problem of oversize singles causing difficult deliveries, as you may find in sheep and cattle. Also, the small size of the kids means that, following the manipulation of any malpresentation, the delivery itself is relatively straightforward. However, as I mentioned before, goats aren't particularly stoical, and any kind of intervention must be carried out with extreme care. They're also rather inclined to get stressed in situations like this, which doesn't help.

For all internal examinations and manipulations, shoulder length obstetric gloves and lubricating gel are an absolute must, and remember to provide appropriate antibiotic cover following any intervention.

Kid rearing

When you take the kids away from their mother at 3 days old, you could simply knock them on the head and eat them at that point. In fact, if you're prepared to do this you might find that you can get plenty more kids from other local goat keepers, less hardened than yourself, giving you a free source of meat for very little effort. On the other hand, you might like to rear the kids in order to obtain rather more worthwhile carcasses – slaughtered at 4–6 months old they're ideal, and are quite easily dealt with at home.

The first, and most important thing in the life of any kid is that it gets sufficient colostrum during the first few days, which is why it's good practice to leave them with their mothers, initially. However, many goats – particularly older animals that have been hand-milked – have rather large teats, so it might be necessary to assist the kids as they make their first few attempts at suckling. After 3 days or so, you'll need to transfer the kids to bottle feeding so that you can start milking their mother. An alternative to this is to leave them together for six weeks, then wean the kids and start milking the nanny. However, this method will give you a considerably reduced yield overall.

If your milk production is solely in order to satisfy the domestic needs of your own household, then there should be sufficient to bottle feed the kids as well. By the time the goat passes her peak of lactation and the yield begins to drop, the kids will have been weaned anyway. If, however, you're producing milk for sale, then it's generally more economical to rear the kids on a milk replacer, provided, of course, that this can be obtained more cheaply than the price at which you're selling your milk. Many goat keepers successfully use calf or lamb milk replacers for kid rearing, as these are generally quite a bit cheaper than products specifically formulated for kids. All milk replacers should be mixed up slightly more dilute than stated in the instructions on the packet, and even natural milk is best fed with a little water added.

To begin with, the kids will need 4-5 feeds per day, totalling around a litre in 24 hours. Gradually, the number of feeds per day

It's common practice to rear kids on a bottle.

can be reduced, and the overall quantity given can be increased, until they're consuming about 2.25 litres a day, split between 2 feeds. However, bottle feeding is a frightful tie, and a lot of hassle, so, if using milk replacer, I'd be inclined to get them onto a cold ad-lib feeding system as soon as possible, using a bucket with teats. Kids can be taught to drink directly from a bucket, as is generally done with calves, but it is never very successful.

Goat kids will begin to nibble at solid food from a very early age, and this should be encouraged by ensuring that fresh hay and concentrates are always on offer, with any uneaten removed and replaced daily. Any uneaten portions can be fed to adult goats, or to other livestock. Fresh water must always be available. Provided that they're eating enough solid food, kids can be weaned abruptly at around 8 weeks of age, or alternatively, gradually cut down the milk feeds (both in volume and in concentration), until ceasing altogether at between 8 and 10 weeks.

Castration

Any male kids being raised for meat must be castrated to avoid the meat being rendered more or less inedible by the male taint, which begins to become apparent from a fairly young age. This is best carried out using an 'elastrator' and rubber rings, applied shortly after birth. (See page 211 for further information on the use of rubber rings.)

Following castration it'll be possible to rear kids in mixed sex groups, which simplifies the management.

Although surplus goat kids are often killed at a few days old I think it's better to rear them in order to obtain decent carcasses.

De-horning

Until 1988 this was something that smallholders were allowed to do themselves, and regional goat keepers' clubs often held 'dehorning days' where those who did not have their own equipment could bring kids along to be disbudded by an experienced member. (No six-day standstills or movement licences in those halcyon days, either!). Now goat kids can only be disbudded by a vet under general anaesthetic. The DEFRA guidelines state that this should be done as early possible,

preferably when 2–3 days old, and certainly no later than 10 days of age. Ironically, the kids seem to suffer a lot more from the after effects of the general anaesthetic then they ever used to following disbudding under the old regime.

Personally, unless you're intending to sell pedigree breeding stock or exhibit at shows, I shouldn't bother with disbudding. Certainly it would be a waste of time and money in the case of kids being raised for meat. Having kept both horned and de-horned goats over the years (including males) I can honestly say there's no significant difference between the two in terms of handling and management.

Goat kids can be disbudded by a vet at up to 10 days of age.

Dairy Production

"A smallholding cannot be considered complete unless it produces its own milk."
Herbert Clarke

"If you had to choose one substance on which to live it would be hard to rival milk."
Patricia Cleveland-Peck

H aving bought your cow, housed her, bred from her, turned her out to graze, and brought her in again for a bit of feed, you are now poised, bucket in one hand, three-legged stool in the other, contemplating that bulging bag of milk. You sit down, grasp a teat in each hand and **crash!** Your bucket is somewhere in orbit, and you are shakily thinking about where you would be now had that scything hoof been three inches or so to the right! Well hopefully no, it won't be like that at all, but of

course it does happen from time to time. The usual scenario goes something like this:

"It's one of those heady, pollen scented evenings of early summer, with a cuckoo calling from the woods above the farm. The cows have been at grass for long enough now to have lost their winter shabbiness and come in for milking looking sleek, and smelling sweetly of clover. I settle down to milk with a pint pot of homebrew within reach, and I'm thinking more about what will be for supper than the job in hand. The rhythmical ping! ping! of milk in the pail plays a calming tune, soporific almost (I did once fall asleep while milking a goat – when I woke up the job was done, but that's a different story). A bee buzzes in through the open door, a forager from one of our hives

in the orchard, and in my drowsy mind thoughts turn to honey or, more probably, mead. *bang!* That buzzing got a bit too close to Rosie's heels! By the time I've rinsed the cloven hoof print from my battered bucket and settled down to milk once again, the bee is long gone and Rosie is chewing the cud as if nothing had happened. Milking continues without a hitch".

The moral of this story? Don't drink and milk, I suppose.

Getting started

A bucket, a cloth, and something to sit on. That's the basic essentials to get you started. Preferably the bucket will be of stainless steel (we've got a couple of splendid ones bearing the legends 'Special Diet Kitchen' and 'Rothschild Ward' – no prizes for guessing where they came from!), and should have a lid, but any food grade receptacle can be pressed into service initially. You could end up spending a fortune on dairy paraphernalia and, although it would be jolly handy to have, much of what is available is not absolutely essential. Better to gradually build up a stock of equipment over time as your experience and commitment develops.

Ideally you will have a designated area for milking. It's not advisable to carry out milking in the same space that is used for housing stock but, having said that, up until relatively recently stall housed cows would have been milked in their standings. Even after the introduction of milking machines most farms initially used an overhead vacuum pipeline, enabling them to continue to milk in the cowshed. We use a small

NB.

Be aware that what I am discussing here is the production of milk for your own use. Producing milk for sale is a whole different ball game involving the Food Standards Agency, Environmental Health, Local Planning Department etc., etc., and is outside the scope of this book.

outbuilding that we call 'The Dairy', which in fact isn't a dairy at all. A dairy is a room for storing and processing milk, and as all our processing is of the 'farmhouse kitchen table' variety, we don't really need a specially equipped area. Our so called 'dairy' is in fact a one-cow-milking-parlour and, as such, is ideally suited to the scale of our operation. The Dairy measures just 12' x 9' and has a wide sliding door. Immediately inside the door, and directly in line with it, is a stall into which the cow can enter forward and reverse out of. The positioning is such that, should the cow be so unladylike as to defecate in the parlour, the muck will fall in the doorway where it can quickly and easily be cleaned away. A light chain can be clipped across behind to keep her in place. Mounted on the wall at the head end of the cow are a feed manger and a self-fill water bowl. The drinking bowl is not a necessity as cows don't stay in the parlour for long, but it has proved handy if keeping an animal in after milking awaiting a visit from the A.I man. The partition forming the cow's stall effectively separates her from the rest of the space within the building. To the right of the door, in one corner, we have a large wash-up sink (with water heater above), and in the other corner is a stainless steel

table (with a shelf underneath for storing odds and ends such as spare buckets and disinfectant. Along one wall is a slatted drainer rack for calf buckets. The trolley mounted milking machine is wheeled forward into position once the cow is in.

Assuming that you've accustomed your cow to the parlour prior to calving, bringing her in for milking should be a simple matter of opening the field gate – she'll trot quite happily across the yard and into the milking stall, where she knows her supper will be waiting. Cows are creatures of habit, and, furthermore, have clearly defined hierarchies and behavioural protocols within the herd – if you have more than one to milk then stick to the same daily order, or you'll really upset the social applecart! While your cow is eating, give her udder a good wash.

I generally draw a squirt of milk onto the palm of my hand to check for early signs of mastitis.

You can buy tubs of disposable udder wipes for this, but we just use a clean cloth and warm water (with a splash of iodine added), which has a soothing effect and can encourage milk let-down in

a nervous animal. After washing, draw a jet of milk from each teat and discard it. This serves a double purpose: firstly, it ejects any muck or drops of dirty water that may be lurking in the teat orifice – you don't want that in the milking bucket. Secondly, it enables you to make a pre-milking check for early signs of mastitis. There is a bit of kit called a strip cup used to collect this first squirt, but I generally draw it onto the palm of my hand where I'll be able to detect any abnormal level of temperature indicative of infection. Any flakes in the milk can be seen and felt. If you do use this method then be sure to wash your hands before continuing.

By the time you're ready to start milking the cow should have finished her grub, but if she hasn't then give her time to do so. Cattle (and other herbivores) in a natural environment are prey species, and are at most risk when they've got their heads down in the grass, so tend to be tense and wary when feeding. Countless generations of domesticity haven't altered this, and in fact may have added to it – a cow with her head in a bucket will not settle till the last crumb is gone, and will be on the defensive lest her herd mates try to steal from under her nose.

A relaxed cow has her head up and is probably chewing the cud. Her eyes may be half shut, but her ears are wide open. Now the milk can flow – you only have to observe animals suckling their own offspring to see that this is so. It never ceases to surprise me that so many smallholders, keeping a milking cow or goats, use feed as a means to get their animals to stand still while being milked. If she won't stand to be milked without bribery then in all likelihood there is something amiss, either in the environment of the milking area or, more probably, in your relationship with your stock. In our experience, animals fed before milking will give higher yields than those that are feeding while milking takes place.

If your cow is fractious and fidgety, it could be because you are nervous. Rather than tempting her with tit-bits you must talk to her to calm her down – It doesn't matter what you say, swear at her if you like, the tone of your voice is what is important. In fact the incongruity of crooning "b****y well stand still you f*****g awkward old ****" in dulcet tones is usually sufficient to raise a smile and defuse the situation.

By hand or machine?

Hand milking is cheaper, quieter, makes less washing up, and is undoubtedly more intimate – a very pleasant and relaxing occupation… when the weather's nice. When it's freezing cold, your hands are chapped, and you've cut your thumb or sprained a wrist, you may view things in a different light and wish you'd opted for mechanisation. In our own case, hand milking became less attractive as soon as we expanded our milking herd to more than one animal. Having a milking machine has not only reduced the physical workload, but has sped up the process no end, as I can be busy measuring out the milk from the first cow and feeding calves while the second cow is milking.

Don't be conned into the belief that hand milking is more 'natural'. More old fashioned it may be, but there is nothing natural about a human being squatting down next to a cow and squeezing away at her udder. Come to that there is nothing natural about attaching a machine to her teats either, but at least the sucking and pulsating action of the milking machine does very closely resemble the suckling action of a calf – an effect you cannot hope to achieve by hand. Machine milking will give you cleaner milk – no hair or dust dropping into the bucket – and what's more, it's consistent. Regardless of who places the cluster on the udder, the sensation for the cow remains the same; an important consideration if you ever need to be away from home. You can quickly teach an animal-sitter the correct way to use the machine, but finding a competent hand milker to cover your absence can be a devil of a job. Every hand milker has a slightly different technique, and even an expert with many years of experience may wreak havoc with the health of your cow's udder simply through subtle differences of wrist action.

A compromise is needed, I feel, and ideally your cows should be content to accept either method. Although we've been using our small portable machine for some time now, we continue to strip out by hand after each milking. By doing this the cows remain quite used to either the feel of the machine or having someone sitting down next to them, and are happy to switch from one routine to the other, if required. We are rather prone to power failures here, and I recall the electricity cutting out when I was in the middle of doing the milking late one winter evening. With a hiss and a clatter the cluster subsided onto the floor beneath the cow as we were plunged into darkness and silence. She didn't flinch. I rummaged about in the dark to find an old hurricane lamp, and milking continued by hand in the half-light shed by a flickering paraffin flame. Time stood still. I felt I could have carried on like that for ever – that is until it was time to do the washing up! How the dairymaids of old ever managed to get their utensils clean in that sort of gloom is beyond me. Probably they didn't. No wonder infant mortality was so high.

While on the subject of washing up, if you look behind the sink in our 'dairy' you'll notice a proliferation of washing up brushes hanging there, of every shape and size it seems. We received a simple lesson on the ease with which cross contamination can occur when Dot washed up the milk churns after having just cleaned her yogurt making equipment with the same brush. You don't need me to explain to you what happened to the whole of the next day's milk! We now use separate brushes for everything – one for the inside of the machine, one for the outside, one for calf buckets, one for churns, etc.

Regardless of whether you have time to do a full wash up immediately after milking you must at least give everything a good rinse, or milk residue will go dry and crusty and be awkward to remove later. We then simply scrub every item several times with extremely hot water and leave them to dry naturally. The milking machine takes a bit more washing than a bucket but it's not a chore. We don't use a chemical disinfectant (except on items that have been out of use for a while) due to the corrosive effect on metal parts, in particular the taps and alloy lid of the milk bucket, but most people do routinely sterilise their dairy utensils with hypochlorite. Or you could use steam. Our dairy sink contains a water heater element and a rack on which to place buckets and things – the addition of a lid turns it into a simple steam sterilisation unit.

Hand milking

The usual practice is to milk out the two fore teats, then the hind pair, before returning to the front ones to strip out, then back to the back ones. Sit down at a convenient height alongside the animal facing slightly aft. Your head should be against her flank with your shoulder nudging in just behind her belly. In this position, when milking a medium sized cow, your forearms will be just resting on your knees. Accompanied by a slight downward stroking motion, take a teat in each hand and, using the thumb and forefinger of one hand, squeeze shut the top of one teat – you must be pretty firm as milk flowing back up the wrong way during milking is painful for the cow and could cause damage to the udder. Now, without any pulling (if anything you should raise your hand slightly), bring the other fingers of that hand to bear on the teat, one by one, gently but firmly forcing all the milk trapped in the teat cistern out through the teat canal and into your bucket. Repeat with the other hand on the other teat, and in the meantime release the thumb and forefinger of the first hand to allow that teat cistern to refill. You'll soon fall into the rhythm of it… first one hand, then the other… back and forth… back and forth… relaxed and unhurried until there's no more milk to be had. Then do exactly the same for the two hind quarters. Stripping is carried out by gently massaging the udder then drawing the thumb and forefinger down the teat to expel the last few drops,

Hand milking is more intimate.

but I stress that it really must be only the last drops – should you commence the stripping action while any significant amount of milk remains then damage to delicate membranes will occur. It is essential that stripping be carried out thoroughly, for if milk remains in the udder after each milking then yield will fall day by day, and eventually the cow will dry off. Having said that, do not fully strip out for the first four days of a new lactation.

Machine milking

Whether you've purchased a machine new or second hand, it's as well to get it checked over by a qualified dairy engineer before you start using it. On a second hand machine there may be parts that need replacing, or a new machine purchased for cows may well have been pre-adjusted to the settings required for goats. Once the machine is properly set up, and you're familiar with its use, you can carry out routine checks and adjustments yourself.

With the machine running at the correct vacuum level, crouch down behind the cow holding the clawpiece of the cluster 'belly up' in the palm of one hand with the teat cups hanging upside down around it – imagine an octopus

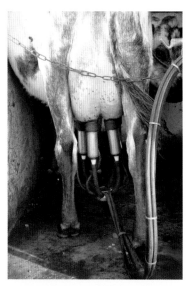

Machine milking is far more convenient.

held upside down with its legs dangling. The design is such that when held like this the suction to each teat cup is cut off. Move the cluster forward between the hind legs and under the udder, then, with the other hand, place the teat cups into position, one by one. As you lift each one, suction resumes, so just pop it onto the appropriate teat and it'll stay there. Cows that have previously only been hand milked usually protest just as the fourth teat goes into position and the full weight of the cluster is felt, so keep your hand on it for a moment or two, just to stop it swinging around until she settles down. You may think that the cluster feels rather heavy, but don't be tempted to support it in any way – the weight is important to prevent the teat cups from gradually creeping up and injuring the udder. A clear section in the milk pipe enables you to see when milking is almost over – avoid over milking, which could damage the sphincter at the teat orifice. Machine stripping consists of pressing down on the clawpiece

Portable milking machine

We bought our little milking unit second hand, without a bucket or cluster, in as-new condition for about £50. The seller, who kept a large number of goats, claimed that the machine was too noisy, which was upsetting things at milking time. I was rather surprised at this, as, generally speaking, animals being milked don't mind a loud background noise, provided that it's constant. In fact, in many cases the sound of the machine starting up as part of the pre-milking routine is often what triggers milk let-down. Subsequently I found out that the goats hadn't objected to the noise in the slightest – it was the owners that found it unbearable in the confined environment of their milking room. I have to admit it is pretty noisy, and several people have suggested that I locate the motor and pump in an adjoining outbuilding and simply run the vacuum line through. However, on more than one occasion the portability of the entire unit has stood us in good stead, for example when a cow has been down after an awkward calving, or in winter when the yard has been too icy for the cows to cross. In these cases we simply take the machine to the animal.

The bucket, lid, pulsator and cluster I managed to scrounge from various sources, with a few spare parts thrown in for good measure, and all the pipe work and teat liners were replaced with 'off the shelf' products by our local dairy technician (at a cost of about £30). The only spare part that's proved difficult to find has been the large rubber washer that fits between the bucket and the lid – the more up-to-date buckets are of a different diameter. Luckily I managed to pick up a couple amongst some boxes of miscellaneous junk at a farm dispersal sale. When they perish I suppose I'll have to improvise something with rings cut from an old tractor inner-tube.

with one hand, while massaging each quarter of the udder with the other.

Whether you milk by hand or machine, apply some udder cream to the teats when the job is done. There are a number of brands of medicated ointment sold for the purpose, but we find plain Vaseline to be better than anything else. And that's about all there is to it! Any whole milk required for the house should immediately be filtered into a suitable lidded container and popped in the fridge – we find that one gallon per day is generally sufficient for all domestic purposes, but occasionally more is needed, for example when making larger quantities of cheese or yoghurt. The rest of the milk can be run through a separator, with the cream being set aside for ice-cream

and butter making. The resulting 'skimmed' milk is what's used for feeding the calves and pigs.

Pasteurised?

Many people ask me whether drinking un-pasteurised milk is safe, to which I generally reply that it's probably safer than crossing a busy road. Certainly I know more people that have been injured in traffic accidents than have become ill through the use of raw milk. No-one could possibly deny that the discovery of pasteurisation brought huge benefits to human health but, just as people who choose to smoke, drive fast cars, or join the army, do so in the knowledge that any of these activities could result in a painful death, so do we choose to drink raw milk. Our cows are regularly tested for both

tuberculosis and brucellosis, and we don't live in a TB hotspot area. That's good enough for us. For the not so foolhardy (or where the household includes the very old, the very young, or anyone who is pregnant) domestic pasteurisers are readily available. Pasteurisation is achieved by holding the milk at 73°C for 15 seconds, or 65°C for 30 minutes, but it will kill off the good bacteria as well as the bad ones.

One final word on pasteurisation: raw milk that has been sitting around for a bit will go sour, and there's no harm in that – sour milk can safely be used for all sorts of things. Pasteurised milk that becomes stale goes rotten. That's nasty.

Milking machine settings

Cow: Vacuum pressure should be between -45 and -50 kpa (-34 to -38 cmHg). Pulsation rate needs to be set at 40-50 per minute, with a pulsation ratio from 2:1 to 3:1 (time liner open : time liner closed).

Sheep: Vacuum pressure should be between -40 and -45 kpa. Pulsation rate needs to be set at 120 per minute (that's 3 times faster than for cows!), with a pulsation ratio of 50:50 (time liner open : time liner closed).

Goat: Vacuum pressure should be between -42 and -44 kpa. Pulsation rate needs to be set at about 90 per minute, with a pulsation ratio of 60:40 (time liner open : time liner closed).

Milking goats

To all intents and purposes, milking a goat is just like milking a cow, except on a smaller scale (and there are only two teats, of course). Being smaller, many people encourage their goats to jump up onto a stand or platform for milking, which brings the udder up to a more convenient height. A similar set-up is often used for milking sheep. For only a couple of goats hand milking would be the norm, but they do take readily to the machine, so this would be worth considering if you've got enough animals to justify the initial outlay.

Just as when milking a cow, it's important to wash the udder before you start, and to apply some Vaseline or udder cream when you've finished. A goat's udder is

Goats are usually milked on a stand or platform.

rather more delicate than that of a cow, so take care to be gentle, particularly when stripping out.

The sheep as a dairy animal

There are currently more dairy sheep in the world than there are dairy cows, so, given that sheep can provide the self-supporter with milk, meat and wool, all from the same animal, why aren't more UK smallholders keeping multi-purpose flocks? I don't know the answer to this, I'm afraid. I do know that domestic milk production is one of the least common smallholding activities these days, due to the unavoidable tie of twice daily milking – many people are running their holdings on a part-time basis, with all enterprises having to be fairly flexible in nature in order to fit in around other, off-farm commitments. This, together with a marked reluctance on the part of British people to try anything 'different', means that small-scale (subsistence) sheep dairying

has never really taken off in this country, which is a shame given the historical importance of ewe's milk. And, in this age of allergies and intolerances, ewe's milk has a very modern significance too – most people (unless they are lactose intolerant) who have been told that they must cut out dairy-based foods are fine with sheep's milk and sheep's milk products. Even in cases of severe lactose intolerance, sheep's milk is well worth trying, particularly if consumed as yoghurt or cheese. Sheep's milk is easily digested, higher in solids than goat's or cow's milk (making it ideal for cheese production), and contains a greater percentage of essential minerals (calcium, phosphorus, sodium, magnesium, zinc and iron) and B vitamins (see table 9, page 446). It has a mild, slightly sweet flavour, and is naturally homogenised. The high proportion of solids-not-fat (casein in particular) means that as little as 4-5 litres may be required to produce 1kg of cheese, as opposed to 9-10 litres of cow's or goat's milk.

Milking sheep on a small farm in France.

The high fat content enables ice cream to be made using the whole milk, without the need to add additional cream or egg yolk, resulting in a product that actually has a lower fat content than cow's milk ice-cream. Sheep's milk yoghurt is naturally thick, and can be used as a low-fat substitute for cream in cooking. Frozen sheep's milk will store well for more than 4 months, and does not separate on defrosting.

The milking flock

Individual animals of just about any breed of sheep can be milked, at a push, particularly if they've previously shown a capacity for a higher than average sustained yield by successfully rearing triplet lambs to satisfactory weights at weaning. If you don't fancy starting afresh then make a selection of the milkier ewes in your existing flock and cross them with a ram of a dairy breed.

A couple of generations of this policy, combined with careful use of performance records, should result in the beginnings of a productive dairy flock. This will have been achieved with considerably less initial outlay than would be the case if a new flock were to be purchased, although it will take longer for yields to reach high enough levels to give a reasonable return. However, you

Rules of thumb for the feeding of lactating dairy ewes

Record milk yields on a regular basis (daily, if possible), and, for a 70kg ewe, feed 0.5kg of concentrate feed / litre of milk produced. This type of feed has a dry matter (DM) content in the region of 86%. Non-productive ewes will typically consume around 2.5% of their own body weight (BW) in DM / day, but high-yielding dairy sheep may manage as much as 4.5%. For the sake of our example here, let's assume a DM intake at peak lactation of 4% of BW. Now, supposing that our 70kg ewe is, at present, producing 3 litres of milk daily. She'll be getting 1.5kg of concentrates, giving 1.29kg DM/day. Her total daily DM requirement is 2.8kg (70kg X 4%), so there's a shortfall of 1.51kg / day that needs to be provided in the form of forage. This can be obtained by feeding 1.7kg of hay (85% DM), 6.04kg silage (25% DM), or from 7.55kg of grazed grass (20% DM).

At times, this level of feeding may not provide sufficient energy and protein, in which case the ewe can be expected to mobilise body reserves. BW losses of up to 100g / day during early lactation are acceptable, but this does emphasise the need for ewes to be in excellent body condition at lambing time. With a bit of commonsense and general stockmanship, you'll be able to tweak these figures according to the nature of your enterprise, the size of your sheep, and your target level of production.

might be glad of a year or two at a lower level of production while you get the system up and running.

As with cattle, dairy sheep exhibit the classic 'dairy wedge' conformation. Think of the difference in body shape between a Jersey cow (dairy) and a Hereford bull (beef) and you'll know what I mean. When selecting your foundation dairy ewes, look for the high tapered shoulder, light forequarter, narrow head and fine bone. These characteristics are totally contrary to what we're looking for when choosing breeding stock for other purposes.

Additionally, the dairy ewe should have good length, a broad deep pelvis, and well-spaced, straight-moving hind legs. Udder attachment must be good (i.e. no droopy tits!), with fairly large teats placed well underneath,

like a goat's. (This teat shape and placement would not be so desirable in a ewe that suckles her offspring). During a lactation period of just over 200 days, a good ewe of one of the recognised dairy breeds may produce a total of 600 litres, although a more realistic flock average of 250 litres should give a justifiable return. Crossbred ewes and ewes of other (non-dairy) breeds used for domestic milk production are unlikely to exceed 150 litres per lactation, although individual animals may well top this figure.

Traditional practice is to hand milk sheep from behind, although I don't suppose it really matters a great deal. Just do it whichever way you feel most comfortable – from behind or alongside.

Electric butter churn and ice-cream maker, together with kitchen utensils used for milk processing.

HOME DAIRYING

For basic milk processing you can manage quite well using general kitchen items such as jugs, pans, dishes, pots, sieves and spoons. As you develop more enthusiasm for home dairying you can think about investing in specialist equipment, but don't let a lack of them prevent you from making a good start.

Cream

You can never have too much cream – it adds a real touch of luxury to everyday cooking. You can separate it simply by leaving the milk to cool then pouring (or spooning) the cream off the top. By this means we're able to obtain about a pint of cream from a gallon of milk. Another way is to siphon the milk from under the cream. Neither of these methods will skim off all of the cream – enough will be left behind in the milk for it to be an acceptable drink – but what cream you do get will be perfectly

adequate for home cooking and butter making.

However, while this works well with cows' milk, sheep and goats' milk is naturally homogenised, so very little cream will rise to the surface for skimming. Therefore you'll need to run it through a separator. In fact, this is the most efficient way to get cream, whatever species of animal you're milking, but they are costly bits of kit. If you do have a separator you should run virtually all your milk through it (just keep enough whole milk to one side for general household use), and use the skimmed milk for feeding to pigs and calves – separators are so efficient that you wouldn't want to use the separated milk for anything else anyway.

Now, with all that cream at your disposal (far more than you could possibly use up on puddings and in cooking), you're ready to start making butter.

Butter

It's possible to make butter very simply by placing cream in a lidded container of some sort and shaking it about. However, for any quantity you'll really need a butter churn. You have a choice of churning by hand or with a motor driven unit. Hand operated 'Blow' type churns can be found fairly easily on eBay, and they seem to sell for a realistic price. Electric churns can be purchased from various smallholding suppliers in the UK, but they're extremely expensive. There are some cheaper ones available on eBay from a Ukrainian supplier, and some from the USA as well. Alternatively, you can make butter in a food processor.

Manual butter churn.

Method

Most domestic butter churns have a one gallon capacity, so start off with 4 pints of cream – it's important that you only fill it half full, as the cream needs plenty of space if it's to be sufficiently bashed about. You can collect up cream over several days until you have enough.

Take the cream out of the fridge about 8-12 hours before you want to use it (to allow it to ripen and come up to room temperature) and pour it into the churn. Begin churning, and it will gradually thicken (like whipped cream) until it becomes difficult to turn the handle. Then, just as you think you're going to have to give up, it will suddenly become a little easier. The sound of it slopping around in the churn will change too. Continue turning until the handle goes very stiff again, and at this point you should have butter. Next drain off the buttermilk by tipping the contents of the churn into a colander or kitchen steamer basket. You can drink the buttermilk, use it in baking, or feed it to the pigs. Rinse the butter with really cold water until the washings run clear. You can just hold the colander under a running tap to do this.

Draining the freshly churned butter.

Turn it out onto a board and leave to drain for 20 minutes or so. Squeeze the remaining water out of the butter. Ideally you should have a pair of Scotch hands for this, although if you're only dealing with small quantities, a couple of wooden spatulas will do just as well. Work the butter until it comes

Home-made Scotch hands.

together into a single lump and no further liquid is coming out

Add as much, or as little, salt as you like, work it in, and then taste. If you find you've been a bit heavy handed with the salt, it's possible to wash some of it out using running cold water. Shape the butter into a block, wrap in greaseproof paper and refrigerate. It will store in the fridge for a couple of weeks, or it can be frozen. We usually get 1½lbs - 2lbs of butter from 4 pints of cream, although the yield will vary with the breed of animal, the time of year, stage of lactation, and diet of the cow. If you used a separator, the yield of butter per pint of cream would be higher. You may even need to add a bit of milk to the cream in order to be able to churn it properly – it might be too thick otherwise.

Work the butter until it comes together into a single lump.

TIP

Butterfat consists of globules within the milk, which, due to their oily nature, float to the surface and are easily separated out. Early in an animal's lactation the butterfat globules are large, but become progressively smaller throughout the lactation. The larger globules are much better for butter making, which explains why we experience difficulty when using cream from later in the lactation. Ripening the cream (for 12 hours or so) before churning may be less effective later in the year, due to lower temperatures. It helps to stand the cream in the kitchen for a while to warm up a bit and, if the butter still won't come, try pouring a cupful of hot water into the churn.

TIP

Don't be alarmed if, after housing your cows for the winter, your butter looses its lovely yellow colour. The colour in butter is due to the level of beta carotene in the animal's diet, and this is something they obtain from grazed grass. Once the cows go back out in the spring, the colour will revert almost immediately.

ICE CREAM

Home-made ice cream is a little luxury that's far superior to the bought stuff. There are so many variations and flavours that you need only be limited by your imagination. If you've got cream and a freezer, you can make it!

This is one area of home dairying where I really think it's beneficial to invest in a good machine from the outset. Thankfully, they're far cheaper and more readily available than most other domestic dairy equipment, largely because they've become popular kitchen appliances. You should be able to pick one up for around £35, although be prepared to pay a lot more for a really good one. Most ice cream makers work by having an inner bowl that you pre-freeze before you start, but the really expensive ones have their own built-in freezer unit. It's possible to make ice cream by hand, but it's very time consuming, and doesn't give the smooth, velvety texture that's achievable with a machine. Dot tends to stick to two or three basic recipes that she knows work well and that everyone in the family likes:

Dark chocolate ice cream

Ingredients
(makes about 1 litre)

1 pint cream
¾ pint whole milk
4oz cocoa powder
4oz sugar
a few drops of vanilla extract

Method

Put the cream and milk in a large jug and stir. If you forget to add the milk then you'll simply end up with chocolate flavoured butter instead of ice cream. Add the remaining ingredients and give it a whizz in a blender, or whisk until everything is well mixed together. Set the ice cream machine running, pour in the mixture, and let it churn for about 25 minutes, before turning it out into a suitable container and putting it in the freezer. It really couldn't be simpler.

Raspberry Ice Cream

Ingredients
(Makes about 1.5 litres)

1lb fresh raspberries
1 pint cream
½ pint milk
4oz caster sugar
1 tbsp lemon juice

Method

Put all the ingredients in a large jug, but reserve a handful or two of raspberries to add later. Mix everything thoroughly using a hand blender. Set the ice cream machine running, pour in the mixture and churn for about 25 minutes. Add the few whole raspberries that you reserved and keep the machine running for a further five minutes then turn it out in to a suitable tub and freeze.

Due to its high fat content, ice cream can be made from whole sheep's milk without the need to add extra cream.

Soft Lemon Ice Cream

Ingredients

3 fl oz water
4 oz caster sugar
Juice of 2 lemons
2 egg whites, whisk
½ pint cream

Method

Place the water, sugar, lemon juice and cream in a jug and mix. Add to the whisked egg white and fold in gently.

Churn in the ice cream machine for about 25 minutes.

There are other ways of making ice cream. Dot used to use a method which involved making 'eggy' custard with the cream, and then cooling it in the fridge before putting it in the machine. However, the custard making process had to be handled very carefully, otherwise vanilla ice cream ended up tasting too much like scrambled eggs! To be honest, if you can make really good ice cream without the need to cook anything, why bother? In fact, the same basic rule can be applied to all aspects of home dairying: just keep it simple!

Heating milk for making yoghurt.

YOGHURT

Yoghurt is one of those things that's so easy to make that everyone ought to be doing it. All you really need is a method of keeping a couple of pints of milk warm for around eight hours. Some people use wide-necked thermos flasks for this, but we put the milk in a plastic tub which we then place in a thick-walled polystyrene box. This was obtained from our local vets, where it had been used to keep vaccines cool. Similar boxes can often be scrounged from the local greengrocer if you talk nicely to him – they deliver delicate things such as watercress in them.

Making yoghurt

Put the desired quantity of milk into a saucepan and bring it to the boil. (In fact, provided that the temperature passes 85°C it'll be ok). Remove the pan from the heat and leave the milk to cool to around 43-45°C (use a jam thermometer to check the temperature), then stir in your chosen starter culture. We always use a pot of Yeo Valley natural live yoghurt bought from the local supermarket for about 50p. Put the milk in your insulated container or use some other means to keep it warm for around eight hours, then check to see if it has gone thick. If not, keep it warm for another couple of hours. Once set, refrigerate.

Before you start eating it, take out a couple of tablespoons to use as the starter for your next batch. Keep this in the fridge until needed.

We usually find we can keep on making yoghurt on a regular basis for 4-6 weeks by keeping our own starters, but after that the quality begins to decline so we nip out and buy a fresh pot of Yeo Valley to begin the whole process again.

CHEESE

Cheese making is a huge subject – vast tomes have been written on the art of it, and there is a strong tradition of farmhouse cheese making in the UK, where recipes have been passed down through generations. We have never been particularly adventurous in this area, primarily because to make the harder, more complex, cheeses not only do you need specialist equipment, but also a place where the atmospheric conditions of dryness and temperature allow cheese to sit and develop its flavour and character without deterioration. We don't have anywhere suitable, so our cheese-making has remained at the most basic level.

Generally we stick to making a basic soft 'cottage' cheese that is ready to eat in 24 hours and will keep for three to four days in the fridge. It's very simple, and the only things you need, in addition to normal kitchen equipment, are rennet and a piece of cheesecloth or muslin.

Soft 'cottage' cheese

Ingredients

3½ pints whole milk
Rennet
Salt and pepper to taste

Method

Using fresh milk, warm it gently to blood heat. You can use a thermometer to check this, but you could just dip your finger in it to see if it's about right. If you're using milk straight from the animal you can omit this step, as it will be the right temperature anyway. Add a tiny amount of rennet, as per the instructions on the bottle. Cover and leave it to stand somewhere reasonably warm. You can use animal or vegetable rennet – it makes no difference to the final product. In a couple of hours or so the milk will have separated into curds and whey. Cut the curd into fairly even sized chunks about the size of an Oxo cube then leave it to stand for another couple of hours until the curds have sunk. This allows the acidity to rise a little and gives the finished product a bit more flavour. Line an ordinary large kitchen sieve with cheesecloth and sit it on top of a large jug. Tip the curds and whey into the cheesecloth, gather the ends of the cloth up around the curds and secure. Leave this to drain in a cool place (or in the fridge) for about 18 hours. You might want to jiggle the contents of the cheesecloth about a little from time to time to encourage drainage. The longer you leave it, the drier your cheese will be, but don't leave it too long otherwise the curd may start to pick up musty flavours from the cloth. The following day, feed the whey to your pigs and tip the drained curds into a small mixing bowl. Add salt and pepper to taste, and anything else you fancy – a crushed clove of garlic perhaps, or chopped fresh herbs – and mix to an even consistency.

You can use this cheese, unseasoned, in any recipes that specify soft cheese, including baked cheesecake. The yield will vary depending on the animal the milk came from – sheeps' milk

will yield more that either goats' or cows'. Only make as much as you can reasonably consume in a few days.

If you feel a bit more adventurous, or are bored with soft cheese, here is another fairly simple drained cheese that can be made with limited equipment. It'll keep for longer than the soft cheese, but not indefinitely. However, we have successfully stored this cheese in the freezer:

Brie-type cheese

Ingredients

3 gallons whole milk
Rennet
Salt
Penicillium Candidum culture

Method

Warm the milk to blood temperature in the same way as for the cottage type cheese. Add an appropriate quantity of rennet as per the instructions on the bottle. Leave in a warm place to coagulate. This should take a couple of hours or so. Once the curds and whey start to separate, cut the curds into even sized pieces, but not too small. Leave the curds sitting in the whey for about an hour. Tip the curds and whey through a cheesecloth and leave the curd to drain for three hours. Once drained, crumble the curd into small pieces and add salt at the rate of about ½ oz for every 1lb of curds. This doesn't need to be exact – you need enough salt to give a good flavour but not so much that it's inedible. We've ruined more than one batch of cheese by making it too salty. Put the curds in small moulds, filling them right to the top, and leave to drain for 24 hours.

Turn the moulds up the other way and leave for another day. Repeat this every day for five days. Remove the cheeses from the moulds and rub all over the surface with salt – this helps the cheese to form a rind – then leave for 24 hours, turn, and leave for a further day. Spray the surface of the cheeses with a dissolved *Penicillium Candidum* culture.

This is purchased as a dry powder, so reconstitute it as per the instructions on the packet and put it in a small spray bottle. It needs to be stored in the fridge between uses.

The cheese should begin develop a nice velvety, brie-like coating after a few days, provided it's not in too cold a place. It wants to be too chilly for a living area, but warmer than a fridge. Leave it, turning it occasionally, for a couple of weeks, by which time it should be ready to eat.

Slaughter and Butchery - Large Animals

"Meat was made for mouths"
William Shakespeare

When talking about home slaughter, I tend to divide animals into two distinct categories: those that can be killed by hand, and those that will require the use of a firearm of some sort. In essence, this is the little and the large. In one category we have poultry, rabbits and very young goat kids (which are often killed at a few days old, as a by-product of milk production). The other consists of adult goats, sheep and lambs, pigs and cattle.

There's a great sense of satisfaction in tucking into a meal that's been wholly bred, reared, killed, butchered and cooked at home, particularly when the whole family has been involved at every step along the way. For us this is the norm, but I appreciate that

for many smallholders new to livestock keeping, it can involve quite a psychological step, this business of eating a piece of mutton that you remember skipping about with the children when it was a lamb. It probably had a name, too. Interestingly, it's always the adults in a household who find this difficult to deal with (though generally, when questioned, they shuffle about a bit and make excuses such as "not wanting to upset the kids"). Children, on the other hand, tend to be remarkably matter-of-fact about the whole process, have no qualms about being present at (or even helping with) slaughter and butchery, and, at mealtimes, are generally delighted to know the name of the animal they are eating, particularly if it's one that they played a special part in the rearing of, such as a bottle fed lamb.

'Home slaughter' is defined as being *"The slaughter of a livestock animal by its owner on their property for their own personal consumption or that of members of their immediate family living there"*. You cannot ask anyone else (even a licensed slaughterman) to kill and cut up an animal for you on your premises, even if it is only for home consumption – you must do the job yourself. In Northern Ireland the law is a little more flexible, in that it states that it **may** be permissible to make use of an itinerant slaughterman, provided he only kills the animal and does not process it in any way.

Why do it?

Why slaughter stock at home rather than making use of a licensed abattoir? For us the answer is simple: why not? It's what we've always done; it's appropriate to our lifestyle, and it works well for us. I'm sure that if there were still small local slaughterhouses in rural areas we'd use them, but the fact is there isn't. Of course, any meat intended for sale **must** go through licensed premises, which in our case involves a 120 mile round trip to deliver the animals to the slaughterhouse. The carcasses are then transported, via another abattoir, back to our local butcher, from where we collect the meat for distribution to our customers. So much for food miles. Is this really the way we should be operating, given the impending fuel crisis that the world is facing? The catchphrase "local food for local people" has rather a hollow ring to it when you consider the huge circular journeys that may be involved. And then there's the stress factor. We like to think that our animals lead a fairly stress-free life, but is this really the case if their final hours consist of a long trailer journey, a strange and frightening environment, and unfamiliar people? For home consumption there's a better way: I slaughter the animal myself, on the farm were it was bred and reared, in familiar surroundings, and with sympathetic handling. In this way we really do know what we eat, how it lived, and how it died.

Various pieces of legislation are in place in the UK to ensure that home slaughter within the law is almost impossible. Strangely enough, pig killing seems to be the least affected. The rules relating to the actual act of slaughter are simple enough, and primarily relate to the welfare of the animal at the time of death, which is as it should be. However, once the animal is dead, things can get complicated.

Should you decide to carry out home slaughter, it's necessary to abide by the following codes of practice:

• No person engaged in the movement, lairaging, restraint, stunning, slaughter or killing of animals shall cause any avoidable excitement, pain or suffering to any animal, or permit any animal to sustain any avoidable excitement, pain or suffering.

• The animal must be killed humanely, in accordance with The Welfare of Animals at the Time of Killing Regulations 2015.

• Animals must be stunned before slaughter.

• No person shall slaughter any animal by a religious method, or cause or permit any animal to be so slaughtered, other than in a licensed slaughterhouse.

• All slaughter waste not intended for human consumption or classified as specified risk material (SRM) must be disposed of in accordance with the Animal By-Products Regulations 2005. This would include hooves, horns, skins and blood.

Acceptable methods

• **Shotgun:** The issue of pre-slaughter stunning can be neatly sidestepped by the use of a shotgun. This technique causes instantaneous death, therefore both stunning and slaughter are carried out in one simple action. It's also more effective in the hands of less experienced users, has simpler licensing / ownership requirements than other weapons (although a license is no longer required for captive bolt stunning equipment), and, of course, has other uses on the holding, such as pest control. We find that a small-bore shotgun (.410) is ideal for slaughtering all classes of stock, without any fuss or unpleasantness. Shot size should not be less than No.6, with a 2½″ cartridge being ok for most situations. (For very large pigs or cattle, use a 3″ magnum, but do check that your gun is correctly chambered to take these longer cartridges. 2″ cartridges are adequate for lambs). Larger bore shotguns may be used equally effectively, but the results can be messy and unappetising.

If you don't have a shotgun or shotgun license, it's still possible to use one on private premises under the supervision of the owner / license holder. Provided that someone within your local smallholding community has both gun and license, it should be possible to carry out your home slaughtering under his watchful eye; an offer of home brew may do the trick. Sadly he cannot be paid in lamb chops – this would constitute supply to a third party, which is illegal. If you have a shotgun license but don't wish to keep a gun on your premises, you can borrow one for up to 72 hours without the need to inform your local police or firearms department. The use of firearms in confined spaces is covered by further complex regulations; avoid falling foul of these by shooting the animal outside.

Apart from a shotgun, other legally acceptable methods for the slaughter of livestock include:

• **Captive bolt pistol:** Captive bolt pistols are no longer subject to firearms legislation, so are readily available. A captive bolt pistol is a stunning device. Immediately following stunning it's necessary to sever all the major blood vessels in the neck with a sharp knife, in order to ensure that death occurs as quickly as possible.

• **Humane Killer, 0.32 calibre free bullet:** A humane killer can be used to kill animals outright, although bleeding should still be carried out immediately. Generally, a humane killer should only be used by a vet, knackerman, or some other suitably qualified person. There is a very real risk of ricochet, should an inaccurately placed bullet happen to pass through the animal, hence the need for proper training in the use of this device.

• **0.22 rifle or revolver:** Only to be used as a last resort, when no other method of humane destruction is available, for example in the case of casualty livestock, in order to prevent further suffering.

There are tight restrictions on what you may do with your home killed meat, and who may consume it. No part of any home killed animal (except in certain cases poultry, rabbits and game) can be sold, bartered, swapped or given to any third party. This would include guests, friends, and family not normally resident in your own home. In the case of home-killed pigs, it's acceptable for the meat to be consumed by yourself and your immediate family living with you in your house. With sheep, cattle and goats, however, the situation is rather different. Due to the Transmissible Spongiform Encephalopathy (TSE) regulations that came into force on 19th April 2002, it's now virtually impossible for anyone to supply privately killed meat to the rest of their own household. This means that private killing of ovines, bovines and caprines is generally only permissible when a farmer slaughters the animal himself, processes it himself, and consumes it himself. Any part of the carcass not actually eaten by the farmer would classify as waste material under EU animal by-products regulation 1774/2002 and should be disposed of in line with that regulation.

It seems to me to be somewhat bizarre that my wife and family are effectively banned from eating an animal that has been reared on our own farm, has been healthy and well cared for, and has been killed in familiar surroundings, simply because it was me who pulled the trigger. Aren't they considered capable of making up their own minds? Should our children have to eat imported meat of doubtful origin, reared under conditions over which we have no control

TSE regulations and Specified Risk Material (SRM):

The Food Standards Agency does grudgingly concede that, in certain circumstances, it may be possible to satisfy TSE regulations at home, in which case meat could be consumed by the whole household. However, this legislation is very difficult, if not impossible, to satisfy adequately in most smallholding situations.

Sheep and goats: The ileum and the spleen must be removed from all sheep and goats, and on those over 12 months of age (or having permanent incisors erupted) you also need to remove the skull (including brains and eyes), tonsils and spinal cord.

Cattle: The tonsils, intestines (from duodenum to rectum) and the mesentery must be removed from cattle of all ages. Over 12 months of age you must also remove the skull (excluding lower jaw, but including brain and eyes) and spinal cord. On cattle over 30 months old you'll also need to remove the vertebral column (excluding tail and spinal processes, but including the dorsal root ganglia).

All of the above SRMs must be stained blue before disposal. Pigs are exempt from TSE regulations, so, of the larger species of farmed animal, these are in fact the easiest animals to deal with in accordance with the law.

In practice, I know plenty of smallholding folk who regularly slaughter their own sheep and goats (and occasionally cattle) for home consumption, and none of them takes the blind bit of notice of the TSE regulations. Neither are they shy about sharing their wonderful home-produced food with their guests. What you decide to do is up to you – just don't blame me if you get into trouble.

simply because they're not yet old enough to handle a shotgun? I could, if I wished, legally kill, process, and sell up to 10,000 chickens per year, yet I cannot feed one home killed lamb to my own family. Where will it all end? And whatever happened to freedom of choice? Maybe you're lucky enough to live in a country where these rules do not apply, or perhaps you are single with no family. Be that as it may, you can rest assured that I, for one, will continue to kill my own stock for my own consumption, and I can't really see the rest of my family being content with a tin of Brazilian Corned Beef whilst I tuck into a roast saddle of mutton, can you?

 TIP

Even if you have no intention of eating your own animals, you should have the knowledge (and preferably the means) to carry out humane destruction of casualty stock for welfare reasons. To avoid prolonged suffering of the sick or injured, it's often preferable to make an on-the-spot decision and carry out the deed immediately. To do otherwise, to leave it to "see if it's a bit better in the morning" amounts to little more than cruelty.

Pig

The killing of a small porker (around 100lb deadweight) isn't a big undertaking, however, the longer you put it off, the bigger he will grow, until in the end you are faced with a mammoth task. I speak from experience.

Generally we kill our pigs late in the evening, leave them hanging overnight to cool, then cut them up first thing in the morning.

This time schedule causes least disturbance to the normal routine work of the holding. Remember not to feed your pig on the day, but on no account should he be without fresh water. Withholding feed not only means his gut will be empty, making for easier evisceration, but, being a bit on the hungry side, he can be persuaded to stand still with a handful of meal, making his final moments completely stress free. Before making a start, think the job through carefully, and talk it over with your helpers. Everyone involved must know exactly where to stand, what to do, and when. You can't afford to make mistakes – that's the sort of thing that gives home slaughter a bad name.

A bed of straw to keep the pig off the floor.

Although the pig will be shot outside, you'll need a draught-free building to work in when you're scalding. We use the dairy; it's clean, easy to wash down, and has water on tap. Use a few sections of straw, well fluffed up, to make a bed for the pig to lie on; keep him off the cold floor at all costs. If necessary, block up holes and gaps under doors with straw to keep out the cold night air. A small block and tackle already in position overhead is handy, together with a gambrel and some meat hooks. The gambrel can be improvised from a bit of mild steel bar, (or double up a short length of chain and hold the ends apart with a spreader, forming an 'A' shape). Get everything set up and organised before you begin. You won't have time to go looking for things after the pig is dead; if you don't get the bristles off him before he cools down, you'll never get them off at all.

Pig killing equipment.

In addition to your shotgun you'll require a knife to stick him with (we use a 7½" cook's knife), a smaller knife (say 6"), and a butchers' saw. (A Jewson's hard point wood saw will do instead of the butchers' saw. Don't try using a hacksaw – it wasn't designed for cutting through organic material.) Later in the process you'll want a cleaver too. You'll also need a scraper of sorts (the real thing looks like a short handled draw hoe, but the edge of a metal saucepan lid works well), a jug, and, of course, hot water. We have found that with the Rayburn going full blast to bake bread, the water coming out of the tap is just the right temperature to scald a pig, i.e. 60°C. In fact, it comes out a bit hotter than this, which makes allowance for some cooling. Six gallons is usually enough for a small porker, so we fill 2 three gallon buckets before we begin. Buckets with lids are best, and warm them before filling. Place the buckets of water next to the bed of straw and wrap them well with old blankets. Now you can begin.

1. Entice the pig out of his sty with a bucket of feed, and as soon as he's fully occupied, shoot him as per diagram (bellow), at a range of 4" - 6". Don't dilly-dally – if you miss the moment he'll soon become suspicious of your behaviour, and things will begin to go wrong.

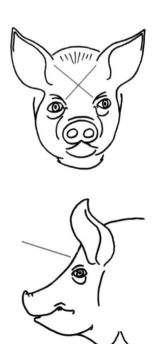

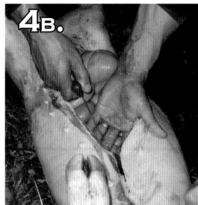

2. The instant that you have shot him, you must stick him. (This needs to be carried out while the body is still kicking, or he won't bleed thoroughly). Insert the larger of your two knives just in front of the breastbone and slightly off centre, at an angle towards the back of the pig, and let him bleed for a moment or two. If you've used a shotgun, which both stuns and kills, then bleeding isn't an essential part of the slaughtering process, however, meat from an animal which has been bled will remain fresh for longer. Now transfer the carcass to your pre-prepared bed of straw, shut the door, block off the draughts and set to work.

3. Fold back the blanket from one of the water buckets and, lifting the lid as little as possible, dip a jug of water. Beginning at the shoulder, slowly pour on the water while plucking at the bristles. All of a sudden they'll begin to slip off easily – you may observe a slight change or tightening of the skin at this point – so stop plucking and get busy with the scraper. If there are two of you on the job, one of you can begin at the rear of the pig, which will speed up the process no end. Keep pouring and scraping until the job is done. Don't waste water on the head and trotters unless you definitely intend to use them to make brawn. As soon as one bucket of water is empty, turn

the pig over and begin on the other side. If you hadn't quite finished the first then you must try to be more economical with water. Once de-bristling is complete you can relax a little, tidy up a bit, and even have a beer, but not too much as there's still plenty to do.

4a. (and 4b) Insert the end of a hosepipe into the rectum of the pig and turn it on for a bit – this will wash out any remaining excrement, reducing the risk of contamination of the meat. Cut around the anus with your smaller knife – three cuts in a triangular fashion should do it, but the knife must be sharp. With the pig lying on his back (stand astride him to stop him flopping over), cut through his breastbone with the meat saw, and continuing with a knife, open the front of his neck almost to the angle of the jaw to expose the oesophagus and windpipe. Now, working in the

other direction, but with the pig still lying on his back, open up the belly as far as the groin. (You can get a knife with a hooked blade especially for this, which reduces the risk of puncturing the guts and contaminating the meat – see page 279.)

5. Next, cut behind the tendons just above the back of the hind trotters (not behind the tendon at the hock joint, which is often referred to as the hamstring), insert a couple of meat hooks and attach to the block and tackle via a gambrel which will serve to hold the hind legs apart, and haul him clear of the floor. All the guts should flop out as you lift him up. Now's the time to pick out any bits of offal you may need, such as intestines for sausage skins, the liver (remember to remove the gall bladder), the heart, and the kidneys. My recommendation is that you hot-foot it straight to the

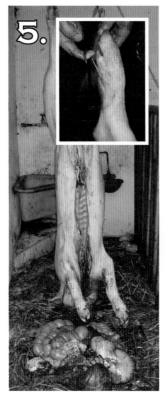

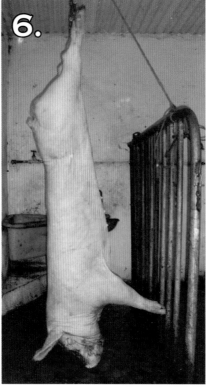

kitchen and get the liver in the pan while it's still warm. Forget the dry, crumbly, grey looking stuff that used to be served up with bacon at school dinners – this will be liver as you've never known before, pinkish in colour, subtle of flavour, and with a truly melt in the mouth succulence.

6. Any remaining bristles can be shaved off using a sharp knife rather in the fashion of a cut-throat razor, then leave the carcass alone until the morning.

While the pig is still hanging, score down the middle of the back with a sharp knife, then cut him in two with the butchers' saw. I don't find this part of the job very easy, and I have heard of people resorting to the use of a small chainsaw, lubricated with vegetable oil. We cut off the head at this point, rather than splitting it. The carcass is then

transferred to your butchers' block (if you have one) or kitchen table (if you haven't), half at a time, to be cut up as you please – joints and chops from a porker; hams and bacon sides from a larger animal. Unfortunately you cannot (legally) ask a butcher to carry out this part of the job for you.

TIP

As the animal wasn't slaughtered on licensed premises, and was therefore not subject to Meat Hygiene Service inspection, any bits and pieces must be disposed of as animal (rather than food) waste. However, as we all know, it's possible to use all of a pig except the squeak, so there won't be any waste, will there!

Sheep (and adult goats)

Unlike killing a pig, where you need lots of hot water, a place to carry out the scalding, and a fairly draught-proof building, you can handle a lamb pretty well anywhere. Often I've carried out the whole process out-of-doors, hauling the carcass up on the overhanging bough of a tree (or the front-end loader of the tractor) where, in cold, dry weather, it can safely remain overnight. For the sake of comfort though, (and to avoid alarming the neighbours), an outhouse is the best place to work. No particular facilities are required, but it's handy if you can rig up a block and tackle from an overhead beam, or failing that, improvise some sort of frame from scaffold poles or similar. In a large agricultural building, the tractor and loader can be brought under cover and used to raise the carcass. You'll not need a lot of space to work, but ideally you'll want room to move all around the animal once he's hanging up. You'll also need somewhere safe to place sharp knives etc., and a small pen to restrain the animal immediately prior to slaughter.

Ideally you'll have had your sheep penned up overnight, with only a bucket of water and a little straw to nibble at. This ensures that his guts are reasonably empty (making evisceration much simpler), and also means he's hungry, which is an advantage – it's a simple matter now to place a pan of feed in front of him, and shoot him as he eats.

Tools of the trade

Including a proper butcher's chopping block. Notice the small knife with the hook-shaped blade – this extremely useful bit of kit is used to open the carcass for evisceration, without any risk of puncturing the stomach (which could cause contamination of the meat). You'll also need a really good sharp knife with a blade length of about 6", and a butchers' saw.

1. With our flighty Welsh mountain sheep, I prefer to restrain them with a halter. The gun (ideally a .410 shotgun) should be held 6"- 8" from the head, and you shoot him in the middle of the forehead, just above the eyes, in a straight line with the neck. The shot makes a small hole in the skull, but completely destroys the brain. Death is instantaneous.

2. Bleeding must be carried out immediately by making a deep cut at the angle of the jaw which severs all the major blood vessels in the neck.

3. Hoist the animal off the floor by the hind legs and let him drain for a while. A simple gambrel keeps his legs apart. Start skinning by making a small incision slightly below, and to one side of, the pizzle (in a male animal), then, with the knife blade facing outwards, open all the way up one side of the 'pee pipe' to where the clear area of skin starts in the region of the groin.

4. At this point, veer off line, cut across the clear skin and all the way up the inside front of the hind leg until just past the hock joint. Repeat for the other side. In the case of a ewe, a single cut up the belly is all that is required, before branching just in front of the udder region.

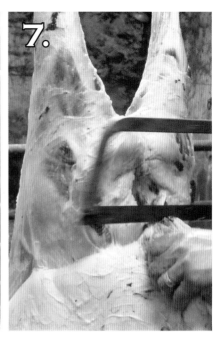

5. Loosen the skin as much as possible on the hind legs before cutting right around and separating the skin from each leg at the hock. Finish skinning the hind legs by pulling down on the hide while 'fisting' with the other hand. This is easy to do in a lamb or kid, but in older animals you may need to resort to the use of a sharp knife to help separate the skin from the carcass.

6. Next, peel back the V-shaped piece of skin formed where your original cut divided; pull it over, between the hind legs, to the back of the sheep, until you come to the rectum. Hook your finger around this, pull out a few inches of pipework, and tie it off with a piece of clean string. Cut the rectum away from the skin then drop the tied off end down into the body of the animal.

7. Saw off the tail close to the carcass, leaving it attached to the skin.

8. Remove the skin from the rest of the body, using your fist, and sometimes a sharp knife, to loosen it as you pull. When you draw level with your original incision, extend the cut downwards all the way to the throat. Skin out the front legs in the same fashion as the rear, and saw off the front hooves just below the knee. Now finish skinning the length of the neck until you reach its juncture with the head.

9. Now score a line down the breastbone with a sharp knife, then saw through it. It's helpful if someone holds onto a front leg to stop the carcass swinging about while you do this. Next, use your knife to open up the animal's neck from breast to jaw, exposing the oesophagus and windpipe.

10. Using a hooked knife, if you have one, open the carcass from chest to crutch. In the absence of a hooked knife, guard the tip of an ordinary blade with

your finger. Whatever you do, take care not to puncture any innards.

11. The guts should now all flop out towards you, although sometimes they might need a helping hand. Locate and remove the bladder (without spilling its contents), and also the liver and kidneys. Carefully cut away the gallbladder from the liver.

12. Cut away the diaphragm from the inside of the rib cage, whereupon all the offal should fall to the floor, remaining attached to the carcass only at the head. Saw off the head, then this part of the job is complete. Don't be tempted to wash the carcass at all. Any visibly contaminated areas should be trimmed off with a sharp knife, once the carcass has cooled.

13. A lamb or kid need only hang for a day or two, but, in the case of a mutton carcass, as shown here, it needs to hang for at least 10-14 days in a cool dry place; the older the animal, the longer it needs. Not only does hanging result in a richer, more complex flavour, but it gives time for enzymes within the meat to soften the muscle fibres, and for connective tissue to relax, giving tenderness. In order for hanging to be successful, carcasses must have a good covering of fat; without this protective layer, meat may begin to deteriorate rapidly after a few days. The carcass doesn't need to be refrigerated, but must be kept reasonably cool, so an unheated store room in winter is ideal. The environment in our store room is ideal for this – it's to the north of our house, and the 2' thick stone walls ensure that the temperature remains fairly constant. In damp weather, a little mildew may appear on the carcass, but this is no cause for alarm – we simply wipe it off with a cloth moistened in vinegar.

14. Butchery is fairly straightforward if you just break the carcass down into easily managed pieces. You can try fancy things like boning and rolling, but this isn't strictly necessary. Any odds and ends that you're unsure about can be minced – minced mutton makes simply the best shepherd's pies and Bolognese.

Disposing of odds and ends

Just as in killing a pig, when it's possible to use "all but the squeak", so it should be possible to make full use of every part of the carcass of a sheep or goat. The liver and kidneys we've already mentioned. The heart, too, makes a tasty dish, or can be included in mince, where it gives an attractive speckled appearance. A quick flick through two recipe books on our kitchen shelf have turned up seven recipes for sheep's heads (and a further 11 for tongues and brains), two recipes for hooves, and one for tails, so that's that lot

dealt with. Use rams' horns for shepherd's crooks, obviously. The hide will make a rug, or slippers, or even a new skin for your banjo. Quite a bit of the intestines can be salted down for sausage skins, and the rest of the innards (together with the lungs and any other bits and pieces) can be fed to the dogs – there's been a huge amount of interest recently in providing more natural diets for dogs and, not surprisingly, they do very well on it. This only leaves one thing: the blood. This should be sprinkled around your raspberry canes, where it'll do a power of good. Now, when an inspector calls, you'll be able to account for every part of every beast!

(Or simply write 'missing' in the flock record book, like everyone else does…)

Cattle

I've only slaughtered cattle on a couple of occasions, for the simple reason that we can't afford to eat beef. We rely on the sale of our young cattle to cover the cost of all our dairy produce. However, there are occasions when we get a 'poor doer' – an animal that doesn't thrive as it should, so can't be sent to market with the rest – and these are the ones for home consumption.

Killing and cutting up a beef animal is essentially the same as dealing with a mutton sheep, but on a much bigger scale. It's not something you'll want to undertake on your own, so enlist the help of a willing neighbour, even if only for safety reasons – you might easily be knocked down and injured by the thrashing hooves of a shot beast, and when there are knives and firearms involved, things could go badly wrong.

Making Bacon, Ham and Sausages

There's actually no need for us to make bacon or ham anymore. The domestic deep freeze reigns supreme as the ultimate meat storage solution, so the salting, drying and smoking of pork for the purpose of preservation is more or less obsolete. But of course we do still make bacon and ham, because we like it! And if we once again found ourselves living somewhere that didn't have the benefit of a reliable electricity supply, we could quickly revert to the old way of doing things. As it is, the biggest advantage of using the freezer in conjunction with the other processes is that we're not wholly relying on the salt for its preservative qualities. Therefore we can get away with using a milder cure, which produces a far more acceptable flavour. The traditional curing process often resulted in bacon so salty that it needed to be soaked in fresh water overnight before use, which would negate a lot of the convenience associated with these types of food nowadays. Having home-cured bacon, ready sliced, in handy sized packs in the freezer, gives us the best of both worlds, I think.

Really, though, it's sausages that provide the smallholder with the perfect equivalent of 'fast food'. A pig can be made into sausages without any specialist butchery skills – there's no need to cut the animal into joints or chops or back or belly, just strip all the meat off the bones and bung it in! In fact, you don't even need to scald and scrape the carcass first – just hang it up and skin it. And a whole pig, processed in this way, will yield an awful lot of sausages. Stored in family sized packs, they can be cooked from frozen, and are just the thing when you come in late at the end of the day with no supper planned, or you need to rustle up a quick meal at lambing time.

Sausage skins

Unravel the large intestines of a pig or sheep, separating it from all attached membranes. Place one end over a cold tap and turn on a steady flow to wash all the excrement from within. Beware of twists!

Cut the intestine into manageable lengths (5' seems to be about right. One whole intestine is about 45'). Turn each length inside out by turning back one end and putting it over the tap (imagine that you're putting the tap into the turn-up of a pair of jeans). Run the water in slowly, and it'll all turn inside out in an instant. Lay out each length on the kitchen table and scrape off the gut lining with the back of a knife. What you're left with will look something like a semi-transparent bootlace.

Store the skins until required in strong brine solution (4 oz salt / 1 pint of water)..

TIP

Before use, untangle an appropriate number of the brined skins, and place them into a bowl or large jug of fresh cold water. I leave an end of each one hanging over the edge of the jug so they don't get tangled up again.

TIP

After threading the whole of a length of skin onto the nozzle of the stuffer – expect some ribald comments if you're doing this with an audience – in preparation for filling, don't tie a knot in the end, otherwise your first sausage will closely resemble a balloon!

Take care not to overfill the skins with the mix as they'll soon tighten up when you twist the links. Keep the bunched skin on the nozzle nice and wet throughout the process to ensure that it slips off smoothly, and without tearing.

Pork Sausages

This basic recipe works just as well with mutton.

Ingredients

2lb lean meat scraps
12 oz fat
1 small glass homebrewed beer or cider
8oz brown breadcrumbs
¼ tsp nutmeg
1 tsp dried sage
½ tsp dried thyme
½ tsp dried marjoram
1½ tsp salt
½ tsp ground black pepper

Method

Thoroughly mince the meat and the fat twice. Add the liquid to the minced meat and fat and mix, then add the remaining ingredients. Mix everything together in a large bowl, ensuring that the herbs and spices are evenly distributed throughout. Fill the skins then hang up the strings of linked sausages (see right) in a cool airy place for a few days.

TIP

Beware of cheap and cheerful sausage making 'starter kits'. If you're serious about home production you really need a decent mincer with a sausage stuffing attachment. Having said that, we filled our first few skins using a funnel and a stick.

Linking

Once you've finished filling the skin you'll have what amounts to one long sausage. Therefore you have to 'link' it. This basically means you twist it at regular intervals to make individual sausages of an appropriate size. However, the resulting string of sausages will tend to unravel when you hang it up, so it's better if you can learn to triple link them:

1) Starting at one end, twist twice to make two sausages of the size that you want; 2) Tie the bit of loose skin at the top end of the first sausage around the twist at the bottom of the second sausage, making a loop; 3) Pull a length of sausage through between the two that you tied together in step 2, until you've got enough to form another sausage and another looped pair the same size as the first; 4) Twist together where the sausages meet. You'll now have a link of three sausages, and another loop as in step 2; 5) Repeat steps 3 and 4 over and over again.

Dried (Continental style) pork sausage

You'll need the widest skins available - the large intestine of a pig is barely big enough. Use 2 parts of lean meat to 1 part of hard back fat. Marinade the lean meat for about 6 hours in dry red wine then mince very finely. Chop the fat into little cubes (¾" or less). Mix together the lean and the fat, and to every 2lb of the mixture add:

¾ oz salt
1½ tsp ground black pepper
3 cloves of garlic (finely chopped or pressed)
Good pinch of coriander
Good pinch of ground ginger
Small pinch of cayenne pepper
Heaped dessertspoon of brown sugar
Good dash of brandy
Big pinch of saltpetre

Mix up all together, and fill the skins. Hang the sausages to dry in a warm place, but not too hot (a room that has an Aga or Rayburn ticking away in the background is ideal) for at least a month. You can cold smoke them if you like. Eat raw.

BACON

You can make bacon from any bit of pork, but using the side will give you classic back and streaky bacon rashers. There's lots of different ways to cure meat, but our dry(ish) curing method is really very simple, and all you need in the way of equipment is a big tub with a lid – a brewing bin or a plastic storage box is ideal. We use a couple of old glass accumulator tanks that were once part of the back-up battery bank for the Bardsey Island lighthouse.

Placing half of a side of pork in the salt tub.

You'll also need:

55lb (25kg) dry curing salt
4 tsp saltpetre
1lb 9 oz dark brown sugar
A handful of juniper berries
A dessert bowlful of the following mix of herbs and spices: black peppercorns, crushed bay leaves, crushed thyme and cloves (adjust the quantities according to taste).

Method

Dump all the ingredients into your tub and mix together really well. Hands are the best tool for this, but you might want to wear a pair of rubber gloves to keep the salt off any damaged skin. Next, rub the curing mixture thoroughly into both sides of the meat then completely bury it, taking care to ensure that it's in contact with the salt at all points (i.e. no air pockets underneath), and that it's not touching the edge of the tub. The following day, and for a further 3 days, you need to turn over and re-bury each piece of meat, then leave them untouched for another 4 days

TIP

Usually, we cut a large side into two (or even three) pieces before curing. We put the first bit in, cover it well with the cure, then put the second piece above it, ensuring it's not in contact with the lower piece, and then cover that as well. Ignore anything you read about boning the side of bacon before curing – you must leave the bones in. Place a flat weight on top of the salt – we use a heavy piece of slate.

(use your common sense a bit here – bigger, thicker bits of meat may need to remain in the tub for a little longer). Next remove all the pieces from the cure, rinse off any excess salt, and hang the bacon up in a cool, fly-free place to dry. After a week, take the side of bacon down and bone it out. Then cut it in half lengthways, just about where the ends of the ribs were, to separate the back from the belly. Now you can slice the whole lot up into rashers and put it in the freezer in suitably sized portions.

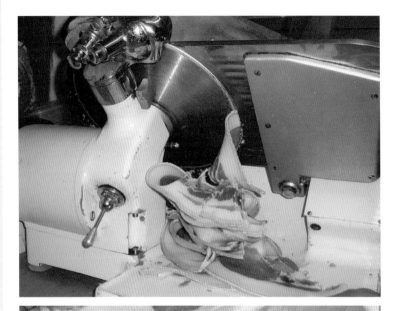

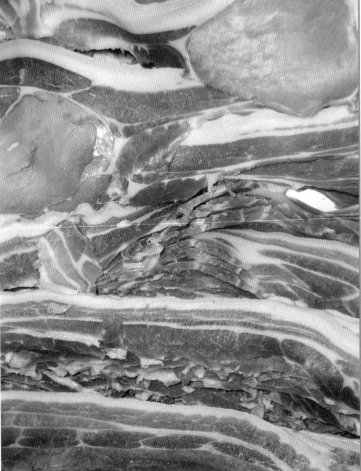

Rashers of home-cured bacon.

TIP

If you want to make the sort of bacon that doesn't require freezing, you'll need to leave the sides in the curing tub for quite a bit longer – maybe 10 days to a fortnight. You can then keep it hanging up from the pantry ceiling and just slice a bit off when required, but the rashers will need to be soaked in fresh water before use, otherwise they'll be unpleasantly dry and salty.

TIP

Don't throw away used salt. A curing tub is like a fine sherry maturing in an oak cask – a little is added, and a little is taken away, but the whole thing never gets emptied. We've been using the same tub of salt for nearly 20 years now, and the bacon just gets better and better! From time to time we drain off the accumulated liquid, and skim off a bit of unpleasant-looking scum, and sometimes we dump in a bit of fresh salt, (together with a few more herbs, spices and brown sugar), but not very often – perhaps once every 4-5 years.

HAM

Ham is made in much the same
way as bacon, except that you do
have to remove the first round
bone (femur) from the leg before
burying it in the salt. This can be
tricky as you need to cut quite a
long way into the joint without
damaging the surrounding meat
too much. Leave the tibia and
fibula *in situ* so that you have
something with which to hang up
your ham.

*Weighing a piece of ham
before boiling.*

Method

Having removed the round bone,
pack the resulting hole full of cure
then bury the joint in the remaining
cure in the tub. Leave it for around
10-12 days (no need to turn this
time) then remove, rinse and hang
up to dry for a week. Remove the
remaining bone from the finished
ham and tie into nice round joints.
Place in a large pan and bring to
the boil. At this point taste the
water, and if it's unpleasantly salty,
chuck it away and re-boil the ham
in fresh water. Once you're happy
with the salinity, add an onion
stuck with cloves and a tablespoon
of brown sugar, and boil for 30
minutes per 1lb, plus another 30
minutes. Next, remove the ham
from the water and place on a flat
board or plate. Put another board
on top and weigh it down until
completely cool. Pressing it in this

*A whole ham, newly removed from the curing tub (visible
behind).*

way makes it much easier to slice.
Now eat as much as you like, and
freeze the rest for later.

Alternatively you can eat
the boiled ham hot, which is
absolutely delicious.

Instead of boiling your ham and
freezing it, you can simply leave
it hanging up to be eaten raw,
Parma style, in wafer-thin slices.
However, it'll be a miracle if the
flies don't get to it in the end. If
you've got a suitable storage area
then by all means give it a go – but
don't say I didn't warn you.

SMOKING

Smoking bacon and ham adds
another dimension to the flavour,
but it isn't essential. In the past
we have hot-smoked both bacon
and ham in an old 45-gallon
oil drum, propped up on some
blocks with a fire (or gas ring)
burning underneath it. A lot of
oak chippings were placed in the
bottom of the drum, and the meat
hung from a rail across the top. An

*The old privy we use as a
smokehouse.*

old blanket and a piece of heavy
plywood sealed up the opening,
ensuring that as much of the smoke
as possible remained inside. It
gets pretty hot in the drum, so a
couple of hours of smoking by this
method is enough.

Now we smoke our produce
hanging from the rafters in a little
stone shed that stands at the corner
of the garden – the old privy. First
we get a good, hot, smokeless fire
going on the floor or in a small
brazier – charcoal is ideal for this.

Once it's well alight we dump
a load of woodchips, shavings
or sawdust (preferably oak, but

287

other native hardwoods are nearly as good) on top and close the door, making sure that all gaps are blocked up. The aim is to let the woodchips smoulder away as slowly as possible, producing lots of lovely smoke, but no flames. We try to keep it burning all day, so from time to time it might be necessary to add more sawdust to keep the fire well smothered. However, it's important that the door is opened as little as possible during the smoking process.

On a really small scale, smoking can even be carried out in a biscuit tin: place a layer of oak chippings in the bottom of the tin, and then, using chicken wire, improvise a rack about half way up. Put your pieces of meat on the rack, shut the lid, and place the whole thing on the hotplate of your stove. This method is ideal for things like fillets of fish, chicken breasts and small pieces of ham or bacon.

PÂTÉ

Dot usually turns the pig livers into a simple pâté, as follows:

Ingredients

½ pig's liver
6 oz butter (plus a little more for frying and for sealing the pots)
2 onions, chopped
1 good-sized clove of garlic
Chopped herbs (rosemary and thyme are particularly good)
Salt and pepper
A capful of alcohol (whisky or brandy)

Method

Cut the liver into small pieces (making sure you remove any stringy bits) and place in melted butter in a large pan on a low heat until it begins to fry gently. Add the onions, garlic, herbs, salt and pepper, and cook for about 10 minutes (until all the liver is well browned) then cover the pan and leave to bubble away for a further 10 minutes or so. Remove the pan from the heat and leave to cool completely, then tip the contents into a food processor, add the butter and alcohol (our original recipe requires brandy, but as we don't usually have any Dot tends to use whisky, which is just as good), and run the processor until the pâté is nice and smooth. Spoon into small dishes (ramekins are ideal for this, and pretty easy to get hold of in charity shops) to within 5mm of the top, then pour over melted butter to seal. You could use lard, but butter is nicer.

The pâté will keep in the fridge for a couple of weeks, but can also be frozen in the pots – just wrap a piece of cling film around each one first to keep them clean. This particular recipe works equally well with other sorts of liver, including duck and chicken.

BRAWN

Ingredients

½ pig's head and 2 trotters
2 onions, cut into large chunks
½ tsp pickling spice
Bouquet garni or mixed herbs
1 tsp salt
¼ tsp black pepper

Method

Remove the eye and discard. Saw the head and trotters into pieces so that you can fit it all in large saucepan and wash well, then soak in salted water for about two hours. Drain and rinse. Place in a pan with cold water to cover, bring to boil, strain, then rinse under cold running water. Return to the pan with fresh cold water to cover, add the rest of the ingredients, bring to boil and simmer for at least two hours. Remove the head and trotters from the pan and cut all the meat from the bones. Skin the tongue and remove the membrane from the brain.

Return the liquid to the heat and boil rapidly to reduce. Taste and adjust the seasoning if necessary. Cut the meat into small pieces and three parts fill a pudding basin or mould. Cover completely with the reduced stock and leave to cool. Ideally, chill in the fridge. When cold and set, run around with a sharp knife, invert the basin over a plate, and shake firmly to remove.

Poultry

"Always keep a cock among your hens – hens like having it off as much as we do."
John Seymour

Despite it's current popularity, the small-scale keeping of hens for their eggs can rarely be justified financially, as the value of eggs produced is unlikely to come anywhere near covering the cost of purchased feed. During the summer you might have a surplus to sell, which helps, but your hens will still need feeding during the long dark days of winter, when egg production is at its lowest ebb. They'll also stop laying when they moult, and when they decide to go broody, and sometimes out of sheer bloody mindedness. During these off-lay periods your loyal egg customers will drift away to other suppliers, and you'll be faced with the task of wooing them once again when the hens do eventually decide to co-operate.

If you want to do the job properly, and generate a reasonable return

from laying hens, then you need to go into it in quite a big way, with guaranteed outlets for what you produce. You'll also need to be ruthless and cull your birds after only two seasons, replacing half of the flock each year, and not many smallholders want to do that (although even the small-scale poultry keeper should be prepared to cull any underachievers in his flock).

We've given up trying to make egg production pay, but we fatten a batch of Cobb cockerels each year. Purchased as day old chicks, for a matter of pence, these remarkable birds just eat and eat, and grow and grow, and are ready for slaughter from around 10 weeks of age. The profit made on them easily offsets the loss made by the laying hens, meaning that our poultry enterprise as a whole is justifiable – we continue to enjoy home-laid eggs, and eat roast chicken too.

On this basis, the best solution from the point of view of egg

production is to keep just enough hens to satisfy your own requirements, but not so many that the cost of feeding them during their downtime becomes excessive. Probably less than half-a-dozen, together with a few ducks to extend the laying season, would be sufficient. If you are prepared to cull a couple of your birds each year, you should replace them with point-of-lay pullets in early autumn, as these will probably lay right through their first winter. The provision of extra lighting in the hen house will help.

Breeds

We've kept numerous pure breeds of poultry over the years – Cuckoo Marans, Barnevelders, Light Sussex, Welsummers, Rhode Island Reds, and Exchequer Leghorns, to name but a few – together with some fancy bantams and a number of recognised commercial hybrids, and without exception the hybrids have been the best. True, they may be a little lacking in character, but they make up for this by laying plenty of eggs and not going broody (well not often, anyway). The huge upsurge in interest in backyard egg production in recent years has led to the creation of a multitude of new hybrids, supposedly ideally suited to small-scale and free-range systems, although our old favourite is the hardy Black Rock, developed in Scotland more than 65 years ago by crossing selected strains of Rhode Island Red and barred Plymouth Rock. They're expected to lay in the region of 280 large brown eggs per year, and are long lived – we had one still laying at 10 years old, having moved house with us twice in that time! The downside to hybrids is that they're not self-replicating, so if you decide to hatch out some chicks they won't be the same as the parent birds. This isn't a problem if you just want to fatten them up and eat them (although they'll take a long time fattening, and cost a fair bit in grub), but as egg layers the home-bred birds may disappoint.

You could, of course, breed your own first cross 'hybrid' laying flock, based on one of a number of recognised pairings, by keeping nucleus flocks of the parent birds. Probably the best known is the result of mating a Rhode Island Red cockerel onto Light Sussex hens. The chicks are sex linked, so you can separate males and females at hatching according to their colour (yellow for the cocks, brown for the hens), and either dispatch the unwanted males, or rear them on a more intensive regime for meat production right from the start.

Buying in

The rise in popularity of small-scale poultry keeping has inevitably resulted in a rise in the price of birds, which isn't helped by the fact that many buyers are either fairly well-to-do folk who want to keep chickens because they're trendy, or newcomers to smallholding who haven't got a clue what they're really worth. Poultry auctions are packed with these people, frantically bidding against one another, while the established poultry keepers rub their hands with glee – and pocket the cash. I've seen fairly non-descript birds selling for as much as £60 per pair under these circumstances, which is many times their true worth. If you really know what you're up to you may still find the occasional bargain at

Poultry may achieve unrealistically high prices at auction.

auction, but the beginner should keep well out of it.

Of course, the high auction prices have had a knock on effect through the whole poultry industry, resulting in higher prices across the board, but at least by buying directly from a reputable breeding company you will know beforehand exactly what you're getting, and how much you'll have to pay. Therefore, my advice is that you go to one of the long-established large-scale suppliers, such as Cyril Bason, where you can expect to be able to buy perfectly serviceable 16-week-old commercial hybrids for as little as £8 to £12, with the added advantage that they'll all have been vaccinated. Point of lay (POL) pullets at around 20 weeks old might cost you a little more, or you could save on the purchase price by buying day-old chicks and rearing them yourself. However, you'd be doing well if you could get them to POL without them ending up costing you more than you would have spent had you bought older birds in the first place.

Another option is to buy one-or two-year-old hens that are being

sold out of a commercial laying flock to make way for the new intake. Some of the more welfare conscious poultry farmers prefer to sell off their older birds rather than wring their necks. Obviously these hens won't give such good results as their younger sisters (which is why they're being sold), but they can be obtained relatively cheaply. However, there is of course the increased possibility of buying in disease if sourcing poultry in this way.

To prevent your poultry from flying, clip the flight feathers off one wing only. Kitchen scissors, dagging shears, or hoof clippers are all ideal for this job.

Housing

Small portable poultry houses (the sort with an attached run) provide the perfect means for smallholders to rotate cropping and land use in the vegetable garden. A lightweight ark suitable for up to half-a-dozen birds can easily be lifted and shifted by two people, giving the hens a fresh piece of ground every couple of days or so. The house

Portable poultry houses are good for rotating land use in the garden.

Electric fencing is ideal for creating runs alongside larger poultry houses.

and run can be moved in stages across a fallow plot, where the hens will do a great job of breaking up the dense mat of vegetation, fertilising as they go. It can also be moved over the residue of harvested crops, allowing the birds to clean up the leftovers and eat any pests such as wireworms and leatherjackets. The construction of a small poultry ark is a simple matter, and, if reclaimed materials are used, will cost next to nothing (if anything). Larger poultry houses, on wheels or skids, aren't moved so often (maybe only once or twice a year), but provide a central point from which a series of enclosures can be accessed in rotation. Electric poultry netting is ideal for creating temporary runs as it's so easy to take down and re-erect on a new site. Regardless of the type of accommodation you provide for your hens, it's advised nowadays that you have a secure covered area in which they can be contained in the event of a bird flu outbreak. Appropriate dimensions for different types of poultry housing are given on pages 163 - 165.

• **Bedding:** A small portable ark doesn't really need any bedding on the floor of the house, as the hens will spend most of their time out in the run anyway. However, a light dusting of wood shavings or crumbly / chopped straw will make your weekly cleaning out routine much easier. Alternatively, fit a 'droppings board' beneath the perches – a removable tray that catches all the muck deposited by the hens during the night, and which can be pulled out for cleaning. Whichever method you use, it's important that the birds are encouraged to roost on the perches, not on the edges of the nestboxes or huddled on the floor.

Larger poultry sheds aren't usually mucked out so often (apart from the area directly beneath the perches), and, as the hens tend to spend more time inside a bigger house, they'll need to be provided with some litter to scratch about in. This usually consists of a base layer of something absorbent such as peat, or partially composted dried bracken, topped off with fresh straw. Don't be tempted to use bark chippings, even though they're often readily available for next to nothing, as they may develop a certain fungus as they break down, which can be harmful to poultry, potentially causing outbreaks of aspergillosis among your birds.

Whatever type of poultry house you have for your laying hens, the nest boxes must be kept clean, which means mucking them out at least once a week, and at any other time you notice that they've become fouled. Bed the nest boxes using a few handfuls of clean wood shavings shaped into a depression in the centre, with a little bit of soft hay on top.

Feeding laying hens

Hens will always be able to supplement their diet by scratching around and finding what they can, provided, of course, that their run is moved regularly, or that they're not too closely confined. However, it's important that you don't overestimate the nutritional value of the free range portion of their food. The amount that they're able to source for themselves should really be seen as a 'top-up', over and above a properly balanced ration, to help maintain good health. They're not going to produce many eggs on free range alone.

TIP

I would strongly advise against purchasing any second-hand poultry houses, no matter how cheap they may be. In fact, having made the mistake once, I wouldn't even accept them as a gift now. The risk that they'll harbour the dreaded red mite is just too great. If the houses have been empty for a while, the little devils will be hungry, and may attack your birds with such vigour that they'll die.

One of their favourite lurking places is under the layer of roofing felt that's so often used to weatherproof the tops of poultry houses, so if you do suspect that one of your coops is infected, the first thing to do is strip this off. Then you'll need to get to work with a blowtorch and pretty well scorch every surface, paying particular attention to cracks and crevices. You'll probably need to repeat this process every day for a week or two to have any chance of eliminating them, and finally give the whole house a good application of creosote before fitting new felt to the lid.

Meanwhile, accommodate your hens elsewhere, in temporary quarters that can be burnt after use, and treat them regularly with a suitable insecticide.

The simplest solution is to give the hens access to a hopper containing balanced layers' pellets (by balanced, I mean that they're basically a complete diet, in pellet form) from which they help themselves as required. This method results in far less wastage of feed than using troughs or simply throwing it on the ground, and may be less attractive to vermin (although some folk will argue that it's more likely to attract pests, as it's always available. Either way, hang the hoppers up to make it harder for rats to gain access). The use of a self-feeder enables the hens to eat as much or as little as they need, depending on the availability of wild food. In addition it's a good idea to throw down a handful of mixed corn in the evenings during winter, with which they'll fill their crops

These birds have access to a self-feeder containing a balanced ration.

before they go up to roost.

However, only provide as much as they'll eat: an excess of corn in the diet will result in your hens

becoming too fat to lay well, so if there's any evidence of uneaten grain remaining in the grass of the run after the hens have gone in for the night, feed a bit less the next day.

• **Grit and shell:** Laying birds will need to be provided with sources of both grit (to aid digestion) and shell (which gives the calcium required for producing good egg shells). Free range birds will find the grit that they need, but housed poultry should be provided with a handful of fine gravel from time to time. We just give ours a dish of all-in aggregate such as is used for making concrete. Calcium can be given in the form of crushed oyster shell (or any other kind of shell). When we lived on Bardsey we used to get a shovelful of broken shells off the beach for our birds. Or you can chuck all your empty eggshells in the bottom oven of the Rayburn to dry, then grind them up and feed them back to the hens. A balanced pelleted feed should contain plenty of calcium, but the occasional occurrence of soft-shelled eggs among hens that aren't provided with an additional source suggests that a bit extra is required.

• **Water:** It should go without saying that poultry must have access to a plentiful supply of clean fresh water. They'll drink a surprising amount, particularly during hot weather and when they're being fed on a predominantly dry diet. It's best to use a water fountain, raised above ground level so that the dish doesn't become fouled, and it should be emptied and replenished at least once a day.

• **Home grown and wild foods:** Traditionally, a large part of the diet of backyard poultry would've been made up of domestic food scraps – a practice that's now illegal (although, of course, many small-scale poultry keepers do still supplement their birds' rations in this way). However, there are crops you can grow in the garden that will help eke out the amount of proprietary feed you need to use, and there are certain wild foodstuffs that you can gather, if they grow on your holding in sufficient abundance:

Potatoes for poultry should be boiled (although not in a domestic kitchen, if you want to keep on the right side of the law) and mixed with mash or pellets. Other roots such as carrots, swedes and artichokes can be boiled as for spuds, or fed raw (either whole, for the birds to peck at, or finely chopped). Surplus peas and beans can be dried and stored, and you could even have a go at growing some grain to feed your fowls. (see pages 120 - 126).

A lot of people say that it's important to provide green food e.g. cabbage tops, bolted lettuces etc. for housed poultry, but ours have never shown any particular enthusiasm for greens. However, something like a cabbage or a sprout plant hanging in the poultry house during winter may help to alleviate the birds' boredom, making them less likely to indulge in bouts of feather picking, cannibalism and egg eating. Wild foods that may be worth collecting include acorns and beech mast, fat hen, groundsel and chickweed.

Regardless of what you might have heard about filling a broken egg with mustard, there's only one really successful way to deal with an outbreak of egg eating: cull the culprits. If you don't stamp it out quick it'll spread amongst the flock, until they're all at it. To prevent it happening in the first place, make sure there's enough nest boxes for the number of hens, collect eggs regularly (cleaning up any broken ones), and provide additional calcium in the birds' diet.

Breeding

Where just a few hens are kept for domestic egg production, it's doubtful whether the breeding of replacement birds can ever be economically justified. However, it's probably something you'll want to have a go at, particularly if you fancy trying to produce your own first cross hybrids from pure parent stock.

• Collecting eggs for hatching:
If you run a cockerel with your hens then, provided that he's doing his job, all of your eggs will be fertile, and potentially hatchable. However, you should only be breeding from the best of your hens, which means you either need to devise a 'trap nest' arrangement (i.e. individual nest boxes that trap the birds when they enter to lay, enabling you to match each egg to the hen that it came from), or you need to pen up your best couple of birds in a separate ark, together with an appropriate cock. This is generally called a trio, although up to six hens may be successfully run with one male for breeding purposes.

Don't collect hatching eggs from pullets (i.e. birds in their first laying season). Any hen chosen for breeding should be in her second year (or older), having already proven herself to be a good layer during the previous season.

Ideally, you'll have your selected hens running with the stud cock for about a week before you start keeping any of their eggs, and during this time it's a good idea to change their diet from layers' to breeders' pellets. The eggs required for hatching should be collected over a 10-day period, or less, and stored in a cool place, as you would with eggs kept for eating (i.e. not in the fridge). The eggs need to be turned from time to time, so if you put them in ordinary egg boxes it's easy enough to turn the whole box upside-down at night, and back up the right way in the morning. Reject any eggs that are undersized, misshapen, double-yolked or cracked.

• Hatching under a broody hen:
If you happen to have a broody hen handy at the time you want to set some eggs, then that's the best option. She'll do a far better job than an incubator. Keep her occupied by sitting her on some 'crock eggs' (i.e. artificial eggs) until you've prepared her new quarters. She'll be quite happy like that for a week or so, and you can dust her with louse powder too. The nest in the hatching box should be formed of slightly damp earth, carefully dished so that eggs cannot roll out. Softer bedding, such as hay, is used to line the depression. Transfer the hen and the crock eggs to the prepared nest, and only once she's settled and

TIP

Unless you actually want to hatch some chicks, a broody hen is nothing but a nuisance – she goes off lay and takes permanent possession of a nest box – so you'll want to get her back into production as soon as possible. Traditionally she'd have been placed in a 'freezer coop' – a small hutch with a slatted floor, placed in a draughty location, and designed to dispel all aspirations of motherhood. We find that a few days' incarceration in a lobsterpot does the trick.

sitting tight (i.e. after a day or two) should you remove the dummies and replace them with real eggs. Thirteen is the traditional number to set under a hen – a dozen plus one for luck.

The incubation period for hens' eggs is 21 days (although hens can also be used to hatch the eggs of other species, which may take longer), and throughout this period you must lift her off the nest for a few minutes twice a day, to eat, drink and defecate. Failure to do this could result in a build up of muck in the nest, which may stick the eggs down (so the hen can't turn them) and attract flies. A foul, maggoty nest isn't conducive to getting healthy chicks.

Once the eggs start 'pipping', usually on day 20, the hen should be left alone, and not until the 23rd day should she be encouraged to leave the nest – briefly – with her new brood while you clean out any unhatched eggs, dead chicks and muck. Some pipped eggs may still be found to contain live chicks at this stage, in which case leave them in the nest for a bit longer – there's a chance that the hen may bring them off over the next few hours, but I doubt it.

Once you're confident that

everything that's going to hatch has hatched you can move the hen and chicks to a broody coop with a secure attached run, and provide a shallow dish of chick-crumbs (either fixed down in some way, or heavy enough to prevent the hen from turning it over – many a chick has been lost under an upturned dish) and a suitable safe drinking fountain. She'll teach them to eat and drink and scratch about, and all you have to do is keep providing food (graduating from chick crumbs to pellets as they get bigger), and gradually increase the size of their accommodation in line with their rate of growth.

By the time they're eight weeks old the chicks will no longer require the warmth of the mother hen, and she'll be pretty fed up with them by this stage anyway, so she can be returned to the laying flock.

• **Hatching in an incubator:** The advantage of using an incubator is that you can plan the timing of your breeding programme and ensure that you get chicks when you want them, without having to wait for a suitable hen to go broody. Therefore, for example, it enables you to hatch chicks slightly earlier in the year than

might otherwise be possible, with a view to having new pullets coming into lay before the winter. The downside, of course, is that you're responsible for all those things that a broody hen does so well – temperature control, maintaining the correct humidity, and turning the eggs. True, some flashy incubators will do all this automatically, but the onus still lies with you to make sure everything's running as it should.

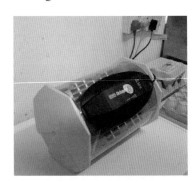

The Brinsea Octagon incubator.

For the small-scale producer, a manually operated (i.e. not automatic turning) table-top incubator capable of holding around 20-30 eggs is probably sufficient, and won't break the bank. We have two – a polystyrene Therbo that's done good service in my family for more than thirty years, and a much newer Brinsea

It happens so often – a missing hen or duck (given up for dead) reappears on the yard with a fluffy brood in tow, or a batch of chicks you're rearing outgrow their brooder sooner than expected. Suddenly you're faced with the problem of having to provide suitable accommodation, fast. After years of cobbling together impromptu poultry housing on the spur of the moment, I believe we've at last come up with the perfect solution – a sheep ring feeder. It's quick and easy to set one up in a suitable location in an outbuilding. The fact that the bottom 12" or so is solid means it's chick proof (and prevents draughts at ground level), and it's simple enough to tie a length of netting around the outside to prevent the parent bird from hopping out. Being round, there's none of the problems associated with chicks being smothered by crowding into corners, and a pole can easily be placed across the top from which to hang a heat lamp, if required. As chicks generally put in an appearance at a time of year when sheep are not receiving supplementary feeding, it makes good use of a piece of farm equipment that would otherwise be standing idle.

Candling

Candling, usually carried out at around day eight, involves the use of light to determine whether an egg contains a viable embryo, or whether it's infertile. If everything's going according to plan then you should see a network of blood vessels surrounding a dark spot within the egg. Any duds can be removed from the incubator at this stage. It's also quite a good idea to candle eggs before you put them in the incubator in the first place, as this will show up any cracks or abnormalities. It also gives you a baseline against which to check progress in a week's time.

You can make your own candling lamp by mounting a light bulb within a small wooden box that has a hole bored in it just large enough to press the end of an egg up against. Candle your eggs in a darkened room, and you'll find that their insides show up very clearly.

Octagon 20. The old Therbo isn't as reliable as it once was, so now we tend to run it alongside the Octagon during the last couple of days of incubation and use it to transfer chicks into as they hatch – a sort of first stage brooder. The reason we do this is that we've found that eggs may hatch over an extended period of several days – particularly if some weren't particularly fresh at the start – and the first chicks to emerge will be needing food and drink before the remainder have finished hatching. Removing them from the incubator at this stage also prevents them from disturbing other eggs that are in the process of hatching.

Turning eggs in the Octagon is simplicity itself, as you just rotate the whole incubator forward or backward at regular intervals. However, in some models (like our

old Therbo) you have to actually open the lid of the incubator and manually turn each egg. In this case it's important that all the eggs are marked, in pencil, with a cross on one side, so that you can tell if they've been turned (e.g. crosses uppermost at night, down in the daytime).

The incubator needs to be sited in a location that has a fairly constant temperature and humidity, not too cold or too hot. A utility room is probably ok, provided that it's not draughty. Set the incubator up and get it running a couple of days before putting the eggs in. The temperature needs to be 37.5°C (although we run ours at 38.5°C as the thermometer is placed a few inches above the eggs), with a relative humidity of 50%. Some incubators have a humidity controller, but in more

basic models it's largely a question of guesswork and following the manufacturers guidelines regarding how much water to put in, and when. At the time of hatching the temperature can be allowed to drop by a degree, and the humidity

Our old incubator doing service as a brooder.

needs to be raised to around 65%. This is in order to prevent the membranes within pipped eggs from drying out and thus becoming too tough for the chicks to break through. Adjust ventilation and add extra water in accordance with the instructions given in the manual for your particular model.

Once hatching is complete, and all the chicks have been removed to the brooder, the incubator should be thoroughly cleaned with an appropriate disinfectant. (For information on hatching other species, see table 10, page 446).

• **Brooding:** If you've hatched your chicks in an incubator then they won't have a mother hen to keep them warm, or teach them to eat and drink, so you'll have to do all that as well (although some people do successfully manage to introduce newly hatched chicks to a hen that they've kept sitting on crock eggs, and let her rear them).

Our brooder is a simple wooden hutch, warmed by an electric greenhouse heater. My father made it years ago, and, although it still works, it's not so dependable as it once was. Now we tend to use a heat lamp suspended over a box instead. Any box will do, but chicks sometimes get smothered by crowding into the corners, so these should be rounded off by taping cardboard across them. As with the incubator, the brooder should be set up and warmed a few days before it's required, so you've got time to fiddle about and get the temperature right. Initially it needs to be set at around 35°C, but this can be gradually reduced down to about 25°C over the first four weeks. Then you can start turning it off in the daytime, gradually extending the length of time that the chicks are without heat, until eventually you leave it off all together. By this time they'll be quite large and well covered with feathers. As with piglets, you'll be able to tell whether or not you're providing enough (or too much) heat by the chicks' behaviour – whether they cluster together tightly, spread out evenly, or move as far away as possible.

Provide a dish of chick crumbs, and encourage your newly hatched chicks to eat it by tap... tap… tapping on the feed with your finger to mimic the pecking action of a mother hen. They'll soon get the hang of it. Some people also advocate teaching the chicks to

drink by dipping their beaks in the water fountain, but we've always found that once they start pecking at the food they'll take to the drink readily enough.

Once they're all feeding well, management is the same as it would be for chicks under a hen – steadily increase the size of their quarters as they grow, and adjust their diet from crumbs to pellets when appropriate.

Vet and med

Poultry are generally pretty healthy. Ours have occasionally been wormed and dusted with louse powder, but that's about it. Once we had a problem with coccidiosis in a batch of young birds (characterised by a thoroughly miserable appearance and the presence of blood in their droppings), but it responded very well to treatment and hasn't occurred since. Red mite I've already mentioned on page 292, but if an individual bird gets sick, for example due to crop binding or egg peritonitis, the best course of action is simply to cull it.

Chickens for meat

If you hatch your own chicks then half of them are going to be unwanted cockerels, destined for the pot. However, they won't put on any flesh if they're running about the place chasing hens all the time. Unfortunately, penning them up for fattening isn't particularly successful either, as they just weren't bred for it. They'll consume vast amounts of food for very little growth, and what weight they do put on is mostly internal body fat. Really, the best thing to do with surplus cockerels is to accept the fact that they'll be lean and rangy (all legs, no breast), and use them just as they are, without fattening, in casseroles and the like. They can be treated a bit like game.

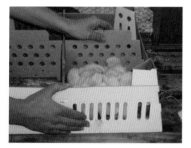

Taking delivery of a batch of meat chicks.

We rear our meat chickens in a deep litter pen, with free access to food and water.

If you really want to produce a decent table bird, then buy in some day old chicks of an appropriate hybrid (e.g. Ross Cobbs) and rear them. If you buy 100 at a time, they only cost about 80p each, but of course not everyone wants to fatten that many chickens. What we do is to join forces with a few neighbouring smallholders and divide a batch of 100 between us. Generally we rear 25 at a time. We start them off in a small brooder, which they outgrow within 2 weeks. Thereafter we keep them in an indoor deep litter pen, with a heat lamp overhead for perhaps as long as six weeks, depending on the weather. We did once try allowing some outdoors, but they really weren't happy, and just sat around looking miserable. The Cobbs aren't bred for free-range rearing, although some other types of hybrid meat birds are, but outdoor fattening will never be quite so efficient.

To begin with we feed them on chick crumbs, changing over to a growers' ration as soon as they're big enough to manage the larger sized pellets. However, this feed contains a coccidiostat (as a preventative against outbreaks of coccidiosis) which has a specified meat withdrawal period, so we put the birds onto ordinary layers' pellets for the last week or so before slaughter.

The rate of growth of the Cobbs is phenomenal, and they're ready to kill at just 10 weeks old, weighing as much as 7lb oven-ready. In that time, a batch of 25 will have consumed 1 bag of chick crumbs (£8.95), 6 bags of growers' pellets (£6.29 per bag) and one bag of layers' pellets (£5.95), giving a total feed cost per bird of around £2.10. Add to this the original purchase price of 80p, and you'll find you're getting a lot of meat for your money. If you sell half of them as oven-ready birds to friends and neighbours (which you can legally do), you'd more than cover the cost of rearing the whole lot.

From time to time we keep a few of the better birds beyond the 10-week optimum, in order to have something suitable for special occasions, and they can reach an impressive size. The last 'big 'un' we killed weighed a whopping 18lb, oven-ready. With chickens that big, who needs turkey for Christmas?

TIP

As with any livestock, some losses are inevitable. When sending out larger batches of chicks (100+), a supplier will often include a few extras to compensate for this. In some cases I'm sure that problems are caused by companies sending out chicks that are, in fact, more than 24 hours old, perhaps in order to co-ordinate a delivery with others to the same area. Older chicks will have exhausted all the natural food reserves that they hatched with, and may literally be starving by the time they reach their destination. You should inspect all new arrivals immediately, and, if you notice any considerable amount of feathering on the wings, or if they've already lost their 'egg tooth', (i.e. if they look older than a day), think twice before accepting the delivery.

Muscovy duck with ducklings.

Khaki Campbells.

Ducks

We keep two kinds of duck – Khaki Campbells and Muscovies. The Campbells are out-and-out egg producers, capable of laying in excess of 300 per year. We find that the ducks tend to come into lay earlier in spring than the hens, so if the hens' laying season can be extended a little at the end of the year by providing extra light (or by buying some POL pullets in autumn) then there ought to be a least a few eggs available for use in the kitchen at all times. However, it really is essential that the ducks be sourced from a true laying strain, not one bred for the show cage.

The housing requirements for ducks is somewhat simpler than for chickens as they don't require perches or nest boxes. In fact they'll drop their eggs pretty much anywhere, given half a chance. Luckily they do tend to lay first thing in the morning, so generally you'll find the eggs in the house when you let the birds out for their breakfast.

Ducks are messy birds, and soon paddle an area into a sea of mud. If you're not able to allow them to free range then they'll need a larger run area per bird than hens do (see page 164). I have heard it said that having a few ducks wandering freely around the garden will help control slugs and snails, but we certainly wouldn't want those clumsy webbed feet trampling all over our precious seedlings.

The feeding of ducks is pretty much as for hens, i.e. layers' pellets during the day, with a handful of mixed corn at bedtime, but you will have to provide them with plenty of water as they'll want to bathe as well as drink. However, they don't actually have to have a pond to swim in.

Be aware that some poultry feeds contain additives that make them unsuitable for waterfowl.

As for the Muscovy ducks, I'm not really quite sure why we keep them. Primarily for their meat, I suppose. Muscovies are the only poultry we have that are truly free range, but thankfully they seem to have the sense to go into the sheep shed at night, or to sleep just in front of the dog kennels, where they're pretty safe from foxes. Equally thankfully they don't seem to have discovered our vegetable garden yet.

We don't feed the Muscovies at all, and they scavenge what they need from around the yard, clearing up any spilt food that the cattle or sheep have left. The only exception to this is when one of the ducks has a brood of little ones, in which case we pen them up for a while and feed them accordingly. Sometimes we'll then keep the ducklings penned up for fattening, but more usually we let them out again once they're strong enough, and let them fatten themselves. The time to kill them is when they first start trying to fly.

When it comes to egg laying, Muscovies are rather crafty: they come into lay very early – around Christmas time – which is handy, and we usually get about a month's supply of eggs before they realise we're taking them and go and make a nest somewhere else, better hidden. They'll then lay a clutch of up to 20 eggs, brood them, and reappear in a month or so with a lot of fluffy yellow ducklings in tow.

I'm sure if we were to manage them a little more closely the Muscovies would be quite productive egg layers, but as it is they don't really cost us anything to keep, and we're content to just take what we can get from them.

Geese

We had a large flock of free-range geese when we lived on Bardsey, which we rounded up from time to time and killed what we needed. Other than that they just did their own thing. There were no four-footed predators on the island, but the gulls and corvids took their toll of the eggs. Sometimes we penned up a couple of the younger birds and fattened them on corn (but usually they got too fat), and often I had a goose egg for breakfast at lambing time, which set me up for the day.

Our attempts at keeping geese on the mainland have been repeatedly thwarted by the fox. Goodness knows why foxes find geese so attractive; they're large, aggressive birds, capable of giving anyone a good buffeting – I think twice about getting hold of a goose myself – yet to a fox they're irresistible. One day we'll try again, but not just yet.

Geese are grazing birds, so fit well into a rotation with your cattle and sheep. They can be driven out to pasture each day, and, provided that your fencing is fox proof (electric flexinets would be worth a try), will happily forage about the fields until bedtime. They'd happily sleep out under the stars, too, but a routine evening feed of a small handful of grain should make

Geese are grazing birds.

them keen enough to return to their shed for the night. And that's about all there is to keeping geese.

A pair of geese – a goose and a gander – should be enough to provide all the goslings required for the average family to consume in a year, and maybe a few to sell oven-ready as well. The goose is a wonderful mother, but you might have some difficulty persuading her to make her nest where you want her to, and not where she wants to. Each egg, as it's laid, will be carefully covered over with vegetation, and well hidden from sight – safe from the prying eyes of predators, and you. However, once she's ready to start brooding she'll line the nest with vast quantities of down plucked from her chest, making it clearly visible and drawing magpies and crows from miles around. If she hasn't had the good sense to nest in the hut you provided her with, the only option now is to build a new shelter over her, as trying to move a broody goose and her nest is seldom successful. Despite these idiosyncrasies I do think it's best

to hatch goslings under a goose, rather than use an incubator or a broody hen.

Geese were traditionally eaten at Michaelmas (29th September), or for Christmas dinner. They're still a popular festive bird here in Wales, despite competition from the comparatively tasteless (yet so much more readily available) turkey. Goslings hatched in the spring will be sufficiently well grown after a summer at grass to satisfy the requirements of either of those feasts, and all you need to do is pen them up about 4 weeks beforehand, and feed them on barley to plump them up a bit.

TIP

Geese are the very devil to pluck, but a tip we learnt from a local farmer's wife is to first lay a damp cloth over the breast of the bird and run over it with a hot iron. The feathers then simply peel off.

Rabbits

Domestic rabbits are well worth considering if you've only very limited space. Even in an urban environment a few rabbit hutches on the patio could go a long way towards satisfying a family's meat requirements. Two breeding does might generate enough offspring to give an average family a good meat meal at least once a week all year round. They don't take up much space and can be fed relatively cheaply, especially if you have enough time to pick plenty of greens for them, and give them your vegetable scraps and stale bread. Breeding and raising rabbits for the table is an excellent project for children, and they'll be very proud to have contributed to the household economy in this way.
Producing rabbits for meat is scarcely more complex than keeping rabbits as pets, and needs only a modest dose of common sense to make it a success.

Accommodation and equipment

As far as equipment and accessories are concerned, nothing additional is required by the breeder than by the pet keeper. You just need more hutches, that's all. Rabbits have traditionally been kept in hutches for almost as long as they've been domesticated (even as early as 100 BC, when semi-domesticated rabbits were kept in communal warrens, the young were often placed in cages for fattening), and they do very well like that, provided that the hutches are big enough. (See page 165 for the appropriate dimensions).

I did once try breeding and raising rabbits in a colony based system, but it wasn't a success. Quite apart from anything else, it became very difficult to monitor health and welfare, and the management inevitably became haphazard.

In hutches, on the other hand, each rabbit can be treated as an individual, any problems are quickly identified, and their needs can be easily catered for. Assuming you're going to keep two does and a buck, you'd need at least five hutches in total – one each for the three adult rabbits, and two (or more, depending on size) for youngsters between weaning age and slaughter. Provided that they're being killed at not much more than 8 weeks old it won't be necessary to divide them into single sex groups for fattening.

When rabbit meat production was more in vogue amongst smallholders, it used to be common to see tiers of three hutches built on top of one another, but I don't favour this. For one thing, there's inevitably going to be a certain amount of urine that dribbles down through the hutch floors, contaminating the quarters below, and secondly, it does mean that the hutches must have opening fronts rather than lifting roofs. This may sound like a minor point, as most hutches do, in fact, have opening fronts, but if children are going to be responsible for the care of rabbits on the smallholding then the lifting roof option will considerably reduce the risk of rabbits jumping (or falling) out of their hutches during routine feeding etc. This is particularly so when the hutch is full of boisterous youngsters. The drawback, of course, is that without the option to stack the accommodation, the 'rabbitry' will to take up more space. My preference is to site the hutches, (singly, not stacked,) under a lean-to, or inside an open-fronted outbuilding, which makes caring for the rabbits much more pleasant in foul weather, and also simplifies the construction of the hutches as there's no need to waterproof them, or even to slope the roofs.

The hutches need to be fully mucked out at weekly intervals, although the dung corner will probably need cleaning more frequently than this, particularly in summer when it'll quickly become smelly and attract flies. For bedding, we always cover the floor of the hutches with wood shavings, and provide plenty of soft hay in the nesting area. At least once a year each hutch should be thoroughly scrubbed out with disinfectant, and rested for a while, which is a good opportunity to carry out any repairs. Drinking bottles will also need to be washed out fairly frequently, as they quickly go green and slimy on the inside, especially in warm weather.

Young New Zealand Whites

On very small holdings, where it's not feasible to keep larger livestock, dung from the hutches is a valuable by-product of rabbit production, having almost twice the nitrogen content of ordinary farmyard manure. Urine can be collected separately by drilling some small holes in the floor of the dung corner (or by making one larger hole and covering it with fine mesh) and placing a bucket underneath. Appropriately diluted, this makes powerful plant food.

Choice of stock

The two most popular breeds for meat production are the New Zealand White and the Californian, which have both been selected for size, conformation and good meat to bone ratio (which may be in the region of 5:1). Both breeds originate from America. The NZ White is the larger of the two, with adults maybe weighing as much as 11lb (5kg).

However, just because a rabbit produces a big carcass does not necessarily mean it produces an economical carcass. Larger rabbits have bigger appetites and need bigger hutches. On a £ per lb basis, it's just as cost effective to use a slightly smaller breed. The best rabbits I ever had for breeding purposes were NZ White x English. Although rather smaller than the pure NZ, they were very robust and seemed to thrive well on a slightly lower spec diet than that required by their parents – evidence, perhaps, of a bit of 'hybrid vigour'.

Breeding

Does will be sufficiently well grown to breed from at around 5-7 months of age, and should be in fit, healthy condition. The buck, too, will be ready to work at about the same age. Female rabbits don't seem to have any specific heat cycle or oestrus period, but it appears that ovulation is triggered by the attentions of the buck, provided that environmental conditions are favourable. In other words, if you keep your rabbits in good health and in appropriate accommodation, they should conceive at any time.

For mating, the doe must always be introduced to the buck, and not the other way round. As I mentioned earlier, on page 240 the females of any species which typically give birth in a nest are inclined to be defensive of their own territory, so if the buck were to be placed in the doe's hutch she'd be likely to attack him. Mating usually takes place very quickly, but may be preceded by a brief chasing game if the doe is playing hard to get. On completion of successful coupling the buck falls sideways off the doe, and sometimes lies motionless on his side for a few moments. The first time I witnessed this I thought the poor chap's ecstatic climax had triggered a fatal heart attack! The doe can be taken back to her own quarters straight after mating, although some breeders like to put them together again after 3-4 days, just to make sure.

Pregnancy lasts for 31 days, give or take a day or so either side. As her time approaches, the doe will be seen to be getting her nest in order, before lining it with masses of hair plucked from her chest. Usually the doe gives birth (or 'kindles') in the nest that she's constructed, although occasionally she'll deposit her offspring all over the place and move them into the nest afterwards. For this reason, it's a good idea to temporarily cover the front of the hutch with an old sack or something similar, so any young born outside the nest don't get chilled, and also so that the doe isn't disturbed.

Once the young are born it's very tempting to take a peek into the nest to check the litter, but this is best avoided initially, as it can lead to cannibalism. If it's essential to handle new-born kits, for example if you want to remove any stillborns, then you should first take some soiled litter from the dung corner and thoroughly rub your hands with it, to mask your scent.

The young rabbits – usually 6-8 in number, but sometimes a lot more – are born blind, deaf, hairless and helpless. Their eyes (and ears) open at about 10 days, by which time they're fully furred, and by 3 weeks old they'll be venturing out of the nest and beginning to eat solid food. The doe can be mated again when her litter is 3-4 weeks old, and weaning takes place at around 6 weeks. The whole batch of youngsters is then moved into a spacious hutch for a further 2-4 weeks for fattening, and by following this plan, each doe may produce 5-7 litters per year.

Feeding

Just because wild rabbits live almost entirely on grass, please don't expect your domesticated bunnies to do the same. The environment in which they're living is so completely different from that of their wild cousins that, understandably, their nutritional requirements are different too. That's not to say that grass (and other greens) isn't good for them – of course it is, and it can be used to form a large part of your rabbits' diet. However, you'll also need to feed some sort of proprietary mix or pellets. Quite apart from anything else, a daily ration of dry feed gives a degree of consistency to the diet, and helps to iron out any differences caused by seasonal availability of various plants etc., and weather conditions (e.g. a load of lush grass picked in the pouring rain, after several weeks of fine weather, would undoubtedly give your rabbits the collywobbles if it was all that they had to eat). The cost of purchased rabbit food can be kept at a reasonable level by buying it in 25kg sacks rather than in little packets from the pet shop. Some good quality hay also adds consistency to the diet.

Feeding pelleted rabbit food is far less wasteful than using a muesli-like mix, because it prevents selective feeding. Rabbits fed on a mix may simply pick out their favourite ingredients and leave the rest.

In addition to the base-line ration of pellets and hay, rabbits will enjoy various garden crops and weeds, which can be used to make up the bulk of their diet. The main thing, though, is not to overload them with too much of one thing. Pick as wide a range of edible plant species as you can each day, which also helps to smooth over the seasonal differences. All types of brassica are welcome, as are root crops and legumes, and also waste products from the kitchen such as apple and carrot peelings. Cooked mashed potato makes an excellent fattening ration, particularly if mixed with some whole oats, but is not so good for breeding stock. Wild plants that can safely be fed to your rabbits include chickweed, dandelion leaves, sowthistle (a real favourite), plantain, groundsel, yarrow, fat hen, grass and clover. They also like dried nettles, which can be cut in the summer and made into a kind of rough hay. Frosty greens shouldn't be fed, so in cold weather it's a good idea to pick a day ahead, so it's got time to thaw properly. Keep an eye on the dung corner at all times, and if you see loose pellets then cut back a bit on the wet food and up the hay. Blackberry leaves and shepherd's purse are both beneficial plants to give to rabbits suffering from scours caused by too many lush greens.

The actual amount to feed is hugely variable, but as a rough guide I would say that the basic diet should consist of around 50g of pellets per day, plus a handful of hay (a loose bundle about the size of the rabbit is what's recommended, although I've never come across one that consumes this much), and whatever greens they'll eat. Pregnant does should be getting twice this amount by the time they kindle, rising to 150g during lactation. However, this does depend on you being able to provide a regular supply of varied green food in reasonable quantities. The weaned youngsters can be fed more or less to appetite (although go easy with the greens initially, until they've become fully accustomed to a solid diet) for the 2-4 week fattening period, or provide up to 50g of mashed potato per head per day, mixed with a similar quantity of oats. Stale wholemeal bread also makes a good feedstuff, and can be given dry or soaked in milk. Any uneaten green / moist food should be removed before the next feed is given.

Provide a mineral lick in each hutch and, of course, plenty of fresh water – incredible as it may sound, a lactating doe with a well-grown litter might consume as much as six pints of water a day.

Health and welfare

Rabbits are, on the whole, robust and healthy creatures. However, there are a few things to watch out for:

• **Myxomatosis:** A virus spread by fleas, and, to a lesser extent, mosquitoes, myxi is the scourge of rabbits everywhere. Most infected animals will die, usually within about a fortnight from when symptoms (swollen head, puffy eyes, swollen anus and genitals) are first observed. I would strongly advise you to have your breeding stock vaccinated, particularly if you also handle wild rabbits. You can also use spot-on type treatments to control fleas on domestic rabbits.

• **Viral haemorrhagic disease (VHD):** Another really nasty virus, which has been a problem in the UK since the early 1990s. VHD is highly infectious, and can be carried to your rabbits on clothes, shoes etc., as well as being transmitted by wildlife. It can survive for long periods in the environment, so it's possible to inadvertently carry the disease for a considerable distance on contaminated items. The disease is invariably fatal,

and its progression is so quick that the animal is often simply found dead. If any symptoms are observed, they consist of bleeding from the nose and anus, together with convulsions and difficulty breathing. Thankfully a vaccine is available, and you'd be wise to have your breeding stock done.

• **Scours:** As I mentioned earlier, scours (or diarrhoea) may simply be caused by an excess of lush green food, although it could be indicative of something more serious. The first thing to do is to try adjusting the diet. If this fails to bring about a result, then you'll have to consider the possibility that your rabbits may be suffering from coccidiosis (see immediately below) or salmonella.

• **Coccidiosis:** This an infection caused by a microscopic parasite, characterised, initially, by severe scouring. It occurs where the husbandry of the rabbits is of a poor standard, with hutches and utensils not cleaned regularly, and where feedstuffs are allowed to become stale and contaminated with faeces. It's possible to buy medicated feed containing a coccidiostat, although there is a brief withdrawal period of 5 days that should be observed before treated rabbits are slaughtered for human consumption.

• **Fly strike:** It's not only sheep that suffer from maggots. Fly strike is surprisingly common in rabbits, and, as they're not particularly demonstrative creatures, may go unnoticed until it's reached an advanced stage. The most important thing is to keep the hutch clean, and therefore less attractive to flies. The rabbits' bottoms should be examined fairly frequently (especially after scours, no matter how slight), and any

soiled hair must be clipped away using a pair of nail scissors.

• **Overgrown toenails:** Obviously, domesticated rabbits don't wear down their claws by digging in the way that wild rabbits do, so it's necessary to clip their claws from time to time. This is easy enough to do using a very small pair of side cutters.

• **Overgrown teeth:** A rabbit's teeth grow continuously, so, unless they get worn down by regular gnawing on something hard, they'll gradually force the rabbits mouth open until eventually it won't be able to eat. Provide a small hardwood log, such as beech, for them to chew at, and regularly include fibrous material like cabbage stalks in the diet.

• **Heatstroke:** A rabbit confined to a hutch can't shift location to get out of the sun – it's wholly dependent on you having sited the hutch in a sensible place. Please bear this in mind when planning the layout of your rabbitry. It's quite a good idea to fill a few plastic bottles with water and keep them in the deep freeze, so on really hot days each rabbit can be given an ice pack to cuddle up to – they will really appreciate it.

The next step

If your young rabbits do well, they should reach a liveweight of about 2.25kg (depending on breed and feeding regime) at 8-10 weeks of age, by which time they're ready to kill, producing a dressed carcass weight of around 1kg.

For information on slaughter and butchery, see pages 308 - 310.

303

Slaughter and Butchery - Small Animals

To the smallholder, one of the advantages of producing meat from small animals, such as rabbits, poultry and young goat kids, is obvious: you won't need a firearm of any kind to slaughter them, as it can all be done by hand. Therefore, even if your location or family circumstances preclude you from owning a gun, or if your holding isn't large enough to support other types of livestock, you can still be pretty well self-sufficient in meat. It also makes a good starting point for anyone planning to make the move into doing their own home slaughter and butchery of larger animals at a later date.

Poultry

On a small scale, poultry are generally killed by neck dislocation. For chickens and ducks under 3kg in weight this involves holding the bird by the legs in one hand, taking the head in the other hand, and, when the bird is calm, you pull downwards on the head while bending it sharply back. This is known as manual dislocation. You'll feel it easily enough when it goes, as the neck suddenly stretches. Don't carry on pulling beyond this point or its head will come right off, which is messy. For bigger birds such as geese, turkeys and some

particularly large drakes, you'll need to use mechanical dislocation or a poultry stunning device, followed by bleeding.

There is a device called a wall-mounted poultry dispatcher (see below) that can be utilised for mechanical slaughter, but I wouldn't recommend it. It crushes, rather than dislocates, the vertebrae, and in my opinion it's not very humane.

Wall-mounted poultry dispatcher.

The broom handle method

The simplest way to carry out mechanical dislocation is by the 'broom handle method', although in fact you need a piece of wood somewhat thicker than a broom handle. Start off by holding the bird by the legs in one hand. Lower it until its head is on the ground then place the 'broom handle' across its neck, just behind the head. Stand on the bit of wood, with a foot either side of the bird's neck, transfer your grip so you have a leg in each hand, and pull upwards

Whichever method you use, the bird will begin to flap its wings uncontrollably as soon as it's dead, which, in some cases, is sufficiently powerful to break the bone and damage the carcass. Therefore it's a good idea to clasp the bird's wings quite tightly to its body until the initial violent thrashings have ceased.

Birds weighing over 5kg must be electrically stunned before bleeding. However, I don't know of any smallholders who weigh their birds before slaughter.

TIP

Be aware that with some ducks, although the body weight may be below 3kg, the length of the neck makes manual dislocation quite difficult (unless you've got exceptionally long arms).

A step-by-step guide to killing and preparing a chicken

1. With the bird held upside-down by the legs in my left hand, I gently but firmly take hold of the head in my right, with its neck between my thumb and first finger. (Most of the instructions I've read suggest that the neck should be gripped between the first and second finger, but I don't find that so effective.) I then pull down on the head while bending it back – effectively bending the neck around the base of my thumb. The action must not be jerky. It's easy enough to feel when the neck dislocates, but you should continue to pull in order to make a good separation into which the blood will drain.

2. As soon as the bird is dead it will begin to flap uncontrollably, often with sufficient force to smash the wing bones. Therefore I clasp the wings quite tightly to its body until the initial violent spasms have subsided.

3. Once I've done the easy bit I hand the bird over to Dot (or one of the children) for the remainder of the job. Dot plucks the bird with it hanging up by the legs at a convenient height, and places a box or bin between her knees to catch the feathers.

4. There's probably a 'correct' order for plucking poultry, but this is the way Dot does it, and it seems to work: Firstly the wings, followed by the neck, then the breast, then the legs, and finally the back. Generally the feathers are pulled against the way they lie, but, to avoid tearing the skin, pull them in the direction in which

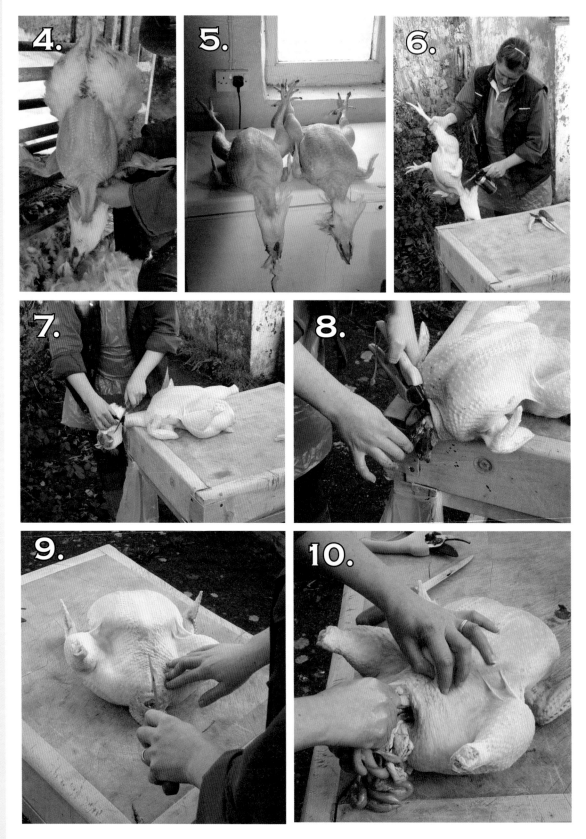

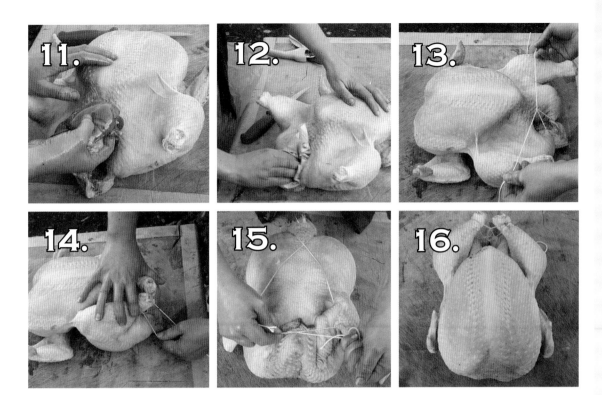

they grow when plucking the neck, shoulders and the front of the breast. Stubborn quills can be removed with a pair of pliers.

5. Two neatly plucked birds ready for further processing. Notice how they've been placed with their heads hanging down in order to keep the blood in the neck cavity.

6. Singeing off the whiskery bits using a blowlamp. A lighted spill of newspaper, a candle or a spirit lamp were the traditional methods.

7. Cut off the scaly part of the legs at the joint. Next, cut off the head at the point where the neck was dislocated. As much of the neck skin as possible should be left on the bird.

8. Having separated it from the skin, Dot cuts off the neck as close to the body of the bird as possible, using secateurs. She also removes the crop at this point.

9. Working at the other end of the bird now, with it still lying on its back, Dot makes an incision between the vent and the rearmost part of the breastbone, just big enough to get her hand through.

10. All of the entrails are removed through the incision, and detached from the body by cutting around the vent.

11. By reaching further into the body cavity, Dot locates and removes the liver, which is used for making pâté, and also the heart and lungs.

12. The inside of the carcass is cleaned by wiping out with paper towels.

13. A simple method for trussing the bird is to start with it lying on its back and tie the middle of the length of string around the parson's nose.

14. Next, pass the string around the legs then back down to the parson's nose, pulling the legs down and together.

15. Turn the bird over so it's lying on its breast, cross the ends of the string above the parson's nose then take them diagonally across the back and under each wing. Tie the ends together in such a way that the neck skin is also secured.

16. Oven ready.

Rabbits

To kill a rabbit cleanly and humanely, you *do not* hold it up by the back legs and aim a karate-like blow (known as a 'rabbit punch') at the back of its neck. Quite apart from the fact that this technique seldom succeeds in killing the rabbit at the first attempt, it'll also cause horrible bruising to the meat around the shoulder area, and probably to your hand as well.

The best way to kill rabbits is in the same manner as for poultry, so you hold the rabbit by the back legs with one hand, and hold its head in the other. Then you simultaneously pull down on the head while bending it backwards, in order to dislocate the neck. If you lack the physical strength and / or size to do it this way then you can place the rabbit on a bench or table, and, when it's sitting calmly, lift its ears with one hand and clout it behind the head with a suitable piece of wood (a hatchet handle is ideal). Some people hold up the rabbit by the back legs and deliver a sharp tap with the hatchet handle, in a variation of the 'rabbit punch'. However, neck dislocation should always be the preferred method.

As soon as the rabbit is dead you should empty its bladder by firmly rubbing with your thumb down the abdomen towards its groin (see photo, page 355).

TIP

In the unlikely event that any of your rabbits weigh over 5kg, they should be killed using a firearm or captive bolt pistol, or electrically stunned and then bled.

Rabbit preparation

• Skinning

I'm sure there are as many ways to skin a rabbit as there are to skin a cat, but this is how I do it:

1. Cut off all four paws at the first joint. I do this by dislocating the joint and then cutting through it with my knife, but some people use a butchers' cleaver to chop off each paw just above the joint.

2. Next I lift a pinch of skin in the lower abdomen region, and make an incision. Take care

only to cut through the skin, and not into the body cavity.

3. I enlarge the incision by tearing the skin, and gradually work my fingers around one of the hind legs.

4. When I can get my fingers right around, I simply pull the skin off the remainder of the leg like pulling an arm out of the sleeve of a jumper, leaving the sleeve inside out. Repeat for the other hind leg.

5. This leaves the skin attached to the back end of the rabbit only at the tail, which I now cut through.

6. The rest of the skin pulls off easily, inside out, as far as the shoulders.

7. I deal with the front legs in the same manner as for the back ones, and then pull the skin off the neck, as far as the back of the head.

8. Cut through the neck, leaving the head attached to the skin.

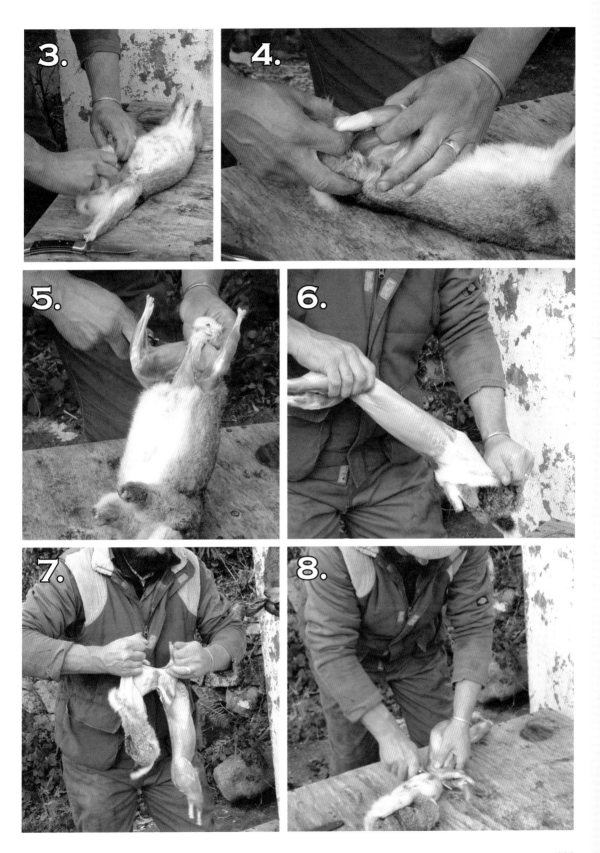

• Paunching

This is much easier if it's carried out after skinning, not before.

1. Slit open the belly of the rabbit from end to end, taking care to keep the blade facing outwards and the point of the knife away from the guts.

2. Next I always run my finger around inside the body cavity to loosen the contents.

3. Most of the innards can then be tipped out in one go, but you'll probably need to hook out the heart and lungs separately. The kidneys are customarily left in the carcass. Remember to retrieve the liver from the pile of offal, and carefully remove the gall bladder.

4. Cut through the front part of the pelvis joint and force the hind legs back, so that you can remove any remaining pipework, and also cut out the anal glands.

5. The resulting oven ready carcass can either be used whole or jointed. Ready for the pot, an adult wild rabbit carcass will weigh something in the region of 1kg (just over 2lb).

Goat kids

NB. The following only applies to kids up to about five days old / under 5kg in weight. Beyond this stage they should be dealt with as for larger animals.

To kill it, the kid must be stunned then bled. Place the kid on the floor and make a sharp noise, whereupon he'll stand still and lift up his head to listen. At this moment you hit him just behind the ears, on the back of his head, with a piece of wood such as an axe handle, hard. Bleeding must be carried out immediately by making a deep cut at the angle of the jaw. To be honest, the blow to the back of the head will, in all likelihood, kill the kid outright, but you should still bleed it anyway.

Very small kids can then be skinned and gutted by following the instructions given for rabbits, and larger ones can be hung up and dealt with in the same fashion as adult goats or sheep.

Beekeeping

The main thing with bees is not to go fiddling about with them all the time. Just let them get on and do their own thing. Many beekeepers seem to feel it's necessary to take their hives apart on a regular basis, and have a good look at what's going on inside. On each occasion the bees then have to waste time and energy repairing the damage and re-organising their disrupted lives, when they really should be busy collecting nectar and making honey. And besides, how would you like it if someone ripped the roof off your house every week or so? The stress would inevitably render you more susceptible to disease, and the same applies to bees.

Personally, the only times I take the lids off my hives are when I add new supers or remove full ones, and I never open the brood boxes. In more than 10 years of beekeeping I haven't seen a queen! Any experienced apiarists reading this are probably frothing at the mouth by now, but the fact remains that our colonies are strong and healthy (having seemingly developed a natural resistance to the dreaded varroa mite), and we get plenty of honey. The hives take up very little space, and my rather relaxed way of keeping bees makes it a truly low maintenance enterprise with a high value output – just what the small-scale self-supporter needs.

(Incidentally I've just read, in a booklet published in 1957 by the then Ministry of Agriculture, Fisheries and Food, that *"The most fatal disease from which queens suffer is beekeeper's curiosity"*, so clearly I'm not the first advocate of a less intrusive approach.)

Getting started

One of the nice things about beekeeping is that you can fit a few hives in almost anywhere. Despite the fact that bees will regularly forage up to 3 miles in search of nectar (and maybe as much as 10 miles, if needs must), you don't have to own vast swathes of countryside to be a successful beekeeper. Even in inner-city locations, beehives can be situated in small backyards, or, perhaps better still, on flat roofs, which keeps their main lines of flight harmlessly out of the way of the crowds on the pavements below. And it needn't just be your own roof or backyard, either – the promise of a few jars of honey might secure you access to all sorts of urban sanctuaries you never knew existed. An increasing number of large companies and organisations see hosting hives as a good way of lifting their eco-credentials, which, combined with the general trend for greening of built-up areas, makes beekeeping just as viable for the urban self-supporter as for his rural counterpart.

Equipment

There's an awful lot of beekeeping kit you could invest in, should you so wish. However, what I'm considering here are just the very basics needed to get you started:

• **Hives:** The classic cottage garden hive, usually painted white and with a slightly pagoda-like appearance, is the double walled WBC. However, this has largely been superseded by the National, presumably on account of the simpler construction of the latter. Second-hand hives (often together with a quantity of accessories and related equipment) do crop up from time to time, usually following the death or retirement of a beekeeper, but you can also buy new ones in a flat-pack format, which is a lot less costly than buying them ready assembled. The cheapest of the flat-pack National hives are made of plywood, and, having ordered one set of parts to use as templates, it wouldn't be difficult to replicate them in the farm workshop. Or you could obtain a set of plans and start from scratch.

Making hives in the farm workshop.

The assembled hive consists of four main sections – the floor, the brood box (where the queen lives and lays her eggs), the super(s) (where the honey is stored), and the roof. The brood box is much deeper than the supers, and therefore requires different sized frames, but for simplicity you needn't have a brood box at all – just use two shallow supers instead, which then means that all your hive parts are interchangeable. Altogether you'll need quite a few supers in order to be able to add more to each hive as those already *in situ* get filled up.

The outside of the hive should be protected with a coat of paint or a non-toxic (i.e. insect-friendly) wood preservative.

• **Frames:** The National super will hold eleven standard shallow frames, but if you use only 9 or 10, and space them out a little further, you'll actually get more honey stored in each super, because the bees will draw out deeper comb to fill the additional space available. (They'll never completely bridge the gap between the horizontal

panels of comb, so you'll still be able to remove individual frames as and when required). Brood boxes, being deeper, obviously require frames of a different dimension, but if, as I mentioned earlier, you opt to use two shallow boxes instead of one deep one, then you'll only need one type of frame for the whole hive – much simpler! Frames often have plastic or metal spacers fitted to the lugs at either end of the top bar, but if you're going to reduce the number in each super anyway then these are superfluous – just space the frames out by eye.

• **Foundation:** Thin sheets of beeswax (often reinforced with wire) embossed with a 'honeycomb' pattern are known as 'foundation'. A sheet of foundation is fitted into each new frame, giving the bees a base on which to build their comb. Actually there's no need for you to fill the whole frame with foundation – just a quarter of a sheet (or even less) at one end, or across a corner, will be enough. The bees will simply follow the pattern and fill the rest of the space themselves. Therefore, a little bit of foundation can be made to go a long way. Once all the frames are filled with drawn comb you just keep on re-using them, so there's no need to buy in (or make) additional foundation unless you're increasing your stock.

Old, damaged comb can be rendered down, and the resulting clean wax turned into new foundation. You can do this yourself, using a suitable mould, or there are companies that offer an exchange service – you send them your beeswax, and they'll send you an appropriate amount of foundation.

Queen excluder.

• **Queen excluder:** The queen excluder is a panel made of thinly spaced wires, moulded plastic or perforated steel that is placed between the brood box and the supers. The name is fairly self-explanatory really – the size of the holes in the excluder are such that the larger queen bee is prevented from entering, and laying eggs in the honey storage sections of the hive.

• **Crown board:** Usually just a simple piece of plywood with some thin battens nailed around the edge to maintain the necessary 'bee space' between it and the frames below. The crown board sits on top of the uppermost super, beneath the roof. This helps to insulate the hive, and also prevents the bees from extending their activity into the roof space.

• **Clearer board:** The clearer board is exactly the same as the crown board, except that it has a couple of rectangular holes in it, so you can fit bee escapes. In fact, you can easily use a clearer board as a crown board, simply by covering up the holes – another example of simplifying the hive components.

• **Bee escape:** This is a simple little one-way valve that allows bees to pass through in one direction, but not to return. Used in conjunction with the clearer board, the bee escape is temporarily installed beneath any full supers that are ready for removal from the hive. By the following day the supers will be more or less clear of bees, and the harvest can be taken. Don't leave it much longer than 24 hours though, because eventually the bees will manage to wriggle their way back in.

• Suit, gloves and veil:
Although in older books we do see photographs of hardy souls examining their hives with only minimal protection (stiff upper lip, and billowing pipe held firmly between clenched teeth), I'd strongly recommend that you cover up. A one-piece overall type suit is best, with integral hood and veil. However, you can buy jacket, trousers and hood / veil separately. Bee suits are usually white, but they're also available in camouflage for anyone who doesn't want to advertise the presence of their hives. Gloves should be made of thin soft leather, allowing maximum sensitivity, and must have gauntlets that cover the forearms. After landing on the outside of the suit, bees will always crawl upwards into any dark crevices, so it's vital that you tuck your trousers inside your boots. Also, make sure that the elasticated cuffs, ankles, hems etc. are in good condition, and if necessary augment them with rubber bands – believe me, if a crowd of bees manages to get inside your suit they really will lead you a merry dance!

• Smoker: The natural reaction of the bees when their colony is threatened (e.g. in the face of a forest fire), is to try to save what they can of their stores. Therefore they rush to gorge themselves on honey, preparatory to taking flight. Once full they become less

Bee space

The discovery of the magical 'bee space', and its incorporation into hive design, is what enables us to keep bees as we do, in removable frame hives. The bee space – a gap of around 6mm (¼") – is the minimum space required by bees to enable them to move around the hive with ease. It's equal to the gap that the bees themselves will naturally leave between panels of drawn comb, so, by constructing the hive in such a way that this distance is left between the various components, and in all the appropriate places, we can ensure that the bees build their comb and store their honey in a way that suits us.

Any smaller spaces within the hive (say, 4mm and under), will be sealed with propolis ('bee glue'), and larger gaps (over 9mm) will have comb built in them (although for some reason bees don't fill up the large gap between the bottom of the brood frames and the floor of the hive – presumably it's too draughty down there).

inclined to sting, so the judicious application of a few puffs of smoke (in imitation of an approaching conflagration) at the hive entrance before lifting off the lid will render the inmates less aggressive. Don't overdo it though.

The most commonly used fuel for the smoker is a rolled-up piece of corrugated cardboard (beekeepers tend to hoard packaging material for this very purpose), but other types of tinder such as dry grass, cotton waste or wood shavings are just as good. Once alight, an

occasional squeeze of the bellows ought to keep it ticking over nicely until required. A tuft of fresh grass stuffed into the spout will help reduce airflow if it seems to be burning too quickly – all you want is smoke, not flames and sparks.

• Hive tool: The hive tool has a blunt, chisel-like scraper at one end, and a hook at the other. It's used for prising apart the hive components (which the bees will have fixed together very securely), scraping away excess wax, and lifting frames. You can just as easily use an old woodwork chisel, or make a simple hive tool from a piece of mild steel bar.

• **Cloths:** It's useful to have a couple of pieces of heavy cotton cloth, hemmed all round, and measuring 18¼" by approximately 24". The two shorter hems should each incorporate a pocket holding a thin wooden batten (e.g. the top bar from an old frame). The cloths are employed while carrying out hive inspections to cover any section of the hive that's temporarily open to the elements. In pairs, the cloths can be used to expose individual frames which might need to be lifted for examination, without unduly disturbing the rest of the colony. I also find these cloths very useful for covering over full supers as I remove and transport them, thus preventing the bees from getting back in.

• **Brush:** A soft brush is handy for gently sweeping bees off sections of comb you might wish to examine, and for brushing away any stragglers clinging to your suit and veil before disrobing.

• **Feeder:** If you leave a full super of honey on each hive at the end of the season, there'll be no need to supplement the bees' diet over winter. However, there are times when some extra feed is beneficial, in particular just after hiving a new swarm – a ready source of food will make them far more inclined to settle down in the home you've prepared for them. To make a feeder you need a plastic container with an airtight lid measuring less than 5" in depth – something like an old margarine tub is ideal. Make lots of little perforations in the top, covering an area about the same size as one of the holes in the clearer board. To feed the bees, fill the tub with sugar syrup (2lb of white sugar dissolved in 1 pint of boiling water, and allowed to cool), fit the lid firmly (pressing down to expel as much air as possible), and invert it over the hole in the clearer board. (If there's more than one opening in the clearer board, block the others using small pieces of plywood, glass or plastic.) Place the clearer board onto the topmost super then install an empty super (i.e. without frames) over that. In cold weather, the empty super can be packed with some insulating material, such as hay. Finish off by fitting the crown board and roof.

A traditional skep.

• **Skep:** While the traditional straw skep isn't really suitable for housing bees on a permanent basis (due to the difficulties associated with harvesting honey from colonies kept in this way), they're very useful for temporarily containing swarms. You can just as easily use a cardboard box, but the bees are much happier in a skep, so are more likely to stick around long enough for you to transfer them to an empty hive.

• **Extractor:** Last, but by no means least, you'll need an extractor. They're expensive things to buy, but you might be able to borrow one from time to time. Your local beekeepers' association may have one that it hires out to members. Frames containing full comb are placed in the extractor and spun very fast, removing the honey by centrifugal force.

Acquiring your first bees

Once you've got bees you'll always have bees, because they seem to attract one another to an established site. However, you will need to obtain some from somewhere to get you started. You could buy them locally (we bought one colony via an ad in the local paper, and another couple from a farm dispersal sale), by mail order (several of the companies that sell beekeeping equipment also supply bees), or you could simply sit back and wait for a swarm to appear. (Even as I write this, there's a swirling mass of bees gradually congregating on a bush in the garden hedge: a swarm flying in from goodness knows where. It hasn't emanated from one of our hives, so we've potentially gained another colony). It helps to stack the odds in your favour if you leave a 'bait hive' ready and waiting. This consists of a brood box containing drawn comb, and possibly a proprietary 'bee attractant'. Hopefully any passing swarm will be drawn to these desirable quarters, and take up residence without any effort on your part at all. As soon as you see activity in the vicinity of the bait hive, indicating that a colony has moved in, provide some food in the form of sugar syrup or a full super of honey, then leave well alone for the remainder of the season. Established beekeepers always have a few bait hives dotted around their apiaries, as it's a very easy way of increasing stock. It also reduces the chances of losing a swarm from one of your existing colonies, because the departing bees, together with their

Main: *A swirling mass of bees.*
Inset: *The swarm clustered on a bush.*

queen, are just as likely to move into the vacant accommodation you've provided as to fly off into the blue yonder.

In the absence of a bait hive, a swarm of bees is likely to be found hanging in a football-sized cluster in a hedgerow or on the branch of a tree. Here they always seem to end up on one of our soft-fruit bushes. But they won't stay hanging up in one place for long – only until their scouts have located a suitable home for the colony, and then they'll be gone! Therefore it's imperative that you act quickly to take the swarm and transfer it to a ready prepared hive. This is where the traditional skep comes into play.

Taking a swarm

Firstly, use a pair of secateurs to snip away the surrounding vegetation, leaving the swarm hanging by a single twig. A little bit of smoke can be wafted around to encourage them to group together more tightly. (Some people advocate misting the swarm with water, for the same effect). Next, position the skep (or failing that, a cardboard box) close beneath the cluster of bees. Now cut through the last remaining branch, whereupon the whole lot will drop into your waiting receptacle. Sometimes the swarm will be on a branch that's too thick to cut, or even clinging to the trunk of a tree, or the side of a building,

In the absence of a skep, simply use a cardboard box.

in which case you can either shake or brush the bees into the skep, or try fixing the skep in position above the bees in the hope that they'll crawl up into it.

Placing a skep beneath the swarm, before cutting through the branch on which the bees are hanging.

The new colony transfered to a hive, and provided with a full super of honey to keep them happy.

comb, with frames of foundation at the outer edges. The skep is picked up carefully then dumped down hard onto the tops of the frames, thus dislodging all of the bees. A few puffs of smoke should send them scurrying down into the brood box, whereupon the hive can be topped off with either a full super of honey or a clearer board and feeder, before fitting the roof.

Moving the hive

Whether you've captured a swarm or purchased a colony, the hive will need to be transported to a suitable site. Late in the day, after the bees have finished flying, the hive to be moved must have its entrance blocked with a small strip of foam rubber, then the whole thing needs to be firmly held together by running a small ratchet strap all the way around – under the floor and over the roof – and cranking it up tight. The last thing you want is for the hive to come apart in the back of your car! The trouble with moving an established colony is that, when released, the foraging bees may return to the original site of the

The skep right-way-up now, containing the bees.

As soon as the swarm is in the skep it should be placed the right way up on a flat surface (such as a square of plywood), and propped slightly open at the base to allow the bees free access. A

period of quiet observation now will soon tell you whether you've been successful – if bees are seen to be leaving the skep, and re-grouping in the vicinity of their original cluster (or departing into the distance), then clearly you've failed to take the queen. Hopefully, though, what you'll see is a general movement of bees towards the skep, as any stragglers rejoin the queen and her retinue now safely contained therein. The swarm ought to remain quite happily in the skep, at least until the evening, at which point you can transfer it to a hive. The prepared hive should consist of a brood box containing, at its centre, frames of drawn

Bee hives in our orchard.

hive, only to perish when they find it gone. To avoid this happening, hives should either be moved in very small increments – say no more than a couple of feet at a time – or in distances of over 3 miles. For shorter journeys, it's often best to move the hive to a site several miles away, leave it for a few weeks, then bring it back to where you want it. However, moving a newly caught swarm shouldn't present these difficulties.

As soon as the hive is in position at the new site you should remove the foam strip from the entrance then retire – the bees will understandably be somewhat irritable after their enforced confinement, and there's no point in aggravating them further by fussing about in the immediate vicinity.

Hive location

As I mentioned before, hives can be sited pretty much anywhere there's space for them, but giving a bit of thought to the location will produce better results. A sheltered position that catches the morning sun is best, with the hive entrance turned away from the prevailing wind. Any vegetation, long grass etc. immediately surrounding the hive should be kept cut back, but it's quite a good idea to have it facing a tall hedge or solid fence, as this encourages the bees to fly high. Raise the hive about 18" off the ground on some kind of stand or platform. This could be as simple as an old door resting on blocks, which would be sufficient to hold two or three hives. On grazing land, the area should be fenced off to prevent damage to the hives by livestock. Some people do allow sheep to graze their apiaries, but, having seen the way our Welsh mountain rams smash things up when the mood takes them, I think it's best to exclude all livestock. Another important consideration is the proximity of a supply of drinking water for the bees. Unless the hive is situated close to a natural pond or spring, or a garden water feature, it'll be necessary to provide water throughout the summer. A small poultry drinker placed on top of the hive would be fine. Put a few pebbles in the dish so that the bees have somewhere to settle while they sip.

The honey flow

In most parts of the UK, the honey season runs from early May through to mid August, although in heather areas the period may be extended to the end of September. However, the peak 'honey flow' (which should be more properly termed 'nectar flow') occurs during a relatively brief spell, between about mid June and late July. Having said that, in mild weather bees can be seen flying at most times of the year.

Early in the year, the bees concentrate their attention on maple, willow and sycamore trees, before moving on to fruit blossom in April. Although most fruit blossom is over and done with fairly quickly, wild crab apples have a long flowering period, running from March right through to June. Bushes such as hawthorn and blackthorn kick in at the beginning of May, and, in arable areas, oilseed rape will be in flower too. Horse chestnut trees also bloom during May. Un-sprayed grassland should have plenty of dandelions, buttercups and daisies from now until late August, and in the garden there's Rosemary.

Other herbs, such as borage and lavender, come into flower in June, as does white clover – one of the principal bee plants. The clover should continue right through until September. Many hedgerow plants, including brambles, thistles and willowherb, provide good food for bees during June, July and August (and maybe even into September).

Taking full supers of honey off the hive for extraction.

Summer flowering trees include holly, sweet chestnut and lime, although these will be finished by the end of July. Ling heather honey is produced during August and September, with the bell heather being somewhat earlier (July). Ivy blossom provides a staple diet during the late autumn, and gorse has flowers on it pretty much all year round.

Although bees will, if necessary, travel considerable distances on their foraging trips, it's obviously more efficient if they can find what they need close at hand. If it were really well stocked with a useful range of bee plants, an acre of land would support a strong colony, without the need for them to fly any further afield. Failing that, there's nothing to stop you taking your hives to where the flowers are, at different times of year. Beekeepers regularly move hives into orchards at blossom time, to the mutual benefit of both the honey producer and the fruit farmer, and likewise where crops such as borage, lavender and oil seed rape are grown. And many hives are transported to the moors for heather in the early autumn – it's almost a cultural thing in some areas.

Control of swarming

An awful lot has been written about the control of swarming in established colonies. Obviously it's in the beekeeper's interest to prevent swarms from leaving his hives as far as he's able to do so, for the simple reason that you lose an awful lot of bees! It can take some time for the remainder of the colony to build back up to full strength, and honey production will clearly be suppressed in the meantime. However, swarming is an incredible natural phenomenon, and there's only so much you can do to stop it happening. Some of the suggested methods are quite invasive, such as regular (weekly) inspections of the brood box and the destruction of any new queen cells discovered, or clipping the wings of the queen bee – but ultimately the root cause of

swarming is often a simple matter of overcrowding in the hive.

Therefore, if you give your bees plenty of space when they need it, the chances of losing a swarm are considerably reduced. One thing you can do is to use bigger brood chambers. The National brood box is 8 ⅞ deep, whereas the supers measure 5 ⅞. Therefore, by using two (or even three) supers in place of a standard deep box (or by placing a super directly on top of the brood chamber, beneath the queen excluder), you're giving the colony a much larger nest area. It's also important that you add more supers for honey storage ahead of peak demand. If a proportion of the frames in these supers contain foundation rather than drawn comb, then there'll be plenty of work to keep the bees occupied, thus distracting their attention away from any thoughts of moving house. If, despite your efforts, a swarm does leave one of your colonies then you simply turn it to your advantage by catching it up and installing it in a spare hive. Where you may only have had one hive at the bottom of the garden, you now have two, and potentially double the amount of honey!

The harvest

Initially, the substance stored in each of the honeycomb cells has a high liquid content. This is primarily nectar. Once the cells are full, the bees raise the temperature of the hive, thus evaporating much of the moisture and creating the end product – honey. Each of the honey-containing cells is then sealed with a wax capping. When approximately three quarters of the comb in the super currently being filled is seen to be capped, a fresh super should be inserted beneath it. This ensures that the full supers are always at the top of the stack, allowing for easier clearing and removal when the time comes.

Once the entire area of comb in a particular super is capped, the honey can be harvested, although it's much better if you leave the full supers on the hive for a while to mature. In fact, it's ok for them to remain *in situ* until the honey flow has finished, simply adding more supers as required – by the end of the season you might have 4 or 5 full supers on the hive, with each one containing in excess of 20lb of honey. However, if you're short of supers you'll need to lift them off as soon as they're full, extract the honey, and get them straight back on the hive again.

Before removing the full supers for extraction they must be emptied of bees, using the clearer board fitted with escapes. Put this in place beneath the supers, and by the next day all the bees should have moved down to the lower parts of the hive. The supers can now be lifted off and transported to a bee-proof place prior to extraction.

Always strap down your hives for winter, or place a heavy block on the roof – the inmates really won't appreciate it if their house blows over in a gale! Mouse guards and insulation may be needed too.

Extraction

The extractor consists of a drum containing a revolving rack or basket. Power is provided either by turning a handle or by a small electric motor. I did once try

attaching an electric drill to the shaft of our manually operated extractor, but it wasn't a success.

The frames of full comb are loaded into the extractor, having first had all the wax capping removed from the cells. This can be done with a hot knife, or with a special uncapping tool, but I simply scratch it off with an ordinary dining fork. After revolving the rack of frames for about 3 minutes to extract all the honey from one side of the comb it might, depending on the specific design (either radial or tangential), be necessary to briefly remove each one and turn it around in order to extract the honey from the other side. All the honey that's collected in the bottom of the extractor drum can now be run out via the bottom tap, through a filter (the leg off a pair of tights is ideal) and into a suitable receptacle. After leaving it to stand for a few days, which allows all the air bubbles to rise, the honey can be transferred to jars for storage. However, that's a bit fiddly, so, unless you're planning to sell (or give away / barter) any of your crop, you might just as well do as we do, and store the whole lot in a big bucket with a tight-fitting lid. Just spoon out what you need, as and when required. Delicious!

The newly emptied frames of comb should be put back into their supers and returned to the hive, where the bees will soon clean off any remaining honey. If it's early in the year they can then be left in place on the hive, and hopefully the bees will fill them up again. Otherwise, take them off when clean, and store away from mice and other pests until the following season.

USING HONEY AND BEESWAX

In the self-supporter's kitchen, one of the principal uses of honey (apart from making mead – see page 333-334) is as a straightforward home-produced alternative to refined sugar in baking, confectionery, puddings and drinks. Now, it might seem crazy to be using honey, with a potential sale value of over £5 / lb, to replace sugar that can be purchased for as little as 80p / lb, but when you consider that the honey hasn't actually cost you anything at all (and is much nicer anyway), it does make sense.

And it's not only sweet dishes that benefit from the addition of a little honey – it can be used as a glaze for roast meats, in salad dressings, and as a preservative. It also has medicinal properties, with many traditional cough remedies, skin care products and sleeping draughts being honey based. Surplus beeswax is also a useful product in its own right, with any not required for making new foundation being used in the home manufacture of furniture polish, leather dressing, candles and hand cream.

If using honey as a direct substitute for sugar in baking etc., use only four fifths of the quantity specified in the recipe, and reduce the amount of liquid added by a quarter. You might also need to add a bit of bicarb of soda, as honey is naturally acidic.

Breakfast

A spoonful of honey is the perfect accompaniment to a bowl of porridge or fresh natural yoghurt, or make your own breakfast cereal as follows:

Ingredients

2 tbsp honey
4 tbsp sunflower oil
3 drops vanilla essence
4 oz porridge oats
4 oz jumbo oats
2 oz sunflower seeds
2 oz chopped hazelnuts
2 oz flaked almonds
2 oz desiccated coconut
2 oz dried fruit

Method

Gently melt the honey and oil. Remove from the heat and add the vanilla essence. Place all the remaining ingredients except the fruit in a bowl, and stir in the honey and oil.

Bake in a large shallow dish at 190°C / 375°F for half an hour, stirring and turning the mixture every 5 minutes or so. When cool stir in the dried fruit.

Leave until completely cold before transferring to an airtight container for storage.

Glaze for roast pork

Ingredients

3.5 fl oz honey
8 oz muscavado sugar
½ pint home-brewed beer or cider

Method

Put all the ingredients together in a pan and heat until it reduces by half. Brush the pork all over with the glaze about three quarters of an hour before serving. Return to the oven and baste frequently until the meat is cooked and the glaze is caramelised. Any left-over glaze mixture, together with the juices in the roasting dish, can be used to make gravy.

Honey and banana ice-cream

Ingredients

5 tbsp honey
1lb bananas
5 fl oz double cream
5 fl oz natural yoghurt
Juice of 1 lemon
2 oz chopped hazelnuts (optional)
2 egg whites

Method

Peel and mash the bananas then add the honey, cream, yoghurt, lemon juice and nuts. Beat well to combine all the ingredients and put in the fridge to chill for a couple of hours. Whisk the egg whites until light and fluffy then fold into the mixture. Churn in an ice-cream maker until smooth and silky (about 30 minutes). Tip into suitable containers and freeze.

Hand cream

Melt together 6 oz of honey, 4½ oz of beeswax and 6 oz of lard, and stir until cool.

Waterproof leather dressing for boots and shoes

Melt together 4 oz of beeswax and 2 oz of mutton fat by heating gently in a double saucepan (or in a tin stood in a pan of water). Stir thoroughly until well mixed then pour into a suitable jar. Keep sealed and warm gently before use.

General purpose polish

Ingredients

4½ oz beeswax
½ oz hard soap – the fag-ends of the bathroom soap bars should do
1 pint turpentine
1 pint rainwater

Method

Break up the soap, put it in a pan with the rainwater and heat gently until dissolved. Melt the beeswax carefully in a double saucepan (or in a tin stood in a pan of water), then add to the turpentine. Pour the warm soap solution into the wax and turpentine mixture, stirring all the while until an emulsion is produced.

For honey beer and mead recipes see pages 327 and 333 - 334.

Section Four
Baking, Brewing and
Preserving

Dot making cider using equipment kindly provided by Vigo Presses Ltd.

Brewing and Winemaking

Alcohol consumption and 'binge' drinking are considered to be evils of modern society, but I think the real problem lies in the fact that everyone drives everywhere these days. Human beings have been enjoying alcoholic beverages for more than 10,000 years, but it's only relatively recently that we've taken to hurtling around at high speed in collapsible metal boxes, with just a painted white line between ourselves and some other idiot hurtling in the opposite direction. It's no great wonder that accidents happen. The trouble is, we're all expected to be able to jump in our cars and go dashing off at the drop of a hat, which more or less rules out a relaxed attitude to drinking. Give someone a night off driving and they try to cram in

enough booze to make up for all the preceding days of abstinence, the consequences of which are invariably bad.

When we lived on Bardsey Island we experienced no such dilemmas, simply because there weren't any cars. Sometimes we went about by tractor, but usually we just walked. We all brewed beer – at least 5 gallons a week, and often more – and that's what we drank, most of the time. If anyone called in, that's what they'd be offered, within reason (although before about 10.00am we might also have offered tea as an alternative.) There were occasions when things got a little out of hand, like when a group of summer visitors dropped in on us around lunchtime to buy a loaf of home-baked bread and

half-a-dozen eggs, and eventually left on their hands and knees at 2.00am the next morning (by which time they'd eaten the bread and the eggs!), but it was all very easy going, and we enjoyed ourselves immensely. I certainly don't remember any harm ever coming of it. Our outdoor lifestyle kept us lean and fit, and beer was just the thing to keep everything running smoothly. Mainland life is tense by comparison, but ideally the situation on a well-managed smallholding should be sufficiently relaxed and self-contained for the consumption of home-made alcoholic drinks to form an acceptable part of the daily routine.

TIP

Whether brewing beer or making wine, cleanliness is absolutely essential. All equipment must be thoroughly scrubbed and sterilised before use. However, there's no escaping the fact that, at best, chemical sterilisers can affect the flavour of the end product. At worst, they could kill your yeast. Therefore, routinely sterilise everything using just plain boiling water. Keep the chemical compounds for cleansing old barrels and bins that have been out of commission for a while. And whatever you do, don't use any fairy liquid or other detergent on your brewing utensils.

BREWING

"Only a pint at breakfast-time, and a pint and a half at eleven o'clock, and a quart or so at dinner. And then no more 'til the afternoon; and half a gallon at supper time. No one can object to that."
John Ridd in R.D Blackmore's *Lorna Doone.*

What is fermentation?

Yeast is a microscopic fungus containing the sugar loving enzyme zymase.

Fermentation is the anaerobic process by which yeast converts sugar into alcohol. In scientific terms, this is written down as:

$$C_6 H_{12} O_6 + yeast = 2C_2 H_5 OH + 2CO$$

(glucose)   (alcohol)   (carbon dioxide)

The maximum amount of sugar that can reasonably be fermented in a gallon of liquid is about 3lb (giving a potential alcohol content, after fermentation, of around 15%). Beyond this point, the high alcohol content tends to kill off the yeast, and any remaining unfermented sugar merely serves to sweeten the finished product. Bear in mind that a proportion of the sugar present will have been obtained from the raw ingredients, so the amount of extra sugar added needs to be adjusted according to the 'sweetness' of the fruit or vegetables used. A lot of traditional country wine recipes include relatively large quantities of additional sugar, and tend to result in rather sticky sherry-like beverages.

Malt extract can be purchased in 25kg drums.

Beer or ale, in one form or another, has been brewed for thousands of years. All sorts of grains and sugars have been used, but, in all likelihood, the earliest fermented drinks made in Britain would have been honey-based meads (see pages 333 - 334). The Romans brought us ale, and the habit persisted after they went home. Hops, initially added as a preservative, weren't included until the Middle Ages, but technically it's the addition of hops that turns an ale into a beer, although nowadays the words 'ale' and 'beer' have become more or less synonymous.

Home brewing is such a simple thing to do (and to do well) that it always surprises me it isn't more widely undertaken, particularly when you consider the cost of drinking in a pub or buying 'decent' bottled beers. It's perfectly legal to brew unlimited quantities of booze for home consumption in the UK. A licence is only required if you want to sell alcoholic

beverages, or if you want to set up your own distillery. This has been the case since 1963, when the need to apply (and pay) for a private brewing licence (introduced in 1880) was removed by the then government. Interestingly, there's never been any similar restriction on the production of wine for home consumption.

Malt

Malt – the principal ingredient of ale or beer – is made from barley. The process of malting transforms the starch content of the grain into fermentable sugar. It is as the barley begins to grow that the starch is naturally turned into sugar, so in order to make malt it's necessary to encourage the grain to sprout, and then kill off the growth at the optimum (i.e. the most sugary) stage. On a very small scale you can do this – as I have done, using home-grown barley – by soaking the grains in warm water and then placing them

in a big old-fashioned sweet jar to sprout, just like growing bean shoots for salad. Lay the jar on its side in a warmish place, shaking it up from time to time. Keep an eye on it, and just before the growing shoots actually push their way through the outer husk of the grains, tip the contents of the jar onto a baking tray and spread them out evenly. Now roast them gently in the oven until golden brown (not black). Before use, roasted grains need to be cracked, which, on a small scale, can be done with a rolling pin.

However, having malted my own barley once, it's not something I'll be doing again. The resulting brew, although recognisable as beer, was scarcely drinkable. Growing barley of suitable quality for malting purposes is a fairly precise science, and best left to the experts, I think.

If you're keen to try brewing beer from scratch, you can buy ready-malted grains from a home-brew shop. In order to make your wort (the liquid that will be fermented into beer) the grains need to be soaked in water (4½lbs to the gallon) for about 2 hours at between 60 and 70°C. This process, called mashing, is the final stage in the transformation of starch into maltose. It needs to be carried out in a bin with a tap at its base, and containing some sort of heater element to maintain the correct temperature.

When the two hours is up, open the tap and let the liquor run out into another container.

TIP

For better results, after 2 hours apply the following test to determine whether the mashing process is complete. Take a spoonful of the liquid and place it in a white dish. Add a couple of drops of iodine, and if the solution turns blue then this indicates that there's still a lot of unconverted starch present, in which case let it mash for another half hour or so before testing again. Drain off the wort when the colour remains unchanged.

Next you need to 'sparge' the mash. To do this, sprinkle more hot water (slightly hotter this time) over the grain in the bottom of the bin, and let it run out through the tap into the second receptacle. A watering can with a rose attachment is just the job for this. Keep at it until you've got a gallon of wort for every 1½ lb of malted grains used. The wort is then boiled up with the required quantity of hops before cooling and adding the yeast.

The grains remaining in the mash tub can be used to make 'small beer' by sparging them a bit more and fermenting the resulting pale liquid into a mildly alcoholic beverage for drinking at times of the day when it's really more advisable to keep a clear head.

Finally, the spent grains can be given to the pigs.

However, when we make beer we by-pass all the mashing and the sparging by using malt extract, which, if bought in sensible quantities (i.e. 25kg drums) doesn't work out too expensive. Not only is it convenient, it's consistent, giving excellent results time after time. For traditional type beers, a fairly dark malt extract is preferable.

Hops growing wild in the hedgerow.

Hops

It's the cone-like flowers of the hop plant that are used in brewing. You can buy dried hops, or grow your own, or you might be lucky and find some growing wild. The first beer I ever brewed was made with wild hops, and much of the beer that we made on Bardsey was brewed using hops that had been growing wild on the island since their introduction by the Augustinian monks in the 13th century. To grow your own hops you need to obtain some pieces of root, which you then simply bury in the bottoms of the hedgerows

around the smallholding. A tall, straggly hedge in a damp-ish spot with fairly deep soil is just the thing for the hop bines to scramble over. Once the roots are established, new bines will grow each year at a phenomenal rate – several inches per day – so from time to time you might need to clear away the old growth during the winter to prevent the hedge from eventually being completely swamped. In commercial hop gardens, all of the annual growth is cut down after harvest. The flowers will probably be ripe for picking from about mid September, when the resinous yellow pollen is at its most fragrant. They can either be used fresh, or dried for storage by hanging in net bags over the Rayburn.

Incidentally, the hop is a natural sedative, so when you fall asleep after a couple of pints of home-brew, don't blame it all on the alcohol!

Equipment

Very little in the way of specialist equipment is needed for home brewing. In fact, most of what you need you probably already have. At the very least you'll require:

A large saucepan: A preserving pan is ideal, although be aware that if it's also used for making pickles and chutney, this could have a serious adverse effect on your beer, unless it's scrupulously cleaned. Stainless steel is best.

A wooden spoon: As with the saucepan, beware of utensils that might be tainted.

A sieve: An ordinary nylon or metal kitchen sieve is fine.

Fermentation vessels: Glass demijohns (preferably brown) can be used for brewing beer, but for a drink that's consumed by the pint (or three), why waste time fiddling about with such small quantities? Get some food-grade plastic bins to hold 5 gallons. Keep the demijohns for experimenting with new recipes.

A siphon tube: Just an ordinary piece of flexible plastic pipe will do, but for added refinement, fit a little tap to one end.

Pressure barrel and fermenting bin.

A pressure barrel or bottles: Barrels are a lot less hassle to use and give you beer 'on tap'. If you prime them with sugar then the addition of carbon dioxide (from a small cylinder) shouldn't be necessary. If the pressure does go you can simply vent the barrel by opening the lid a touch, and drink up the remainder quickly, before it goes bad. (However, this will only work with barrels that have their tap positioned at the bottom).

Bottling beer is a bit of a palaver, as each bottle has to be scrubbed out and sterilised, and each one needs to be individually primed, filled and sealed. Having said that, beer does generally keep better in bottles, and they give you the benefit of portability,

should you wish to take some into the hayfield with you. (Although we've successfully transported a 10 gallon barrel on the back of the tractor!). If you can get hold of some empty 'Grolsch' style bottles (the ones with the flip tops) that makes sealing them a lot simpler, otherwise you'll need:

Crown corks and a corking tool: Crown corks are the little metal caps found on ordinary beer bottles. Buy them from any home brew supplier. You'll need a special tool to put them on. The really basic ones you hit with a hammer, but after a few smashed bottles (and a lot of mess), I decided to invest in a lever-operated corking tool, which is very easy to use. You just have to be aware that the rim depth and thickness may vary between different makes of bottle, and adjust the tool accordingly.

A basic recipe to make a gallon of beer

This simple recipe makes a good starting point for anyone new to the world of home brewing. It's the recipe I followed when, at the age of 14 or thereabouts, I discovered some hops growing wild in the hedgerow on my parents' smallholding.

Ingredients

1lb dark malt extract
1 tbsp black treacle
½ pint dried hops
Brewer's yeast
A little sugar

Method

Boil the hops, malt and treacle in 8 pints of water for one hour. Meanwhile, place 1 tsp of dried

yeast, 1 tsp of sugar and ½ pint of tepid water in a gallon jar. When the boiled hops, malt and treacle have cooled to tepid, strain the liquor into the jar with the yeast, then top up to 1 gallon with tepid water the next day. Ferment for about 5 days in a warm place. Before siphoning into bottles, place one level tsp of sugar in each bottle (known as 'priming'). Seal the filled bottles and leave in a warm place for a further 4-6 days, and store the bottles in a cool place for at least a week before drinking.

Brewing 5 gallons of strong beer

This is our 'standard' recipe that's stood us in good stead for a long time. It's been honed over the years to give the best possible result in terms of both quality and cost. Furthermore, it has an international reputation!

Ingredients

3 lb dark malt extract
2lb granulated sugar – if you keep bees then reduce the cost by using just under 2lb of honey instead
5 tbsp black treacle
4 tbsp dark brown muscavado sugar
2 oz dried hops (Keep the cost down by growing your own).
1 sachet dried brewer's yeast ('Muntons Gold' seems to be the best), or some of the sludge from the previous batch of beer
2 oz granulated sugar to prime the barrel

Method

Put the malt extract, sugar, and dried hops in a large pan together with three or four pints of water and bring to the boil. Simmer for an hour. I wouldn't recommend

Boiling up the hops, malt and other ingredients.

you leave it unattended – keep an eye on it, and stir it from time to time, as it will froth up considerably. Believe me, you really don't want to it boil over onto your hotplate. After an hour, strain the liquid into a fermenting bin, rinsing through with a kettleful of boiling water to wash all the malt off the hops. Top up to just under 5 gallons with cold water.

Straining the liquid into a fermenting bin.

It should now be at a suitable temperature to add the yeast. For your initial brew you'll need to use a bought beer yeast, although sometimes the first batch of beer made with a new yeast does have a slight 'tang' to it, probably caused

Main: *Adding the yeast.*
Inset: *Sachets of dried brewer's yeast.*

by the nutrient that's included in the sachets. Stir it in well, cover, and leave in a warm place to ferment for about a week.
After about a week, carefully siphon the liquid off into a pressure barrel, or into bottles, whichever you prefer. It's a good idea to 'prime' them with a little bit of sugar to ensure a secondary fermentation (so you get some fizz and a head on your beer).

Fermentation under way.

A teaspoonful of sugar per bottle is enough, or a couple of ounces in the bottom of the barrel.
Once all the beer is bottled, or barrelled, go back to your fermentation bin and you should find a lovely brown sludge in the bottom of it. This sludge is mostly

Siphoning into a pressure barrel.

yeast, so spoon some into a clean glass, and cover. Unless you're starting another brew immediately (and why not?), put the glass of yeast in the fridge, where it will keep for a couple of weeks or so, until you have your next brewing session. We have on occasion stored the yeast sludge in the freezer for several months, and managed to successfully restart it on defrosting.

Set aside a spoonful of yeasty sludge to start your next brew.

If you can keep your hands off it, leave your beer in the bottles or barrel for at least a week before drinking. The longer you keep it, the more it will improve, up to a point.

Nettle beer (2 gallons)

This is a useful recipe for when times are hard and you can't afford malt extract. Interestingly, the colour (and flavour) of this beer is remarkably similar to that brewed using malt, not green as one might expect.

Ingredients

4lbs young nettles
1lb soft brown sugar
1lb honey
2 tsp ground ginger
Water
Brewer's yeast
Granulated sugar for priming

Method

Boil the nettles in 6-8 pints of water for half an hour then strain the liquid onto the sugar, honey and ginger. Stir until everything is dissolved. Top up to 2 gallons with cold water and add the yeast when cool enough. Cover and ferment in a warm place for 10 days then siphon into primed bottles. Seal and store in a warm place for 3 days, before moving them to somewhere cooler. If possible, keep for at least a fortnight before drinking.

Cost

Although it remains considerably cheaper (and nicer) than bought beer from either the pub or the supermarket, the cost of making beer at home has risen sharply in recent years, primarily because of the increasing price of malt extract. This is partly due to the closure of many of the old maltings, leaving only a handful of larger companies holding a monopoly on the production and supply of malt extract, and also due to a relatively recent change in the way that malt extract is classified for VAT purposes. In the past it was designated as a food item (a necessity), but it has since been reclassified as a food supplement (a luxury). This means that it is now subject to 20% VAT, which has pushed up the price considerably. In an attempt to try and mitigate these price increases we compromise by substituting a proportion of the malt with sugar (or, better still, home produced honey).

Brewing cost per pint at the time of writing:

Malt extract (£64.00 for 25kg) = 9p
Sugar (59p per kg) = 1½p
Yeast (£1.56 per sachet) = 4p
Hops (£5.00 per 100g) = 6p
Total: 20½p per pint

Obviously this only covers the raw ingredients, and makes no allowance for the cost associated with boiling the water and so on, but even so, a pint of home-brewed beer is still a cheaper drink than either orange juice or shop-bought milk!

Kit beers may cost in the region of 30–60p per pint, depending on quality. Some kits require you to add extra sugar, so this is something to bear in mind when comparing prices.

Honey beer (1 gallon)

Ingredients

1lb honey
½ oz dried hops
4 oz dark brown sugar
Water
Brewers' yeast
Granulated sugar for priming bottles (1 tsp per bottle)

Method

Boil the hops and the brown sugar in 6 pints of water for an hour. Strain, and dissolve the honey in the hot liquor, top up to 1 gallon with cold water, allow to cool then add the yeast. Ferment for a week then siphon into primed bottles and seal. Store the sealed bottles in a warm place for a few days before transferring to somewhere cooler.

Demijohn, bottles and corks.

The S.G. of a liquid that contains about 3lbs of sugar to the gallon will be 1.115, so, if this is the starting point for your wine, and you ferment it until the S.G. is somewhere in the region of 1.000 (i.e. all of the sugar has fermented out), then the alcohol content of the finished wine will be just over 15%.

Glass demijohns: These 1 gallon (4.5 litre) vessels are very easy to pick up from charity shops, car boot sales and Freecycle. You'll also need large corks or rubber bungs to fit the necks of the demijohns. Some should have holes bored through them to take an airlock.

Airlocks: An airlock is fitted to the fermentation vessel to enable CO_2 to escape without allowing air to get in. They come in various designs, but the basic idea is that the gas has to pass through water contained in the U-bend of a glass pipe. The steady plop… plop… plop… of gas bubbling through the airlock is the surest sign that fermentation is underway.

Siphon tube: As used in home brewing (see page 325).

Filter: You can buy a fancy kind of filter, but generally an ordinary funnel containing a folded filter paper will do. Un-scented disposable nappy liners also make good filter papers.

Pectic enzyme: Most fruits contain high levels of pectin, which can result in a hazy wine, particularly if they were overheated during preparation. The addition of a pectin destroying enzyme not only reduces the likelihood of a haze appearing, but also aids the juice extraction process.

WINEMAKING

"Wine is the most healthful and most hygienic of beverages."
Louis Pasteur

Winemaking at home always strikes me as a rather hit-and-miss affair. Sometimes the results are very, very good, and sometimes they're appalling. Certainly we find it difficult to achieve the regular, consistent high quality that's easily attainable with home-brewed beer.

Wine (of sorts) can be made from almost any plant material, although fruits and flowers are the most popular ingredients. Oak leaves, onion skins and bean pods are best left to the really dedicated enthusiasts, in my opinion.

The basic essence of making wine is that you extract the flavour and colour, together with any sugar present, from your raw ingredient by whatever is the most appropriate method (pressing, steeping, mashing, juicing, boiling etc.), add the required amount of additional sugar and acid, together with a suitable yeast, and leave to ferment.

Equipment

Food grade plastic bins and buckets: Used for preparing the must (i.e. the liquid that will become wine), and for fermenting larger volumes.

Stainless steel preserving pan, wooden spoons etc.: Some ingredients may need to be boiled, and all will need to be stirred from time to time. As I mentioned before, scrupulous cleanliness is essential, particular with utensils that are used for purposes other than winemaking.

Hydrometer: The hydrometer is an optional extra for the more scientifically minded winemaker. It's used to determine the specific gravity (S.G.) of a liquid, and, by taking readings both before and after fermentation, it's possible to calculate the alcohol content of your wine. For example, the S.G. of water is 1.000 (at 15°C).

Citric acid: Some ingredients – root vegetables in particular – contain insufficient acid for efficient fermentation, so you'll often see lemon juice and / or peel included in country wine recipes. Alternatively, you can buy citric acid in powder form.

Tannin: Tannin is found in the skins of black grapes, and is one of the things that give red wines their distinctive character. Most other raw ingredients don't contain enough tannin, so some recipes may include powdered grape tannin (obtainable from home brew shops) or tea leaves.

Wine yeast: You can buy many different sorts of yeast for making different sorts of wine, but we just use a general purpose wine yeast for everything. It comes as a powder, complete with nutrient.

Bottles: Accumulate a stock of second-hand bottles and just keep on re-using them. Green or brown glass is best, so wines don't lose their colour.

Corks and corking tool: New corks can be purchased from home brew shops, or you could use plastic stoppers which have the advantage that they can be re-used.

If using natural corks you'll also need a corking tool, which may be a simple bit of kit you hit with a mallet, or a more sophisticated lever operated tool. Corks should be soaked for a few minutes in boiling water before insertion, to ensure that they're both soft and sterile.

Recipes

Rather than waste a lot of time (and sugar) experimenting with obscure ingredients, it's best to find a few simple recipes that work well for you, and stick with them. A recipe is only ever a starting point – make your own adjustments through trial and error. Here are a few that have given us reasonably consistent results over the years.

Apple wine

This recipe makes almost 1½ gallons of sweet wine. For a long drink, dilute slightly with cold spring water.

Ingredients

15lb mixed apples, well chopped
Granulated sugar (at least 3lb)
1 gallon cold water
Wine yeast

Method

Put the chopped apples in a suitable bucket and pour the water over them. Add the yeast, cover the bucket and leave in a warm place for 1 week, stirring twice daily. Strain off the liquor and press the remaining fruit to extract as much juice as possible. Measure the total volume and, for every gallon add 3lb of sugar. Ferment using an airlock and rack when clear, then bottle.

Chopped apples for winemaking.

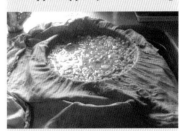

Straining apple wine.

Rhubarb wine

Ingredients

5lb rhubarb
2½lbs granulated sugar
1 gallon boiling water
Wine yeast

Method

Chop the rhubarb and pour over it one gallon of boiling water. Mash well, cover and leave to stand for 24 hours. Mash again and strain off the liquid. Dissolve the sugar in the liquid, put it in a suitable fermentation vessel and add the yeast. Leave to ferment in a warm place then rack and bottle.

Gorse flowers.

Blackcurrant wine

Ingredients

4lb blackcurrants
2½lbs granulated sugar
6 pints water
Wine yeast

Method

Preparation is as for the rhubarb wine above, but using only 6 pints of boiling water. Top up to 1 gallon, if necessary, after the initial fermentation has subsided.

Plum wine

Ingredients

6lb plums
2¾lb granulated sugar
6 pints boiling water
Wine yeast

Method

Put the fruit in a bucket and pour the boiling water over it. Mash well then cover the bucket with a cloth and leave for 4 days, stirring occasionally. Strain, dissolve the sugar in the liquor and add the yeast then leave in a covered bucket for a further 2 days. Pour into a fermentation jar or demijohn, top up to 1 gallon if required, and fit an airlock. Rack when clear and keep for a further 3 months before bottling.

Sloe and elder wine

Ingredients

2¼lb elderberries
1lb 10 oz sloes
2½lb granulated sugar
6 pints boiling water
Wine yeast

Method

Put the fruit in a bucket and crush it with the end of a rolling pin (or something similar). Pour over the boiling water, leave to cool then add the yeast. Cover and leave for three days, stirring daily. Strain the liquor onto the sugar, stir until dissolved then pour into a demijohn. Top up to 1 gallon with tepid water and ferment using an airlock. Rack as necessary, and bottle when the fermentation is complete.

Gorse wine

Ingredients

1 gallon gorse flowers, fully opened and picked on a hot day
2½lbs granulated sugar
2 oranges
1 lemon
6 pints water
Wine yeast

Method

Boil the water and stir the sugar into it, making sure it all dissolves. Put the orange and lemon peel (no pith) into a fermenting bin and pour the hot, sugary syrup over them. Leave it to cool then add the orange and lemon juice, the flowers and the yeast. Cover tightly and leave to ferment for a week, stirring daily. Strain the liquid into a demijohn and top up to 1 gallon with tepid water. Ferment using an airlock and rack when there is an appreciable deposit, and the wine is just beginning to clear. Bottle when the fermentation has ceased, and the wine has cleared.

Parsnip or carrot wine

Ingredients

4lb parsnips (or carrots)
3lb granulated sugar
1 gallon water
2 lemons
A handful of raisins
Wine yeast

Method

Cut up the parsnips (or carrots) and boil together with the lemon rinds and raisins, until just prickable with a fork. Over-boiling will make cloudy wine. Strain off the hot juice and stir in the sugar and lemon juice. Add the yeast when cool then transfer to a demijohn. Ferment well, and rack several times before bottling.Keep as long as possible – it tastes like sherry.

Ginger wine

Ingredients

3 oz crushed root ginger – whack it with a rolling pin!
3lb granulated sugar
2 oranges
2 lemons
½lb raisins
6 pint water
Wine yeast

Method

Peel the fruit thinly, avoiding the pith, and place the peel, fruit juice and raisins in a bucket. Boil the water with the root ginger and the sugar for half an hour, then pour over the peel, juice and raisins, adding the yeast when cool. Cover the bucket and leave for a week. Strain off the liquid into a demijohn and top up to 1 gallon with tepid water. Ferment using an airlock, and rack as necessary. Bottle when fermentation is complete.

Sloe gin

Ingredients

1lb sloes
8 oz white sugar
750ml (standard size) bottle of gin

Method

First prick the sloes all over with a fork – a tedious business, so you can cheat by freezing them for a while, which will split the skins. Put them in a large Kilner jar, together with the sugar, and pour in the gin. Seal the jar and give it a good shake from time to time, until all the sugar has dissolved. Leave to steep for a full year before straining off the liquor into clean bottles.

The same basic methodology can be applied to other fruits. My mother used to make a marvellous drink we called 'summer fruits', which consisted of gradually filling a large sweet jar with layers of various fruits, as each came into season. As each new fruit was added it would be covered with a layer of sugar then topped up to that level with brandy. Eventually, when the jar was full, it would be sealed and left for a year. After straining off the liquor, the leftover fruit can be mixed with stewed apple and baked in a pie. Delicious!

CIDER

Here in the UK, where grapes don't grow particularly well, cider is probably the ultimate self-supporters drink. Nothing added, nothing taken away, just pure apple juice fermented. Some folk don't even add yeast, relying instead on the naturally occurring fungal bloom on the skin of the fruit itself.

The trouble is, if you're going to do the job properly (i.e. in sufficient quantities to be worthwhile) you need an awful lot of apples, and some pretty hefty equipment. With a suitable cider press you might get 1 gallon of juice from about 15lb of apples, but if using inefficient improvised apparatus you may need nearly double the quantity of fruit to obtain the same volume of liquid. A fairly effective press can be made by fitting a hydraulic vehicle jack into a strong wooden frame, but there's also some very good apple processing kits on the market now, which contain everything you need to extract the juice from your own fruit and turn it into cider on a modest scale (about 2½ gallons at a time).

If you haven't got an orchard, then plant one. However, it takes a long time for new trees to come to full fruition, so in the meantime you'll have to scrounge windfalls from trees in residential gardens, and maybe unsold fruit from greengrocers or supermarkets. This can be surprisingly productive, and I know of people who've been able to establish themselves as artisan cider makers with hardly an apple tree to their name.

Cider apple variety 'Brown Snout'.

To make 'proper' cider you really need to use cider apple varieties, but you can get away with using any sort of apples, provided that you have a good mixture of types. Use cookers in preference to eating apple varieties, and perhaps throw in a couple of handfuls of crab apples as well. When you've got enough you need to leave them in a heap for a week or two to mature and soften.

Pressing apples.

Cider is probably the ultimate self-supporters drink.

Before pressing, the apples need to be milled, which basically means they're chopped up into very fine pieces. The resulting 'pomace', as the chopped apple is called, is made into 'cheeses' by placing it between layers of strong hessian. The cheeses are then compressed to extract the juice, and it is this juice, and nothing else, that's made into cider. If the apples were washed (as in the case of shop leftovers) then yeast will need to be added, but otherwise you could just chance it and hope that the fermentation starts up on its own. If you're unable to build, borrow or buy the necessary equipment to do the job properly, here are some easy alternatives to traditional cider making:

Simple cider

This can reasonably be made using a basic improvised press.

Ingredients

25lb mixed apples
9 oz granulated sugar
Cider yeast

Bottling cider.

Extra sugar for priming bottles

Method

Extract as much juice as possible from the apples then top up to 1 gallon with water, if required. Stir in the sugar until dissolved then add the yeast. Ferment for one week, then filter and ferment for a further week. Prime each bottle with a teaspoon of sugar before filling, and keep for at least a

couple of weeks before drinking. (NB. 9 oz of sugar is the minimum to add, and will result in a dry cider. Experiment with further amounts for an increasing degree of sweetness – a matter of personal taste.)

Smallholder's cider

(No specialist equipment required)

For anyone who's not really geared up for cider making, but who finds themselves with a small quantity of windfall apples to experiment with, this recipe is definitely worth a try:

Ingredients

3lb washed windfall apples
1 oz crushed root ginger
½ tsp cloves
½ tsp cinnamon
1½lb granulated sugar
1 gallon water
Cider yeast
Extra sugar for priming bottles
(1tsp per bottle)

Method

Finely chop, mince or grate the apples (I whizz them in the food processor, a few at a time). Put the apple, cold water and yeast in a bucket, cover and leave to ferment for a week, stirring daily.

Strain onto the sugar and spices, squeezing as much juice from the apple pulp as you can. Stir well to dissolve the sugar, cover and ferment for a further 5 days. Siphon into primed bottles, seal and store for 2 weeks before drinking.

KID'S DRINKS

Here are a couple of very mildly alcoholic fizzy drinks to be enjoyed by younger members of the family:

Elderflower champagne

Ingredients

12 heads of elderflowers, picked on a hot day
1lb granulated sugar
1 lemon
2 tbsp cider vinegar

Method

Place the blooms in a bowl with the juice and the cut up rind of the lemon (but minus the pith). Add the sugar, vinegar and 1 gallon of water, stir to dissolve the sugar, cover with a clean cloth and leave to stand for 24-36 hours. Strain the liquor into strong screw-top bottles and keep for a fortnight before drinking. Even better is to make 5 gallons at a time and strain it into a pressure barrel. You'll notice that no yeast is included in this recipe – the naturally occurring yeast in the elderflowers is sufficient.

Elderflowers.

Ginger beer

First you need to start a ginger beer 'plant', by putting 2 oz of fresh baker's yeast in a jar together with 2 teaspoons of granulated sugar, 2 teaspoons of ground ginger and ½ pint of tepid water. Cover the jar with a piece of clean cloth or paper towel, held in place with a rubber band, and leave in a warm place. Every day, for 10 days, you must 'feed' the plant by adding a teaspoon of sugar, and one of ground ginger. When the 10 days is up, strain the liquid through a piece of muslin, or a very fine sieve, into a clean bowl. Add 1 pint of warm water, 1lb of granulated sugar and the juice of two lemons, and stir until the sugar has dissolved, then add a further 5 pints of cold water. Bottle into screw-topped fizzy pop bottles and keep for at least a week before drinking. The sediment remaining in the sieve should now be divided in half. Put each half into an empty jar, add ½ pint of warm water to each one, and you now have two ginger beer plants. One you give away to a friend, and the other you carry on with as before.

MEAD

Mead – made from honey – is almost certainly the oldest form of alcoholic beverage known to man. Like cider, it requires little or nothing in the way of additional ingredients, making it an ideal drink for the true self-supporter. You could simply mix honey and water, bung in some yeast, and leave it to do its own thing, but it would be a long time doing it. Honey contains no acid or any of the other nutrients required by yeast to enable it to work efficiently, so for the best (and quickest) results these need to be added.

Mead is sometimes flavoured with spices or fruit juice, but the basic recipe remains more or less the same:

Put 3lb of honey in a pan together with 6 pints of water, the juice and zest of 2 lemons, and a teabag. Bring gently to the boil and simmer for 5 minutes, scraping off any scum (made up of beeswax and bits of bee) that forms on top. Remove from the heat and strain into a suitable fermentation vessel, and when sufficiently cooled, add a good quality active wine yeast containing nutrient. Top up to 1 gallon with water after a day or two, once the initial vigorous fermentation has died down. Ferment out using an airlock, and rack at least once before bottling. Keep it for as long as you can – several years, if possible – before drinking.

VINEGAR

Just occasionally you'll get a batch of beer that goes 'bad', and turns into perfectly acceptable malt vinegar all by itself. The few times this has happened it's been because, for some reason, I didn't get around to barrelling it when I was supposed to, and eventually it was forgotten. Five gallons of vinegar will pickle an awful lot of onions, so you don't want to go letting that sort of thing happen too often!

You can, of course, deliberately turn beer into vinegar, perhaps to make use of a batch that's a bit below the usual standard, or maybe just because you need some vinegar and would rather make your own than buy it. The method below is how I've done it in the past, and is a variation on that described by John Seymour in *The Complete Book of Self-Sufficiency.*

To make 5 gallons of vinegar you will need:

2 fermentation bins (without their lids), one of which must have a tap at the base.

An old cotton bed sheet.

A quantity of beech wood shavings.

A couple of pints of malt vinegar.

5 gallons of poor quality beer.

Method

Soak the shavings in the vinegar and place them in the bottom of a bin with a tap at the base. (You'll need enough shavings to fill the container to above the level of the tap). Fold up the sheet and pack it down tightly on top of the shavings.Pour the beer into the bin on top of the sheet. Position the bin containing the beer above the other one, and leave the tap slightly open. Allow the beer to drip slowly from one container into the other, over the course of a week or so, then leave it to stand for a further week.

The same basic method can be applied to wine, except that you'd use an appropriate wine vinegar rather than malt vinegar, to initiate the process.

Bread and Baking

"Bread is the staff of life."
Jonathan Swift

"Not everyone has a field of wheat, but we can all bake our own bread." Paul Peacock

Good bread forms a central part of the smallholder's diet. It's a rich source of complex carbohydrates, is low in fat (if that's what you want; if not, just spread more butter), is a plentiful source of B vitamins, and the micronutrients phosphorus, potassium and magnesium. It's perfectly feasible to bake all your own bread – better bread than you can possibly buy – and at a lower cost, too, lower even than the cheapest, nastiest, white bread you can find.

We buy our flour in 16kg sacks from a small commercial bakery, and have done so for many years.

It's 80% wholemeal, and we find that it can be used for all of our baking needs. If a recipe calls for particularly light flour then Dot just sifts the bran out and adds raising agents where appropriate. Currently we're paying £12 per sack, which works out at 75p per kg. Supermarket own brand strong brown bread flour is around about 85p per kg, so we're saving about £1.60 with each sack purchased. It doesn't sound a lot, but when you consider that this flour is used for all of our bread and baking, it adds up to quite a bit over the course of a year. If you choose to use white flour, you'll be able to bake your bread for less, but it won't be anywhere near so nice or so good for you.

To do a bake of three family sized loaves (with each roughly equivalent in size to a purchased 800g loaf) requires about 1.5kg of flour (plus a little bit extra when kneading). To turn this amount of flour into bread requires 20g of dried yeast (64p per 125g), 15ml of vegetable oil (13p per 100ml), and a tablespoon of salt which, at only 38p per kg scarcely has any impact on the overall price. Therefore the cost of the ingredients for a home-made family loaf is in the region of 41p.

Would you believe it?

When we first started buying our flour in bulk 22 years ago, it came in 32kg sacks costing £5 each (i.e. 15½p per kg). This means that the price has risen by 480% since then.

Even the cheapest loaf purchased from one of the main supermarkets is going to cost you 50p, and, to be honest, I wouldn't want to eat it. In truth, cheap wrapped sliced bread isn't really bread at all, merely some sort of flour based product designed as a means of conveying jam to your mouth because you're too polite to just eat the jam by the spoonful straight out of the jar. Some of it isn't even raised with yeast. If you're not used to eating such rubbish it'll undoubtedly give you indigestion when you do. If you are used to eating it, and you stop, you'll suddenly feel a whole lot better than you did before.

A higher quality loaf (of the sort that's actually edible) retails for around £1.10, so two-and-a-half times the cost of home-made bread. Over the course of a year, if your family were to eat a loaf every day, as we do, you'll save around £255 by baking your own. Bread making isn't nearly as time consuming as you might imagine. True, it's quite a long process from beginning to end, but while the

335

bread's rising, and subsequently baking, you can go off and do all sorts of other things. The actual hands on working time required to produce three loaves is only in the region of 10-15 minutes.

To get consistently good results you must use a type of flour that suits your taste, your oven, and your baking style. Once you find one that you like, stick with it if you possibly can. For the sake of simplicity, choose a general purpose flour. Avoid strong bread flour and 100% wholemeal flours, as neither of these will make good cakes, and in the case of wholemeal flour, any bread you make may be a little too solid for some tastes.

The 80% wholemeal flour that we use contains enough bran to give it good flavour and plenty of fibre, but it's not so heavy that it can't be used for general home baking. It's the only type of flour we ever buy. If you can't find anything suitable,

consider mixing wholemeal and white flour to give you an appropriate blend. Actually, you'll probably find that mixing together bags of supermarket white and supermarket brown to give a 50% wholemeal flour will actually cost less than bulk buying, as white flour is so cheap.

A 16kg sack of flour lasts us for about three weeks, and that does all bread, cakes, pastry etc. Not every family will use as much as we do, but once you've settled into a baking routine you'll be able to work out exactly when you need to re-stock, and budget accordingly. If you can't find a friendly baker to supply you with flour, there are a number of online sites where you can place bulk orders. Many specialist millers supply it in 25kg sacks, but they're fairly pricey, and often you have to pay a heavy delivery surcharge. However, there are economical deals to be found if you shop around.

TIP

Bread freezes well, so it may be worthwhile baking larger batches in smaller households, and storing some for later use. Rolls in particular keep well in the freezer, and can be defrosted relatively quickly when required, making them a good standby.

The other essential component of proper bread is the yeast. Without this the dough won't rise. There are various forms available, ranging from fresh (which has a limited shelf life and needs to be 'started' before adding to the flour), through to dried granular yeast which keeps for ages, and can be added to the flour straight from the packet. This latter option is undoubtedly the simplest, and is relatively inexpensive. It's better to buy it in tubs rather than sachets, as some recipes may require a bit more or less than a sachet typically holds.

Dot's favourite is Doves Farm quick yeast, but unfortunately we're unable to source it locally at the time of writing. Having said that, bread yeast is becoming easier to find in shops, particularly since the advent of domestic bread making machines, so you shouldn't have any trouble buying something suitable.

Bread makers

Bread makers have undoubtedly made home-baked bread more popular and accessible, and, dare I say it, rather fashionable too. Suddenly it's become easy to have fresh loaves on hand without any of the perceived hassle of baking it. If you live alone, or have a small family, heating up a whole oven just to bake one loaf doesn't make a lot of sense in terms of energy usage, so a bread maker may be a good investment. However, if you have a higher demand for bread in your household then using a machine that's only ever going to make one loaf at a time is definitely not the answer. You need to bake a whole batch of loaves then use the residual heat in the oven, or a lower shelf at the same time, to cook something else that doesn't require quite such a high temperature, thus making full use of the stove while it's hot. Dot can bake up to four loaves at a time in the Rayburn, and at the rate of consumption of a loaf a day, we'll eat it all before it goes stale.

The other advantage of not using a bread maker is the absence of that irritating little hole that you get in the bottom of a machine-baked loaf.

A basic bread recipe

This recipe makes three family sized loaves, or 24 rolls.

Ingredients

1.5kg flour
1 tbsp cooking oil
1 tbsp salt
2 pints water, approx., at blood heat
Yeast (and possibly a little sugar)

Method

Where the yeast is either fresh or needs reconstituting before use, add about ¾ oz (20g) to the warm water in a jug, together with two teaspoons of sugar, and mix well. Leave this somewhere warm for about 15 minutes, by which time it should have a nice frothy head on it.

In the meantime, put the flour in a very big bowl and mix in the salt and oil. Add the yeasty water to the bowl and mix until all the flour is incorporated. If using easy blend yeast, simply add it directly to the flour, and stir in before adding any water.

Add as much extra water as you need to make a dough. You may end up using as much as 2½ pints in total when using wholemeal flours, but white flour requires less. Knead the dough (either in the bowl or on a floured board) until it's smooth and elastic; 5-8 minutes of kneading will probably be enough.

The dough should half fill the bowl at this stage. If it takes up more space then your bowl isn't big enough! Cover the mixing bowl with a clean tea towel and leave to rise in a warm place. Prepare your bread tins by lightly greasing the insides with a used butter paper or an oil spray then flour all the greased surfaces.

Once the dough fills the bowl (after about an hour), turn it out onto a floured board and knock it back (i.e. thump it about a bit to get the air out). Cut into three equal pieces, shape to fit, pop it in your bread tins, cover and leave to rise for a further twenty minutes or so. You'll know it's ready if it springs back into shape when you gently poke it with your finger. Put the tins of dough into a hot oven (about 230°C), but handle them gently; if the dough sinks when you lift the tins (probably because you've left it to rise too long) then you'll have to turn it out, knock it back, and leave to rise once more.

After about 35 minutes baking, move the loaves around the oven to ensure they get an even colour. When they look done, turn them upside down in the oven (still in their tins) and cook for another 10 minutes. Take the loaves out, remove from the tins (they should just slip out if you greased and floured them properly), and leave to cool, right side up, on a rack.

TIP

If the loaves stick in the tins, pop them back in the oven upside down for another five minutes and try again. If this still doesn't work, dropping the tin on the floor is usually enough to dislodge the loaf (although this might not work if you don't have a hard floor in your kitchen).

If you want to make rolls, rather than loaves, divide the dough into 24 equal pieces at the knocking back stage, knead each piece into a small bun shape then place on baking sheets. Leave plenty of room between them as they'll expand to fill the gaps. Leave to prove until approximately doubled in size, then bake for 25 minutes.

Don't ever wash out your bread tins. To do so will inevitably result in the next few batches of bread sticking in the tins, regardless of how thoroughly you've greased and floured them.

Dot's a bit of a purist when it comes to bread, and insists on always rising it twice. The resulting bread is lighter, has a better flavour and a more elastic texture, and it doesn't really take up any more time doing it this way. Only when she suddenly realises late in the evening that there's no bread for lunch tomorrow does she rise the bread just once. In this situation, knead well after the initial dough mixing, shape, and put straight into tins. Leave until well risen (it will take about an hour) then bake as usual. The bread will be ok, but probably a bit more dense than normal.

Given that making bread at home gives such a good return on the time invested, and is nicer and cheaper than can be bought, there really isn't any excuse for not baking your own. Of course, this philosophy isn't restricted to bread: the same argument can be applied to home baking in general, which includes cakes, biscuits, pastry, puddings and pies. Making full use of the general purpose

plain flour by incorporating any raising agents required, which removes the need to purchase self-raising flour, and by the addition of a fairly small range of general baking ingredients, you should be able to keep the cake tins full. Try to organise your baking in such a way that you can make combined use of the oven, and keep the cost down even more by replacing sugar with honey from your bees, and by using eggs from your own hens or ducks. The use of home-made butter instead of margarine will lift your baking to a whole new level too.

Some ingredients, such as dried vine fruits, will need to be purchased, but make the most of whatever seasonal produce you have to enhance your baking whenever possible. Dried or fresh raspberry, apple pieces or strawberries make a nice addition to muffins, carrot cake is well known, and dried elderberries could be used in any recipe that specifies currants. You are limited only by your imagination.

ALTERNATIVES

Bara Brith

Tea breads are not technically bread, but closer to a moist fruit cake where tea is the liquid ingredient. Generally these are made as loaves, keep quite well, and are excellent spread with home-made butter. This is our version of a true Welsh classic:

Ingredients

6 oz sultanas
8 fl oz cold tea
4 tbsp pumpkin marmalade
(see page 65)

12 oz flour
3 tsp baking powder
6 oz dark soft brown sugar
2 eggs

Method

Put the sultanas and marmalade in a jug. Ordinary Seville orange marmalade will do just as well. Add the tea and leave to soak for 30 minutes. Mix together the dry ingredients and add the contents of the jug and the eggs. Stir well until everything is incorporated then pour the mixture into two lined, medium-sized loaf tins. Bake for about 45 minutes at 170°C. Check the loaves by poking a skewer into the middle. If it comes out clean, they're done. Cool on a wire rack, removing from the tins after ten minutes.

Soda bread

Also known as quick bread, this can be a useful standby when you're really tight for time, as it doesn't require rising with yeast. This means that it can be mixed and baked straight away, and you can be eating it within about 35 minutes. The following recipe is for plain soda bread, but it can be flavoured with all sorts of things. Cheese and mustard are a good combination.

Ingredients

1lb flour
1 tsp salt
1 tsp bicarbonate of soda
12½ fl oz buttermilk (skimmed milk will do if you haven't any buttermilk)

Method

Combine the dry ingredients then add the liquid. Mix well and work the dough until it becomes smooth. Shape into a ball about 7" across, and cut a deep cross into the top. Bake in a preheated oven at 200°C for about 30 minutes until done.

Bun loaf

This yeast-raised fruit bread is perfect for breakfast, and is delicious toasted. The additional ingredients that enrich the dough slow down the action of the yeast, so bear in mind that it'll take much longer to prove than a standard bread mix.

Ingredients

1lb plain flour
½ tsp salt
1 tsp ground mixed spice
2 oz soft brown sugar
2 oz margarine
½ oz instant dried yeast
8 fl oz warm milk
1 large egg, beaten
4½ oz dried mixed fruit
2 tbsp water and 2 tbsp granulated sugar to glaze

Method

Put the flour, salt, spice, brown sugar and yeast into a bowl and stir well. Rub in the fat and add the fruit. Pour in the warm milk and beaten egg, then mix to a dough. Turn it out on the kitchen table and knead for 10 minutes until the dough is smooth and elastic; this type of mixture needs more working than standard bread dough in order to achieve the desired consistency. Leave in a covered bowl, in a warm place, to rise until doubled in size and springy to the touch (probably about two hours, but it could be as much as three). Knock the dough back a little and divide into two equal pieces. Shape and place in small greased bread tins, or as rounds on a

Hot cross buns.

baking sheet if you prefer, and leave to rise again for half-an-hour or so. Bake at about 200°C for 20-30 minutes until well browned. To glaze, put the water and granulated sugar in a small saucepan and bring to boil. Simmer for two minutes and then brush over the top of the loaves as soon as you remove them from the oven.

You can use exactly the same recipe for hot cross buns. To make the crosses, mix up a paste from white flour and water and pipe across the tops of the buns just before you put them in the oven. Bake and glaze as above.

Flatbreads

These are very simple to make, and a good accompaniment for chilli-con-carne, stews and curries.

Ingredients

½ lb brown flour
1 tsp salt
1 tbsp oil (olive oil is best if you have it)
Sufficient water to mix

Method

Put all the ingredients in a bowl and mix to a dough. Knead for 5-10 minutes until the mixture feels soft and a little stretchy then leave to rest for 30 minutes. Cut the dough into eight pieces and roll each one out fairly thin. Spray or wipe the Rayburn hotplate with a little oil, and cook directly on it. Give each flatbread about 2 minutes then flip over to cook the other side until browned. Keep warm in the bottom oven until ready to eat.

Jams, Pickles and Chutneys

However carefully you plan your fruit and vegetable cropping, you'll sometimes harvest more than can be reasonably consumed at the time. As mentioned previously, freezing gives poor results where most vegetables (and some fruits) are concerned, and given that you can't really turn everything into wine, the making of jams, jellies, chutneys and pickles offers an alternative use for the surplus. These preserves store well, so you can really stock up when there's a glut of garden produce.

Equipment

Preserving pan: First things first; invest in a good pan. It's no good trying to make any of these things without one. We use a stainless steel, heavy-bottomed stock-pot for all our preserving needs. The main thing is that you get one that's big enough: about 2 gallons should be sufficient.

Wooden spoon: You'll need a big, long-handled wooden spoon. It's quite a good idea to keep one

specifically for this purpose. Most importantly, don't use the same spoon for stirring pickles and chutneys as you use when making wine or beer. Cross contamination with vinegar will ruin your home-brew.

Jars and lids: Whatever type of preserve you're planning to make, you'll need jars to put it in. Jams, jellies and chutneys require a container with a lid that'll make an airtight seal. For pickles this is desirable, though not always essential. It's possible to purchase glass jars of all shapes and sizes, but there's absolutely nothing wrong with using second hand jam jars, provided that the lids are in good condition. These should be checked before use to make sure that the rubber lining on the underside is intact, and any that show traces of damage or rust should be discarded. Even if you don't buy any food items in glass jars you can ask your friends and neighbours to save their empties for you, rather than putting them in the recycling box.

Jelly bag: Required for making fruit jellies. You could buy one, but it's just as effective to use a linen tea towel, a piece of muslin, or an old cotton pillowcase.

Sugar thermometer: Not essential, but extremely useful when making jams and jellies. The same thermometer can be used if you make toffee or fudge.

Ladle: Just an ordinary soup ladle will do.

Jam funnel: Highly recommended to keep things tidy when you're ladling your finished preserve into jars. Not only does it make it easier to get the stuff into the jars in the first place, it avoids drips and dribbles running down the sides, and reduces the likelihood of bits of fruit getting stuck on the lip of the jar, which would prevent the formation of an airtight seal.

Sticky labels: All home-made preserves should be labelled to show what's in the jar. It's also sensible to include the date on which it was made. Write them in pencil, not ink, so the words won't fade if the label gets damp.

JAM

Jam is simply fruit and sugar boiled up to make a preserve that sets when cooled, and it's the balance between the pectin extracted from the fruit, it's acidity, and the amount of sugar included that defines the quality of the set.

Fruit for jam making needs to be firm, leaning towards the under-ripe, and it should be blemish-free. You can, in theory, use any type of fruit, but not all have the necessary quantities of pectin or the right levels of acid for a successful outcome. Pectin is a naturally occurring 'glue' which helps plants maintain their cellular structure, and it's an essential requirement if your jam is to set. Where the main ingredient is deficient in pectin you'll need to add some extra, either in the form of another fruit that's rich in it, as pectin stock, or by using purchased pectin (such as 'Certo'). Fruits generally considered good sources of pectin include cooking apples, redcurrants, blackcurrants, gooseberries, cooking plums and damsons. All of these should produce well-set jam without the need for any additional pectin. Early blackberries, loganberries, raspberries, dessert plums and gages all have some pectin, and

can set jam, but sometimes a bit extra will make all the difference (e.g. blackberries are often combined with apples). Fruits that'll struggle to make a set jam include cherries, strawberries, late season blackberries and rhubarb.

If you do want to make jam out of these you'll definitely need some extra 'glue'. Generally speaking, pectin-rich fruits also have sufficient acidity for jam making, but where this is low it can be bumped up by adding lemon juice, or a small amount of an acidic fruit such as redcurrants or gooseberries.

TIP
To make pectin stock, collect the peel and cores of apples that you've used for some other purpose and extract the pectin from them by cooking gently in a very small amount of water for about an hour. Strain the liquid through a jelly bag, then cool and subsequently freeze in suitable portions. When making jam, a block of frozen stock can be added to the fruit before stirring in the sugar. It won't affect the flavour of the finished preserve.

Sugar is usually added in the form of white granulated, although you might consider using a special preserving sugar, which is basically the same as the normal stuff, but with added pectin. However, it's more economical to use ordinary sugar together with Certo or home-made pectin stock if you need the extra gelling agents.

Basic method

Sort out your jars and lids before you begin, making sure that

they're clean inside and out, and any old labels have been removed. They must be sterilised, and the simplest way to do this is to put the glass in a medium oven, and put the lids in a bowl and pour boiling water over them. The sterilised jars need to be kept quite warm; if you let them cool down they'll crack when you pour hot jam into them later.

Also, before you begin, put a small plate in the fridge in readiness for testing the setting point of your preserve.

The cooking process is broadly the same for all jam making: put the fruit into your big pan, add water and acid, as per the recipe, and simmer gently until its structure has broken down. Don't skimp on the simmering, as it's this gentle cooking that releases the pectin from the cell walls of the fruit. If the contents of the pan are rather runny (i.e. too great a water content), you'll need to simmer with the lid off for a while to reduce it, otherwise the end result won't be good.

TIP
If you're using fruit that's previously been frozen, don't add any water, and reduce it until it's quite thick before you add the sugar, otherwise the jam just won't set.

Once the contents of the pan has achieved the desired consistency, add the sugar. Stir continuously until it's all dissolved then bring the jam to a rolling boil. Always stirring first, use your thermometer to check the temperature from time to time; it needs to reach 105°C.

If you think it's somewhere near

Ladling jam into hot jars.

ready, retrieve your plate from the fridge and drip a spoonful of jam onto it. Move the preserving pan off the direct heat while you wait for the stuff on the plate to cool – a minute or two will suffice. Then, to test if setting point has been reached, push your finger through the middle of the jam on the plate. If the surface wrinkles, and the gap made doesn't fill up again, it's ready. If neither of these things happens, return the pan to the heat and boil for a little bit longer before repeating the test.

As soon as setting point is reached, line up all the hot jars and fill them to just below the neck using a ladle and jam funnel. Screw the lids on tightly then give all the jars a quick wipe over to remove any sticky splashes, and leave to cool. Once it's completely cold, stick on the labels, and you're done.

TIP

If you've tested your jam and it doesn't seem to have reached setting point, take care when you re-boil to make sure that it doesn't go over 105°C. If it gets too hot it won't set either.

TIP

Sometimes the boiling jam develops a bit of frothy scum on top. Skim this off into a pudding bowl, leave to cool, and eat on fresh bread or scones for tea.

Strawberry and redcurrant jam

Ingredients

2lb strawberries
1lb redcurrants
2 tbsp lemon juice
1 pint water
3lb granulated sugar

Method

Simmer the redcurrants in the water until soft then add the strawberries. Add the lemon juice and cook for about 10 minutes, then mash the fruit and simmer until thick. Add the sugar and stir until dissolved then bring to the boil and test for set when the correct temperature is reached. Ladle into warm jars and seal.

TIP

If your jam doesn't set make light of your failures: jam that fails to set makes a lovely syrup to go on ice cream.

Plum jam

The following recipe is also suitable for bullaces or damsons.

Ingredients

4lb plums
4lb sugar
¾ pint water

Method

Wash and sort through the plums, discarding any that are over-ripe, then place in the pan with the water, bring to boil and simmer until soft. Add the sugar, stirring until it's dissolved, then bring to a rolling boil and cook until setting point is reached. Most of the plum stones will rise to the surface while the jam is boiling, so it's a fairly simple matter to fish them out with a drainer spoon as they appear. Ladle into warm jars and seal.

JELLIES

Fruit jellies are made in much the same way as jam, and are good for utilising fruit that's fiddly or time consuming to prepare. The primary difference is that when making jelly the cooked fruit is strained before the sugar is added, which means that any pips, seeds, or bits of skin will be removed. Jellies often don't set as well as jams, so it's best to stick to pectin-rich fruits (e.g. gooseberries, redcurrants and cooking apples) and hedgerow crops such as rowanberries and crab apples. The aim is to end up with a fruit jelly that's clear, has a good colour, and a rich flavour.

Basic method

The process begins with cooking the fruit to extract the pectin in the same way as for jam. You'll probably need to add some water, but do check the specific recipe first. Simmer gently for an hour or so until the fruit is soft, and then strain.

Scald your jelly bag (or whatever you're going to use) first, and make sure that you've set everything up ready to catch the juice. You can lay the cloth in a colander and sit it over a jug or pan to catch the liquid, or you can tie the bag or cloth and hang it up to drip into a large bowl. You can even buy a special 'jelly bag stand', but they're not really necessary – just improvise something. Leave to drain for about an hour (certainly don't leave it much longer than that) and, no matter how tempting it might be, you mustn't squeeze the bag. If you do, your preserve will be cloudy. Measure the volume of juice then work out how much sugar you will need. Most recipes will tell you to add a certain weight of sugar per pint of liquid. Put the liquid into a clean preserving pan and heat gently, adding the appropriate amount of sugar, and stirring until it's dissolved.

Bring to boil once more, check for setting point and ladle into hot jars, as for jam.

Blackberry and apple

Ingredients

5lb blackberries
4lb cooking apples
1 pint water
14 oz sugar per pint of juice

Method

Wash the blackberries and chop the apples, but don't remove the peel or cores then put in the preserving pan with the water and simmer. Once the fruit is really soft, pour it into the jelly bag and strain for an hour or so. Measure the juice and add the appropriate quantity of sugar then bring to the boil and cook until setting point is reached.

Redcurrant

This is particularly delicious as an accompaniment to roast meat, particularly mutton.

Ingredients

4lb redcurrants
2 pints water
1lb sugar for each pint of juice

Method

The method is the same as for the blackberry and apple jelly.

Pickled shallots.

PICKLES

Essentially these are vegetables or fruit (and sometimes fish or eggs) preserved by immersion in vinegar. The type of vinegar used may vary between recipes, but in most cases it's malt vinegar, often with spices added to improve the flavour of the end product.

Alternatively, distilled vinegar is often used for pickles where the colour and appearance are important, or you could make your own cider or wine vinegar from a failed batch of either of these brews (see page 334).

Turning malt vinegar into spiced pickling vinegar

Put a tablespoon of pickling spice into a litre of vinegar and leave it to steep for two months before use.

If you're not able to wait that long you can heat the vinegar together with the spice until it boils, then remove from the heat and leave to cool with the lid on.

Some people then strain the liquid to remove the spices before use, but we don't.

Peeled shallots sprinkled with salt prior to pickling.

Pickled Onions

You can grow varieties of onions specifically for this purpose, but we find that the shallots work really well. Peeling them isn't a pleasant job, but if you do it with the bulbs under water you'll find that your eyes don't sting half so much.

Method

Put a layer of peeled shallots in a large bowl and sprinkle liberally with table salt. Add some more shallots and then more salt, alternating until they're all used up. Leave to stand for 24 hours. Pour into a sieve or colander to drain, and then wash the salt off with lots of cold water. Do this thoroughly otherwise you may find that your finished pickle is so salty that it's inedible. Once the shallots are free of salt, drain then pack carefully into jars. Pour in the spiced vinegar, taking care to ensure that there are no air bubbles in the jar, then seal. Keep for a few months at least, before eating. That's all there is to it.

TIP

If you prefer your shallots a little less crunchy you can use hot vinegar to fill the jars.

There are several classic pickles including red cabbage and beetroot (which is cooked before the addition of vinegar) that are made in essentially the same way, but below is a recipe for something a little different:

Crunchy courgette pickle

This is an easy pickle to make that looks attractive in the jar. Cucumbers can be used equally successfully.

Ingredients

10lb courgettes, sliced as thinly as possible
2½ lb onions, sliced
Salt
4 pints distilled vinegar
2 tbsp white mustard seed
3 tsp celery salt
3tsp turmeric
3lb granulated sugar

Method

Place a layer of sliced courgette and onion in a large dish and sprinkle with salt. Repeat these layers until all the vegetables are salted and leave to stand overnight. Drain any liquid from the courgettes using a colander and wash well in cold running water to remove the excess salt – you can taste a bit to see if enough salt has been removed – then squeeze out as much liquid as you can. Boil up the vinegar, sugar and spices, and pour over the courgette and onion mix then pack into warm sterilised jars and seal.

TIP

As an addition you can include a few pieces of red and yellow capsicum pepper with the sliced courgette or cucumber, to give an attractive appearance.

TIP

When you've eaten the last pickled onion from the jar, don't throw the vinegar away. Strain it and use it again.

Fruit and vegetable gluts can be preserved in the form of jams and chutney.

CHUTNEY

Chutney making isn't an exact science, and, unlike jam, if you don't get it quite right it'll still be chutney, even if the flavour isn't what you expected. Generally speaking, the main vegetable or fruit (which will give the finished product its name) is chopped and cooked together with vinegar and a selection of other ingredients (usually, but not exclusively, onions, apples, dried fruit, sugar, and spices) to produce a condiment that has a thick consistency and a well rounded flavour. Most chutney needs time to mature before you start eating it; about two months is sufficient, but longer is better.

We tend to use dark brown sugar as it produces chutney that has sweetness without being too sugary, and gives a lovely rich colour. The exception to this is where ripe tomatoes are the main ingredient, in which case granulated sugar would be added instead. As far as vinegar is concerned, the same guidelines apply as for pickles. Spices can be used whole or ground, but the latter is probably more appropriate as it'll disperse more evenly through the whole batch.

TIP

Where a chutney recipe specifies sultanas or raisins, use the best quality you can afford, otherwise you might find that the flavour of your finished product has musty undertones. We avoid this problem by using dried pitted dates instead.

Basic method

Some chutney recipes give quite detailed instructions on cooking times, and the order in which different ingredients should be added. However, in our experience you won't go far wrong if you simply pile everything into a big pan, stir well to mix it all up then simmer until cooked. Once everything is soft and the consistency is even, it's done. However, it's quite possible that the chutney may still be too runny at this point, so just leave it to bubble with the lid off. Dot often leaves it overnight on the cool side of the Rayburn to reduce. Once it's really thick you can pot it into warm, sterilised jars and seal.

Apple chutney

A firm family favourite that's quite quick to make, and simple too.

Ingredients

7lb cooking apples
1lb dried pitted dates
3lb dark brown sugar
1½ oz ground ginger
1 oz garlic
1 tsp mixed spice

345

A selection of jams, pickles and chutneys in recycled jars.

Beetroot and Ginger Chutney

(We find this is a good imitation of Branston pickle.)

Ingredients

3lb cooked beetroot
1 lb onions
1 lb cooking apples, peeled and cored.
1 lb stoned dates
3 tablespoons ground ginger
2 lb dark brown sugar
2 pints vinegar
1 tsp salt

Method

Peel the cooked beetroot, cut into small chunks and place in the preserving pan. Chop up the onions, apples and dates and add to the beetroot, together with all the other ingredients. Mix, cover and bring to the boil, then cook steadily until it looks pulpy. Remove the lid and reduce until the required consistency is reached. Ladle into warm jars.

Seal in the usual way.

1 tsp cayenne pepper
½ tsp salt
2 pints malt vinegar

Method

Prepare the apples by peeling and removing the cores then chop roughly and add to the pan. Chuck in all the other ingredients and mix well then bring to the boil and simmer with the lid on until the apple is soft. Remove the lid and reduce until the required consistency is reached then bottle in the usual way.

Ripe tomato relish

It might seem like a bit of a waste to use ripe tomatoes in chutney, but sometimes you just get more ripe fruit at one time than you can comfortably eat. This relish is delicious and goes well with cheese, cold meat and sausages.

Ingredients

12lb ripe tomatoes
1lb onions
1½ lb granulated sugar
¼ oz paprika or cayenne pepper
½ oz salt
1 pint distilled vinegar

Method

Skin the tomatoes by pouring boiling water over them – the skin should then peel off easily by hand if they are ripe – and cut them up. Chop the onions and put them in a preserving pan with the tomatoes. Add the sugar, spices and salt, pour in the vinegar, and boil until everything's soft. Remove the lid and reduce. This may take quite a long time as the tomatoes will release a lot of liquid. Bottle as usual when sufficiently thickened.

Section Five
Wild Harvest

Rabbits, Game, Deer and Wildfowl

"Subsistence hunters are amongst the happiest, most respectful and knowledgeable people that I have met." Guy Grieve

Almost without exception, the 'how-to-do-it' books written during the golden age of self-sufficiency (i.e. 1970s to early 1980s) had fairly substantial sections on the hunting and trapping of wild animals for food, yet this information generally isn't included (or at best, is merely touched upon,) in more recent publications. Even new editions of older works have had these sections revised and curtailed. John Seymour's *Complete Book of Self-Sufficiency* is a case in

point – the original version had a full four pages concerned with the shooting or snaring of all kinds of game, including deer and pheasants, but in the more recent edition (published in 2003) this has been reduced to a mere two. Why is this? I can only put it down to some kind of misguided political correctness, which assumes that the modern day self-supporter doesn't like to consider such things. Or perhaps it's an attempt to make these publications a little more palatable to a largely urban readership. Either way, I think they've got it wrong.

At any rate, I can assure you of one thing – it's not because we've

eaten all the wildlife! Most of the traditional quarry species are thriving in the UK, together with an interesting 'newcomer' – the wild boar.

I don't believe that there can be any ethical objections to the self-supporter routinely sourcing some of his meat from the wild, particularly when doing so can be combined with pest control (e.g. protection of his own and / or his neighbours' crops), provided, of course, that it's carried out humanely. Neither is there any reason why you shouldn't enjoy the thrill of the chase, (the primitive instinct of the hunter lies very close to the surface in all of us,) but to kill for sport alone is an abomination. Shoot to eat, or to protect your livelihood (e.g. in the case of a marauding fox in the vicinity of your poultry run, or the carrion crows that attack your newborn lambs) and you won't go far wrong.

(Ironically, although sport is considered to be one of the 'good reasons' for the granting of a firearms certificate, shooting for the pot is not! What is the world coming to?).

Shotguns and other firearms

For the sake of simplicity, we can divide the available armoury into four main categories: shotguns, rimfire rifles, centrefire rifles, and air rifles.

The inside of the barrel of a shotgun is a smooth cylinder, and it fires a charge of shot consisting of sometimes as many as 400 tiny pellets. Range is relatively short (maybe 40 yards optimum), but the spread of the pellets gives a fairly wide margin of error, and the ability to take quarry on the move. The rifle, on the other hand, fires a single projectile through a spirally grooved (or 'rifled') barrel, the grooves imparting a spin to the speeding bullet or pellet, which helps to keep it going in a straight line once it's left the muzzle of the gun. The use of a rifle is a precision exercise, and the potential effective range is many times greater than that attainable with a shotgun (except in the case of low-powered air rifles).

For the benefit of anyone who might be thinking pure survival tactics, I'd better just point out that hunting with a bow and arrow is illegal in the UK.

Shotguns

The size of a shotgun is denoted by its bore, i.e. the internal diameter of the barrel. It is calculated thus: if a single lead ball were made to exactly fit the barrel, how many of those lead balls would together weigh 1lb? Therefore higher numbers denote smaller diameter barrels. However, very small diameters are specified in fractions of an inch (e.g. .410). Just to confuse the matter further, there's usually a constriction, known as 'choke', at the muzzle end of the barrels. The choke restricts the spread of the group of pellets, so the tighter the choke, the greater the effective range. Double-barrelled guns will have a different degree of choke in each barrel, and some shotguns may have 'variable chokes' that can be screwed into the muzzle(s). The choice of choke will depend on the type of shooting for which the gun is intended – snap shooting bolting rabbits in

dense undergrowth will require a much more open choke than, say, taking long range shots at flighting wildfowl on the marshes. Shotguns may be single- or double-barrelled, with the configuration of the two barrels being either side-by-side or over-and-under. Some single-barrelled shotguns have a 'pump action', and a magazine capable of holding a number of rounds. This is restricted to three cartridges on an ordinary UK shotgun certificate. The quintessential English sporting shotgun is the double-barrelled, side-by-side 12-bore. This gauge is popular the world over for small game such as pheasants, rabbits and pigeons. Their popularity means they're very easy (and cheap) to buy second hand – less than £150 would get you a serviceable bit of kit – and cartridges, in a range of different shot sizes, are readily available. The 'standard' 12-bore cartridge contains 32 grams (1⅛ oz) of No.6 shot (i.e., 304 pellets, each measuring 2.6mm in diameter), which is adequate for most situations. (Although I'd always keep a box of larger shot cartridges, such as No.1 or BB, in stock, ready for when Charlie tries to raid the hen coop). The shot are usually made of lead, although alternative products (usually steel) must be used for wildfowling (i.e. shooting ducks and geese in wetland habitats).

The drawback to the 12-bore is that it is large, fairly heavy, and very noisy. One shot is enough to startle the whole countryside, so the element of stealth that's so essential when carrying out pest control on a small acreage is immediately lost. However, with more and more women taking up shooting these days, many smaller gauge shotguns such as the 16-,

20- and 28-bore are coming on to the second hand market, although I believe that the ideal calibre for the smallholder is the diminutive .410, the traditional poacher's tool!

Rimfire rifles

The little .22LR is the most commonly used small-bore rifle in the world. Although there are other .22-calibre rimfires (such as the WMR), the LR (or 'Long Rifle') is the one that nearly everyone cuts their teeth on. They're cheap to buy second hand (£100 would get you something pretty good), and there's plenty to choose from. At one time, most livestock farmers would have owned a .22LR, as it was considered to be the most suitable gun for humane destruction of casualty animals, and for carrying out home slaughter. However, this is no longer the case.

Theoretically the .22LR could be (and has been) used on any UK quarry, if you could get close enough, but this wouldn't be legal or humane. Basically, it's a pest control round, and is the ideal gun for rabbiting. Some police forces will also allow the .22LR to be used on foxes, but others won't. In most cases it will just specify 'vermin' on the licence.

Most of the readily available .22LR ammunition is 'subsonic', in so far as the projectile (which weighs something in the region of 2 grams) travels slightly slower than the speed of sound, at around 1,050 feet per second. Without the supersonic 'crack' experienced with faster rounds as they break the sound barrier, .22LR subs are extremely quiet, and the addition of a sound moderator to the barrel of the rifle makes it almost silent. This means that rabbits can be

Main: *.22 rimfire rifle.*
Notice the torch mounted above
the 'scope to enable night shooting. **Inset:** *Segmented ammunition.*

picked off one after another, without alarming the rest of the colony, and without disturbing anything or anyone in the surrounding countryside.

There are downsides, however – the relatively slow bullet speed means that it has a frightening tendency to ricochet, and the trajectory (flight path) of the .22LR is, at best, described as 'rainbow-like', meaning that it's essential to become fully familiar with the required degree of hold-over at different ranges before attempting to hunt live quarry. The risk of ricochet can be reduced, to an extent, by the use of segmented ammunition (which will also increase the terminal effect on your quarry), but familiarity with the trajectory can only be gained through experience. Thankfully .22LR ammunition is remarkably cheap (around 7p per shot), so you can well afford to spend some time punching holes in paper targets before taking to the field. The optimum effective range of the .22LR would be in the region 50-80 yards, although shots up to – and exceeding – 100 yards may

successfully be taken by skilled marksmen.

Despite the overriding popularity of the .22LR, there's a new kid on the rimfire block – the .17HMR. Often described as the 'Marmite calibre' (you either love it or you hate it), the .17HMR is based on a .22 cartridge case necked down to take a .17 inch diameter projectile. The result is a bullet that flies very fast (around 2,550 feet per second) and very flat, giving outstanding accuracy at extreme ranges. The risk of ricochet – always the bugbear of rimfire rounds – is almost completely eliminated, due to the fact that frangible bullets travelling at that speed simply break up on impact. So what's not to like? Well, for one thing, it's noisy. Even with a sound moderator fitted, the crack of the supersonic round may be enough to startle the bunnies. Also, the light weight of the bullet (approximately half that of the .22LR) means that its accuracy is adversely affected by wind and rain. The ammunition, which is expensive, has been subject to some quality control issues, with

occasional split cases and blocked barrels, and the destructive nature of the disintegrating bullets means that unless rabbits are shot in the head only, the carcasses will be more or less inedible.

Centrefire rifles

Unless you've got deer on your land (or are culling deer for a neighbour in return for a share of the venison), or are going into fox control in a big way, or have wild boar rampaging through your vegetables, you're not going to be considering centrefire rifles. Having said that, with appropriate training, and assuming you live in the right sort of area, there's no reason why semi-professional deer management couldn't form an interesting sideline to running a smallholding.

A good entry level centrefire calibre is the .243, which is legal for use on all types of deer found in the UK, and foxes too. Now, some folk may tell you that the .243 is unnecessarily large for taking the smallest species such as muntjac and Chinese water deer, and others will say it's "not man enough" to tackle a big red stag, but the fact remains that it's a good all round general purpose deer calibre, ideal for the occasional user who hasn't the luxury of being able to afford a cabinet full of specialist rifles for different purposes. A lot of people start off with the .243 before moving on to other calibres as their interest develops, which means that there's always plenty of them on the second hand market, and because they're so popular the ammunition is readily available.

One significant difference between rimfire and centrefire cartridge cases is that the latter can be reloaded, which might appeal to the waste-conscious self-supporter.

Air rifles

Personally, I won't consider hunting with an air rifle, and this is why: once upon a time, when I was in my mid-teens, an old buck rabbit was feeding in the lettuce field alongside my parents' driveway. I stalked him with my air rifle, well within range, took careful aim, fired and missed. The next morning, and every morning for a week, I repeated the exercise with the same result, merely startling the rabbit and making him bolt for cover. By the weekend I'd had enough of this ritual, so I borrowed my father's 12-bore and shot him dead. Success at last, although on processing the rabbit I discovered five airgun pellets – one for each day of the week – lodged under his skin, and all within the supposed 'kill zone' of the chest and neck. Since then I haven't felt comfortable with the use of air rifles for hunting live quarry in the field, and mine is now reserved for 'light duties' such as humane dispatch of small vermin at point-blank range (e.g. rats caught in live traps). I'm also inclined to be sceptical when I hear people talk about having made a 'clean miss'. How do they know?

Having said all that, it was a long time ago, and there are some very good – and very powerful – air rifles on the market nowadays, which can be extremely effective in the right hands.

Air rifles can be categorised in 3 ways: firstly, by calibre; secondly by their mechanics; and thirdly by power.

• **Calibre:** The most popular airgun calibres are .22 and .177.

Main: *.243 centrefire rifle equipped with 'scope, bipod and sound moderator.* **Inset:** *Some popular calibres and cartridges (L-R): .410 shotgun, 3" case; .410 shotgun, 2.5" case; 12 bore shotgun, 2" case; .243 centrefire rifle; .22LR rimfire rifle; .177 airgun pellets.*

The .22 is generally reckoned to be the best hunting calibre (because the pellets, although slower, are heavier, and therefore retain more energy), although I've heard people recommend the .177 for shooting pigeons due to the fact that the smaller-sized pellets are better at penetrating dense feathers.

• **Mechanics:** Airguns may be powered by a large spring, or by a reservoir of compressed air. In the case of spring-operated rifles, it's necessary to compress the spring before each shot, by either breaking the barrel or by the use of a separate lever, depending on the specific design. On firing the gun, the spring is released, which drives forward the piston and hence expels the pellet. On the compressed air models, known as 'pre-charged pneumatics' (or PCPs) there is a small cylinder that needs to be charged from a diver's bottle, or by using a hand pump. The number of shots that can be fired from each refilling varies from as many as 500, down to under 50 in the case of high-powered rifles.

PCP air rifles are generally considered superior to springers, and are quieter too. With a sound moderator fitted they're almost silent. They're also more expensive.

• **Power:** Air rifles delivering 12ft lbs of energy (giving a muzzle velocity of 580 feet per second in the case of .22, or 800 feet per second for .177) or under, are, at the time of writing, exempt from any kind of licensing*. However, airguns with more power than this will require a section 1 firearms licence. There are no limits on the quantity of airgun ammunition you may buy or hold in stock.

The attraction of the 12ft lbs air rifle to the smallholder is understandable – he can wander into his local gun shop, and, without any of the preamble usually associated with purchasing a firearm, he can buy exactly what he wants, together with a lifetime's supply of pellets, and wander out again. Thereafter he's beholden to no-one, which is something that appeals to the self-sufficient mindset. Provided that the user is well aware of its limitations (e.g. short range), and puts in plenty of practice (don't even think of going hunting until you can regularly place five consecutive shots onto a ½" target at an appropriate distance), it ought to be capable of taking rabbits and other small game out to about 30 yards but I have my reservations. (*NB Since this was written airgun licensing laws have been introduced in Scotland).

The higher-powered air rifles (known as 'FAC Air', because of the need for a Firearms Certificate in order to acquire one) are capable of delivering muzzle velocities of up to 1,030 feet per second, which is only marginally slower than the subsonic .22LR. Given that .22 airgun pellets only cost about £12 for a tin of 500, doesn't this make FAC Air the obvious choice? Well, it's not the speed of the projectile as it leaves the end of the barrel that's important, but what it's doing when it reaches its target. Although the muzzle velocities are almost the same, by the time it connects with a rabbit at, say, 65 yards, the .22 airgun pellet (which weighs less than a gram) will only be travelling at 550 feet per second, delivering 11ft lbs of energy, whereas the rimfire bullet will be travelling at around 930 feet per second and delivers 77 ft lbs of energy. Therefore, although the .22LR ammunition is 3 times the price, it's giving you much more than 3 times the stopping power.

Firearms and the law

It's not my intention here to go into any great detail regarding firearms law. You can find all that out for yourself, if and when you decide

to take up shooting. What I will do, however, is to explain the basic licensing procedure:

There are two main types of licence that will be of interest to the self-supporter – the Section 1 (Firearms) Certificate and the Section 2 (Shotgun) Certificate – both of which are issued by your regional police force.

The granting of a shotgun certificate is relatively straightforward. You submit the completed application form, together with a number of passport-sized photographs, and the name, address and signature of an appropriate referee, and, provided that you have no previous convictions, or a history of domestic violence or mental health problems or anything like that, your certificate will be granted. You do not need to give a 'good reason' for the possession of a shotgun, and nor do you need to provide any evidence that you have access to land to shoot on. You will, however, need to demonstrate that you have made suitable arrangements for the safe storage of your shotgun(s), which generally means you'll need to install a BS7558:1992 standard gun cabinet.

The certificate allows you to acquire any number of shotguns (and any amount of ammunition for them), provided that they fall within the definition of Section 2 of the firearms act, and to shoot them over any land where you have the authority, or have been given permission, to do so. On that land you may pursue any of the quarry species that can legally be shot with this type of gun, subject, of course, to any close seasons or other restrictions that might be temporarily or permanently

imposed, and to the permission of the landowner.

The procedure for the granting of a firearms certificate is more complex. This time, your application form and photographs will need to be endorsed by two referees, and you will also need to provide a 'good reason' for possessing the firearm(s) that you wish to obtain. You must specify precisely what calibre you would like to acquire, together with the amount (and type) of ammunition you may want to purchase or store at any one time. Sound moderators will need to be specified separately. You also have to provide details of the land that you will be shooting over (which will be checked by the police to ensure that it is suitable for the safe use of the calibre that you're requesting), and list the quarry that you intend to shoot. Before your certificate is granted you will be visited at home, and interviewed by a Firearms Examination Officer, who will also check your storage facilities. You might be required to install two cabinets, in order to be able to keep the guns and their ammunition separately.

Your certificate may be granted subject to certain 'conditions', the most common being that you can only use it on land that has been deemed suitable by the Chief Officer of Police for the area where the land is situated. This is known as a 'closed ticket'. After a year or two you might be able to apply for your certificate to be 'opened', which will then allow you to form your own judgement as to whether or not a certain piece of land is appropriate for the safe use of that specific calibre of firearm.

The firearms certificate only allows you to acquire the guns specified on it. If you wish to purchase additional Section 1 firearms, or you want to replace one of your guns (even if the replacement is of the same calibre), you will need to apply for a variation to your certificate. You will also need to make a request in writing if you want additional quarry species to be listed on your certificate. At the time of writing, the cost of an application (or renewal) for either a shotgun or a firearms licence is not extortionate, and can be reduced by applying for the two simultaneously. Once granted, the certificates remain valid for five years, unless revoked.

Rifle accessories

• **Telescopic sight:** Rifles are invariably fitted with telescopic sights nowadays, and quite rightly so – we owe it to our quarry to be as efficient as possible, and good quality optics make all the difference. Many 'scopes have a variable degree of magnification, although in all honesty, once you've discovered the setting that suits you best, you probably won't change it again! However, in low light conditions, such as when rabbiting at dusk, it can be helpful to wind down the magnification as daylight fades, enabling you to bag another couple of bunnies before complete darkness descends. In addition, some 'scopes have an illuminated centre spot, which is also beneficial at dusk. The reticle (crosshairs) may include a pattern of dots or gradations which are used for estimating range and hold-over.

Something in the region of 3-9 x 50 would be more than adequate for most situations, and always buy the best you can afford.

• **Sound moderator:** Until relatively recently it was very difficult to get permission to have a sound moderator on your rifle. However, in the light of health and safety concerns regarding loss of hearing amongst professional stalkers engaged in deer control on Forestry Commission land, the Home Office guidelines were amended, and their use is now more or less universal.

• **Sling:** Although a shotgun can comfortably be carried, broken, in the crook of your arm, the same cannot be said for a rifle. Therefore it's usual to fit a sling so you can carry it over your shoulder. Whether or not it should be carried muzzle up or muzzle down is a matter of much debate. Personally I carry mine muzzle end up, as it feels more comfortable that way. If you're worried about rainwater entering the barrel, or the possibility of getting a twig in it as you move through woodland, put a small piece of insulation tape over the end. There's no need to remove it before taking a shot – it'll be blown away as soon as you pull the trigger.

• **Bipod:** It takes a lot of practice, and a very steady hand, to be able to shoot confidently and effectively without any kind of additional support for the rifle. Therefore, in the interests of improved accuracy (and humanity) it's quite in order to make use of a bipod. The bipod attaches to the front sling stud, and is a great aid to precision when shooting from the prone position. Standing shots may be similarly supported by the use of 'sticks', which might, quite literally, consist of a couple of straight hazel sticks cut from the hedgerow and joined near the top with a piece of old inner-tube.

• **Lamp:** A small but powerful, narrow-beamed torch which clamps onto the top of the telescopic sight is just the thing for shooting rabbits at night with the .22LR.

In conclusion…
At the very least, I think that the self-supporter should equip himself with a double-barrelled .410 shotgun chambered to take 3″ magnum cartridges, and a .22LR rimfire rifle. It's interesting to note that the 'Savage Survival Gun - Model 24', issued to members of the USAF during World War II, was a double-barrelled firearm in over-and-under configuration, with the top barrel being .22 rifle, and the bottom being .410 shotgun. Its purpose was to enable ditched aircrews to live off the land, and if that's not self-sufficiency, what is? However, if force of circumstances dictates that only one gun can be acquired, it would have to be the .410.

TIP
Never refer to your gun as a weapon – it isn't! It only becomes one when placed in the hands of a soldier or a lunatic.

THE QUARRY

This isn't intended to be a comprehensive list of all the species of birds and animals that you can legally shoot or trap in the UK. There are, for example, 'sporting' birds such as the snipe and woodcock, which simply don't fall within the scope of the self-supporter's radar. They're beautiful to observe in their natural environment, cause no damage, and their small size means that they're not even worth shooting on culinary grounds – a dainty morsel,

Sporting rights

Even though you may own the land, you do not necessarily own the sporting rights. This is something that your solicitor should have checked up on at the time of purchase. Have a look at your title deeds, and if you see something like *"The land in this title is subject to the following rights reserved unto the vendor and his successors in title the exclusive right of preserving shooting hunting fishing fowling and sporting over and taking all and all manner of game hares rabbits and wildfowl and fish from the property, and the right to enter upon the property for all or any of the purposes aforesaid"* then, basically, this means that a previous owner (not necessarily the one you bought the holding from) has retained the sporting rights. In most cases this will date back to the time when many small farms and smallholdings were part of large country estates. When the estate was broken up and farms sold off to the tenants, the original landowning family will have kept the shooting rights, which they may then either use for their own recreational purposes, lease to a syndicate, or sell to another individual or company. The owner or tenant of the sporting rights has full rights of access over all parts of your land, and if you shoot any game on your own land you could be prosecuted for poaching.

It all sounds rather archaic I know, but if you do find yourself in this situation then you're just going to have to learn to live with it, I'm afraid. Get to know the people involved, and you'll probably find they're quite willing to discuss ways to ensure that the level of disturbance is kept to a minimum, and will probably heed your requests to keep out of certain specific areas (such as the garden). They may also be prepared to carry out certain works, such as installing new gates and stiles, fencing, tree planting etc., which will be to your mutual benefit. Other benefits to living on a properly managed shoot include a reduced fox population (good news for your chickens!) and a regular supply of courtesy game for your dinner table.

perhaps, but hardly the sort of dish that's going to feed a hungry family! What we're looking at here are primarily the edible 'pest' species, where control is justified on the grounds of preventing damage to crops or vulnerable habitat, or those animals and birds that are found in sufficient abundance that a regular harvest can reasonably (and economically) be taken, often to the benefit of the remainder of the population in that area (e.g. in the case of deer, where the general health of the wild herd may be maintained or improved by the removal of the aged and the infirm, and by reducing overall numbers to a level that their territory can sustain).

Rabbits

Despite repeated decimation by myxomatosis, the bunny always bounces back, forming the mainstay of the self-supporter's wild harvest. Myxi seems to be more or less endemic in the rabbit population these days, and flares up at roughly seven year intervals. So, sometimes you might have plenty of rabbits on your patch, and sometimes none at all! After each outbreak it may take a few years for the population to build back up to shootable levels. When at full strength, rabbits pose a very real threat to the productivity of your smallholding. It's estimated that seven rabbits will eat as much grass as one sheep, and even a single rabbit can wreak havoc in the vegetable garden. If you multiply that by the fact that there are around 50 million rabbits in the UK, you'll understand why they're the number one agricultural pest, causing damage to crops and pasture valued at about £100 million per year!

The best way to get rabbits is to lie in wait for them on summer evenings with the .22LR on a bipod. Provided that you stay still you don't need much cover – maybe just a rise in the ground or a clump of nettles to lurk behind will be fine. Reconnoitre the area first, during daylight hours, in order to pace out the exact distance between the warren and your favoured hidey-hole, and to ensure that you'll be firing into a safe backstop.

Having been laid up all day, rabbits are very keen to feed at dusk, so even if you've disturbed them while getting into position, you'll seldom have to wait more than twenty minutes or so for them to reappear, and then you simply pick them off one by one as they emerge, until it's too dark to carry on. Head shots are preferable, although shots to the chest are equally effective. Leave the dead rabbits where they lie, and collect them all up at the end.

Rabbits are also active at dawn, although if they're startled and run back to their burrows they'll usually remain down below, having just spent the night feeding.

Rabbitting with the .22LR

Emptying a rabbit's bladder.

Ferrets, nets and snares

Ferrets and ferreting: Ferrets are likeable creatures that deserve a place in the smallholding menagerie. Quite apart from their usefulness at times when the rabbit population is high, they can also be used to control rats, and make good waste disposal units for all the by-products of your poultry enterprise, such as cracked eggs, casualty birds and offal. And when meat is scarce they can be fed reasonably cheaply on cat biscuits.

Keep them in a dry, spacious hutch, with cosy nest quarters and a large play area, provide a few bits of plastic drainpipe to keep them amused, and above all *keep them clean*, and they'll give good service for years. Jills (females) can be housed in pairs or groups, but the male, or hob, needs his own quarters, as two hobs kept together may fight. If the hob is kept with the jill(s) then obviously they will breed, and he is then rather inclined to eat his own offspring. (Having said that, a couple of the hobs I've had have made exemplary fathers, and would sleep in the same nest as the jill and her kits with no sign of harming them at all.) Handle your ferrets frequently, especially the kits as they're growing up, and they'll always be tame and trustworthy. You also need to accustom them to being carried in a small box or bag, as that's how you'll transport them to the field.

Therefore 'walked up' shooting is more productive in the mornings, taking one rabbit from each spot and moving on. Use the .22LR off sticks (or off hand, if you've got the skill) on more open ground, where you'll be shooting sitting targets at longer ranges, or the .410 if expecting short range shots at bolting rabbits in broken cover.

At night rabbits can be shot by using a lamp attached to the 'scope of the .22LR, or, if you have an accomplice, using the .410, with one of you shooting and the other holding the torch. Dot once shot seventeen rabbits in twenty-seven minutes like that.

Everything you read about preparing wild rabbits for the pot will tell you to paunch them straight away, but I don't bother.

It's usually pretty late in the evening by the time I get back from a shooting session, so I just empty their bladders and hang them in a cool place overnight, ready to deal with in the morning. Also it's much easier (and cleaner) if you skin a rabbit *before* you paunch it, which again is contrary to what many writers suggest. Skinned and gutted, and ready for the pot, an adult wild rabbit carcass will weigh something in the region of 1kg (just over 2lb). (See pages 308 - 310).

Often I don't paunch the rabbits at all, or even completely skin them. I simply peel back the pelt from the hind legs, which I cut off and put to one side, and then I feed the rest of the rabbit – skin and guts and all – to my sheepdogs. This is a win-win situation, as we get the prime joints for ourselves, and a free meal for the dogs. They do very well on it too, as it's a completely natural diet.

The essence of hunting rabbits with ferrets is that the ferret explores the underground network of burrows that makes up the warren, and you catch the rabbits as they're flushed out. Contrary to popular belief, ferrets don't need to be hungry to work – their naturally inquisitive behaviour

Ferrets deserve a place in the smallholding menagerie.

A correctly set purse net.

means that no tunnel will remain un-searched. In fact, hungry ferrets are a nuisance as they're inclined to kill underground and lay up. Usually it's the more agile jills that are used for hunting, as, quite apart from anything else, they're generally lithe enough to fit through the meshes of your nets without getting in a frightfully bad-tempered tangle.

Bolting rabbits can be taken with a shotgun, but this is noisy, and, unless there are several of you and you're all good shots, quite a few will be missed. There's also the risk that someone will get carried away and shoot one of your ferrets as she pops up to see what's going on. A better (and quieter) method is to use purse nets. A purse net, strategically placed over the entrance to a burrow, works on the drawstring bag principle. A bolting rabbit hitting the centre of your net

is neatly bundled up in an instant, ready for you to dispatch.

The correct way to set a purse net is to have it draped loosely over the hole, with the peg knocked into the ground above, and the bottom ring pushed lightly into the soil just inside the mouth of the burrow. It's crucial that you cover all the entrances to the warren because, if you miss one, you can bet your bottom dollar that that's where the rabbits will exit! Most warrens have a hidden bolt hole at some distance from the main entrances, so you must find this and cover it too.

Once you've set all your nets, and waited a while for the rabbits to settle down after the disturbance you've been creating over their heads, you can enter your ferrets. If a ferret refuses to go below, and perhaps fluffs up her tail like a bottlebrush, don't force her in – it could mean there's a badger down there, in which case you'll

have to give up and go elsewhere. Hopefully, though, your ferrets will snake away down the tunnels, and the hunt is on!

For a little while nothing will happen above ground. Then you'll begin to hear the drumming of rabbits' feet, and all of a sudden they're hitting your nets! You have to work quickly and quietly, killing the rabbits and re-setting the nets, and all the time keeping an eye open for your ferrets re-emerging – you don't want them setting off for the next warren on their own. To kill a wild rabbit, hold it by its back legs and dislocate its neck, rather in the same manner as for poultry. This can be done while they're still in the net.

At the end of the hunt it's essential that you collect up all your nets, as, left behind, they pose a real danger to wildlife and farm animals. It's also essential that you take all your ferrets home with you. Should one of the team fail to put in an appearance, the best thing is to block up all the holes except one, and just inside that one (effectively blocking the entrance) you place a cage trap baited with a nice piece of fresh rabbit liver, and containing some soft bedding material. Nine times out of ten that'll do the trick. The alternative is to dig down and get her out, having first located her using a 'line ferret' – a grumpy old hob on the end of a long piece of string – but it's pretty tedious work. Ferrets can be fitted with radio transmitter collars, which greatly simplifies the matter of locating one that's gone missing below ground.

The season for hunting with ferrets is during winter, when there shouldn't be any baby rabbits to cause distractions. However, rabbits appear to be breeding more or less all year round these days, so it seems that there's always the risk of your ferrets coming across youngsters, which they'll almost invariably kill below ground.

Long netting: A long net is precisely that. Sometimes up to 90 metres in length, they're set up between the rabbits' burrows and their feeding grounds, to intercept them as they race for home. Like the fishing nets described on page 365 the long net is 'set on by the third', meaning that it takes 150 yards of netting to make a working net of 100 yards. This gives it the required degree of bagginess. Similarly, although the panel of netting measures about 62" wide, the working height of the net is only 30". The net has strong head and foot lines, and is supported by lightweight stakes (similar to flexinet fence posts) at about 7 yard intervals.

Usually the net is set up at night,

very quietly, between the feeding rabbits and the hedgerow where they live. Given that you'll be doing this in the dark, it's something that needs a lot of practice first, otherwise some horrendous tangles will ensue. Working a long net is generally a two man job – once the net is in position, one member of the team waits at one end, with his finger resting on the head line, while the other person takes the long route around to the other side of the feeding rabbits, without disturbing them. Then he begins to walk steadily down the field towards the net, zig-zagging back and forth, and maybe pulling along a small tin containing a couple of stones on the end of a piece of string. The man by the net will feel the vibration as a rabbit hits, whereupon he can quickly dart along the length, locate the rabbit, kill it, disentangle the net, and return to his former position to await the next one.

Another way of using a long net is to set it out in the daytime and then furl it up so that the rabbits pass underneath it on their way out to graze. Then, when you return at night, you pull a trip line which allows the net to drop down into a working position. Not surprisingly, this method is called 'drop netting'.

Long nets measuring 25 to 100 yards in length cost less than £1 per yard to buy, or you can get a roll of nylon twine and a netting needle and make your own.

Snares: Having spent a lot of time trying to perfect the art, I've reached the conclusion that snares are neither efficient nor humane as a method of catching rabbits, so I won't recommend their use. The only time that I will consider

setting a snare is when I'm pulling out all the stops to deal with a fox that's been giving us trouble. All snares must be free-running (i.e. they mustn't incorporate any kind of locking device), and should be checked at least three times a day.

Pheasants

If you live in an area where pheasants are reared and released for sporting purposes, then you will have pheasants too. In fact, they're a damned nuisance in the vegetable garden, and will often be hanging around your poultry runs on the look out for spilled grain. It's hardly worth wasting powder and shot on these birds, because they're almost as tame as domestic fowl, and can be trapped very easily. All you need is an old chicken coop. Leave it wide open, and baited with corn for a few days and then, last thing in the evening, fix a small funnel of wire netting in the entrance. The pheasant is an early riser, and will be up and about before you are in the morning, so, hopefully, by the time you wander out to feed your hens, the spare coop will be full of nice plump pheasants. The last time we did this the coop, measuring just 3' x 4' contained nine birds.

The truly wild pheasant is a different proposition altogether, and far too wise to be conned in this way. You'll need to stalk within range and get him with the .410. Of course, it's not really the 'done thing' to shoot a pheasant on the ground, but personally I much prefer it when they're standing still! After all, we're talking here about clean kills and a meal on the table, not high flyers for the wealthy gentry.

Plucking and preparing a brace of pheasants.

Cock pheasant and, inset, the hen bird.

Pheasants fly up to roost at around dusk, where they can be seen silhouetted against the evening sky.

Pheasants go up to roost at around dusk, when, silhouetted against the evening sky they present a very easy target. This sort of behaviour is seriously frowned upon by the sporting fraternity, but I can assure you it's a very efficient and humane way of harvesting pheasants, and, if it's on your own land, who's to say otherwise?

Before plucking and drawing, pheasants should be hung by the neck in a cool place for up to a week.

Hares

In my opinion, hares should be spared, as they have suffered considerably from changing farming practices, making them something of a rarity in areas where they were once common. Having said that, it does seem to be localised, and some parts of the country still support fairly high populations, where they're considered to be a pest. If you live in one of those areas then you may well be justified in adding them to your menu from time to time. Hares are best shot with the .22LR. It's amazing how often, on skinning a hare, you find quantities of shotgun pellets lodged under the skin – evidence of someone else's 'clean miss'.

Preparation is as for rabbits, although, being game, hares should first be hung for about a week with their guts in.

Pigeons

The woodpigeon population of the UK is rising rapidly, with recent estimates placing it somewhere in the region of 15 to 20 million birds. As an agricultural pest they are second only to the rabbit. Therefore, I don't think we need

experience any qualms about shooting them for the pot and to protect our crops, which they'll destroy given half a chance. On a smallholding scale, it would only take a few hungry pigeons to completely wipe out your cabbage seedlings or garden peas. On a bigger scale, flocks of pigeons descend in their thousands to feed on emerging rape or ripe cereal crops, and, like locusts, they leave very little behind. They're fond of clover too, so even the grassland farmer isn't immune.

Although you'd hardly credit it when you see them boldly swaggering along your brassica rows, pigeons have an acutely nervous disposition, which makes them very wary. They've also got exceptionally good eyesight. Therefore, in order to get within range you must give them the confidence to come in to land exactly where you want them to, and that means using decoys. Being a gregarious bird, all of the passing pigeon's natural caution seems to disappear when he sees what appears to be a flock of his friends calmly feeding down below. The decoy pattern needs

to be set out downwind of where you've got your hide, as pigeons always land into the wind. They always feed facing into the wind too, so make sure you place the decoys the right way around or not a single bird will be drawn down!

The incoming pigeons tend to alight just behind your decoy birds, so arrange them so that that point corresponds with the optimum range for your gun (the .410 firing 3″ cartridges will be fine, but if you're going to be doing a lot of pigeon shooting then a 12-bore would be better). Now, when everything's in place you must retire to your hide. Keep completely still and out of sight, just peering through a fringe of vegetation, and don't show yourself until the moment that you fire. The time to take the shot is just before the pigeon alights, as he flutters his wings and momentarily appears to hover in preparation for landing. Dead birds can be added to your decoy pattern as the day progresses, as the more decoys there are, the greater will be the lure to passing flocks.

Although decoying is the most efficient way of taking pigeons, occasional birds may be bagged by waiting beneath their favourite sitting trees, or by intercepting them as they flight to and from the woods where they roost.

To prepare pigeons for the pot they can be plucked and gutted, then jointed for use in casseroles, although many people simply remove the breast meat. They don't require hanging.

Squirrels

The grey squirrel is a non-native species that causes untold damage in the British countryside, not only to habitats, wild birds and garden crops, but also to the indigenous red squirrel, which has more or less been wiped out. Although they may look like endearing bundles of fun as they race about in the treetops, you'll view them in a different light once they get into your veg plot, your feed store or, worse still, the roof of your house. Thankfully, they're rather nice to eat!

Squirrels are a pest, but thankfully they're rather nice to eat!

Shooting them presents something of a challenge, but they're relatively easy to catch in live traps, whereupon they can be humanely dispatched using an air-rifle at close range. Preparation is more or less the same as for rabbit, although they're not so easy to skin.

Ducks and geese

Wild ducks aren't really likely to feature much on the self-supporters menu, although if you've got a pond on your land, and a large number of ducks take up residence, you might feel justified in removing some in order to maintain the ecological balance. The best time to get them is as they fly to or from the pond at dawn or dusk.

Similarly, wild geese aren't really the quarry of the smallholder either, although sometimes big flocks do descend on winter sown cereal crops, where they are a serious pest indeed. As with ducks, you can shoot them as they fly to or from their feeding grounds, or use decoys to entice them within range. Geese are strong birds, so you'd need a 12-bore and some fairly hefty cartridges.

Deer

Of the six types of deer found in the UK, only two – the red and the roe – are native species. However, fallow deer – introduced by the Normans – have been here so long that most people consider them to be native too. The other three species – sika, Chinese water deer and muntjac – are all the descendants of escapees (or deliberate releases) from private collections during the 19th and 20th centuries. All six species are afforded the protection of the rather complex 'Deer Act', and, with the exception of the muntjac, all have a specified close season, when they can't be shot.

The right to control deer (provided such control is carried out within the conditions of the Act) lies with the occupier of the land on which they're found, so, if they're plentiful in your area there's no reason why you shouldn't enjoy venison from time to time, particularly if they've been damaging your crops. However, the ethos of deer control lies very much in management of the wild population, with numbers always being maintained at a level that's appropriate to the local ecosystem.

Minimum rifle calibre requirements for the different species are detailed in guidelines issued by the Home Office, although, as I mentioned earlier, the .243 is generally regarded as a good all rounder. There's also a clause in the Deer Act which allows for farmers (and presumably smallholders) to kill deer on enclosed agricultural land using a 12-bore shotgun firing AAA size pellets or solid slugs, for the purposes of preventing damage to crops or growing trees. However, this is only ever considered as a last resort, where

Roe deer are one of the UKs native species.

the damage being caused is serious. You would have to be very close for it to be effective, and I don't think it can possibly be very humane. It is illegal to shoot deer at night (i.e. from one hour after sunset until one hour before dawn) unless a special licence has been granted, and it's also illegal to use any kind of trap or snare for the capture of wild deer.

Using a rifle, deer are generally shot through the heart (the point of aim lies just behind the foreleg, about ⅓ of the way up the body), and are immediately 'gralloched' (gutted) where they lay. The carcass is then hung – either with or without the skin, depending on personal preference – for about a week before butchering.

Deer tend to be most active at dawn and dusk and, particularly on smaller parcels of land, one of the most effective ways of taking them is from a high seat or some other raised vantage point overlooking an area where they regularly pass or stop to feed. Although this perhaps lacks some of the romance associated with hiking over the heather-clad hillsides in pursuit of your quarry, it's certainly a magical experience to be hiding up a tree at daybreak, watching the countryside wake up around you.

Wild boar

I think it's quite exciting that these large (and potentially dangerous) animals are once again roaming the British countryside, after an absence of more than 300 years, but that's easy for me to say – they haven't spread this far yet! The farming of wild boar (possible only with a special 'Dangerous Wild Animals Licence') was very popular during the late 70s and early 80s, and, although the occasional break-out did occur, the malefactors were generally rounded up fairly quickly and returned to the fold. Then came the great storm of 1987, which caused chaos across southern England, bringing large trees crashing down onto the secure fences of wild boar enclosures, whereupon they simply walked out to freedom, and in sufficient numbers to establish a free-living population. At least that's the story I heard! Since then numbers have steadily increased, and their range has gradually expanded, augmented, no doubt, by some deliberate releases, and escapees to which a blind eye was turned.

Anyone who's ever kept domestic pigs outdoors will appreciate the damage that can be caused by a sounder of wild boar passing through a field of crops or someone's vegetable garden. They make a pretty fine mess of pasture, too. Understandably, if a family of boar takes up residence on your land, or even if they just pay you

After a long abscence, Wild Boar are once again free-living in the British countryside.

a visit from time to time, you're going to want to do something about it.

At the time of writing, wild boar are not a protected species in the UK, in that they do not have a 'closed season' or anything like that, yet neither are they classified as vermin. The decision as to whether boar should be controlled, and the choice of methods used, lies entirely with the occupier of the land where they're found. So, for the smallholder or farmer, that does at least enable you to act to protect your crops. They can be caught in live traps, then humanely despatched, or they can be shot in the field, often by making use of a bait station. Sometimes this is carried out at night by the light of a full moon. However, if you're thinking of carrying out the shooting yourself then you must have "Wild Boar" (or possibly "Any Other Lawful Quarry") specified on your firearm certificate, and it's recommended that you use a rifle with a calibre not less than .270. Under certain

circumstances, farmers may be able to use a 12-bore shotgun firing solid slugs for the control of boar, but again this needs to be specified on a firearms certificate, rather than on an ordinary shotgun licence.

Wild boar carcasses are skinned, rather than being scalded like domestic pigs.

Did you know?

The meat of the wild boar is called venison, not pork.

Details of the open and closed seasons for game shooting in the UK are given in table 12, page 447.

Harvest from the Sea

"The sea is never more than a few hours from us in the British Isles… and of course if you live near the sea it is madness not to make use of sea fish." John Seymour

And quite right he was too. It is hardly coincidental that there are high densities of original smallholdings (and by original I mean those that have always been small, not the more recently created smallholdings which come about when farms are amalgamated into larger units, and one of the old houses gets sold off with a couple of acres and some outbuildings) in the coastal regions of the British Isles – particularly where the inshore fishing is good. These holdings would traditionally be farmed with one foot in the sea, so in a year when the potatoes (or

wheat or whatever) failed to give a satisfactory return, perhaps the herrings would fare better, and *vice versa*.

This situation has been maintained in many areas right up to the present day, so, for example, here in Pen Llyn it's not uncommon to see lobster pot ropes or fishing nets hung in the rafters of someone's lambing shed, or to spot boat engines alongside balers in farm workshops. It is this dual existence – the safety net of having two income streams – that has enabled these small farms to remain viable.

If you're currently living on a coastal holding then you will probably have adopted the fishing / farming lifestyle already, in which case the remainder of this

article will be old hat to you, but, as John Seymour said, we are never more than a few hours from the sea in the British Isles, so it's not unreasonable to suggest that anyone with a decent freezer could enjoy a fish supper at least once a week throughout the year as the result of a couple of summer weekends by the seaside. When planning your self-sufficient menu think beyond pork, mutton, chicken and eggs, and consider mackerel, lobster, crab or skate.

A bit about boats

Although fishing by rod and line from the shore can produce good catches, it's unlikely to be a really worthwhile use of your time if it's your intention to land a year's supply of seafood. I think it would be fair to say that for the best results you'll need a boat. It's possible, in many seaside areas, to book a day fishing on a local charter boat – a boatman who knows the area can take you to where the fish are feeding with the minimum of delay, and if the mackerel are in it will be money well spent. Share the cost amongst a group of you. Alternatively, buy (or build) your own craft.

I've been messing about with boats on and off since childhood (my father was building a sailing boat in the dining room of our house at the time that I was born, so I grew up with it really), but it wasn't until we moved to Bardsey Island and began to fish for lobster and crab as a supplement to our small income, that I had to take boats (and the sea) more seriously. Lifting lobster pots into a small boat in a choppy sea is a very different ball game to dinghy sailing on inland waterways with a safety boat standing by.

Our first fishing boat, Arianne, was an Orkney 14, not much more than a large rowing boat, strongly constructed of fibreglass (nicely finished off with a hardwood trim) and powered by a 20hp outboard. A touch over engined perhaps, but we were fishing in a dangerous area, and would often have to dart into rocky inlets to retrieve pot ropes and make a quick exit before the next breaking wave – many times I've been glad of a turn of speed. Lobster pots were lifted by hand which limited me to fishing single pots, or at the most a string of two, but she did have a proper pot handling bench and bait table which made sorting the catch and re-baiting very simple.

Arianne would be a very practical craft in our present situation, and often I've regretted parting with her. She could be mothballed on her trailer in a corner of the shed for most of the year, taking up little space, costing nothing to keep and not suffering any deterioration, all ready to be towed down to the beach for the mackerel season. Our second boat was an altogether more substantial affair, enabling us to make the crossing from Bardsey to the mainland under our own steam, rather than relying on others for a lift. Gladys B had a 70hp engine and, being too big to row, carried a 7.5hp outboard as an emergency backup. She also boasted a hydraulic winch, enabling me to fish longer strings, and in deeper water too. We had about 50 pots at that time, and lobstering began to make a more significant contribution to our annual turnover. Had we continued semi-professional fishing after our return to mainland life, then Gladys B would have been quite adequate.

Our current vessel is not at all practical in the way the previous two had been, but is very, very beautiful. Moonbeam was built in 1952 of clinker mahogany planking on oak ribs, and sports a traditional gaff sailing rig. Auxiliary power is provided by a diminutive British Seagull outboard motor, also circa 1950, which pushes us along (just) on an extremely noisy 10:1 two-stroke mix. She can be rowed if all else fails. Being wooden she is better off kept afloat as planks dry out and shrink during periods ashore, meaning she leaks like a sieve after launching. It can be rather alarming putting to sea with water bubbling up through the floorboards, so we try to convince ourselves that the mooring fee is a justifiable expense!

The catch

(NB. It is inevitable that the following discusses what is most appropriate in our own locality. Other areas will be different, but you'll get the general idea.)

Mackerel have always been regraded as the summer holiday fish – they appear each year in early July, and can be caught in abundance up to the end of August. All seaside shops seem to sell mackerel fishing tackle, or 'feathers', regardless of whether mackerel have ever been seen on that stretch of coastline. You can quite easily make your own lures by binding a piece of something shiny to the shank of a size 1/0 hook. A strip cut from the inner bag of a wine box is ideal. If you're serious about stocking up on fish for the whole year then the mackerel is the one to go for – we find we can easily catch the 250 or so we require in a couple of summer evenings, and they freeze well. The usual method of fishing

(if from a boat) is by 'jigging' with a short rod or handline. Attach half a dozen or so lures to the main line at intervals of about a foot, via droppers or snoods of approximately 4". A 4 oz weight (heavier where strong tidal currents are likely to be encountered) is tied to the end of the line, about 18" below the lowest lure.

Handlines for mackerel fishing from a boat.

Pay out plenty of line over the side of the boat until you feel the weight touch bottom probably, then commence jigging – raising and lowering the tip of the rod (or your arm if using a handline) to keep the lures on the move. After a few minutes of jigging, haul in a couple of feet of line and jig again. Keep repeating this hauling / jigging exercise until you've brought the lures back to the surface. Hopefully before you get this far you'll have discovered the depth at which the fish are feeding. Bang! Half a dozen good-sized mackerel on the end of the line will leave you in no doubt as to whether or not you've got a bite! Get them aboard as quick as you can and chuck the line over again – if you've hit a shoal you may be able to land the year's supply in a very short space of time.

One nice thing about mackerel is that they require so little preparation prior to freezing, simply head off, tail off, innards

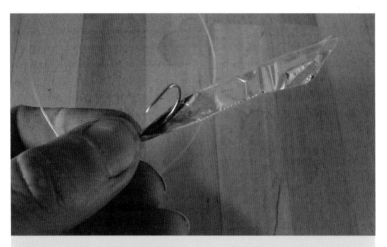

A home-made lure, using a strip cut from the inner bag of a wine box.

Mackerel ready for the freezer.

out, job done. No fiddly skinning or scaling. Larger fish can be filleted. Heads and guts go in the pig bucket, which is probably highly irregular. The chickens enjoy them too. Or store the bits and pieces in a tub of strong brine ready for use as lobster pot bait.

Pollack and coalfish can be taken on the same lures as for mackerel – in fact it's quite usual to land a mixture of species. Best sites are rocky gullies and inlets or, if boat fishing, in the region of underwater rocks, wrecks or reefs. Both are members of the cod family. Coalfish is the tastier of the two and is usually sold in fishmongers under the name of coley. Larger pollack can be filleted and smoked (just improvise something) then used in any recipe requiring smoked haddock.

If all else fails, or if it's too rough to set out in the boat, you could try fishing for wrasse. Use a simple set up of a single hook on a weighted line, baited with prawn or limpet, and fished a couple of feet off the bottom alongside a stone jetty or steep rocky shore. Beware of the sharp spines on the dorsal fin of these colourful fish – they aren't poisonous, but can inflict a painful puncture nonetheless. Recipe books will tell you to skin or scale wrasse, both of which are nigh on impossible. Gut them, then bake whole, wrapped in tinfoil with a bit of butter, some lemon and a bayleaf. When you peel away the tinfoil the skin comes off too. Cook grey mullet in the same way.

Lobsters and crabs can be caught in pots (or creels) almost anywhere around the British Isles, although on some coasts it is necessary to go a long way offshore in search of a suitable spot. In rocky areas they can be taken close inshore. Without a boat you could lower a pot from an overhanging rock into a deep gully, or wedge a baited pot amongst the rocks at low tide. Spring tides (i.e. the large tides that occur every fortnight) would be best. Return 12 hours later to see

what you've caught. Lobster creels come in many shapes and sizes, but the parlour pot is probably the most popular, certainly in this area anyway. Pots can be purchased, either just the frames or covered and ready to use, but anyone who is fairly handy could make a few. Have a good look at some stacked up on the quayside, then replicate in the farm workshop. Bits of old trawl net that get washed up on the beach from time to time will do for covering the frame, which should then be bound with old rope to prevent the net from chafing through. The parlour pot is divided into two sections by a one-way funnel, also made of netting. The lobster or crab enters the first compartment via a large entrance neck (to the inner rim of which is attached your bait), and from there moves through to the 'parlour' from which there is no escape. Crabs and lobsters can be stored in keep pots until required – there is no need to provide food, they will filter feed quite happily. They will also quite happily eat one another, so it's necessary to band their claws to prevent carnage. Use rings cut from an old bicycle inner tube.

There are legal size limits below which you must not land lobsters and crabs, even if only for your own consumption (carapace length 87mm for lobsters, width 130mm for crab), and in some areas local bye-laws prevent the landing of 'V-notched' lobsters, marked by means of a notch in the tail. Notched lobsters are usually berried hens (i.e. females carrying eggs) which have been returned to the sea. As proven breeders they ensure good stocks for the future. Areas where this is carried out have seen considerable increases in catches after a few years, reversing the damage done by years of over fishing. Dogfish, conger eel and octopus all crop up from time to time in lobster pots, and all are edible. Any conger over 5' long makes a fairly lively companion in a small boat, so you may rather tip them back in the sea. Cook dogfish Moroccan style. To skin a dogfish pour a kettleful of hot water over it and the sandpaper-like skin will simply rub off. The same trick works for skate.

Prawns can also be taken in pots, though of course they must be covered with much finer netting. Alternatively, follow the tide out with a prawning net. Only keep the big ones and please, cook them as soon as you can, don't leave them sitting around in a beach bucket of tepid water to die slowly. Cook prawns, lobsters or crabs by plunging directly into fiercely boiling salted water (3 tbsp salt per 2 pints of water). A few minutes will do for prawns, but up to half an hour should do for a really big lobster.

(If you have any doubts about the preparation of seafood (or indeed, if you are not even sure if your catch is edible) then consult *Simply Fish* by Jenny Baker. Mrs Baker does for fish what Jane Grigson does for pork.)

While you're pottering through the rockpools with your prawning net, gather a few winkles too. It's no more tedious than blackberry picking. We used to sell them by the hundredweight as children, and I know one fellow who bought his first lobster boat on the carefully saved proceeds of childhood winkle picking.

If you're lucky some local person may let you into the secret of where to safely gather mussels. If you are so privileged, keep

Main: *Parlour pots.*
Inset: *Although dark blue when caught, lobsters turn red when cooked.*

the information to yourself, and don't gather more than your fair share. Keep them in fresh running water for a few hours before cooking, and discard any that do not close firmly, or which have cracked shells. Once cooked, any not required immediately can be frozen.

Nets and netting

Nets can be a very practical way of making fairly large catches in a relatively short space of time, but are liable to be misused, in which case they may pose a threat to wildlife. My own experience of netting is limited to three types, and I'll briefly describe each:

Gill net: This is a simple net which hangs like a curtain vertically in the water and, as its name suggests, catches fish around the gills. Set across an inlet by tying to rocks either side, or lay along the beach at low water – the incoming

tide will lift the net. They are very useful for taking grey mullet in estuaries. Nets can be purchased in various lengths, ready set up with a weighted footrope and headrope with floats at regular intervals, or buy the components and set up your own. A gill net should be 'set on by the third' to give the required degree of bagginess, i.e. 100 yards of stretched netting when set up will give a working length of 66 yards. Our own is a small section salvaged from a huge length of discarded netting found washed up on the shore.

Seals are not averse to free lunches, and, having found your net, will cruise up and down its length removing any fish, and tearing great holes in the mesh in the process. Limit your activities to one, or at most two tides then clear off before they discover what you're up to.

A properly set gill net seems to present little risk to other marine

Tim, late 1980s, with pollack caught in a trammel net.

life, but damaged or discarded sections floating horizontally on or just below the surface are dangerous. Never abandon your net, and get it in quick if foul weather threatens.

Trammel net: The name comes from the French *'tres mailes'*, meaning more or less "three meshes", which is what it is. Two sheets of wide mesh hang one either side of a very baggy finer net. Fish swim through the wider net and hit the central curtain of fine mesh, which they then push through the wide net on the opposite side, resulting in each caught fish hanging in a sort of

pocket. Set in open water they are useful for taking shoaling fish such as mackerel. We made excellent catches of coley in a trammel, until one night a pack of dogfish cruised into the net and made a bit of a mess of things.

Tangle net: The way in which this net operates is fairly self-explanatory. It lies on the seabed and quite simply tangles up anything that swims into it. Used locally for catching crayfish or 'spiny lobster', we have enjoyed eating the bycatches such as big tope and skate. The tangle net is totally indiscriminate in its action, and really I cannot recommend it

due to the high risk posed to non-target species such as diving birds and sea mammals (except perhaps under genuine survival conditions, in which case you'll be eating the seals and the seagulls anyway...)

No boat? No problem!

If kayaks were good enough for Eskimos in arctic waters, then they're more than adequate for us in more temperate climes. For anyone living at a distance from the coast, the advantages of a kayak are obvious – they take up so little storage space, and, being lightweight, can easily be kept hanging from the rafters in an outbuilding when not in use. Then, when the fishing season comes along, you simply pop your kayak on the roof of the car and head for the seaside. And when you get there, you don't need any special facilities for launching either, so you can drop your craft in to the water pretty much anywhere you can safely access the shoreline.

Kayaking is a popular sport right now, so second hand ones are readily available, on eBay and other similar sites, for very little money. However, in keeping with the ethos of self-sufficiency, you really should build your own. It's much more fun that way, too. Suitable plans for the construction of an epoxy-ply sea-going kayak will set you back about £50 (try selway-fisher.com), and you'll need to allow yourself about a week to build the basic hull. Painting and fitting out will take a bit longer.

A home built kayak is ideal for coastal fishing.

The usual method of construction is known as 'stitch and tape'. Having measured, marked and cut out all the various components from standard 8' x 4' (1200 x 2440mm) sheets of 4mm thick plywood, you drill small holes along the joining edges and 'stitch' the hull together using short lengths of copper wire, twisted together on the outside. When you're happy with the shape you seal all of the seams on the inside using fibreglass tape and epoxy resin. Once the resin has set, the protruding ends of the wires can be snipped off prior to finishing the outside of the hull. After fixing down the deck, the whole of the kayak can be coated with glass cloth and epoxy before sanding and painting. Don't forget to make a paddle as well – use a simple wooden pole for the loom, and fashion the blades from plywood offcuts.

Accessories such as hatch covers, cleats and deck bungees can be bought online, and you use these to fit out the kayak to suit your own requirements.

The easiest way to fish from a kayak is by using a handline, and you simply drop any fish you catch into a plastic bag between your knees.

Foraging

"The most complex and intimate relationship that most of us can have with the natural environment is to eat it". Richard Mabey

Foraging is fun, but, despite being a free source of food, the amount of time taken up may be disproportionate to the gain. However, there are certain edible wild products of the fields and hedgerows that may grow prolifically around your own holding, and these should be seen as a welcome additional crop. Stick to the reliable favourites that'll give you a harvest year after year without you having to go and search for them. Anything else you're able to gather on country walks should be seen as a bonus.

Some basic foraging rules

• **Don't trespass:** Only gather wild food from your own holding, or in areas where you've been given permission to do so.

• **Don't pick from roadside verges**: Plants will be covered in residues from vehicle exhausts, mud and dirt – not really what you want to be eating. It's best to steer clear of places frequented by dog walkers too; big dogs can cock their legs much higher than you might think.

• **Look after the source plants:** Don't strip so much out of a plant that you compromise its chances of survival. We avoid using wild sources of roots for the simple

reason that you would have to destroy the whole plant to get to the edible bit. An exception to this would be horseradish, which is quite rampant in some areas, although we don't have any around here. Harvesting nuts and fruit shouldn't have any negative effect, but do leave some for the local wildlife.

• **Identify before eating:** This is especially pertinent to fungi. Correctly identifying what you've found can be tricky, and a good field guide is essential for anything remotely unusual. There are relatively few poisonous plants in the UK, but it's better to be safe than sorry. Bear in mind that even some widely accepted foodstuffs can have disagreeable side effects if you overindulge, so be sensible and don't gormandise.

Field and hedgerow

The type of environmentally sensitive land management that most smallholders aspire to, with its traditional mixed species hedgerows and diversity of habitats, ought to favour the presence of a number of useful wild food plants. Where practical these should be encouraged to flourish, and utilised.

Gorse: The flowers are what you're after here. Best picked on a sunny day in late April / early May, when they'll be giving off their amazing coconut scent. They can be used to make a really light, fresh wine (see page 330) that ferments out in as little as six weeks, and can be drunk shortly after bottling – any wine that you can make and drink in the same year has got to be a good one. You shouldn't have any difficulty finding them; the bright yellow flowers aren't shy about

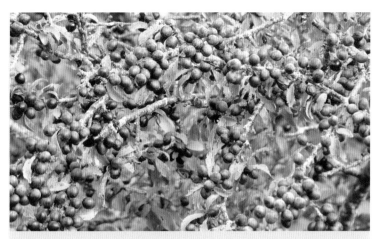

A hedgerow blackthorn covered in sloes.

advertising their presence. Take care when gathering them though, as everything's a bit prickly. Provided that you pick in the same direction as the way in which the prickles point, your fingers shouldn't suffer too much.

Sloes: Sloes are the fruit of the blackthorn, and are commonly found in hedges during the autumn. Blackthorns can be found all over the UK, and are easily identified in spring by the clouds of white flowers that cover them, usually in early April. They can be differentiated from hawthorns in that not only do they bloom a month earlier, but they also do so before they come into leaf. Late September and early October are the best time to pick sloes, once the fruit is plump, but before it starts to get overripe. Again, take care when harvesting as the thorns on the bushes are wicked. Sloes are very, very tart. You can try eating one if you like, but I doubt you will want a second. However, they do make really good wine, jellies and jams, especially when used in conjunction with other ingredients. They contain plenty of pectin, so any jam or jelly made with these should set well. If using them for winemaking, add some pectolase to avoid the risk of a pectin haze developing. The making of sloe gin is another popular use for these fruits (page 331). Sloes can be used fresh, but freeze equally well, so harvest plenty in a bumper year.

Hawthorns: These produce little berries known as haws that can be harvested and used to make jelly, although they're probably best mixed with some other type of fruit such as crab apples, otherwise the resulting jelly can be rather dry and rubbery. Hawthorns come into leaf in mid April and flower during May, hence why it's known as the May tree. Haws will be ready for picking at around about the same time as sloes.

Rowanberries: The fruit of the Rowan, or Mountain Ash, can be used for the same purposes as hawthorn berries. The trees are distinctive, and are popular in urban parks and communal spaces. Berries hang in clusters and can be picked a bunch at a time, removing them from the stems later on in the kitchen. They're ripe when they're a deep orange colour, usually from mid August onwards.

Rowan jelly

This makes an excellent accompaniment for both meat and game.

Ingredients

2lb rowanberries
Juice of 1 lemon
1 pint water
Sugar

Method

Wash the berries carefully and place them, with the water, in a heavy bottomed pan and simmer until tender. Strain the liquor through a jelly bag, leaving it to hang for approximately 1 hour. Measure the strained liquid, pour it back into the pan and add the lemon juice. Add 1lb of sugar for every pint of juice extracted, and bring to the boil.
Boil until setting point is reached then pour into hot, sterilised jars immediately and seal.

Elder: An elder tree – common in field boundaries around the farm – will give you two different crops in the same season, provided that you don't overexploit it. Elderflower heads should be picked when the florets are fully open on a dry, still, sunny, and preferably hot day, as it's the pollen which gives these flowers their distinctive flavour. Use for making wine, champagne (see page 333) and cordial. The former is a light wine that ferments out quickly, elderflower champagne is a refreshing fizzy drink – ideal after lugging in a crop of hay – and the cordial you dilute and drink like squash.

Harvest elderberries in the autumn.

Gather the heads whole and later remove the berries from the strings using a fork, in the same way as for blackcurrants. Elderberries are less astringent than sloes, so have a wider range of uses. In addition to the usual jellies, jams and beverages, they can be dried and used like currants. Combined with sloes they make a particularly fine table wine (see page 330).

Elder trees can be propagated very easily from woody cuttings, so you could plant a few about the place if you haven't got enough. They also benefit from being cut back pretty hard from time to time.

Rose-hips: The autumn fruit of the wild rose (or dog rose) is an elongated, pinkish-red berry that's loaded with vitamin C. Rose-hips contain four times the vitamin levels found in blackcurrants, and twenty times more than oranges, hence the supposed medicinal qualities of rose-hip syrup.

The seeds contained within the fruits are covered with stiff hairs, which are an irritant and may cause problems if ingested. If you're planning to dry rose-hips, or use them for jam making, then you need to slice them in half and remove the seeds, but if you're making something that will be strained or filtered then you should be able to get away with leaving them in. Rose-hip jelly is good, or include them with other fruits in a general hedgerow jelly recipe.

Wild blackberries: Brambles are found in abundance on most smallholdings, and can be used in exactly same way as cultivated blackberries; the flavour is the same, although the fruits are significantly smaller. Use for winemaking, in puddings (e.g. blackberry and apple crumble), and for jam.

Giant puffballs.

Fungi: Foraging for wild mushrooms is a popular pastime, which some people are quite obsessive about. Armed with a good field guide you could waste days at a time trying to track down an elusive delicacy, and even then, would you be sure you'd identified it correctly? The result of making a mistake could be most unpleasant. However, there are a few common species that are clearly recognisable, and if you're lucky enough to have them growing on your farm you should treat them as a welcome crop. Horse, field and parasol mushrooms are easy to identify, with the parasol being our particular favourite. They're all delicious fresh, fried with a dash of Worcestershire sauce, or dried. The giant puffball is another one that's unmistakable. It must be harvested while white and firm (i.e. before the spores that give it its name begin to develop), and should be cut into slices and eaither fried and eaten straight away, or dried in the bottom oven of the Rayburn for a day or two, for later use in soups and stews. Stored in an airtight container and used sparingly, a big one, dried, may keep you going for more

Slices of puffball drying in the bottom oven of the rayburn.

than a year. Parasol mushrooms dry well, too. The flavour of dried mushrooms is quite intense, so you only need to use a little at a time in your cooking.

Hazelnuts: The hazel is a tree-like shrub that can quite frequently be found in hedgerows. They're easily spotted by the yellow catkins that develop early in the year, before the hedge is clothed in foliage. The most difficult aspect of harvesting any nuts is leaving them on the bush long enough to ripen, yet getting them picked before the squirrels eat them all. Weight for weight, hazelnuts contain 50% more protein, 7 times the fat, and more than 5 times more carbohydrate than eggs, so a little goes a long way. Nuts are borne on

Date and hazelnut fingers

Ingredients

2 eggs
6 oz soft brown sugar
3 oz wholemeal self raising flour
2 oz wheat bran
2 oz hazelnuts, roughly chopped
4 oz dates, chopped
A pinch of salt

Method

Whisk together the eggs and sugar until light and fluffy then add the rest of the ingredients and mix thoroughly. Spread the mixture over a lined Swiss roll tin and cook at 180°C for approximately 30 minutes. Leave to cool and then cut into slices.

the bush in pairs or trios, and they should be picked dry then stored in their shells. Hazel trees are useful to have around the farm as, apart from the potential nut harvest, they're excellent for coppicing.

A hazel that's regularly cut will produce a multitude of straight poles as it re-grows, which can be used for fuel, making hurdles, and are particularly popular with stick makers. Managed in this way a hazel tree may live for several hundred years, but if left to its own devices the life span is much shorter. Wild hazels won't produce nuts until they're more than six years old, so don't coppice too frequently. The other alternative would be to coppice half of each shrub at a time.

Sweet chestnuts: Sweet chestnuts closely resemble conkers (horse

chestnuts), but are smaller, the nuts are less glossy, and the cases are densely covered with fine prickles (as opposed to the rather crude spikes seen on the husk of a conker). They're well worth the effort of collecting if you're lucky enough to have access to a chestnut tree. They usually start to drop in the early autumn, but these first ones will be under-ripe and may be of no use. Instead, look out for those that fall from late October, which should be ideal for use in the kitchen. You can eat the chestnuts raw, but usually they're roasted. Traditionally, they're placed in the ash of a hot fire, or next to glowing coals. The skins must first be split with a sharp knife, otherwise they'll explode, although if you're game enough you could leave one chestnut un-split amongst the others, and when that one goes bang you'll know that the rest are done.

Chestnuts are widely used in stuffing to accompany roast poultry, or they can be boiled, puréed, and then frozen for later use.

Beech mast: The nuts of the beech tree are very small, and most of the cases are likely to be empty as squirrels will probably have got there first. You've a better chance of getting a meal by trying to bag the squirrels for the pot (see pages 359 - 360)

Edible garden weeds

Early in the year, when the winter crops are looking tired and the spring sown ones have barely poked their heads above ground, you can find plenty of alternative green stuff in the garden – provided that you're not too tidy a gardener. Bear in mind that there's no real definition of a weed; it's

Chickweed growing amongst the crops on one of our vegetable plots.

just a plant that's growing where it isn't wanted.

Chickweed: This is a staple crop for us during the 'hungry gap'. It grows all over the vegetable plots given half a chance, but as it's relatively easy to weed out there's no harm in allowing some to flourish. The leaves are too small to be picked individually, so use scissors to cut what's needed for the kitchen. In preference, look for the smooth stemmed variety. Chickweed deteriorates once it gets close to flowering, so June is probably about the latest you'd want to harvest it. We tend to eat it chopped up and mixed with onion, garlic and some chive flowers to make a good salad. The best chickweed is always found between the rows of early spuds.

Nettle soup.

Main: *Fat hen.*
Inset: *Stinging nettles can be used in the kitchen.*

Stinging nettles: Another very successful garden weed. They put down a huge network of roots that makes them very hard to get rid of, and provides plenty of opportunities for them to spread. Most grazing livestock tend to avoid them (although goats will eat nettles, and other animals may do so when they're dry), but they're beneficial to many garden insects, including red admiral, small tortoiseshell and peacock butterflies. Nettles need to be picked early in the year, preferably before June. If harvesting later in the year, just take the small young leaves at the top of the stems.

The early spring leaves can be made into a very drinkable beer (see page 327), or used as another spinach substitute. They also make a good soup following the same recipe as that for lettuce given on page 90.

Horseradish: This large, dock-like weed was abundant where I grew up in East Anglia. The grated roots should be mixed with home-made mayonnaise to make horseradish sauce as an accompaniment to meat and fish dishes. Horseradish thongs for planting can be purchased from some seed companies, so it might be a good idea to try to establish some around the holding.

Dandelions: You can use the leaves, flowers and roots of this versatile plant. The leaves are always quoted as being good, but you must blanch them first, otherwise they're extremely bitter. Cover a dandelion plant with an upturned flowerpot for a few days until the leaves turn very pale, then pick and use in salads. The flowers make a good wine, and the roots, if dug up in the autumn, dried and ground, apparently make a decent coffee substitute, although we've never tried it.

Ground elder: Ground elder is a bane for gardeners as it's very invasive, and once you've got it you'll have a real job getting rid of it. However, take some comfort from the fact that if you can't eradicate it, you can at least eat it. Cook and use just like spinach. It has quite a tangy flavour.

Fat hen: An extremely successful and prolific weed, with each plant capable of producing around 20,000 seeds. It's been used as a food plant since prehistoric time, but fell out of favour when spinach arrived on the scene, even though it contains higher levels of both iron and protein. Pick young, fresh leaves, then cook and use as spinach.

Section Six
Technological
Self-Sufficiency

Water and Sanitation

Despite dire warnings about shortages, there's exactly the same amount of water on earth now as there was when the world began. What is getting scarce is clean water, because we've messed it up.

Global distribution and seasonal patterns are also shifting, and the result is that mains water supplies are inevitably going to become more expensive, and more tightly restricted (e.g. by hosepipe bans and suchlike). The vast majority of UK properties are connected to the mains, and, if you've got it, the chances are you'll use it, simply because it's so convenient. However, you should be taking steps to reduce your dependence:

• **Use less:** How often do you really need a bath or shower? Once a week is more than enough; the nation's obsession with cleanliness is not only wasteful, it's unhealthy too. And when you do fill up the bath tub, make the most of it – filling a bath just for one person is nothing but extravagance. (Incidentally, a shower typically uses only 16% of the water required for a bath, so unless you can get 6 people to use one bath, you're better off all taking a shower.) Discourage people from leaving a tap running while they're cleaning their teeth, and keep a jug of water in the fridge so that no-one has to run the kitchen tap 'until it comes cold' when they want to make a glass of squash. Fit automatic drinkers in livestock pens, and make sure you repair dripping taps and overflowing troughs promptly.

• **Harvest rainwater:** When we lived on Bardsey the water that came out of the taps in our house was rainwater, collected in big tanks from the roofs of the farm buildings. We used it for almost all purposes, including cooking, making tea and cleaning teeth, and it never did us any harm. Mind you, it was a bit of a funny colour sometimes! We cleaned out the tanks when they ran dry one summer, and found that the filter that should've been on the end of the outlet pipe had disintegrated years ago. We had access to spring water as well, but we were usually too lazy to fetch it, as it involved carrying it uphill to the house by the bucketful.

Although you might not want to make exclusive use of rainwater, you should at least be collecting as much as you can for smallholding purposes such as watering the garden and filling troughs for livestock. In the house, rainwater is perfectly acceptable for running the washing machine, flushing the loo or having a bath.

• **Re-use grey water:** It's ridiculous to allow the contents of the bath to flow away down the plughole, and then use fresh water to flush the loo! Leave the water in the bath and provide a bucket for flushing the toilet – a bucketful of water scooped out of the bath and tipped into the lavatory pan is all it takes. Bathwater can also be used in the garden, as can water from the basin and the washing machine, provided that you always use eco-friendly soaps and detergents. If your house is situated on higher ground than your garden then simply pipe the waste outlets to a conveniently situated tank from which to fill your watering can. The water does get a bit smelly at times, but the plants don't seem to mind. However, it's best to avoid using it on the leaves of vegetables that'll be harvested and eaten fresh, such as salads. From time to time the tank needs to be emptied for cleaning (a winter job, when water's not needed in the garden), and the accumulated sludge can be tipped on the compost heap.

• **Look for an alternative supply:** If you live in an old property then there's a fairly high chance that there's a disused well on the land somewhere, so search until you find it. Old maps may indicate the location, and local knowledge will help. Once you've found it, it'll need cleaning out, but after years of neglect may be structurally unsafe. There are companies that specialise in bringing old wells back into commission, so if you're in any doubt seek advice, particularly if your well is a deep one.

If you live in an old property there's a fairly high chance that there's an old well on the land somewhere.

Borehole drilling rig.

Springs, wells and boreholes

What's the difference? A spring occurs where groundwater naturally issues from the surface. This often occurs at the foot of a slope, where the underlying strata is exposed. Spring water is rainwater that's percolated through the soil until its downward progress is arrested by a layer of impermeable rock. As such it's not a deep groundwater source, so may be subject to contamination by surface activities (e.g. effluent from livestock farming).

Where this type of water doesn't issue from the surface, but instead collects in a depression in the underlying rock, a hole dug down to it is what's generally known as a well. Although some wells are very deep (with the deepest ever hand-dug well being a staggering 1,285 feet / 392 metres), most are not, and, like springs, can become contaminated, and are subject to the vagaries of the climate. Most of the wells in use today are very old, and may have historical significance. For new installations, the ancient art of the well digger has been superseded by the borehole drilling rig. Incidentally, what appears at first glance to be a well often isn't – it may simply be a sump that collects and stores water from an adjacent spring, prior to it being pumped to where it's needed. We have three of these 'spring sump' wells on our land, one of which provides the sole water supply for a neighbouring property (so isn't available for our own use). One supplies our cowshed and dairy, and has, at times in the past, been piped to the house, but it's unreliable and tends to dry out in the summer. The third, and potentially most useful, lies at some considerable distance downhill from our yard and buildings. We've tried pumping it up, but it appeared to cost more to run the pump than if we'd we bought the same volume of water from the mains supply. However, having installed solar panels since then, we now ought to be able to run an electric pump reasonably cheaply, so we'll probably revisit the idea in the near future.

A borehole is a narrow shaft (usually around 4″ / 100mm diameter) drilled down to considerable depth in order to tap into water stored in aquifers (porous rocks). Boreholes are unlikely to become contaminated by activities on the surface (so can be installed more or less anywhere, including urban areas), and aren't significantly affected by periods of drought. Although it may cost in the region of £100 / metre to drill, a borehole provides a long term reliable supply, and is therefore an economical alternative to mains water for properties that aren't already connected. If you already have a mains supply, a borehole may still be a worthwhile

Our spring, at the bottom of a steep slope.

If you're using a dual water system (i.e. both mains and own supply, alternating between them as requited) you must ensure that there's an air gap between the two. One way to achieve this is to have both supplies feeding into a header tank, with the inlet pipes positioned higher than the maximum water level. This reduces the likelihood of untreated water being sucked back into the mains system in the event of a drop in pressure, and potentially contaminating someone else' supply. It also prevents you from inadvertently filling your well with mains water, which would be an expensive thing to do.

Also, if you're using a hosepipe to fill troughs for livestock, the end of the pipe mustn't be allowed to contact the surface of the water, again in order to prevent contamination of the mains supply.

investment, particularly if your water usage is at the higher end of the scale, for example as a result of irrigating the garden or providing drinking water for livestock. If you're prepared to do the pump installation and plumbing work yourself, the price of the installation can be kept at a reasonable level.

Dig your own well

A very simple shallow well can be constructed as follows:

First locate a suitably damp area and dig a trial hole (about the same size as you'd need for installing a new gatepost). Monitor the water level in this hole for a full year, and if it always has at least a bit in the bottom then the site is probably good enough. Next, you need to get hold of one of those big black plastic tanks that are used for storing orange juice – they hold about 1,500 litres and cost in the region of £150. You'll also probably want to hire an excavator.

Drill lots of holes all over the

This well is actually a 'spring sump', collecting water from the spring pictured above

bottom of the tank and for about 12″ up the sides then bury it up to the neck in the ground. Put about 18″ depth of fine gravel in the bottom to act as a filter, and that's about all there is to it.
For watering the garden you simply bail the water out with a bucket when you need it. In the interests of safety, always re-fit the lid of the tank between uses.

Abstraction licences

A water abstraction license won't be required if you're drawing less than 20m³ per day from your own supply (10m³ in Scotland). An average household uses in the region of 1m³ per day, so, unless your well or borehole serves a number of properties, licensing isn't something you're going to have to worry about.

Using your own supply

Whatever the nature of your supply, you need a means of getting it from its source to where you need it, and this is usually (but not always) going to require a pump of some sort. For a fast-flowing spring, a hydraulic ram pump provides the best solution, for the simple reason that, once installed, it incurs no further running costs. The ram is operated by water power alone, with approximately 80% of the water that flows through it being used to pump the remaining 20% uphill, often over a considerable distance.

Filtering system for a private water supply.

Hydraulic ram pumps have been manufactured in the UK for over 200 years by Green & Carter Ltd., but if you'd like to have a go at making your own there are numerous plans available online.

Wells and boreholes will need a submersible electric pump, operated by a float switch in an above-ground header tank. From here the water may either be gravity fed through the household plumbing, or pumped on demand. It's common practice to install a pressure vessel in the system in order to even out any variations in supply pressure, provide a boost where necessary, and deliver water to the taps and appliances in a predictable fashion.

It's also a requirement that you have your water supply tested and fit appropriate filters to deal with bacteria and heavy metals, although we never have.

TIP

If drawing water from a well or spring for domestic use, it would be wise to exclude livestock from the immediate vicinity of the source.

Sanitation

If there had not already been flush toilets in our house when we moved in, we certainly wouldn't have bothered installing any. They represent a shocking waste of both water and nutrients. The 'bucket and chuck it' system we had on Bardsey was perfectly adequate – basically a bucket beneath a wooden seat in the little stone outhouse originally built for the purpose. After each use a sprinkling of wood ash or sawdust was added, to keep everything as odour-free as possible, and when full the bucket was emptied onto the current compost heap. This would then be covered over with grass clippings or some other similar compostable material. We had a 'solids only' policy for the bucket, largely because this meant I was less likely to slop its contents into my boots when carrying it down the garden path. Men were encouraged to pee directly onto the compost heap, but women tend to feel a bit exposed doing this, so we provided a separate bucket for their convenience (which they then emptied onto the heap themselves). Non-flush toilet systems are often fitted with separators nowadays, although men, take note – you do need to be seated for urination for

A 'bucket and chuck it' loo needn't look out of place in any bathroom.

these to be effective. Provided that urine is separated out at source (i.e. before it's had a chance to come into contact with faeces in the bucket), it's basically a sterile fluid, and if you don't want to use it on the garden it can be safely disposed of via a soakaway.

Modern composting loos can be fairly complex pieces of equipment, often incorporating heater elements, electronic fans and ventilation pipes. Some models are also rather bulky, due to the storage chamber, and they're expensive. However, there's absolutely nothing wrong with installing your own home-made bucket system, which can be done quite tastefully, and needn't look out of place in any bathroom. However, you might want to compromise by installing a bucket loo in a downstairs cloakroom, and having a more conventional system for upstairs bathrooms: the potential for disaster while carrying a full bucket down a carpeted staircase just doesn't bear thinking about. Or build yourself a bungalow.

Natural woodland regenerates about 3,000 kWh / acre / year

Fuel

It's clear that we can't go on burning coal, oil and natural gas for evermore. Quite apart from all the damage it does to the environment, these resources are going to run out. Nevertheless, we do still want to be able to heat our homes and cook our food, and we need a renewable way of doing it. On a larger scale, some really big commercial farms are installing anaerobic bio-digesters that process all the waste from their livestock (and from crops grown specifically for this use, such as maize), producing methane gas that's burnt for heating and electricity generation purposes. The remaining 'digestate' – the sludge that's left over in the bottom of the digester – is then spread on the land as an organic fertiliser. However, for an anaerobic digester to be sufficiently efficient to be worth bothering with you'd have to invest in an awful lot of expensive kit, and you'd probably have to keep it operating at maximum capacity to justify the initial outlay. If this means growing extra crops to feed the beast then it also means less ground would be available for growing what you need to feed yourself, so you'd be no better off. Several smallholders working together as a co-operative might manage to run a small one – just about – but for most people, domestic methane production it isn't going to provide the answer we're looking for.

What's needed, therefore, is a rapidly renewable source of energy that can be converted into a useful form reasonably easily, while delivering ecological benefits, and on a small scale the only thing that's realistically going to satisfy these requirements is wood. But you do need a surprising amount if it's going to be your sole source of heat. An acre of natural woodland could regenerate the equivalent of 3,000 kWh per year; a stacked cubic meter of mixed species firewood, at less than 20% moisture content, might have a calorific value of around 1,500 kWh, and the average household uses 14,000 kWh per year for the purposes of heating, hot water and cooking. Do the sums and you'll see that if you were to rely purely on the natural harvest of your woodland (e.g. dead branches, wind-blown timber, thinnings etc.), you'd need access to about nine acres in total. But, of course, this isn't what you do. You will undoubtedly get some of your fuel from natural woodland and hedgerow maintenance, but for the remainder you'll plant fast growing species, and coppice them. Willow,

Coppicing our willow plantation for the first time.

underutilised patch of wet ground, and every single one grew. The first coppicing, some few years later, obviously yielded only 90 poles (of varying thicknesses up to about 6″ in diameter), but this was enough to heat our house (excluding hot water and cooking) for approximately 3 months. Each stump has subsequently thrown out around 12 shoots, so the next harvest should result in considerably more timber, although I may not wait until the trunks get so thick before cutting. Bearing in mind that you could plant 2,700 of these trees per acre (at the spacings suggested above), you'll appreciate the potential, although for the best results you'd want to plant a hybrid variety specifically bred for firewood production. See table 11, page 447 for additional information relating to the fuel values of different types of timber.

Felling licences

Be aware that you may need a felling licence (available from Natural Resources Wales, or the Forestry Commission in England or Scotland) if you want to fell more than 5m³ of timber in any one calendar quarter (or sell more than 2m³ of your home-grown timber in any one calendar quarter). However, a licence won't be required for very small trees (3″- 4″ in diameter), for coppicing trunks up to 6″ in diameter, for felling in orchards or gardens, or for dealing with dangerous and diseased trees.

A felling licence may include a condition that requires you to replant, and subsequently maintain, the area.

for example, can be cut on a five year rotation, and might yield as much as 5 tonnes (approximately 15 stacked cubic meters) per acre per year. Therefore, ⅔ of an acre of willows, together with whatever other timber you can scavenge from around the place, could theoretically do it. But, of course, it won't. Theory is all very well, but we also have to take into consideration the fact that even the best wood-burning stoves are only 80% efficient. More typically the figure is closer to 60%.

Therefore, if I was starting from scratch, I'd want to plant at least an acre (preferably more), and also include some other species, such as ash, within it. Willow can be planted simply by poking cuttings into the ground at appropriate spacings (1 metre between trees and 1.5 metres between rows, for firewood production), and leaving them to it. The last time we did this we just cut 90 pieces that had sprouted from a couple of stumps where the council had chopped back a roadside tree, stuck them in an otherwise

After coppicing, each of the willow stumps has thrown up about 12 new shoots.

Processing and seasoning

Despite the fact that it's a renewable resource, don't for a moment think that wood is a cheap fuel. If you were to buy in what you require, already cut and split, it would work out more expensive than burning coal, oil or gas (but it would be cheaper than using mains electricity for heating purposes). To process a year's supply of your own timber it'll take two people working more-or-less full-time for a week, and that doesn't make any allowance for extracting it from the forest in the first place. This is all very well if it forms part of your general strategy of woodland management (for which grant funding may be available) on the holding, but if you're taking time off from paid employment specifically to cut firewood, you really do have to ask yourself whether it's worthwhile, particularly when you factor in the cost of running your chainsaw.

One way of keeping the processing cost down would be to have your tractor turning a PTO driven circular saw while at the same time powering a hydraulic log splitter. This enables two people to work simultaneously, achieving a fairly high work rate per hour, and the slow-revving diesel engine of a tractor is much cheaper to run than a chainsaw. But you'd still need your chainsaw for felling the trees, snedding (removing

The first harvest from our coppiced willow.

side branches), and cutting them into manageable lengths for manhandling to the circular saw table.

TIP

If your stove is capable of burning 20″ logs (as many are), don't waste time and fuel cutting your firewood into 10″ lengths.

Once harvested, firewood ideally needs to be reduced to below 20% moisture content before burning. Some timbers, when freshly cut, may contain up to 65% moisture (e.g. poplar), whereas others, such as ash, have a moisture content of only 35% – which is why ash burns pretty well even when green. The general rule of thumb is to season firewood for a year per inch of thickness, so splitting it all before stacking will hasten the process. Either way, you need to be cutting a few years ahead of your requirement. We split our firewood manually using a large axe, and we're quite happy doing it that way. However, we don't – at present – use wood to satisfy all of our domestic fuel requirements. When we do we may well invest in a mechanical splitter (or simply buy another axe).

Splitting logs before stacking will hasten seasoning.

Renewable Heat Incentive (RHI)

Certain wood-fuelled ('biomass') boilers may be eligible for the government's Renewable Heat Incentive scheme, in which you'll be paid for the heat you generate. At the time of writing, the biomass domestic tariff for new applicants is 5.14 pence per kWh. Air source and ground source heat pumps, and solar thermal installations, may also qualify for payment, with the current rate for solar thermal being 19.51 pence per kWh. Payments are made quarterly, over a seven year period, and if you also use the heat generated to take the chill off your workshop, or for other smallholding purposes such as grain drying or heating a greenhouse, you may be eligible for the commercial payment rate which, although lower, is paid out over a much longer period.

Power

Like it or not, we've become an electricity dependent race. Even those who opt for an off-grid lifestyle generally do so by generating their own electricity, rather than managing their affairs by candlelight. Although total dependence on any one thing in particular isn't ideal, there's no getting away from the fact that electricity is a powerful tool, and is here to stay. It certainly makes life easier around the smallholding if you can use a drill, a milking machine or an incubator whenever required, and having a readily available source of electricity to run a home office may be what turns a rural lifestyle into an economic reality for many people. Almost without exception, the smallholding handbooks written during the 'golden age' of self-sufficiency (i.e. mid 1970s to early 80s) have something to say about electricity generation, and some even include plans to build your own wind turbine. I'm not aware of anyone who actually did this, but a lot of people talked about it. Output figures quoted for a home-built domestic-sized installation were up to 2kW, with commercially available wind chargers capable of powering up to a dozen light bulbs being considered good value at around £400 (in 1976). Photovoltaic generation was dismissed on account of the cost – estimated to be in the region of £10 - £15 per watt – although solar thermal water heaters were quite popular.

We may laugh at these figures now, but to be honest not much progress was made until the introduction of the Feed-In Tariff (FIT) in 2010. With the government prepared to pay for small-scale electricity generation the whole alternative energy industry leapt forward, and rooftop solar installations (up to 4kW) became the 'in' thing, together with a rising number of wind turbines and small-scale hydroelectric projects. The FIT scheme enables householders to use the National Grid as a huge battery, feeding electricity into it when a surplus is generated, and drawing electricity from it when required, and to be paid for all that they produce – even the portion that they use themselves.

The rise and fall of the FIT

At its inception in 2010, the domestic FIT paid householders something in the region of 42 pence for each unit of electricity generated. In the absence of 2-way 'smart meters' it is deemed that, of the total amount generated, half will be used at source, and the remainder exported to the National Grid. For this amount an export tariff (initially 3 pence per unit) is paid. These payments are index linked, so will rise with inflation over the 25 years of the scheme. If you could afford to install solar panels in 2010 it was basically a licence to print money, and could add a useful additional income stream to a smallholding business. If you didn't have the capital you went and asked your bank, and they said no. In their eyes, the FIT tariff had no track record, so wasn't considered a sufficiently

reliable source of income against which a client could borrow. Meanwhile, the FIT for new installations was steadily being reduced, and the duration of the scheme was cut back to 20 years.

Eventually the banks all woke up and started falling over one another in their scramble to fund micro generation projects. However, by this time the government had moved the goalposts by introducing new criteria for eligibility, one of which was the requirement that your house had an Energy Performance Certificate (EPC) rating in bands A–D, which pretty well ruled out old stone farmhouses.

While homeowners battled with EPC assessors, the FIT continued to fall, to the extent that the whole scheme is now playing into the hands of the large-scale commercial producers with their multi-acre solar farms and massive turbines.

However, although the FIT for new domestic solar PV installations is now down to under 5 pence per unit generated (plus an additional payment of about the same amount per unit on the 50% estimated to have been exported to the grid), rising energy costs and a reduction in the capital outlay required mean that a small-scale solar PV system is still a worthwhile investment, by virtue of the savings made to your electricity bill.

Throughout the lifetime of the FIT scheme, the rate at which alternative energy generating technology has been changing is phenomenal, to the extent that whatever I write today will no doubt be out of date by the time you read it. Therefore, the most appropriate way for me to summarise the potential of small-scale electricity generation for household use is in the form of a case study.

Alternative energy case study

When they moved into their new self-built, low-impact, off-grid home, the first thing that Richard and Tracey Wilson realised is that they'd have to drastically cut their electricity consumption in order for their new lifestyle to be a success. In their old house they'd been using in the region of 25kWh per day, and Richard reckoned this would have to be reduced to below 4kWh if they were to be able to afford to install the necessary equipment to supply their own power.

The first step was to measure the consumption or check the specification of all of their electrical appliances to find out what their peak wattage was, and to calculate the duty cycle of each item. They then considered where savings could be made by changing patterns of use, or by switching over from electricity to another energy source for some things (e.g. wood burner or solar thermal to heat hot water in place of electric immersion heater, etc.). It soon became clear that big savings could only be made in relation to the high-cost items such as fridges and freezers, dishwasher, entertainment system etc., some of which would need to be replaced with more efficient units. Smaller savings could be made at a lower cost, for example, by changing all light bulbs to LEDs.

Having set a target for their electricity usage, Richard and Tracey set themselves a budget for

Richard and Tracey's low-impact home, with solar PV and solar thermal installations visible on the roof.

the purchase and installation of the power system, and the replacement of some of their inefficient appliances, and began to plan how they'd be able to generate and store the required amount of electricity. A wind turbine was briefly considered, but this clearly wouldn't have been efficient on a small scale due to the close proximity of trees, and there would have been difficulties associated with planning permission had they wanted to install a larger turbine.

Eventually they decided upon solar PV, together with a diesel powered generator, and started watching eBay for bargains…

Their first system, powered by an 800 watt solar PV array and a 6000kVa / 4800 watt generator, consisted of a 12v 1500watt 50amp inverter charger, together with six 2v 1550ah second-hand battery cells, giving a total capacity for stored energy of 18.6kWh.

However, in order to prolong the life of the cells it's advisable not to drain them to below 50% charge,

Top to bottom: *Water temperature; Battery charge level; Solar thermal controller; Current meter.*

The 'nerve centre' of the Wilson's off-grid system.

meaning that they'd have almost 3 days worth of useable stored power in the event of not being able to generate for any reason. All of the equipment was sourced for relatively little money, although the high price of solar panels at that time was a limiting factor.

The battery bank.

From this small beginning the system was upgraded in stages to a 12v 2500 watt 120amp inverter charger, and an additional twenty-four 12v 700ah cells (wired together to create 4 x 12v batteries), which, with the existing battery bank, gave a total capacity for stored energy of 52.2kWh.

After taking into consideration the fact that these were second-hand cells, and also the fact that they shouldn't be drained to below half charge, this was expected to provide up to 4-5 days' worth of stored power. The solar panels were replaced with a 1200 watt array, which was deemed to be the optimum size required to produce enough daily energy for most of the year, at a viable cost – any smaller than this would result in insufficient production during spring and autumn, and making

it larger wouldn't make winter production any more successful due to the false horizon created by surrounding woodland when the sun is low in the sky. The generator was also replaced, although this was partly driven by the need to reduce noise output.

At this point the government announced the introduction of the FIT, which, initially, gave a short time window during which people with self-installed systems were able to apply. Although being off-grid meant that the Wilsons wouldn't qualify for the export tariff, they were able to claim the generation payment, which was then in the region of 42 pence per unit, and rising in line with inflation. This means that while their solar PV system supplies all of their energy requirements in spring, summer and autumn, the income received from the FIT tariff during this period pays for all of the red diesel required for running their generator during the winter, with enough left over to fuel their tractor and other machinery.

Lessons learnt: If starting again, Richard says they'd have installed more solar PV from the outset, and used 24v or 48v for the battery system. Two inverters would be fitted, giving extra capacity and security in the event of one unit failing. The solar thermal would be dispensed with, and instead a diverter would be used to re-direct surplus electricity into the hot water system. It's also interesting to note that while their solar PV installation cost in the region of £2.80 per watt, the same can now be had for around 50 pence per watt, so for anyone starting from scratch now the most significant expense is likely to be buying and maintaining a suitable generator.

ALTERNATIVES TO SOLAR

Wind power

Despite the popularity of wind power among the early pioneers of self-sufficiency, and during the first couple of years of the FIT, rapid advancements in photovoltaic technology, coupled with planning objections to the siting of turbines, mean that wind generation on a domestic scale has largely been superseded by solar panels. Most of the wind turbines you see being erected now are in fact commercial installations.

Wind turbine on a local farm.

That's not to say that wind power doesn't have its place alongside solar PV for small-scale systems – after all, it does tend to be windy in winter, when the sun doesn't shine so much – but do bear in mind that while a 15 metre diameter turbine on top of a mountain may generate more than 387,000 kWh per year, a smaller (domestic-sized) unit with a diameter of 3 metres in a more sheltered location may only be capable of producing 2,900 kWh per year.

At the time of writing, prices for small wind turbines range from around £2,000 for a 1kW rooftop model up to £30,000 for a 6kW pole mounted installation.

Diesel power

When we lived off-grid on Bardsey Island we had an old Lister generator which we ran on red diesel, eked out by scrounging 'waste' fuel from the lighthouse. We powered up the 'genny' for a few hours each evening, even in summer (in order to keep the contents of our freezer frozen), and our total electricity bill came in at around £80 per year, if I remember correctly. We had no capacity for storing electricity, so it was a simple case of when it was on it was on, and when it was off it was off. For us, at the time, it was a perfectly satisfactory system, but it's not particularly eco-friendly, and with fuel prices as they are now it wouldn't be justifiable anyway (unless you make your own biofuel from waste cooking oil – see page 388). However, as we've seen in the previous example, a diesel powered generator does provide a useful backup to alternative energy systems (which may be influenced by climatic and seasonal variation) in an off-grid situation.

Water power

If you've got a suitable watercourse on your property then hydro is the way to go, as it'll generate 24 hours a day, 7 days a week, all year round, whether the wind blows or the sun shines (droughts notwithstanding).

To calculate the potential hydroelectric output (in watts) of a stream, you need to know the flow rate (in litres per second) and the fall (in metres). The sum goes like this:

Watts = flow x 9.81 x fall x 0.5
(where 9.81 is the gravitational constant, and 0.5 the estimated efficiency of the equipment).

Therefore, a small stream like ours, with a flow rate of around 60 litres per second and a fall of about 3 metres, could potentially generate 7734 kWh per year. With this in mind, I think we need to take a closer look at it.

Transport and Machinery

Transport

It's a sad fact that rural areas are very poorly served by public transport. An even sadder fact is that people living in rural areas make very little use of the service that is provided, with the result that buses are often observed trundling around country lanes with virtually no-one on board. There appears to be something of a stigma attached to being seen using public transport ("Maybe the Joneses next door will think we're too poor to run a car?"), which really needs to be addressed. Having said that, although the cost of travelling by bus is pretty low compared to other forms of public transport, and is often cheaper than taking the car, this advantage fades away if you're travelling in a group: to take a family of five (even if the two youngest can go half price) on a bus trip is considerably more costly than taking the car, and when you factor in the inconvenience as well, it seems hard to make a positive case for travelling by bus. However, the majority of the cars that I see passing our farm in the mornings, as folk travel to work, contain only the driver, meaning that people are, in fact, opting for a more costly mode of transport. If only those cars were full. What a difference it would make! Apparently, one bus carrying 20 passengers causes less pollution than 15 cars carrying the same number of people over the same route, but what if only 5 cars were used, with each of them being full? Car sharing is one way of really cutting down both

travel costs and carbon emissions, while enjoying a certain amount of convenience (e.g. not being tied to a timetable or a roundabout route). Some larger workplaces run shared transport schemes, and people should be encouraged to make use of them. There are also a number of regional and national lift sharing schemes, and internet sites, that offer a way of finding someone to share your car, or to enable you to arrange a lift if you don't have a car of your own. Shared journeys may be short or long distance, regular, occasional, or one-off trips. The person sharing the car is generally expected to make a contribution towards the cost of the journey, and by doing this both of you manage to save money. The more people you can squash in, the more money each of you saves. It's not designed as a profit making exercise for the driver though; making money from car sharing could invalidate insurance cover.

Despite all of the above, the smallholder faces a real dilemma. The general ethos of sustainability suggests that we should be doing these things, but could you really fetch a six-month supply of bread flour from the wholesaler, and bring it home on the bus? Or would your car-share companion appreciate sharing a seat with half a pig that you've just collected from the abattoir? And what about transporting livestock? Like it or not, the busy smallholder is going to need his own vehicle, and a fairly hefty one at that. The only thing you can hope to do is to make your vehicle usage as cost effective as possible:

• Share regular journeys, such as the school run.

• Walk, cycle, or use public transport as an alternative whenever the opportunity arises.

• Plan carefully in order to combine a number of activities into one journey.

• Lengthen the period between routine shopping trips.

• When travelling any distance towing a trailer, try to organise a pick up and delivery for the part of the journey when you'd otherwise be travelling empty.

• Use online planners to find the shortest or most efficient route.

• Managing a fragmented smallholding can involve lots of short journeys between fields, which, over the course of a year, may equate to a considerable distance. This cannot really be justified, so consider scaling back your activities and renting outlying ground to a neighbour.

• Use your tractor on the road for short-distance towing. This may mean that you can get away with running a smaller, more economical car.

• Carry out regular vehicle servicing (e.g. oil and filter changes etc.) yourself, which should help reduce maintenance bills. We fail miserably in this respect.

• Always drive in a fuel-efficient fashion, and switch off the engine if waiting in a queue of traffic.

• Don't travel if you don't need to.

Road trailers

Even if you only keep a few animals for domestic production, you should have a livestock trailer of some sort, in case you want to take a poorly sheep to the vet or something like that. A small trailer that'll take up to half-a-dozen sheep or a few pigs or goats can easily be towed behind an ordinary family car. We've fitted a roof-rack to our little livestock trailer, which has considerably increased its versatility.

If you're planning on livestock being the principal enterprise on your holding then you'll probably want a much bigger trailer (and correspondingly bigger vehicle), although you could make use of a local haulier to take cattle or sheep to market for you. You might also want a flat trailer for transporting hay, straw, building materials, animal feed etc.

MACHINERY

It's not really possible to provide a standardised list of the smallholder's machinery requirements, due to the huge variability between smallholdings. If you just have a small- or medium-sized vegetable plot, and keep only a few animals for subsistence purposes, then you won't need any machinery at all. However, even between larger smallholdings of the same size the requirements will differ according to the type of land and the nature of the business: the equipment needed for growing 20 acres of vegetable crops in East Anglia will be quite different from what the 20 acre beef and sheep producer in North Wales might want. There's also the question as to whether a high degree of mechanisation is justifiable, when each implement might only be used for a few days in the year. There's a balance to be struck, and the answer probably lies in having the necessary equipment to carry out all the basic day-to-day work yourself, while engaging the services of an agricultural contractor for specific tasks. However, if you keep livestock in a predominantly arable area (or conversely, if you want to grow crops in a stock-rearing part of the country) you might struggle to find a local contractor who's able to satisfy your demands.

Tractor

You may not need a tractor, but if you do the key considerations are size, safety and versatility. Another consideration is power, although this requirement is entirely dependent on the nature of your holding and what implements you may be intending to use.

Our dinky little Renault.

• **Size:** Here I'm talking about physical size rather than engine capacity. You may want to use your tractor inside buildings for mucking out, so think about height and width. Also, consider the dimensions of your gateways. It would be a shame to have to re-design the layout and infrastructure of your holding just because you went and bought an oversized tractor. However, I don't rate compact tractors very highly – all the ones that I've had anything to do with were about as much use as a wheelbarrow, but much more expensive. There are plenty of mid-sized tractors available that would be ideal for

Having a front-end loader on the tractor enables us to keep the cost of purchased straw down, by buying big bales.

A popular smallholders tractor, the Massey Ferguson 35X

small-scale farming purposes. If you'll be using it on sloping ground, consider also where the centre of gravity lies – a tall tractor is inevitably less stable than a machine of smaller stature, even though the width of the two may be the same. I found this very noticeable when I changed from my old Ford 4610 to a Renault 70-14. The Renault is the same width as the Ford, and is marginally more powerful, but smaller and therefore more stable.

• **Safety:** Your tractor must be fitted with an anti-roll bar or safety cab to protect you in the event that the whole thing tips over on a slope.

• **Versatility:** If you're going to have a tractor then you want it to be capable of doing as much as possible. To my mind, having a front-end loader, together with appropriate attachments such as bucket, muck fork, bale spike etc., is absolutely essential – to the extent that I wonder how we ever managed without one. You'll also need power take-off (PTO) capability in order to use any machinery with revolving parts (e.g. tedder, baler, rotavator etc.), three-point linkage for the attachment of implements that need to be lifted clear of the ground, draw bar (both pin and ball hitch types) for towing, and hydraulic spools for operating items such as tipping trailers, log splitters etc. Also, consider whether you might require four-wheel-drive.

• **Power:** Most smallholders will be looking for a tractor in the 20 to 60 horsepower range, depending on the expected workload. For light duties such as tedding, small-scale row crop cultivation, pulling a small trailer or carrying a link box, a machine at the bottom end of the range will be fine. However,

Biodiesel

The diesel engine was originally designed to run on peanut oil, so it seems fitting that we should manufacture biofuel for modern diesel engines out of waste vegetable oil. In fact, older vehicles will run quite happily on straight vegetable oil (SVO) with no further processing required. I ran my old Daihatsu Fourtrak like that, using bottles of cheap cooking oil purchased from the supermarket. It was fine in summer, but in winter needed to be mixed 50:50 with conventional diesel. I think lots of other people started doing the same when the price of road fuel rose above £1 per litre, so the supermarkets weren't slow to raise the price of vegetable oil to the point where it was no longer a viable alternative.

For use in newer vehicles, vegetable oil (often waste collected from catering outlets) will need to be properly converted into biodiesel, otherwise expensive damage to delicate parts may occur. Complete biodiesel manufacturing kits can be purchased easily enough online.

You can use up to 2,500 litres per year of home-made biodiesel (or SVO) as road fuel without the need to register with HM Revenue & Customs, or pay any duty. However, you do need to record how much you're using, and keep the records for 6 years.

A friend of ours with a small farm in France took the whole biodiesel thing a step further by growing and pressing his own rapeseed. The oil fuelled his tractor, Landrover and generator, and the residual cake from the pressed seeds was fed to his sheep. Whether you could do this economically on a small scale in the UK I don't know, but if you live in an arable area where oilseed rape is grown, you might be able to purchase some of the crop from a local farmer.

The basic process, using waste cooking oil, is as follows:

1. Warm the oil slightly and filter it.

2. Heat to 100°C and hold at that temperature for a while to drive off any moisture – this is a very inefficient way of doing things, so avoid, if possible, by sourcing oil that doesn't have excessive water contamination.

3. Determine the acidity of the oil by titration.

4. With the oil held at around 60°C, add an appropriate quantity of methoxide (made by mixing methanol and sodium hydroxide). Somewhere in the region of 20% of the volume of the oil is usually required. Wear gloves, goggles and a face mask for this step.

5. Mix thoroughly.

6. Leave to settle and separate, after which glycerine is drawn off the bottom (which can be used as a bio-degradable hand cleaner), and you'll be left with useable biodiesel.

once you start wanting to bale your own hay, spread manure or feed silage to your animals, you'll need something with a bit more oomph. A few 'old favourites' that have stood the test of time as smallholder tractors are the Fordson Dexta (32hp), Massey Ferguson 35X (44hp), Massey Ferguson 135 (45hp), and the Fordson Major (50hp). Our first tractor was a classic 'Little Grey Fergie', but at only 20hp we soon found it inadequate, particularly given the challenging nature of our terrain. However, for occasional use on a very small holding it would have been fine.

Remember that you can use red diesel in your tractor, for agricultural purposes. This is considerably cheaper than road fuel, as it attracts a lower rate of duty. However, it's not particularly easy to get hold of in small quantities. Unless you can justify installing a tank and having a large volume delivered, the best option is usually to buy some in jerry cans from a neighbouring farmer.

Implements:

As with the tractor, your equipment requirements are largely dependent on the nature of your holding. However, based on the assumption that you'll have a diverse range of enterprises on your small farm, the following implements are worthy of consideration:

(Most of these items have already been discussed in greater detail in other sections of this book, so the following list is merely a summary).

Mechanically there's very little that can go wrong with a muck spreader – a couple of bearings and a drive chain, and that's about it – and there's not much to choose between models in this respect. What really makes a difference to how long the machine will last is the thickness of the steel that the drum is made from. On second-hand machines the metal will have worn pretty thin, and new 'economy' models aren't up to much, either.

• **Muckspreader:** See pages 137 and 139. Mucking out your livestock buildings directly into the spreader saves a certain amount of double handling. An alternative way of spreading manure is to fork it off the back of a slow-moving trailer into the path of a chain harrow being dragged along behind.

If considering purchasing a new muck spreader, it's worth paying a bit more for better quality.

• **Harrows and roller:** See pages 138 and 140.

• **Topper:** See page 140.

• **Fertiliser spreader:** See pages 26 and 137. Also used for spreading lime and broadcasting seed. In addition to tractor-mounted models you can get small ground-wheel driven spreaders, or even really tiny 12v ones for fixing to the rear rack of a quad or the tailgate of a pickup.

• **Haymaking machinery:** Mower, tedder and baler. See pages 146 - 149. You'll also want a bale spike if you're planning on making silage, see pages 148 - 150. A double spike on a front-end loader

can also be used for moving big 'heston' bales, which is a worthwhile consideration if you buy in hay or straw, as big bales invariably work out cheaper than little ones.

• **Rotavator:** See pages 55, 62 and 128. If the only vegetables you grow are for your own consumption then you'll probably manage quite well using hand tools or a small garden rotavator. However, if you're thinking of growing forage crops for your livestock then you'll need the capability to cultivate a larger area, and if the same machine can also be used in the vegetable garden that's good. Consider laying out your plots to facilitate this.

• **Ridging tool:** See pages 70 and 85.

• **Link box:** Fits on the three-point linkage of the tractor for use as a general carry-all. See photo, page 378.

• **Plough:** See page 122.

• **Sprayer:** See page 137. A small knapsack sprayer can also be used to apply disinfectant in livestock buildings and trailers.

• **Trailer:** See pages 146 and 386.

Farm dispersal sales are a good source of second-hand machinery.

Sharing

Often it can be hard to justify the cost of acquiring a particular piece of kit if you only use it occasionally, but you might find that someone else has one that they don't mind you borrowing from time to time. We've been very lucky in this respect, and during our early years at Ty'n-y-Mynydd, the generosity of our farming neighbours allowed us to make use of several tractors, large and small livestock trailers, flat-bed trailer, tipping trailer, roller, tedder, mower, baler, mini-digger, gardening tools, a rotovator, and numerous other smaller items.

Now we're more established we find ourselves in a position where we're able to return the favour, or take our turn at helping others just starting out in smallholding.

A word of warning though: think about what you'll do if something gets broken while you're either borrowing it or lending it out. It does happen, and it could potentially lead to a dispute. Use common sense to decide who pays for repairs; if it's something minor then the borrower should sort it out, but if a more serious problem crops up then it may have been something just waiting to happen, and simply be bad luck that it occurred while the item was on loan. Negotiate, and pay up with a smile, if necessary; good will among farming and smallholding neighbours is invaluable.
Also on the subject of sharing, consider joint ownership of some larger pieces of equipment, or even livestock; where flocks and herds are small it makes sense to share rams, bulls and boars.

Small native ponies are phenomenally strong in proportion to their size.

THE WORKING HORSE

Unless you have a considerable area of woodland requiring sensitive timber extraction, there's no place for heavy horses (or any other kind of horses, come to that) on a productive smallholding. A full-size working horse is going to use up the equivalent of almost 2 acres of your holding, just in order to exist. Could you afford to take that much of your ground out of food production? I'm all in favour of a low-impact lifestyle, but you can hardly call it 'sustainable living' if you starve yourself to death in the process. You could reduce the pressure on your land by buying in all the feed and hay the horse requires, (and if he's a big one, and working hard, he'll require a lot), but you'd still need to find at least an acre of reasonably good grazing (which wouldn't stay good for long). What's more, horses are expensive to buy, incur exorbitant maintenance and repair bills, and have no residual value at the end of their useful lives.

Whichever way you look at it, the idea of having heavy horses on smallholdings, in lieu of tractors, is a non-starter, but what about little ponies? They don't eat much when they're not working, or take up much space either. The smaller types of native pony will thrive on a mere postage stamp of rough pasture, with perhaps just a handful of hay when the weather's really bad. They're also phenomenally strong in proportion to their size, far more intelligent than horses (making training so much easier), and readily available (for very little money). Although a pony is never going to be able to carry out the heavy tasks for which we use the tractor (e.g. mucking out the livestock buildings or baling hay), it could go a long way towards replacing that ubiquitous Jack-of-all-trades, the quad bike.

Hoeing field-scale vegetables.

The Saddlechariot

Despite its diminutive stature, pulling a wheeled vehicle carrying a grown man is no problem for a native pony. The saddlechariot makes things even easier: by virtue of the position of the rider giving perfect balance to the vehicle, strain on the animal is reduced to only one fifth of that inflicted by more conventionally designed traps and carts. The real beauty of the saddlechariot, however, lies in its unique safety mechanism – if things get out of hand you simply step off and pull the 'rip cord', whereupon the whole thing detaches itself from the pony, with no risk to either man or beast.

Animal welfare and user safety are the principle aspects of the design. In fact, the design is so pony-friendly that the average bomb-proof outgrown children's mount can be put straight to harness, with no further training required, and start earning his keep about the place.

Use of the saddlechariot on the smallholding is limited only by your imagination, as almost any piece of equipment designed to be towed by a quad bike or ATV can be operated equally easily behind the chariot. It'll even pull a small trailer. There's no brightly painted woodwork, polished leather, burnished brass, or any of the other paraphernalia usually associated with horse-drawn vehicles, just a practical down-to-earth bit of kit. Whether you're popping out to the shops, off to check the sheep, or need to fetch a load of firewood, you simply hitch up and go.

Could this be the organic quad-bike of the future? Low impact, low cost, low maintenance, and above all… fun!

Dot hauling timber by pony power.

Pony health and hoof care

Provided that he isn't allowed to become too fat, a squirt of wormer paste from time to time, an annual vaccination, and an occasional hoof trim are pretty much the only routine maintenance a small pony will require.

Although I'm equipped to trim a pony's feet myself, the vast majority of horse owners will employ a professional to carry out even relatively minor aspects of hoof care, particularly in animals that have been shod. In fact, the Farriers Acts of 1975 & 1977 make it illegal for anyone other than a qualified farrier to shoe horses, but native ponies shouldn't need shoes anyway.

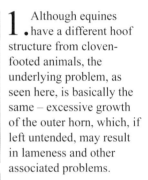

1. Although equines have a different hoof structure from cloven-footed animals, the underlying problem, as seen here, is basically the same – excessive growth of the outer horn, which, if left untended, may result in lameness and other associated problems.

2. Using a pair of pincers identical to those used for trimming the feet of cattle, the farrier first removes the surplus growth of outer horn.

3. A few moments spent removing the overgrown material has the hoof immediately looking much better.

4. The final shaping is carried out using a handheld rasp.

Section Seven
The Smallholder's
Workshop

The Smallholder's Workshop

A ny experienced workshop owners might like to skip this section, rather than be told, like grandma, how to suck eggs!

A Place To Work

You don't actually need a very big workshop. Larger projects can be carried out in other buildings when they're not taken up with livestock. In our sheep shed we have, amongst other things, dismantled and reassembled our baler, put a new engine in our car, and built any number of poultry houses. My sister constructed a sailing dinghy in the shed where we rear calves, and more recently our youngest daughter Rhian and I built a couple of kayaks in the same area (see page 367). However, projects like these are few and far between, and it would be an uneconomical use of space to have an area solely designated for such tasks. The exception would be where the smallholder has a specific

Building kayaks in the shed where we usually rear calves.

workshop skill, such as motor vehicle maintenance, welding, or furniture making, which he's intending to develop into an income-generating enterprise. Quite apart from the area required for actually carrying out such projects, additional space might be needed for certain dedicated items of equipment, and room to operate them safely.

For the non-specialist, a general purpose workshop is largely a storage area for tools and materials, and a place for carrying

out smaller repair and construction jobs – usually the sort of things that can be done on a bench. The main requirement, therefore, is for plenty of shelving and racks for tools. An electricity supply is more or less essential, as is good lighting. Bulky items such as rolls of fencing wire, drums of paint and larger bits of timber can be stored somewhere else, although smaller odds and ends will need to be kept close at hand. Store garden tools and equipment elsewhere too – there's no point cluttering up the workshop with spades and forks and stuff like that.

The floor area of my own workshop is about 256 square feet, and that's about the minimum you could get away with, I reckon. Most of that area is taken up with storage, and the woodwork bench (with more storage beneath) occupies much of the remaining clear space. A rack for holding lengths of timber is directly in line with the doorway, meaning that longer pieces of wood can easily be accommodated. Plenty of shelves and a small loft in the apex of the roof provide further useful storage space, and there's also a separate area within the workshop for all metalwork related items, machinery parts, and so on. (If I had the space, I'd have a completely separate workshop for metalwork and machinery maintenance). Potentially hazardous operations like welding are carried out outdoors, or in another building, depending on the weather. Flammable liquids such as petrol, oil, creosote and large tins of paint are kept in a designated chemical store some distance from the workshop. Even so, I keep a fire extinguisher just inside the workshop door, where it's easily accessible from within or without.

Basic equipment for the non-specialist

The content of anybody's workshop is a personal thing, so far be it from me to tell you what you ought to have in yours. Amongst other things, mine contains the head of an African buffalo, a pair of ice-skates, several broken banjos and some old leather horse-harnesses. I don't need this stuff, and neither do you, but there's also a lot of things in there that I know you will need. So, for the benefit of anyone who's starting from scratch, I'll run through a few suggestions. However, there's no need to go rushing out and buying all these things at once – build up a stock of equipment gradually, and source things second-hand where possible.

Work bench

A decent bench is central to any workshop. You won't be able to buy one sturdy enough, so make your own from some really hefty (3" thick) bits of timber. Ideally it needs to be 3' wide by 34" high, and at least 5'6" long, although clearly the size of your bench is going to be partly determined by the amount of workshop space you've got – you'll want to be able to work all round it, and still leave some room for storage. A woodwork vice can be permanently attached to the bench. You'll also need a metalwork vice, but this should be in a separate part of the workshop, perhaps attached to a small bench of its own along with other related equipment such as a grinder. It's a big mistake to carry out metalwork on the same surface that you use for woodwork, as shards and filings will ruin any piece of timber that they become embedded in.

A separate area for metalwork.

A pair of trestles is invaluable for jobs that can't be brought into the workshop (make your own), as is a folding 'workmate' type bench.

Hand tools

Saws

A good quality traditional wood saw is a joy to use, but they're expensive and take a lot of looking after. On the smallholding, where you're quite likely to be abusing your saw by cutting plasterboard, plywood, old pallets, breeze blocks and telegraph poles, in addition to conventional timber, you'd spend more time sharpening and maintaining the tool than actually using it. On the other hand, the modern hardpoint saws are ridiculously cheap (about £8 at the time of writing), and lethally

sharp, so buy several and replace as required. For general purpose use (i.e. both ripping and cross-cutting), look for one with 7 teeth per inch. You'll also want a tenon saw, bench hook and mitre block (you can make the last two items yourself).

A coping saw and a key-hole saw are both useful at times, although in my workshop they've been superseded by the electric jigsaw (see page 399).

If you do opt to use traditional wood saws then you'll also have to have a little gadget for setting the tooth angles, and the right sort of files for sharpening.

For metalwork, a hacksaw is needed. Get a 12" one, and plenty of spare blades.

Another saw, the bow saw, used for cutting logs, has more-or-less been made redundant by the chainsaw but you might want to keep a small one with the garden tools for pruning fruit trees.

Plane, spokeshave and / or drawknife

All three of these tools are used relatively frequently, when shaping new handles for spades, forks and shovels. The plane, however, should really be kept for jobs where a decent finish is required, such as making bookshelves and other simple furniture for the house. I have three – a chunky little smoothing plane, a much longer Jack plane, and an even longer try plane. However, for most general purposes a good smoothing plane will suffice. And while we're on the subject of smoothing, you'll also want a stock of sandpaper in various grades, and some emery paper too, and wire wool.

A range of hammers, L-R, club, claw, warrington, ball pein, tack.

Hammers and mallets

Hammers are for hitting metal (including nails), and mallets are for hitting wood. Don't go clouting a wooden chisel handle with a hammer, please. Exceptions to this rule are the copper mallet, which is used on certain metals where there's a risk that being hit with a hammer would cause distortion, and the rubber mallet, used when any of the aforementioned tools would be too severe.

You'll probably only need one wooden mallet, but you'll want a selection of hammers including:

• **Claw hammer:** The amateur's first choice, because it enables you to pull out any nails you've knocked in wonky. When using the claw, always place a piece of scrap wood under the head of the hammer. Not only does this protect your work from damage, it provides a fulcrum for additional leverage and results in a straighter pull.

• **Warrington:** A Warrington pattern hammer has a straight, chisel-like pein instead of a claw opposite the face. They always feel better balanced in the hand than a claw hammer, so would be my first choice when doing repetitive nailing jobs like fixing down floorboards (but I'd keep a claw hammer within reach, just in case…).

• **Ball pein:** A small ball pein hammer is what's used for peening rivets, so you'll need one when replacing handles on garden tools. You might also want a big one in the metalwork department.

• **Tack hammer:** Looking like a miniature Warrington, the tack hammer is used for knocking in small fixings such as panel pins, glazing sprigs, and those fiddly little gimp pins used in the construction of beehive frames.

• **Club hammer:** The club hammer needs no introduction. Weighing in at around 4lb, and with a short, thick handle, it's used in conjunction with tools such as cold chisels and bolsters, and for hitting things in general, when you're at your wit's end. The head of the club hammer also makes a useful mini anvil, for jobs like riveting or straightening bent nails.

• **Sledge hammer:** The sledgehammer is broadly similar to the club hammer, but larger, and with a much longer handle. Used for smashing up hardcore and things like that, it can also be pressed into service, at a pinch, for knocking in fence posts, but it's not nearly so effective as a proper post knocking hammer, and will result in more split stakes.

Whenever you're using a hammer as a 'gentle persuader', it's a wise precaution to protect the item being bashed using a piece of softwood.

Hand drill and brace and bit

Although it's easy to reach for a power drill these days, the simple hand drill shouldn't be overlooked, particularly for delicate jobs. Make sure you buy one with two cogs on the shaft – the poorer quality single cog models are wobbly to use and will wear out fairy quickly. Drill bits are rather like spanners, in that expensive ones are just as likely to get broken or lost. However, cheap twist drills will soon lose their edge. Learn to sharpen them and they'll last a lot longer. You'll want a countersink bit, too.

Another traditional hand tool that's by no means obsolete is the brace and bit – perfect for boring through wooden gateposts for the fitting of hinges. The brace needs to be of the ratchet type so it can be operated close to the ground. You'll want a 1" diameter auger bit for the gateposts.

Whether or not you'll need any additional sizes or styles of bit will depend on what other woodwork you'll be doing.

Chisels

For woodwork, you will, at the very least, require a sturdy 1" wide chisel when putting up new fences, for cutting mortises in the straining posts and so on. Whether or not you need any other sizes and styles will depend on the amount of more detailed carpentry you're intending to do.

Cold chisels are for use on stone and masonry, and you'll need a couple of fairly big ones, and a bolster (for cutting bricks and blocks) too. A very small (and fairly sharp) cold chisel is useful for slackening off nuts which have lost their corners and therefore can't be gripped with a spanner.

Using a brace-and-bit to bore a gatepost prior to fitting a new hinge.

Oilstone

Essential for keeping planes and chisels sharp. Get someone to teach you how to sharpen these tools properly – it makes a world of difference.

Try square, sliding bevel and marking gauge

Even if your carpentry skills don't extend beyond knocking together poultry houses from reclaimed materials, you'll want to neatly square off plank ends, accurately replicate angles, and mark out timber for cutting.

Tape measures

A pocket-sized tape measure is absolutely indispensable in the day-to-day running of the holding, and I always carry one. I also have a 30 metre tape in the workshop, which really only gets used when we're putting up a new building or carrying out major alterations. A strong steel rule is worth having in the workshop, too. It doubles as a straight edge for marking and cutting.

Spirit level, plumb-bob and string line

The plumb-bob and string line can be improvised as and when required. The spirit level is used, amongst other things, when setting gateposts and strainers in a new fence line – attention to detail makes all the difference.

Screwdrivers

The length of the shaft on a screwdriver should be directly proportional to the width of the blade (I forget the exact ratio). That is to say, fat screws need long screwdrivers. A shaft that's too short provides insufficient torque, so those stumpy little screwdrivers that you sometimes see in sets are little more than a gimmick. You'll need several different sizes

of both slotted and Philips style, including some very small ones for household and electrical repairs. There's also a host of 'new' fixings such as Torx and Pozidrive that you might come across – these each require their own style of driver.

Punches

You'll want a dot punch (or centre punch) for marking metal prior to drilling, and a flat-headed punch for burying nail heads (and dismantling old pallets – see overleaf). You might also need some roll-pin punches. A leather punch is also handy, even if only to put extra holes in your belt to stop your trousers falling down, when the stress and worry of running a smallholding reduces you to mere skin and bone – or at the other end of the belt, for when the good life is just too good!

Awl, bradawl and gimlet

The bradawl and gimlet are both used for making small holes in timber, to give a start to nails or screws. The bradawl is the smaller of the two, and resembles a very small, very sharp screwdriver. The gimlet is threaded, so can be used to bore a slightly larger hole. Providing a start in this way ensures that the nail or screw goes in the right place first time, and reduces the likelihood of the wood splitting as the fixing is driven home. An awl is simply a sharp spike fitted to a palm-sized handle, and is useful for jobs like making holes in leather prior to stitching.

Clamps / cramps

A selection of G and F clamps in various sizes is invaluable. If you're planning on doing a lot of carpentry then you might want a couple of pairs of sash cramps too.

Old pallets will yield up a lot of useful timber, ideal for the construction of poultry houses, rabbit hutches and the like. However, the secret lies in stripping them down without smashing any of the planks. You can't pull the nails out, or cut through them, or prise the timber apart, so what's the answer?

Using a flat-headed punch against the heads of the nails, you simply drive them right through the planks and into the battens. Each plank can then be lifted off intact – undamaged, apart from small neat holes where the nails were. Once you get into the swing of it, it doesn't take long.

It also works a lot better if the wood is wet, so leave the pallets out in the rain for a while first, to soften up.

A selection of clamps in use.

Files and rasps

You'll need a small selection of these. The ones that get the most use here are the round ('rat-tail') and half-round files. Equipment such as chainsaws and traditional hand saws will require their own special files for sharpening.

A surform type rasp is just the thing for shaping goats' hooves after trimming.

Paintbrushes

It's not worth splashing out on expensive paintbrushes for the kind of rough-and-ready paint jobs that the average smallholding needs to keep things up and running, so, unless you're undertaking more detailed work, like varnishing woodwork, the packs of cheap brushes you find in discount stores will be fine. You'll also need some bigger 'emulsion' brushes for applying whitewash to masonry, creosote to hen houses, and waste oil to machinery. Keep separate brushes for each of these tasks.

Rather than cleaning a paintbrush after use, try wrapping the bristles tightly in cling-film. This will keep them soft and pliable, ready for next time. Obviously this method is only any good if you'll be using the brush again fairly shortly, and with the same kind of paint.

Scrapers

Not only useful for removing loose or flaky paint – jolly handy for cleaning out poultry nest boxes and scraping crusted droppings off perches too.

Crow bar

Nothing to do with crows I don't think, just a hefty wrecking tool with a hook and claw at one end, and a pry bar at the other.

Trowels and floats

You'll need a large bricklayer's trowel, a smaller one for pointing, and a metal float. If you also need a wooden float then make your own. Make a wooden hawk, too – a board on a handle, which you use to hold a dollop of mortar or plaster at a convenient height for

Pliers, cutters and grips

In addition to an ordinary pair of 'combination' pliers (square nose, with wire cutter), you should have longnose pliers, surclip pliers, and fencing pliers (see page 49).

You might also want a pair of pinchers (for pulling out nails), side cutters (small ones can also be used for de-tusking piglets), tin snips, and mole grips. If you've got any domestic plumbing work to do then some sort of pipe cutter is also a good thing to have.

Pop riveter

This has been superseded, to an extent, by self-drilling screws.

the job you're doing – particularly useful when pointing.

Soldering iron and blowlamp

The soldering iron is for small jobs such as electrical repairs, and the blowlamp is for heavier tasks like plumbing, singeing chickens, and turning rams' horns. You'll need flux and solder as well, and an asbestos-style mat to prevent damage to the surrounding area.

Grease gun and oil can

These need no explanation. Save a lot of mess by using grease cartridges in the gun. Grease and oil machinery both before use and before storage.

Drain rods are absolutely essential.

Drain rods

Absolutely essential – so much so that I should probably have put them at the top of the list. With appropriate attachments, the same rods can be used for cleaning chimney flues.

Electrical power tools

Drills

A conventional electric drill has uses over and above the simple drilling of holes, as there are a number of other attachments such as wire brushes, sanders and hole-saws that can be used. In addition to an ordinary power drill you should also consider getting an SDS (Special Direct System) drill.

With the correct bits, this has the capability to hammer-drill through solid stone and concrete, and can be used in the 'hammer only' setting with chisel attachments. Cordless drills always appear to be a convenient option, but in my experience they never last very long, are never powerful enough, and the batteries are always flat when you need them. Whether you opt for mains- or battery-powered drills (or both), always choose ones with a variable speed facility and reverse function.

I also have a pillar drill in my workshop, but I inherited it. It's doubtful whether I could ever have justified buying one.

Jigsaw

I find a really good quality jigsaw absolutely indispensable, although if you'll be doing a lot of woodwork you'll probably want some heavier duty fixed equipment such as a bench saw and planer / thicknesser. For everyday applications, though, the jigsaw is more than adequate. Mine will tackle timber up to 85mm thick, steel up to 10mm thick, and aluminium up to 20mm thick. Combined with the ability to cut curves and bevels, this makes it a very versatile tool indeed. Removing the base plate also allows me to cut corrugated steel roofing sheets.

Jigsaw.

Angle grinder

The angle grinder is another indispensable electrical appliance. Quite apart from its use in cutting and shaping metal, it can also, with appropriate discs, be used to cut through stone, brick and concrete. The discs are relatively cheap, so you can afford to keep a selection of the different types in stock. Angle grinders come in different sizes, depending on the diameter of the discs they use. A big 9" (230mm) grinder will tackle pretty much anything you care to throw at it, but, if you're doing a lot of metalwork, you might also want a much smaller 4½" (115mm) grinder for cleaning up surfaces to be welded.

This is particularly the case when carrying out tasks such as machinery repairs, where the parts to be joined may be inaccessible to larger diameter discs.

Bench grinder

I don't think I'd have bought a bench grinder if I hadn't picked one up cheap at a farm dispersal sale. However, now I've got one I do find myself using it fairly regularly. It's particularly good for sharpening drill bits and hand shears.

Extension leads

You'll certainly need several.

Spanners, wrenches and sockets

Spanners are a nightmare to keep track of: you take them out into the hayfield to keep the baler running sweetly, and lose them on the headlands; you stuff them down behind the seat of the tractor where they become irretrievably absorbed into the gooey detritus that accumulates in such places, made up of grease, rust, grass-seeds,

The sort of spanners known as 'combination' wrenches (open spanner at one end and a ring spanner at the other) are good, because two can be linked together for extra leverage.

 TIP

A knackered socket set ratchet mechanism can be given a new lease of life by welding it up and using it thereafter as a solid drive.

mud and dead flies; they fall out of the door of the Landover whenever anyone gets in, and are promptly driven into the ground. And, if you're really incautious, you lend them to people. Either way, the life of a spanner of a useful size is pretty short. (Those of obscure dimensions, on the other hand, clutter up the tool box for years and years, impotent, yet taunting you with their unsullied newness). Good spanners aren't cheap, and won't last any longer. The best bet is to buy a few of those cut-price spanner sets you see on market stalls and in bargain stores to start you off, and simply put 'spanners' on your Christmas present list every year thereafter.

Adjustable spanners are handy too, but don't get used as often as you might think.

If any of your agricultural implements are of the 'vintage' variety then the odd box of ancient spanners you might come across at a farm dispersal sale are worth bidding on, as some old nuts and bolts won't be compatible with modern tools.

Sockets are rather like spanners in their habits, so I wouldn't bother splashing out on fancy gear, except for one thing: the ratchet drives in cheap socket sets are rubbish. Thankfully this item can be bought separately, so get a good one. You'll also need a solid bar drive

– the combination of a solid bar and a length of pipe will give you immense leverage for undoing stubborn things like tractor wheel nuts. Individual sockets can also be purchased separately, enabling you to add a few bigger sizes to your collection (again, thinking tractor wheel nuts here).

In addition to a ½" (13mm) drive socket set, wheel braces and some spark-plug sockets, it's also a good idea to have a smaller ¼" (8mm) drive set of sockets for fiddly jobs. And you'll want an adapter for using these in conjunction with a brace or power drill – small sockets will get a lot of use like this, particularly if you're attaching cladding or roofing sheets to a building with self-drilling screws.

Some Allen ('hex') keys are also worth having, although any piece of equipment that requires these for assembly or adjustment (garden machinery, power tools etc.) usually comes with a few in appropriate sizes as part of the package.

Larger Items

Welder: You can buy a basic arc

Above all else, you must have a decent Stilson in the spanner box. The Stilson and the club hammer are the two most reached-for tools when dealing with recalcitrant farm machinery.

Mortar and concrete

Mortar is made from sand and cement, with perhaps some lime added too, whereas concrete consists of 'all-in' aggregate (a mixture of ballast and sand) and cement. Different mixes are used for different purposes.

Mortar is used for laying bricks and blocks, pointing and rendering. A general purpose mix is made up of 1 part cement to 4-5 parts of soft sand (or 1 part cement, 1 part hydrated lime and 5 parts of soft sand). A slightly stronger mix is required for pointing, so use 1 part cement to 3 parts of soft sand (or 1 part cement, ½ lime and 4 sand). Concrete is for laying slabs, for example foundations, floors and driveways. Larger areas should be reinforced by the inclusion of metal bars or mesh. For general use, mix 1 part cement with 5 parts all-in aggregate (or, if mixing your own sand and ballast, use 1 part cement, 2 parts coarse sand and 3 parts aggregate). Where additional strength is required you can change the proportions and use 1 part cement to 4 parts aggregate, or even 1:3.5.

If a particularly good finish is needed, for example on internal domestic floors which are to be tiled, the concrete is often topped with a thin screed consisting of 1 part cement to 3 parts medium or coarse sand.

Both mortar and concrete must be prevented from drying out too quickly, so in hot weather cover your work with plastic sheeting or dampened sacks. You don't want newly laid concrete getting rained on either, so protect it with plastic sheeting, if required.

welder for around £60, new. This means that for simple repair and fabrication jobs it's cheaper to buy the equipment and do it yourself, than to pay a professional. On the other hand, you might already be a skilled metal worker, in which case you may be able to justify investment in a more heavy-duty bit of kit, with a view to offering your services to others. Personally, while I'm happy to carry out small welding jobs around the farm, I never tackle repairs to anything where the failure of a joint might result in a nasty accident (e.g. load bearing parts of agricultural machinery). I'm aware of my limitations, and am happy to pay for a proper job when need be. However, the cheap welder that I bought nearly 15 years ago has paid for itself many times over.

Don't forget, if you're using a welder you'll also need gauntlets and a face visor.

Concrete mixer

If you don't own a concrete mixer, make sure you know someone who does. Smaller quantities of mortar or concrete can be mixed by hand, using a shovel, on a flat board (an old piece of plywood will do) as follows: Thoroughly mix the dry ingredients in the correct proportions for the job (see box, left), then make a well in the centre of the heap. Pour water into this depression, a little at a time, and mix well. Repeat the process of heaping up the mixture, making a well, adding water and re-mixing, until the correct consistency is reached. Ideally, when you riffle the surface of the mix with the shovel or a trowel, it should hold the marks without them crumbling at the edges (too dry) or disappearing into puddles (too wet).

TIP

To clean the inside of a concrete mixer after use, let it run for a while with a bucket of water, a shovelful of gravel, and a couple of large stones or half bricks in the drum. Also, always clean mortar or concrete off shovels and trowels before it sets.

TIP

The addition of a squirt of fairy liquid to mortar during mixing makes it much easier to work with when laying bricks or blocks.

TIP

Dampen bricks and blocks before laying in dry weather, otherwise they'll draw moisture out of the mortar before it has a chance to set. Likewise, moisten walls before rendering.

Pressure washer

You'll probably need one in order to comply with regulations relating to the cleanliness of your livestock trailer. Also useful for washing down animal housing after mucking out.

Compressor

Like the concrete mixer, if you don't own one yourself, make sure you know someone who does. You can't afford to waste good haymaking weather trying to pump up squishy tractor tyres by hand.

Petrol powered equipment

Whether or not you have a lawn mower will depend upon how fussy you are about lawns. What you will need, though, is a heavy duty strimmer / brushcutter, and a decent chainsaw. It's worth going on a chainsaw course, because, quite apart from the safety aspect,

Chainsaw law

The laws relating to either domestic or commercial use of chainsaws differ slightly. As an agricultural holding you're classified as a commercial user. You, the owner / occupier, can use your own chainsaw on land that you farm without any kind of training. Your employees (if you have any) will need to have a certificate of competence, unless they've been using chainsaws since before 1998. You are responsible for ensuring that they have received appropriate training, and are provided with suitable protective clothing.

You cannot lend, hire, give or sell your chainsaw to anyone else unless they hold a certificate of competence. Although it is not a requirement that you, personally, have been properly trained and wear protective clothing, the HSE may prosecute you for failures in this respect.

you'll learn to sharpen it properly. A small garden rotavator can be useful for taking some of the hard graft out of preparing your vegetable beds, particularly if you're trying to incorporate manure. Additional attachments – such as potato ridgers – can be obtained, but we've never found them very effective. If you're serious about growing any significant amount of veg then you'll probably graduate to tractor mounted equipment fairly quickly.

Generator

Like it or not, our lives have become more or less dependent on electricity, and smallholders are no exception to this. Whether you rely on mains power or produce your own from renewable resources, a back-up 'genny' is a worthwhile investment, even if only to save the contents of your freezer during a power cut.

Paints and potions

Creosote

Proper old-fashioned coal tar creosote is no longer available to domestic users. Thankfully, agriculture falls within the definition of 'industrial', so we can still buy it. It's just the thing to treat timber poultry houses, fence posts, garden sheds, etc. The modern alternatives are not nearly so effective.

Linseed oil

For finishing wooden tool handles, making polish (see below) and softening putty.

Meths

Methylated spirits can be used to remove stubborn sticky marks and glue residues, such as where price labels have been removed from items. It can also be used as a de-greaser, prior to gluing or painting. It's highly flammable (burns with an almost invisible blue flame), and is used to pre-heat paraffin-fuelled pressure stoves and lanterns (e.g. Primus and Tilley).

Turps

Turpentine substitute or white spirit. Use as a thinner and for cleaning paintbrushes. It can also be used, together with linseed oil, meths and white vinegar, to make a simple furniture polish – two parts linseed oil to one part each of the other ingredients. (To make beeswax polish, which also uses turps, see page 320.)

PVA wood glue

Apart from its use as a timber adhesive, PVA is also used, diluted with water, for bonding concrete surfaces prior to laying floor tiles etc.

2-part resin glues

2-part epoxy resins, such as Araldite, form an incredibly strong bond and can be used for sticking non-porous materials such as metal and ceramics, in addition to materials like wood and masonry. It's essential that the surfaces to be glued are free from grease or the epoxy simply won't set, and remains soft and rubbery.

Once dry, epoxies can be sanded and painted. Epoxy resins are commonly used in boat building these days (see page 367 and following), and can be purchased in suitably large quantities from yacht chandlers.

Other glues

Clear adhesive such as UHU for small household repairs; contact (rubber-based) adhesive such as Evostik for sticking leather, rubber etc. (e.g. shoe mending); latex-based glue such as Copydex for

use on textiles. Also wallpaper paste, which needs no explanation.

Modern adhesives

Modern adhesives such as 'Gripfill' have awesome sticking power, and have replaced nails and screws in many applications. I have used them for, amongst other things, fitting wooden skirting boards and architraves to masonry and plastered surfaces without the need for any other fixings. It's definitely worth keeping a few tubes in stock, but be aware that their shelf life is rather short.

Pastes and fillers

Polyfiller, putty, fire cement, mastic etc.

Paint and varnish

These are generally the sorts of things you'll buy in for specific jobs, but do keep in stock some masonry paint for the dairy, cowshed, and other outbuildings (the modern equivalent of whitewash), and some red-oxide primer for coating exposed metal after repairs to machinery etc. For occasional touching up jobs you're bound to have an accumulation of half-tins and leftovers of gloss, undercoat, primer and emulsion.

TIP

Keep a selection of small quantities of different types of wood dust, and also powdered horn, bone etc., in little pots. When mixed with an appropriate adhesive, these can be used to make more-or-less invisible repairs in matching materials.

Nuts, bolts, nails, screws and washers

Nails are most definitely *not* 'use once and throw away' items. Old nails can be straightened and re-used many times over, so whenever you're dismantling something, salvage as many as you can. Sort roughly according to size and style, and store in appropriately labelled containers.

On the other hand, once screws or bolts become bent, they're rendered more-or-less useless due to damage to the thread. Therefore take care when removing, to extend their useful life. As with nails, sort second-hand screws and bolts into different sizes and types for storage. The same applies to nuts and washers.

While it's always best to recycle products wherever possible, there will be times when it's necessary to buy new fixings, particularly if you're undertaking a big construction job such as putting up a new outbuilding – a repetitive task such as laying roof sheets or fitting Yorkshire boarding will use up an awful lot of nails. For these jobs, buy in bulk, if possible, because the little plastic pre-packs you see on sale these days work out awfully expensive when you need more than just a few.

One of the most useful types of fixing to keep in stock are self-drilling screws that can be zapped into almost any material using an 8mm socket in an electric drill. Different types are available for fixing into steel, timber or concrete. Uses include fixing roof cladding to steel or timber purlins, attaching gate hinges to metal stanchions, and fitting galvanised sheeting to gates.

You'll also want staples for attaching fence wire to posts (see pages 48 - 51).

Other odds and ends

Offcuts of leather and old rubber inner tubes for making emergency washers.

Lead flashing (for roof repairs or making fishing weights).

Candle wax (for greasing sledge runners).

Whipping twine and / or strong waxed cotton thread.

Paraffin and lanterns etc., in case of power cuts.

Puncture repair kit (together with tyre levers).

Fuses, fuse wire and electrical insulation tape.

Ptfe tape. Used to ensure a watertight joint in compression type pipe fittings – wrap a length of ptfe tape around the thread before tightening.

Penknife: Not exactly a workshop tool, as it should be in your pocket at all times. I favour a fairly large one with a lockable blade, but the law says if you're carrying a penknife in a public place, it must be non-lockable, with a blade of less than 3″ in length.

TIP

To clear an airlock in domestic plumbing, use a length of hosepipe to connect the kitchen cold water tap (which runs directly from the mains) to the affected tap, having first removed the washer and temporarily replaced the top. Turn both on for several minutes.

Always have 2 wheelbarrows - one for dry / clean, and the other for wet / dirty.

Garden, yard and woodshed tools

In the garden you'll need a digging fork (straight, square tines), spade, rake, two kinds of hoe (Dutch and draw), dibber (an old spade handle), small trowel, string line, measuring stick (make your own), and watering can. Around the yard you'll want a muck fork (curved, rounded tines), pitchfork, shovel, stiff broom and yard scraper. It's also a good thing to have a couple of different wheelbarrows, one of which is used for muck, compost, earth, stones, concrete etc., and the other for carrying 'dry' stuff like hay and straw, and for bringing in the vegetable harvest. Hosepipes are something else you'll want plenty of, both in the garden and around the yard.

The scythe is a tool that's largely been superseded by the strimmer, but there are times when you might want to use one (see pages 124 and 125). Likewise, the grass hook or slasher – I find ours very useful for cutting isolated thistles in areas where they can't be tackled by machine. If you're intending to do any hedge laying (see pages 47 - 48) you'll also need a billhook, although a chainsaw is often used instead these days.

In the woodshed you'll want a

Chopping kindling using a small hatchet.

felling axe and a hatchet. The big felling axe is used for splitting logs, and the little hatchet for chopping kindling. If you're processing a lot of firewood you might consider it worthwhile investing in a hydraulic log splitter, but I've never felt this to be necessary, despite the fact that our central heating is wood fired. Splitting wood with an axe is a very satisfying (and warming) task.

TIP

Always empty the water out of hosepipes during the winter. You may well need to use them in a hurry to provide drinks for thirsty livestock whose usual supply has frozen. In this situation, it's very frustrating to find that your hosepipes have also frozen solid.

Arts and Crafts

Here, I feel, we're treading on difficult ground. The arts and crafts movement is often considered to be synonymous with alternative living, and many smallholders I know are indeed accomplished craftsmen. Yet I wonder – was it an interest in arts and crafts that led them to adopt a self-sufficient way of life, or did the change of lifestyle come first? Either way, in most cases, craft activities play little or no part in the actual day-to-day running of a food producing smallholding (I mean, what use is a corn dolly, really?).

However, the skilful master of a craft who finds a ready market for the output of his creativity has a prime opportunity to generate some cash revenue, and it's even better if the raw materials required can be grown on the holding.

Take basket making as an example: you really would be wasting your time if you decided to make baskets specifically in order to carry produce in from the garden, particularly when there are so many discarded plastic containers lying about, just crying out to be put to good use. However, basket making as a craft, with income generated by doing demonstrations at rural events, and the sale of finished articles, is an avenue well worth pursuing. To get this good you have to practice, and all those early attempts (and any later efforts that don't quite reach the required quality standard) are the ones that get used around the home and holding, in place of the ubiquitous plastic bucket.

On this basis, anyone thinking of incorporating some sort of art or craft into their (probably already diverse) portfolio of smallholding enterprises ought to ask themselves the following questions:

1. Can the raw materials be produced sustainably on the holding (or sourced free of charge)?

2. Do you have sufficient skill (or the opportunity to learn)?

3. Do you really have time to pursue this new interest?

4. Is any significant capital investment required (e.g. for the purchase of specialist tools or equipment)?

5. Is the end product likely to be saleable?

6. Do you have any marketing experience?

7. Will sub-standard or unsold items be of any practical use on the smallholding?

Obviously the answers to questions 2, 3 and 6 are a personal matter, but with respect to the other points, let's consider a few options:

• **Working with wool:** Fleeces are a low-value by-product of domestic meat production, and your sheep will grow new ones every year, so raw wool is a sustainable product of the holding. Spun yarn is definitely marketable, as hand-knitting remains a popular pastime, and you could add further value by producing finished items for sale. Any garments that don't quite make the grade can be worn by yourself and your family. A basic spinning wheel and associated equipment will set you back about £400. (See pages 408 - 413 for further information on spinning, weaving and dyeing.)

• **Woodland crafts:** If you've got plenty of trees on your holding then green woodwork, such as chair bodging, is a sustainable craft, provided that you plant more trees as you go along – it would be a great pity to run out of the basic raw material through lack of foresight. The tools and equipment required are minimal, and you may find you've got what you need in the workshop already. Hand-made chairs sell well, and any that are a bit wobbly will be fine around your own kitchen table. If you want to learn more about woodland crafts I recommend the book *Green Woodwork* by Mike Abbot (ISBN 0-946819-18-1).

Charcoal burning could also be considered under the heading 'woodland crafts', as could hurdle making.

• **Basketry:** As with woodland crafts, the raw materials required for basket making may already be growing around the farm. If not you can plant some willow and coppice it from time to time (see pages 378 - 380). No special tools are needed, and either the end product will be saleable, or, as with many of these traditional pastimes, there's money to be made by doing demonstrations at country fairs. Poorer quality baskets will be useful on the smallholding, but that use is fairly limited.

• **Furniture making / restoration:** The making of furniture, apart from the chairs mentioned above, requires seasoned timber, which you'd usually have to buy in.

Pottery

If there's a good source of suitable clay on your farm then you could dig it up, make it into pots, and sell them. But you'd be selling your land, bit by bit, which clearly isn't sustainable in the long term. Really, you'd have to buy in clay of the right type if you were planning on making more than just the occasional item. There'd also be a fair amount of expenditure on items such as a wheel and kiln. However, there's no doubt that pots are saleable, and the rejects might be useful in the kitchen.

Left: Handmade pottery by Tim's mum.

Before and after: We've given these discarded items of furniture a new lease of life.

That's not to say that you couldn't produce it yourself, if you've got suitable mature trees. My father made some very nice furniture from wind-blown timber, and I'm accumulating a store of suitable wood by the same means. However, it does need to be milled, for which there'll be a fee (although I'm planning on settling the bill by barter). If you've got a ready supply of timber then making furniture is one of those things that's probably justifiable, even if purely for home use. It doesn't take a huge amount of skill to build a bookcase or a bed that's better than anything you could buy.

Furniture restoration, in its simplest form, just means taking something old and tatty and making it look nice again. It's amazing what stuff people throw out or that can be obtained through Freecycle. The nicest pieces of furniture in our house were once someone else's rubbish. House clearance sales and auctions are also sources of old furniture in need of a makeover, and once restored they can often be re-sold at a reasonable profit, provided you didn't pay too much for them in the first place, and that no major structural repairs are required.

• **Leatherwork:** Animal skins are another by-product of your meat producing animals, which may go to waste if you can't find a use for them. Curing skins to make rugs is simple enough, but tanning hides (for leather) is a different matter. We've only done it once, and aren't planning on having another go any time soon, although kits can now be purchased to make the job easier. If you don't fancy trying it there are companies that'll tan your hide for you. Small leatherwork items such as purses, belts and bracelets always seem to sell well at craft fairs and the like.

Ammunition wallet, stick barette and knife pouch made from recycled leather.

Second-hand leather is also a useful source of the raw material, and you can often pick up old saddlery items for next-to-nothing at auction, or leather handbags in charity shops and car boot sales. These can be recycled and used for the making of small hand-crafted items for personal use.

To ensure evenly-spaced stitches when sewing leather, mark out the line of the seam using the prongs of an ordinary dining fork, prior to making holes with an awl. The two pieces of leather can be temporarily glued together (UHU is good), which will be sufficient to hold them in place while you make the holes and do the stitching.

Curing skins

After successfully removing the skin from the animal, lay it out and scrape off any remaining flesh, fat and connective tissue. It may also be possible to remove some of the membrane at this stage. Most books recommend the use of a blunt blade for this job, but we have found that a very sharp knife and a steady hand are preferable. The skin can now be salted if it is not possible to continue with the process at this stage.

Scraping a sheepskin prior to curing.

Place the skin in a container containing a 10% solution of formaldehyde and leave for a week, stirring occasionally. If the skins have been salted they should be thoroughly rinsed before placing in the formalin solution. Formaldehyde solution can be purchased from agricultural merchants as it's used for foot-bathing cattle and sheep, but you'll have to dilute it to get the right concentration.

At the end of the week the skin is removed from the solution and thoroughly washed several times with clean cold water. Shake off as much water as possible and tack out the skin (hair side down) on a board. Rub a hide de-greasing agent into the skin with a nailbrush. (The product we used to use doesn't seem to be available any more, but a search of taxidermy supplies companies will turn up several options.)

Allow to dry for a day or two, and before completely dry, rub all over in a circular motion using coarse sandpaper on a block. Apply more de-greaser and leave until the next day. Repeat the sanding and dressing, and continue to repeat day after day until all the membrane is removed.

Remove the skin from the board and wash carefully in warm water with a little washing up liquid. Rinse in clean cold water and leave to dry out at room temperature. It may be desirable to re-fix the skin to the board (fur uppermost this time) while it dries, but we don't usually do this.

Once the skin is dry you'll probably have to work it over a beam (or the back of a chair) to make it nice and supple, and apply a leather dressing such as neatsfoot oil.

Spinning, Weaving and Dyeing

Fleeces stored in paper sacks in a suitable environment (cool and dry) will remain useable for a long time (years, even) and, provided that they were properly rolled at shearing time, it should be a fairly simple matter to unroll and lay them out correctly for sorting. Alternatively, fleeces destined for home spinning could be sorted at shearing time, and the various different parts packed separately ready for use.

Rolling a fleece at shearing time.

Unfortunately, domestic processing of home-produced fleeces into everyday items of family clothing cannot be considered a worthwhile activity, even for the most dyed-in-the-wool self-supporter. In terms of the time and effort involved, you'd end up with very expensive garments. What's the point, when you can pick up a pure wool jumper in a charity shop for a couple of quid? Yet producing wool for sale to the British Wool Marketing Board (BWMB) isn't a financially justifiable activity either, with the price received scarcely covering the cost of shearing. In the case of coloured sheep, where the fleece may fetch less than 10 pence per kg, shearing can become a rather a costly business, unless you do it yourself.

Despite the fact that small-scale hand spinning of your own fleeces won't be justifiable as the sole source of the family's winter woollies, you're bound to want to have a go at it at some point: it's great to have a jumper made from the fleece of a favourite animal, or, in my case, from the fleece of the very first sheep I ever sheared.

As your skill develops, it may be possible to start adding value to those otherwise worthless coloured fleeces, by producing yarns for sale in a variety of natural shades. We sold quite a bit of wool like this when we lived on Bardsey, with Dot spending some of the long winter evenings spinning both white and coloured fleeces (and mixtures of the two), for sale via an 'honesty box' system to summer visitors.

From this point, it's but a short step to producing a range of finished items in natural colours – artisan products for sale at the higher end of the market – and suddenly the idea of keeping sheep for their fleeces doesn't seem so bad after all.

Lay the fleece out skin side down on a clean surface, and begin by removing any contamination. Very heavily contaminated fleeces, for example from sheep that have regularly slept under the hayrack during the preceding winter, are of no use to the hand spinner. Matted fleeces should also be rejected. Any second cut wool (little short pieces, caused by the shearer going over the same part of the sheep twice, in order to tidy up a bit he's missed) should be picked or shaken off, and the belly wool can be put aside for felting. The remainder of the fleece is then divided up into about seven different areas. There's a traditional pattern to this, but use your judgement a bit as individual fleeces vary. Basically, put wool that looks and feels similar together. The best quality wool is found on the shoulder, and then the back. Other areas that should be separated out are the sides, neck, haunches, tail and hind legs, and the forelegs. In the case of coloured sheep you may wish to further sub-divide each category according to shade, but this isn't essential; some nice random effects can be created by spinning the wool as it comes.

Carding combs and prepared rolags.

Carding

Before spinning, wool needs to be teased out and fluffed up. This could be done by simply pulling apart a piece of the fleece with your fingers, but a bit more care in preparation will result in a better yarn, so it's best to 'card' the wool. This is also a good opportunity to remove any remaining debris, and to blend different colours.

A carding comb is a slightly curved rectangular wooden bat, about 8" x 5", with a handle on the long edge. The convex face of the bat is covered with 'card cloth' which has closely spaced rows of bent wire teeth. Carders are always used in pairs.

Method

With one card held face-up in the left hand (if you're right handed), lay staples of wool on the teeth, side by side, parallel with the handle. Cover the surface completely, but not too thickly. Commence carding by holding the other card face down in the right hand and brushing it gently across the wool on the first. Repeat this a few times. Most of the wool will transfer to the other card, and you'll see that the fibres are gradually being combed into line with one another. Next, transfer all the wool back onto the teeth of the first card. Repeat the process of combing and transferring several times, until you've created an even mat of wool with all the fibres more or less aligned. Remove the mat from the combs by stripping it gently from one card to the other, and back again. Lay the resultant light, fluffy rectangle of wool on the concave back of one of the cards, and roll it into a sort of long, airy, sausage shape, such that all the fibres are curled. This is called a rolag. Make quite a few rolags while you're at it, and stack them loosely in a box or basket, so that once you start spinning you won't have to keep stopping in order to prepare more wool.

If you intend to develop your wool processing activities into a cottage industry scale operation, then it would be worth buying a drum carder.

SPINNING

Spinning basically consists of drawing out the parallel fibres of a rolag and twisting them into a continuous thread of the required thickness. This can be used directly for weaving, or two or more may be plied together to form a yarn suitable for knitting.

Drop spindle

Simple to make, or cheap to buy, the drop spindle remains an excellent way for beginners to gain a 'feel' for the wool, and develop the rhythm of co-ordinated hand movements required, before moving on to a more expensive spinning wheel.

To make a drop spindle, all you need is a slightly tapered stick, around 10" long, and a wooden disc about 4" diameter by ¾" thick. The stick should have a notch in its thinner end (like a crochet hook), and the disc (or whorl) needs a hole through the centre, slightly smaller in diameter than the thicker end of the stick. When the stick is pushed through the hole, thin end first, the whorl should slide almost to the other end, leaving an inch or so of the thicker end of the stick protruding.

Drop spindle.

Using the drop spindle.

Method

You'll need a short length of yarn, already spun, as a leader. Attach this to the spindle just above the whorl, then pass it under the whorl and wrap it round the spindle a couple of times. From here, it goes back over the whorl and all the way up to the thinner end of the spindle, where it is held in place by a half hitch around the notch. The free end needs to be about 8″ long. Now, dangle the whole assembly in front of you by holding the end of the leader between the finger and thumb of your left hand. Together with the leader, also between the finger and thumb of the left hand, pinch a piece of the fluffy end of a rolag. With the other hand, give the spindle a good twirl in a clockwise direction, then pinch the leader and rolag just below the left finger and thumb. The two hands now move apart, drafting some of

the wool from the end of the rolag between the finger and thumb of the left hand. When a section of suitable length and density has been drawn from the rolag, pinch more tightly with the left hand and release your grip slightly with the right. The right hand now slides up to meet the left, allowing the turning spindle to twist the fibres into a thread. The end of the leader and the new thread should join seamlessly. Don't allow the twist to pass the left finger and thumb or it'll tangle up the rolag, making subsequent drafting very difficult.

Continue repeating the sequence of hand movements until you've spun sufficient yarn for the spindle to touch the floor. At this point you'll have to stop, undo the half hitch and the turns under the whorl, and wind the yarn onto the spindle. Once again, pass the yarn under the whorl before taking it back to the top of the spindle and securing it with a new half hitch. If you didn't give the spindle enough of a spin it may well stop rotating before it reaches the floor, then begin to unwind; if you don't spot this happening, your yarn will break. Experience will soon teach you how much spin to give, and how finely you need to draft the fibres from the rolag.

Spinning wheel

Spinning with a wheel uses exactly the same sequence of hand movements, although it's simplified by the fact you're working in a horizontal plane, and you get to sit down. There is, of course, the added complication of having to operate the treadle, but once you get the hang of it you'll find that a natural rhythm develops, and you'll carry on without even thinking about it. The action of the treadle turns the large

wheel, which in turn drives the bobbin and flyer mechanism via a drive belt (just a piece of string, really). The bobbin rotates at a slightly different speed than the flyer, either faster by virtue of there being two drive belts on different sized pulleys, or more slowly by using a braking system, depending on the design of the wheel. In the first case, the spun yarn is drawn onto the bobbin, and in the second case the yarn is wound onto the bobbin by the flyer.

Attach a leader of spun yarn to the bobbin.

Just as when using a drop spindle, begin by attaching a leader of spun yarn. This is tied to the shaft of the bobbin, and wrapped around a few times. It's then carried over the hooks of the flyer, before exiting via the spindle eye – you'll need a little wire hook to pull it through the hole. As before, spinning commences (in a clockwise 'Z-twist' direction,) by joining the leader to the end of a rolag. As you spin you'll need to shift the yarn onto the next hook of the flyer from time to time, to ensure that the bobbin is evenly filled.

Plying

A single strand of twisted yarn will, if given half a chance, begin to unravel itself. However, if two or more yarns are run together, while applying a twist in the opposite direction, a state of

Main: *Spinning wheel and Lazy Kate.*
Inset: *Drafting fibres from the rolag.*

Plying together two yarns of different colours.

equilibrium is reached, resulting in a stable yarn. This is called plying. Single strand yarns are used for weaving, but for knitting you'll need 2- or 3-ply. Some interesting variations can be created by plying together bobbins containing different coloured wools.

Method

Put two or three filled bobbins in the Lazy Kate, making sure that the larger diameter ends are all at the same side. Place the Lazy Kate behind and slightly to the left of you, either on the floor or on another chair. Fit an empty bobbin on the wheel, and attach a new leader. Tie the ends of the yarns to be plied to the free end of the leader, then begin to treadle the wheel in an anti-clockwise ('S-twist') direction. The action of the hands is very similar to when spinning, except that there's no drafting to be done, so the left hand stays still. For making 2-ply, one yarn passes between the thumb and first finger of the left hand, and the other between first and middle fingers. Pressure of the fingers controls the speed at which the yarn is pulled off the bobbins on the Lazy Kate. The right hand gently holds the two threads together and slides back towards the left, allowing the twist to develop in front of the fingers. When the two hands meet, the

right pinches the yarn and moves forward again, allowing the plied yarn to be wound onto the bobbin on the wheel, while drawing another length from the bobbins held on the Lazy Kate. Repeat these movements, over and over, until the bobbin on the wheel is full (i.e. when you've used up half the wool on the Lazy Kate). Now, to empty the bobbin of plied wool, you'll need to wind a skein.

Winding and washing

Skeins are wound using a Niddy Noddy, which isn't half as bizarre as it sounds. The Niddy Noddy is made of wood, about 18" long overall, and shaped like a capital letter I, except that the two cross pieces are perpendicular to one another. You could easily make one by pushing pieces of dowel through holes drilled at each end of a piece of broom handle.

The wool is wound onto the Niddy Noddy in a continuous fashion, around one end of one peg, then one end of the other, then back to the other end of the first peg, then the other end of the second.

Two Niddy Noddies, one bought and the other home-made.

As with everything we've seen so far, there's a rhythm to this: up and over, down and under, up and over, down and under, with the right hand winding the yarn, while the

A skein wound on the Niddy-Noddy.

holding. However, you'll find that each dye bath you make up takes you on an interesting voyage of discovery – the colours never come out quite like you expected, and very rarely do you get the same colour twice!

(See table 13, pages 448 - 449 for a comprehensive list of dye plants and recommended mordants.)

The basic method of obtaining dye remains pretty much the same whatever plant is used, in that the vegetable material is boiled to extract the pigment, although there are a few (lichens in particular) that need to be fermented (in urine, of all things!). A mordant is used to ensure that the dye is colour fast, and may also be used to modify the tone.

Mordants

Some dye plants contain their own mordant, such as the tannin in oak, or the oxalic acid in rhubarb, in which case no fixative will be required.

However, in most cases a chemical mordant will need to be used, the commonest being alum (potassium aluminium sulphate), chrome (potassium dichromate), tin (stannous chloride), and iron (ferrous sulphate). A couple of less frequently used mordants are lime (calcium oxide) and copper sulphate. Cream of tartar is often added to alum in order to brighten a colour, and in some cases washing soda, or even common salt, can be used for mordanting. Depending on the chemical being used, and the intended effect, mordanting can be carried out before, during, or after dyeing, or before and after.

left hand, holding the centre of the shaft of the Niddy Noddy, twists it back and forth in time with the movement of the right. When you've wound a whole bobbin full of plied wool onto the Niddy Noddy, tie around the skein fairly loosely in four places using short lengths of yarn, before slipping it off. You could now simply roll this into balls and start knitting, but you'll end up with a greasy 'fisherman's jersey' smelling strongly of sheep. It's best to wash the skeins at this stage, and, if you do want to make a weatherproof sweater, re-oil it with purified lanolin during the final rinse. Or soak the skeins for a couple of hours and wash in cold water only (no soap) – this will remove most of the odour, but leave the lanolin, which will be ok for outdoor garments.

For more thorough washing, soak the wool in warm water before washing in 'hand hot' water with a detergent (Fairy Liquid). Very grubby wool will need washing more than once. Rinse several

times in tepid water, before hanging the skeins up to dry on a broom handle. Another broom handle slipped through the bottom of the skeins will keep them taught and prevent kinking. Excess water can be gently squeezed out, but not wrung – handle the wool very tenderly throughout the whole washing process, or you'll end up felting it. Wool that has been thoroughly washed in this way can be dyed.

Some spinners prefer to wash (and dye) fleece wool before spinning. Certainly this keeps the spinning wheel and other equipment much cleaner, but washed wool has a 'dry' feel to it, and is much harder to spin than its greasy counterpart.

DYEING

When introducing colour to your creations, it adds a nice touch if you use natural dyes from plants which can be grown in the kitchen garden, or encouraged to proliferate naturally around the

Mordanting with alum and cream of tartar before dyeing

It's not possible here to give detailed instructions for the use of all the various mordants, but alum, being the commonest used (and the safest), seems like an appropriate example. The addition of cream of tartar will result in brighter colours. Too much alum makes the wool go all sticky, so make sure you weigh the ingredients carefully.

Method

For each 4 oz (approx. 2 skeins) of washed yarn you'll need 1 oz of alum, ¼ oz of cream of tartar and 1 gallon of soft water (rain water is good). Heat the water to around 30°C in an old saucepan – stainless steel is preferable, as it won't have any affect on the final colour, but aluminium pans are ok for use with alum. Don't use chipped enamel saucepans, or the iron will 'sadden' the dye. If you do want to produce subdued colours, then ferrous sulphate can be added later. Dissolve the alum and cream of tartar in a small quantity of boiling water, and stir the solution into the saucepan. Thoroughly wet the wool with clean, fresh water, and place it in the saucepan containing the mordant solution. Gradually, over a period of about an hour, bring the saucepan to the boil, turning the wool gently a few times. As soon as boiling point is reached reduce the heat and simmer gently for a further 45 minutes. Turn off the heat and allow the yarn to cool in the liquor. After this, the wool can either be stored damp for a couple of days, after which it will be in an ideal state for dyeing, or it can be dried and stored for future use, in which case it will have to be thoroughly wetted again. If you're

storing skeins of pre- mordanted yarn, remember to label each one according to the substance used.

Simple dye recipes

Uusing 4 oz of wool pre- mordanted with alum and thoroughly wetted

Yellow / green

Simmer 8-10 handfuls of onion skins in soft water for about 30 minutes then strain out the skins and allow the liquor to cool to hand heat. Place the wetted wool in, making sure that it is completely submerged, and bring the pan slowly to the boil. Simmer until the wool reaches the desired colour. This method will result in varying shades of yellow. The addition of iron to the dyebath gives greens. (A bright orange can be obtained from onion skins by mordanting with tin, but this is not such an easy substance to use as alum).

Purple / blue

Crush 2lb of elderberries, put them in a pan of cold water, heat slowly, and simmer for 45 minutes or so. Strain off the berries and allow the liquor to cool to hand heat. Place the wetted wool in, making sure that it is completely submerged, and bring the pan slowly to the boil. Simmer for half an hour or more, until sufficient depth of colour is achieved. Leave the wool to soak in the dye overnight to give a lovely purple colour. This can be made bluer by the addition of a handful of common salt to the dye while the wool is soaking.

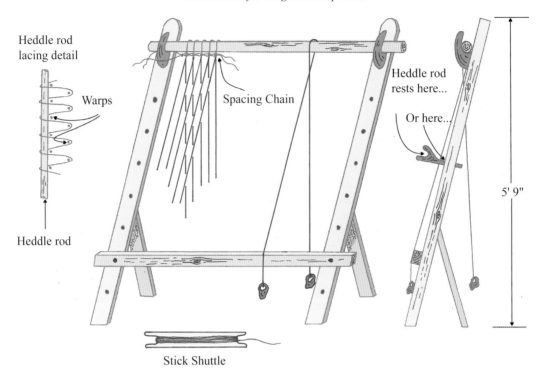

Mediaeval style weighted-warp loom

Heddle rod
lacing detail

Warps

Spacing Chain

Heddle rod
rests here...

Or here...

5' 9"

Heddle rod

Stick Shuttle

Weaving

My experience of weaving is limited to the use of a Mediaeval style loom that my father built, on which we made some interesting wall hangings, but even where a more up-to-date piece of equipment is used, the principle remains the same.

A loom, of any design, is basically a frame (either vertical or horizontally mounted) on which one set of threads (the warp) are held taught, while another thread (the weft) is woven in and out of them, from one side to the other, and back again, and so on, until an appropriate length of cloth has been formed. The weft is generally wound onto some sort of shuttle (we used a stick shuttle), or can be pulled through using a long flat piece of wood with a notch forming a hook at the end. Care must be taken not to pull the

weft too tight, or the shape of the finished piece will be distorted. After every few passes with the shuttle, the weft can be pressed firmly into place with a heavy wooden comb.

Our Mediaeval vertical frame loom is a 'weighted warp loom', in that the warps are held taught by weights tied to the ends (in our case, stones with holes in, gradually accumulated over many trips to a shingle beach).

The two uprights of the vertical frame have holes drilled at intervals along their lengths to allow for re-positioning of other components as the length of cloth on the loom grows. The top cross member is the beam, over which the threads are hung when warping up. The warps are then tied in place, tight to the beam, with a 'spacing chain'. The lower cross member of the rectangle is

also the shed rod. Alternate warp threads hang in front of or behind the rod, creating the 'shed' – the gap through which the shuttle containing the weft is passed. Of course, it's necessary to bring the hindermost warps to the front before sending the shuttle on its return journey, otherwise you'd simply undo what you'd just done. For this, another, movable, horizontal bar, called the heddle rod, is used. All the warp threads that hang behind the shed rod are loosely laced to the heddle rod. Pulling the heddle rod forward (where it is held by a couple of notched pegs located in the holes in the uprights) moves the warps into the alternate position.

Section Eight
Making Ends Meet

Generating an Income

"...confusing, perhaps, busy-ness with progress, and money-handling with money-making" Adrian Bell – author of the 1930s farming trilogy Corduroy, Silver Ley and The Cherry Tree

As I mentioned at the very beginning of this book, you will need to generate some monetary income in order to be allowed to exist in this day and age. Unfortunately it's not sufficient to be simply self-sufficient. If you're burdened with heavy borrowings (e.g. mortgage), or have rent to pay, then the need is rather more pressing, and you may have to look outside the farm gate for part-time employment opportunities, or consider diversification projects. What you mustn't do, though, is allow your smallholding activities to degenerate into an expensive hobby, paid for by ever-increasing hours worked elsewhere, otherwise you might just as well sell up and go back to town.

Produce and livestock sales

The initial target here must be to sell at least enough of a surplus to cover not only the production costs of whatever you're selling, but the cost of whatever you've used for home consumption too.

This is the very essence of viable self-sufficiency. If, in addition, you make some profit, then that's good. What you'll probably find is that while most of your farming activities come close to breaking even, there'll be one that does so much better than the rest – perhaps a crop that's particularly well suited to your land, or a direct marketing venture that just happens to strike the right chord with your customers. You should consider making this your 'principal enterprise', i.e. the one that helps to support any other aspects of your business that are important from the point of view of domestic food production,

but may be less able to deliver a financial gain. In our own case this is the sheep flock: whereas all of our other livestock, poultry and gardening activities are carried out primarily for subsistence purposes, the sheep are managed on a commercial basis. Other people might find that it's their pigs that give the best return, or their vegetable growing, or whatever. Either way, some degree of specialisation may be required in one aspect of the smallholding business in order to make the whole worthwhile.

Livestock sales

The livestock keeper is lucky, in so far as there's an existing well-established marketing infrastructure that he can tap into. Of course, there's plenty of alternative sales opportunities too, which may be more appealing to the small-scale producer, but it's good to know that there's always this safety net. Having said that, while most auction centres regularly handle sheep and cattle, there are not so many that take pigs, and even fewer that sell poultry and goats on a regular basis.

TIP

Whenever you're selling animals through a livestock market, try your best to pen them up in matching groups with respect to characteristics such as size, weight, age, sex and appearance.

• **Breeding stock:** Sales of breeding stock are generally held in the autumn. If you keep pedigree animals and register them with the relevant breed society, there'll be dedicated sales organised specifically for

The small-scale livestock producer can tap into an existing marketing infrastructure.

members. However, you must be aware that, no matter how well bred they are, not every animal you produce will be of a suitably high standard to sell in this way. Particularly in the case of males there's only a limited demand, so if you take the whole lot to a society sale expecting to achieve 'pedigree' prices you'll be disappointed – the majority may scarcely achieve slaughter prices, in which case you'd have been better to have sent them straight for killing and saved yourself the entry fee.

In addition to breed society sales, many livestock markets are now holding their own annual sales of rare and minority breeds, which provide a useful outlet for the more run-of-the-mill pure bred animals of this type.

Some pure breeds of livestock also have a strong commercial following, whether registered or not, so there's generally a reasonable demand for these at an ordinary weekly market at the right time of year. Certain crossbred cattle and sheep are also popular for commercial production, so again, the weekly market is probably a good bet for these. One advantage of the ordinary routine livestock auctions is that you can be sure that the price you receive represents a fair value for those particular animals on that day. In addition to the above, you've always got the option to sell breeding stock straight off the farm, which is how many small-scale livestock producers prefer to operate.

• **Store sales:** Often, when managing livestock on smaller acreages, where grazing may be in short supply at certain times of year, it's best to sell all of the

Many livestock markets now hold sales of rare and minority breeds.

animals not required for future breeding, or home consumption, on a pre-determined date, regardless of whether or not they're ready for slaughter. Let someone else do the job of fattening them up. This approach makes grassland management so much easier, and may actually increase the overall productivity of your flock or herd due to more grazing being available at key times (e.g. tupping and lambing), and reduce your feed bills over the winter. Once again, the local market may be the best bet for store sales, or via a livestock dealer.

• **Deadweight sales:** The sale of animals directly to an abattoir is a good option if you haven't got time to take them to an auction or to devote to marketing. In some cases a local fieldsman will come out to your holding and make a selection of what's ready for slaughter, and may even arrange transport to the abattoir. You'll be paid on a deadweight basis (i.e. so much per kg, based on the weight of the carcass, not the live animal), and should get feedback relating

to how well each animal graded. This is useful as it enables you to monitor performance and maybe adjust your breeding programme or feeding regime to ensure that more of your animals achieve a higher specification.

• **Primestock sales:** Most of the livestock markets that sell stores will also hold primestock sales, although possibly on a different day of the week. These can be a useful outlet if you've got a small number of animals ready for slaughter that are surplus to your domestic consumption requirements. They'll be weighed (and possibly graded) when they arrive at the mart, and most of the buyers will be working on behalf of the large abattoirs. They'll bid on lots of smaller batches to make up the total number they need, so you shouldn't be disadvantaged by only having a few on offer, provided that they're of reasonable quality.

TIP

Do you know what your animals are worth? Many smallholders don't, with the result that transactions are often based on wild guesses. On the one hand, there's the inclination to over-value, and hence charge far too much. The losers here are usually newcomers to smallholding, who, knowing even less about market trends than the vendor does, pay the asking price and are subsequently disappointed. On the other hand, not knowing the true value of what you're trying to sell may leave you open to exploitation by unscrupulous dealers – although to be honest, all the livestock dealers I've ever dealt with have been very fair. I suggest it's worth the while of any livestock keeper to make a point of visiting the local auction market from time to time, even if that's not the way you want to sell your own beasts. The bottom line price for any animal is what it's worth for slaughter, and you can work upwards from there, adding value on the basis of pedigree information, breeding potential, etc.

TIP

A livestock dealer is a very useful contact for the smallholder to have, as you'll often find yourself with small numbers of stock to sell, rather than the large batches of evenly-matched animals favoured by the major buyers. A dealer working in conjunction with a number of smallholders can, in effect, co-ordinate the marketing of stock from those holdings. Many livestock dealers are themselves smallholders who have diversified into the 'buying and selling' side of things to generate a bit of cash flow and make ends meet. They have nothing to gain (and their reputation to lose) by messing you about, or ill treating your animals.

• **Direct marketing:** Here I'm referring to sales of meat directly to the consumer, thus cutting out quite a few middlemen. For this to be possible, the animals must have been slaughtered in a licensed premises, not at home (except, in

Some of our lamb, packaged and labelled for sale direct to the consumer.

certain cases, poultry and rabbits). It's quite common for smallholders to sell pork by the half pig, or boxed lamb, to friends and family, and if you're having a couple of animals killed for the freezer then selling a proportion of it to help cover costs is the sensible thing to do. However, for direct marketing to have any significant influence on your turnover you'll need to do more than just sell the odd bit of meat here and there.

A chap I know, a very successful small-scale pig breeder who direct markets all of the pork he produces, once told me that the best view you can have from your

farmhouse window is chimney pots, meaning, of course, that you need a customer base right there on your doorstep to make it pay. The rise in popularity of farmers' markets and internet sales have made it easier to connect with a more distant clientele, but time spent manning a market stall is time spent off the farm, and distributing produce by mail order brings its own complications. We used to sell quite a lot of lamb and pork directly to the end user, but eventually the rising costs of slaughter, butchery, packaging and delivery meant that the margin was scarcely any greater than if we'd sold the animals to the abattoir, and it involved a lot more work, so we gave it up. However, if you live in a well-populated area (and have a local slaughterhouse) then it's definitely worthwhile.

• **Adding value:** If you're already direct marketing meat then the next logical step is to add value to the product by processing it in some way (such as turning beef into burgers, or pork into sausages), or provide an additional service such as hog roasts and catering. Some abattoirs that are also licensed cutting plants would be able to process the meat for you, and you could collect it from them for immediate delivery to the customer (provided that you can maintain the correct temperature during transport). Alternatively you could collect the whole carcasses from the abattoir and process them yourself, but your home would need to be registered as a food premises with the local authority / Food Standards Agency, and would be subject to inspections.

You can also apply the same principle to dairy products, and I can think of a couple of local examples of farmers and

TIP

Believe it or not, the most profitable thing to do with a pig is to turn the whole animal into sausages. It sounds incredible when you consider the retail value of the high quality cuts, but if you do the sums you'll find that it is so.

smallholders now retailing cheese and ice cream made from home-produced milk on their own holdings. However, the capital investment required to establish this type of venture may prove to be prohibitive for very small-scale livestock keepers, and just bear in mind that if you convert an outbuilding or part of your house into a dedicated food processing facility, it may then be liable for business rates.

Produce sales

Selling garden produce is in some respects easier than selling livestock, as there's not the same degree of legislation involved, but on the other hand you don't have the auction system to fall back on in quite the same way. Although there are such things as produce auctions, they're probably not really appropriate in this situation. At the most basic level, you could simply set up a roadside stall and honesty box at the farm gate, in order to raise enough cash to cover the cost of purchased seeds. You can sell eggs like this too, as the current egg marketing regulations don't apply in full to small-scale

You could simply set up a roadside stall and honesty box at the farm gate.

producers (i.e. less than 50 birds) selling directly to the consumer from the farm or at a local market. The next step-up is probably Country Markets (formally the WI markets), held on a weekly basis in many rural towns. We sold almost £1,000 worth of produce through the local Country Market in our first season at Ty'n-y-Mynydd, which was a great help. It wasn't only vegetables – we sold quite a lot of Dot's baking as well.

Farmers markets may be a useful outlet for smallholding produce.

Value can be added by turning surplus garden crops into jams and chutneys, and by using home-produced eggs (and home-made jam) in cakes.

Monthly farmers' markets provide another outlet. Being involved can be quite a commitment, and there are fairly stringent standards that must be adhered to. If you only have a limited range of products to sell you're going to run into problems regarding seasonality: some very high value crops – such as raspberries – are only available for a brief period (and are subject to failure), so what are you going to sell for the rest of the year in order to justify your position as a stallholder? You might find that car boot sales are more suited to disposing of an occasional vegetable glut, without the commitment of paying for a regular pitch. You could also sell surplus seedlings and plants at the same time.

Veg box schemes are a very good idea, although as I mentioned earlier when talking about direct marketing of meat, you do need a local customer base. One of the beauties of these schemes is that customers pay by subscription, so your cash flow is regular, and you can budget accordingly. You also know precisely how many boxes you need to fill on a weekly / fortnightly / monthly basis. Once again, seasonality is likely to be an issue, but you could team up with other small-scale producers to ensure a year-round supply.

There's also been a rise recently in the number of small community-run shops, and these are often willing to offer stuff for sale on behalf of local producers.

Agricultural and environmental payments

It seems to be the fashion in some areas for smallholders to denigrate the wider agricultural industry, and to distance themselves from their larger farming neighbours. This serves only to drive a wedge through rural communities, creating a counterproductive 'us and them' environment. There's no legal distinction between a farm and a smallholding, so if you've got a holding number (which you must have if you keep any livestock) then you'll be classed as a farmer, albeit perhaps a very small one. You'll also be burdened with a considerable amount of bureaucracy and paperwork.

This situation does have its compensations, however, in that you may find yourself entitled to claim some of the farm subsidies and environmental payments that are available. Under the current 'Basic Payment' system, farm subsidies are accessible to smallholders, provided that they're actively engaged in agricultural activity on at least 5 ha / 12.35 acres of eligible land (3 ha / 7.41 acres in Scotland). I spoke recently with a young couple on a modest-sized holding who are claiming nearly £10,000 per year in agricultural and environmental support. That's not to be sniffed at, whatever you consider the rights and wrongs of the system to be. No-one will come running after you to tell you what you can claim, so keep an eye on industry matters, and ensure you're on all the right mailing lists to be kept informed of what's available.

A brief word of caution about this: although environmental schemes may at first glance seem to be more in keeping with the smallholder's ethos, I wouldn't advise signing up to such a scheme during your early years on the holding; the requirements are often very restrictive, and could seriously limit the food-producing capability of your land. At a later stage, when you've got the whole place up and running to your satisfaction, then environmental scheme prescriptions can be tailored to incorporate your existing activities.

Capital grants

The availability of capital grants seems to vary considerably between regions. We've been extremely lucky here in Wales in that we've had access to 'Farming Connect' to facilitate applications for funding to the Welsh Government.

Broadly speaking, capital grants for agriculture (smallholdings included) are likely to fall into one of three main categories:

• Farm Improvement (such as new livestock housing)

• Diversification (tourism, farm shops, educational visits, equestrian etc.)

• Environmental Enhancement (which would include creating ponds or wetlands, tree planting projects etc.)

There's a considerable amount of overlap between these schemes, so an application that fails in one category may be re-submitted to another category in a slightly different guise; e.g. an application for a grant to erect a new shed for milking goats may be rejected under the heading 'Farm Improvement', but may be perfectly acceptable as 'Diversification'. Boundary fencing probably wouldn't attract funding as a farm improvement either, but by agreeing to do a bit of double fencing, hedge planting or clawdd restoration, you could probably pass it off as 'Environmental Enhancement'. Anyone whose smallholding is their principal occupation, and which meets any minimum acreage requirement, should have no difficulty in satisfying the various eligibility criteria, but, as I mentioned earlier, it is down to you to seek out what's available, and to actively pursue the various options.

You may also find that there are capital grants available from local government in your area towards the cost of repairing or upgrading your living accommodation. Known as 'Discretionary Housing Renovation Grants' (or something similar, depending on where you are), these may cover anything from replacing a few windows to a full restoration, with funding up to 100% in some cases (means tested). Assessment is made on a points system, and you'll get a lot more points for having no bathroom or kitchen than you would for a rotten window frame. The higher the total number of points, the higher your chances of making a successful application. There are similar schemes that can provide funding for the installation of boilers, central heating systems and insulation, in order to make your home more energy efficient.

Support payments

Don't be ashamed to claim whatever benefits you may be entitled to. You may not pay any income tax, but your parents probably did, and they surely wouldn't be averse to you claiming a bit of it back. But when I say 'entitled to', that's what I mean. There's no need to cook the books; social security benefits are designed to assist low-income families, and you'll certainly fit that description. Only claim what you're genuinely entitled to, and you'll find the system very supportive. This shouldn't be considered a long term solution to the financial situation, but can be a huge help during the first few years of a new venture. Having made a claim it is, of course, up to you how you spend that money. With a bit of luck, your frugal self-supporting lifestyle should mean that you don't actually need as much money to live on as the government thinks you do, and therefore a certain amount of what you're entitled to claim in benefits may be surplus to your immediate requirements. You could use this surplus cash to rent additional land, or even to make repayments on a business loan used to buy yourself some ground. We managed to purchase 35 acres like that, and you can do a lot with 35 acres, even if it is halfway up a mountainside somewhere at the back of beyond. This strikes me as a very responsible use of support payments, as, by increasing the size of our holding (and hence our productivity) we're ultimately reducing our reliance on hand-outs.

Diversification

Diversification isn't a new idea; farmers have been exploring other ways of making a living for years. Some are hugely successful – to the extent that the new business totally eclipses the old one – whereas other projects make a more modest contribution to the overall viability of the holding.

Some new ventures are simply an extension of what's already being carried out, for example, the pig farmer who starts doing hog roasts; the market gardener who establishes a farm shop; or the cereal grower who plants a novel crop, and as such are really covered under the heading 'Produce and Livestock Sales'.

Others involve the establishment of a completely new enterprise, but one which fits in well with existing activities. In many cases traditional farm outbuildings are utilised for alternative ventures, but often this involves considerable capital expenditure to convert them into offices, holiday lets, or business units. However, there are some slightly less ambitious projects that may appeal to the smallholder operating on a limited budget:

• **Farm based tourism:** Tourism has long been the prop that holds up small farm businesses, particularly in coastal areas. I don't think it would be unreasonable to say that a lot of the smaller farms around here simply wouldn't exist without this seasonal injection of cash, and many of them have been taking 'paying guests' or offering B&B for generations. Camp sites and caravan parks have proliferated, and in summer the beaches are thronged with visitors, which is all good for the local economy.

Whether or not you could fit tourism into your own smallholding activities is another matter. B&B is great if you've got a large, underutilised, tidy house with good access and plenty of parking, but if yours is the sort of place where muddy children and animals wander freely in and out, tractors have a habit of breaking down and blocking the driveway,

and the pigsties really do need mucking out more often, then maybe it's not for you. And you might not even be able to feed your home-produced meat and milk to your guests anyway (at least, not without incurring lots of additional expense), which for me would rather defeat the object.

Campsites are another thing I fight shy of – those serried ranks of tents and caravans look far too much like housing estates relocated to the countryside for my liking – but I know that some smallholders make rather a good thing out of it. There does seem to be a certain amount of infrastructure required, such as toilet and shower blocks, tarmac roadways and electrical hook ups (for which it's likely you'll have to apply for planning permission), and in order to justify the costs of installing these the site will need to be fully booked throughout the season.

On a smaller scale, you could establish a campsite for up to three touring caravans on a minimum five-acre plot, or tents for up to 28 days, without planning permission being required.

The recent trend for 'glamping' (glamorous camping, often with an eco twist) is perhaps playing more into the hands of the smallholder, and there's very few of us who couldn't find a small corner of the farm to make room for a yurt or tipi. Glamping seems to attract a clientele who are more sympathetic to the self-supporter's lifestyle, and their demands are minimal. Most of them are simply wanting to 'get away from it all' for a few days, so the seclusion of a site that has just one or two simple camping units offers the right appeal. If you've got an outbuilding that can be converted

Our bell tent has proved very popular with 'glampers'.

Smallholders often team up with schools to provide rural learning opportunities.

TIP

In addition to establishing whether or not your tourism venture requires planning permission, you must also ensure that your farm insurance policy provides adequate protection.

into a basic bathroom (or you're able to construct a composting loo and solar shower), and can install a standpipe for drinking water, then that's all you need in the way of fixed infrastructure. A wigwam or bell tent can be erected wherever you've got a suitable level site, and tastefully furnished with rugs and bedding. A barbecue (together with a selection of pots, pans and utensils) supplies all the cooking facilities required, and provided there's somewhere to light a campfire then everyone's happy.

Again, you're subject to the '28-day-rule', which some people attempt to circumvent by moving the whole set up to a different location from time to time. At the end of the summer you simply pack everything away, and there'll be nothing to show for it except a bit more cash in the bank.

The total cost to us in setting up a single glamping unit based on a 4 metre diameter canvas bell-tent was in the region of £1,250 (including not only the purchase of the tent, but all furniture, bedding and equipment), and it generates an income of £40 per night throughout the summer. Tidying up between guests is a bit of a chore, but on the whole folk do leave things in a reasonable state of cleanliness.

• **Education:** Here I'm talking about smallholders linking up with schools and other educational establishments to provide 'outdoor learning' opportunities. In many cases grants may be available to help set up and run this type of venture, or you may be eligible for charitable status, particularly if you're prepared to work with disadvantaged or disabled young people. If what you want to do is likely to deliver real benefits to the local community then you may be successful in sourcing private funding to help purchase equipment or fit out the facilities you may need (e.g. disabled access toilets).

Some agri-environment schemes provide additional payments for farmers who agree to host educational activities (in which case you wouldn't be able to charge a fee for visiting groups), or you could simply offer a service at a certain price to local schools and colleges – if what you're able to provide offers good educational value, or the opportunity for youngsters to develop new skills, then they should be prepared to pay for it.

• **Training:** The number of smallholders currently running training courses for beginners worries me. It seems that anyone who's been keeping hens or pigs or sheep for a couple of years suddenly feels qualified to start teaching others how to do the same – probably because they see it as an easy way to make a bit of money out of an enterprise that's otherwise a financial drain.

The problem of 'the blind leading the blind' is a very real one in the smallholding world, and I regularly encounter the same mistakes and misconceptions being passed on to the next generation of novices by people who are really only beginners themselves.

Having said that, if you do have sufficient knowledge and skill (I would say at least 10 years of farming experience), and suitable facilities, then by all means give it a go – it's hugely rewarding, and you get to meet some really interesting people. However, to do the job properly (which may mean purchasing specialist equipment, paying additional professional tutors, and providing accommodation or catering) will require some outlay, so don't expect to make huge profits.

Running courses may be profitable sideline, if you've got sufficient experience.

Employment

I don't believe that it's possible to make a really good job of running a smallholding if you're engaged in full time employment elsewhere.

Quite apart from anything else, livestock may require attention at any hour of the day or night; to leave them untended could have serious welfare implications. You may find yourself having to pay someone to work on the holding in your absence, so you'll have to put in even more hours off-

farm to raise the funds to pay their wages. It's a vicious circle that won't bring you any closer to living the dream. If there are two of you that's not so bad, one to work on the holding and the other conventionally employed, but even so there will be times – haymaking for example, or at lambing – when the work of the holding demands all hands. Given that it'll be necessary, in the early years at least, to have some other source of income, the answer to the dilemma probably lies in seasonal employment. Contract lambing always stood us in good stead – not lambing our own sheep until mid March enabled me to put in 2½ months work on other farms first. Sheep shearing is another good one, if you've got the necessary skill, or there's harvest work, fruit picking, relief milking, fencing, hedging, drystone walling, mole catching; the possibilities are endless. You'll notice that all the jobs I've mentioned here are agriculturally orientated, and for a very good reason: quite apart from the valuable experience, it'll keep you in the picture. You'll get to hear of things on the rural grapevine that you'd have missed if you spent all week in town; land to rent perhaps, or useful items for sale. Much of our equipment, including our previous tractor, was purchased from farms on which I worked, often with a certain amount of barter. Being an accepted member of the farming community also considerably reduces the likelihood of you being ripped off.

The internet has added another powerful string to the smallholder's bow, in that it's now possible to run an office-based business from just about anywhere – you can work 'off farm' without even going out of

your own gate! This situation lends itself to anyone wanting to downshift without fully letting go of their previous occupation – secretarial work, journalism, accountancy, website design, and so on, are all jobs that can be carried out at home, with hours structured to fit in around the work of the holding. The internet's also a great marketing tool for artists, craftsmen and small-scale producers to sell their wares, whereas previously they'd have had to attend events, hold exhibitions, and maybe locate themselves close to a large customer base.

We've also discovered that music is an exportable commodity, with son Iestyn being an accomplished folk fiddler. He's been able to pay his way from a very young age by performing at local social functions, later graduating to larger

Music is an exportable commodity - son Iestyn pays his way by playing the fiddle.

festivals and concerts. This has resulted in far less demand for 'pocket money' being placed on our scant resources than might normally be experienced by parents of a teenage boy. Now, as a student, he's finding that the ability to come out of a pub with more money than he went in with, and free drinks all evening to boot, is a very useful skill to have.

VAT

Register for VAT – there's a threshold of turnover above which you must be registered, but what I'm talking about here is voluntary registration for smaller businesses. If you opt for 'cash accounting' then the paperwork involved isn't onerous. Many of your inputs, including vet and med, fencing materials, contractors' charges, animal handling equipment etc., (but not feed, hay or straw), will have VAT charged on them, but most of your outputs, such as garden produce, livestock and poultry sales etc., (but not casual labour), are zero rated. Therefore you may make a net gain by reclaiming the VAT you paid on inputs; it's a big help to be able to knock 20 per cent off the vet's bill.

Credit

Use credit wisely. An ordinary 30-day account at your local farm suppliers actually gives you 60 days credit if you take care to make purchases on the first of the month. With a bit of planning it's possible to arrange things in such a way that your feed merchant finances the lion's share of any enterprise where animals require a couple of months fattening before sale. A good example of this would be rearing a batch of table birds to be killed at 10 weeks:

In Conclusion

Looking over what I've just written, it gives the impression that there's an awful lot of begging and borrowing involved in getting started in smallholding, and yes, I have to admit, it does feel like that initially. A bank generally expects a new farm business to be holding it's own after four years, but a big farm has a correspondingly big turnover, so can take bigger risks. On a smallholding, where finances tend to be rather more precarious, I think we should expect seven years before seeing light at the end of the tunnel, and that's only if the tunnel remains straight. In recent years there's been BSE, changes to the tenancy laws, a huge hike in property prices, foot and mouth disease, and two rounds of CAP reform, each of which has added a new bend in our route.

From time to time, during the seven years or so that it takes you to establish your smallholding business, someone will get up on their moral high-horse and tell you you're nothing but an idle waster, scrounging to live off the state, and why can't you go out and get a 'proper' job? Well, let them have their say then just carry on with what you're doing, for sooner or later the time will come when you can begin to 'repay' your debt to society by turning around and giving a helping hand to those coming up the ladder behind you.

As part of the traditional network of smallholdings and family farms in a well-maintained landscape, you'll be putting far more back into the rural community than you've ever taken out.

1. Purchase day old chicks, together with a fortnight's supply of feed, on the 17th of the month.

2. On the first day of the next month, purchase (on account) enough feed for the next 8 weeks.

3. Slaughter poultry between the 26th and 28th of the month following. This gives you a couple of days in which to sell enough oven ready birds to cover the feed bill, which will fall due for payment on the 30th. Settle the account promptly, and you won't incur any interest charges.

Non-Cash Revenue

Produce for your own consumption

As a self-supporter, a significant proportion of your annual turnover may be in the form of 'non-cash receipts', (i.e. goods taken from the business for your personal use), and these need to be properly accounted for, as they're taxable income. Therefore, any of the produce of your holding that you consume needs to be appropriately valued and written down in the relevant place in your financial records. You don't need to give these items their full retail price, yet neither do you simply put them in at cost of production. Something approaching wholesale value is about right.

It's also worthwhile, for your own benefit, to record transfers of produce between the different enterprises on your holding. For example, you have a cow giving 3 gallons of milk per day. One gallon of this you use in the house, so it'll be accounted for as a non-cash receipt (NCR), as described above. Another gallon is used to feed the cow's own calf, so this remains within the cattle enterprise. The third gallon, however, you give to your pigs. Therefore, this transaction is shown as income to the cattle enterprise, and a corresponding sum is entered as expenditure in the pig account. Similarly, if you make hay you'll know what costs to allocate to the forage account (fertiliser, diesel for the tractor, contractors' charges etc.) and you'll be able to 'charge' each of your livestock enterprises accordingly for the hay that they use. Only by doing this can you

have any idea whether or not your various activities are paying their way, or whether one profitable enterprise is simply masking the loss made by the others.

Barter

In its simplest form, barter involves a straight swap – you have something your neighbour wants; he has something you want. You exchange goods and everyone's happy. It's a time-honoured way of doing business, particularly in the agricultural world. However, even these types of deals need to be recorded as 'contra transactions'. So, let's presume that you run out of hay, and John Jones is getting short of potatoes. You swap three of your bags of spuds for three of his bales of hay. You then need to enter this in the income side of your account book as:

Sold to John Jones, 3 sacks of potatoes @ £5 / sack (contra)

And on the expenditure side: Purchased from John Jones, 3 bales of hay @ £5 / bale (contra)

The corresponding date enables a cross reference between the two entries in the book.

Contra transactions can start to get a bit complicated to account for when the exchange of goods didn't happen on the same day, when barter only partially covers the full value of the deal, or when one of the items has VAT on it and the other hasn't. The temptation is just to 'say nowt', but these are the type of transactions that VAT

inspectors are very aware of, and will be expecting to see from time to time in an agricultural business, so it's best just to write everything down and keep your nose clean. Sometimes.

Time banks

Time banks are, I think, a wonderful idea, and should be more widely adopted among smallholding communities.

They're based on the principle that everyone's time is worth the same, whether he be accountant, solicitor or odd-job man. Doing a few hours work for someone else in the group enables you to put time in the bank, which you can then spend on employing the services of another group member. Using the same three professions as an example, let's begin with the odd-job man taking three hours to mow the solicitor's lawn. He's then got three hours credit at the bank. A few weeks later he needs a bit of help with his tax return, so he 'spends' his three hours by asking the accountant to fill in the forms for him. The accountant, who's getting on in years (and now has three hours credit in the bank), feels it's about time he started putting his affairs in order, so his neighbour, the solicitor, spends an afternoon helping him re-draft his will. And so on. Everyone is using their own specific skills to the benefit of the community, nobody's out of pocket, and nobody feels like they've been taken advantage of.

Obviously this type of scheme is not to be confused with the more general ethos of helping your neighbours in times of crisis, which is something I hope you would do anyway, without thought of reward.

Household Economy

"Frugality and economy are home virtues without which no household can prosper."
Mrs. Beeton

Frugality

If you're really serious about trying to lead a self-sufficient lifestyle then you probably won't have much spare cash to splash around. However, there are always going to be some things that you have to purchase because you can't produce them, or because it's not worthwhile to attempt to do so (either financially, or due to the time that would need to be invested). Grocery shopping is a chore that'll be considerably reduced by growing your own food, but it won't go away altogether. Before you start filling your trolley, have a think about the following:

• Once your smallholding is operating productively, the amount of stuff you actually need to purchase on a regular basis could be quite small. Keep yourself well acquainted with the contents of your freezer, the crops in your garden and the stores on your shelves, and you won't end up purchasing a lot of unnecessary extras.

• Develop a basic range of meals that you can cook entirely from home produce and store-cupboard staples. This means you'll always be able to rustle something up with what you have to hand. We all like a treat from time to time, and might want to cook a 'special' meal for a particular occasion

using purchased ingredients, but if you start to do it on a regular basis, your shopping spend is going to creep up. Also consider that your standard range of meals will change in accordance with whatever crops you have available at the time, so won't become monotonous – there shouldn't be any need to buy extra stuff to give yourself variety.

• Throw brand loyalty out of the window! Keep a close eye on the price of the products you put in your trolley, and switch brand if there's a cost benefit in doing so. You don't necessarily have to opt for the cheapest alternative, as quality is important too, but there's a balance to be struck.

• Buy-one-get-one-free (BOGOF) and other multiple purchase deals are frequently blamed for contributing to the massive problem of food waste, but you should take advantage of these offers where the goods are non-perishable, or where you can freeze, preserve, or use it all before it starts to deteriorate.

• Before shopping, make a list, then stick to it. Unnecessary impulse buys will inflate the grocery bill. If you do fancy a treat from time to time look in the cheapie bin for stuff that's been reduced because it's getting close to its sell by date.

• Shop around. Split your list between different outlets if you need to, in order to get the best deals, but only if you can do it without having to get in the car to move from one shop to another. If this is the case, anything you save

on the shopping will quickly be outweighed by extra travel costs.

• Keep records of domestic expenditure, and give yourself a weekly / fortnightly budget to cover everything, then stick to it.

• Bear in mind that the items you expect to be the cheapest are not always so. Things like crop failures, changes in exchange rates (or any other worldwide financial disturbance), and the current value of oil can affect prices in unexpected ways.

• Buying in bulk is often cited as a means of saving money, but it doesn't always work out that way. Do some sums to ensure that the unit costs are actually lower, and allow for any extra expenditure such as delivery charges or travelling further to get to a bulk outlet.

Think about how you'll store bulk food purchases.

• If you're purchasing food items in bulk, you'll need to think more carefully about storage – a bit of mouse damage to a small packet of porridge oats is neither here nor there, but if your oats are in 15kg sacks you stand to lose a lot

Section Eight | Household Economy

more. Use airtight tubs and lidded buckets to store dry items and those that are vulnerable to pests. Empty sheep lick buckets that have been thoroughly cleaned are ideal for this. Label the outside of the tubs with a permanent marker pen, so you know what's in them without having to take the lids off, and if you see any sign of rodents in your food storage area do something about it immediately.

• Plan ahead and cut down on the number of shopping trips you make; weekly down to fortnightly, fortnightly down to monthly, etc. When we lived on Bardsey Island we didn't have the option of nipping down to the shops if we ran out of something, so Dot went ashore to do some shopping at six monthly intervals. (I remember someone asking me, with a hint of envy, where I had managed to find a wife who only wanted to go shopping twice a year.) Extensive lists were made before she set off; we pored over previous purchase invoices, carried out a careful stock take, and wrote down anything we needed as the thought popped into our heads. We did run out of things from time to time, and if we did we went without, and learned to plan a little better next time. I accept that at the time we only had ourselves to please, and no growing children to keep happy, but it does illustrate the point that you can get by without stuff if you have to (with the exception, perhaps, of toothpaste and loo rolls).

• Don't get too hung up about 'use by' or 'best before' dates. Tinned food will last for years provided that the tin itself remains in good condition, with no rust or dents, and hasn't become distorted or blown. We've often eaten tinned stuff that was several years out of

TIP

The lower legs off old pairs of trousers that have gone at the knee make very useful storage bags. Simply turn the leg inside out, bind the cut end tightly shut (or sew it, if you're feeling fussy), turn it back in the right way, and that's all there is to it. I use these handy bags for keeping a small selection of appropriate spanners with each piece of machinery, so I can easily carry out simple tasks (such as fitting new shear-bolts to the baler) in the field. They could also be used for storing dried beans or peas, or carrying ferrets. Filled with sand and tied at both ends they're very good for weighing down tarpaulins, holding back floodwater, or for use as a sturdy rest when zeroing a rifle 'scope.

date, with no ill effects. As far as perishables are concerned – meat and fish in particular – your nose is a pretty good guide; if it smells ok, then it almost certainly is, but make sure it's well cooked, just in case. I've never been able to understand why 'use by' dates are provided on packs of hard cheese – it just gets better as it gets older. We're currently eating a round of Cheshire cheese we were given over a year ago; it's been in the fridge, wrapped in greaseproof paper (not plastic) all this time, and it's splendid.

Make do and mend

We live in a 'throw away' society, where the majority of items seem to have a kind of built-in obsolescence, and many things are designed with the intention of making them impossible for the user to service or mend. On our bookshelf is a copy of the *Reader's Digest Repair Manual,* published in 1972, which provides detailed illustrated instructions on how to

carry out home maintenance tasks, and gives guidance on repairing a wide range of household items, from spectacles right through to cars, caravans and lawn mowers. Although a lot of the DIY stuff in the book is still relevant, sadly most of the repair instructions are not.

As technology becomes more complex, opportunities to mend things decrease, but it's not all doom and gloom – some basic items can still be fixed with glue, screws, or a new bit of wire. If you're mechanically minded (unlike me), fixing farm machinery, mending vehicles and repairing the kid's bicycles may just be a case of purchasing the new parts (or sourcing them from the local scrapyard, or through Freecycle) and bolting them on. If you're paying for repairs, then most of the bill will be made up of labour.

Finding alternatives to commercially manufactured goods can also be a real money saver,

Woolly jumpers and suchlike can be unravelled and the yarn re-used to create new items – we've knitted hats out of old socks, and Dot made me a wonderful thick jumper using oddments of re-cycled wool. It's a basic design, consisting of two matching rectangles (one for the front and one for the back) and a tapered piece for each sleeve. A thin knitted strip is then stitched on around the neck. The whole thing is knitted in stocking stitch, except a little bit of rib around the hem and the cuffs, so it could hardly be simpler. There's not really any need for a pattern as such – just use a tape measure so you know when you've knitted enough.

at the expense of just a little time and effort. It's quite possible to make some items that are as good as any over-the-counter product, using re-claimed materials. For example, old floorboards from demolition sites are a great source of free timber if you want to knock up some bookshelves or build yourself a garden shed.

Clothing: It's probably fair to say that most of our clothes are so exhausted by the time we've finished with them that they're only fit for the rag-bag. However, there are a few options for recycling and re-using worn out garments.

Old work boots can be cut up and used for any project where a small piece of leather is required, and for many years Dot pinned up her hair with a stick barrette that I fashioned out of a piece cut from just such a boot (see pages 406 - 407). Worn out wellies can have the tops chopped off to make slip-on galoshes, which are very handy if you just need to pop out to the garden to pick some beans for dinner. The cuffs of favourite jumpers should be cut off when they're worn and frayed, and the sleeves rolled back and hemmed to make them ¾ length. Jeans can, of course, be patched and patched again. Having said that, it's probably not worth doing this with the cut-price clothing that's often sold in discount stores and supermarkets – it's so cheap as to be semi-disposable – but where an item is of good quality, it's well worth attempting to get some extra use out of it.

Don't neglect to try and make your clothing last longer in the first place, and wearing overalls for farm work will certainly make a big difference. It's so easy to rip things when they catch on a gate latch, or tear your jeans when you trip over trying to catch an escaped ewe, and a cheap pair of overalls will bear the brunt of the damage. They'll also take most of the heavy soiling, making the washing of clothes so much easier.

Hair care: I've never been to a hairdresser and, quite frankly, the thought of paying a complete stranger to wield a pair of very sharp scissors around my ears is positively terrifying. Throughout my childhood my hair was cut by my mother, followed by a succession of fellow students, and now Dot plays the role of family barber. This isn't an onerous task as the girls (aged 13 and 15 at the

Dot and the girls with their easy care long hair.

The first rule of recycling is reuse, so keep used jam jars for re-filling with home-made preserves.

time of writing) have never had their hair cut, and Dot's hasn't seen a pair of scissors since I gave it a bit of a trim nearly twenty five years ago. She hasn't washed her hair for 20 years, either, although you wouldn't know it to look at it. The human scalp will produce as much sebum as is needed to keep hair healthy, but constant washing strips out the natural oils, thus increasing their rate of production. It becomes a vicious circle – the more often you wash it, the more frequently you will find you need to. Dot had already 'trained' hers to being washed only once a fortnight, and then a busy lambing period stretched that to three weeks. After another six or seven weeks she just rinsed her hair in warm water, and that was that. All it needs to remain looking good is thorough routine brushing, and maybe a rinse in cool water only (no soap) once or twice a year. Whoever said long hair takes a lot of looking after?

Recycling: The first rule of recycling is reuse. This applies to both household and non-household stuff. Keep used jam jars for bottling chutneys and preserves; retain empty beer and wine bottles for refilling with home-brewed booze; tatty towels can be used in the dairy or as hand wipers in the lambing shed. The list goes on: tin cans (of which there won't be many) make useful storage containers in the workshop, as do the bottoms of plastic milk cartons (which are also good cut up and used as plant labels); plastic 5-gallon oil-drums can have the tops cut off and be given rope handles to become 'farmer's

Cut the top of a 5-gallon drum and fit a rope handle to make a 'farmers' handbag'.

handbags' – useful for storing and carrying stuff about; cardboard can be hoarded for mulching under fruit bushes, and old newspapers too (although keep some for winter fire lighting); fruit punnets make ideal seed trays, and the inners of used loo rolls make good pots for plants that don't take kindly to root disturbance. These are just a few examples, but the options for reuse of stuff that might otherwise be considered rubbish are limited only by your imagination and ingenuity.

Charity shops

Charity shops are an extremely useful resource for the low-income household. I don't think we bought new clothes for any of our children until they were at least 10 years old (and not many after that), having clothed them entirely out of charity shops and with hand-me-downs from friends and neighbours. This goes for Dot and me too. If you don't mind wearing clothes that aren't hot up-to-date fashion, then these outlets are a great source of reasonably priced, often very good quality, clothing (and if you keep them long enough they'll come back into fashion anyway). Of course you need to be a bit picky: avoid clothes that are more worn than first appearances suggest, and watch out for unsightly stains. Pricing can be a bit erratic, but if you keep your eyes open you will find bargains. I think one of the best Dot ever found was an almost brand new 100% wool La Tricoteur Guernsey jumper (current retail price about £100) for £1.50. Charity shops are also a good source of useful books, and I don't think it would be unrealistic to state that about 90% of all the titles listed on pages 450 - 451 came from charity shops. Do bear in mind, though, that charity shops are only able to function thanks to the donations they receive, so if you have any unwanted clothing in good condition then do your bit by donating it – just take care that you don't accidentally buy your own stuff back again.

Freecycle

These web-based groups match people who have things they want to get rid of with those who can use them. The basic aim is to keep usable items out of landfill sites. As the name suggests, everything is offered free of charge. Goods are offered by posting email messages via your local Freecycle group, the proviso being that all items are free, legal, and appropriate for all ages. If you're looking for something in particular you can also post 'wanted' messages, and you may find that there's someone out there who has just what you're after. We've picked up several bicycles like this, a flute for Rhian, and a lovely old sewing machine. Make sure you check the specific guidelines for your regional group as they can vary between areas. You can join as many Freecycle groups as you like, but if anything crops up that you're interested in you'll have to travel to look at it, so it's best to keep it local.

Waste disposal

Disposal of domestic waste shouldn't really be a big issue for the self-sufficient family – there won't be much. There certainly shouldn't be any food waste: When you've grown and produced it yourself you'll really understand its value, and want to make use of every bit. Anything that's left over gets composted. Previously some of this would have been fed to the pigs and the poultry, but of course that's no longer allowed.

Our lovely old sewing machine, acquired via Freecycle.

Because you won't be buying many packaged foods domestic waste plastic will also be minimal, and what little there is has become much easier to recycle through council doorstep collection schemes. Some plastic packaging you'll be able to re-use anyway.

Cardboard and paper have already been mentioned, although whatever you don't have a use for can be collected for recycling, as can any tins, bottles and jars that you don't need. Rather more problematic are substances such as polystyrene, which may form part of the packaging when you buy delicate items. However, we tend to save it up for use as insulating material or buoyancy.

Used batteries also present disposal problems, so equip your household with rechargeable or wind-up torches.

Domestic waste mustn't be confused with agricultural waste, such as empty feed sacks, silage wrap, veterinary medicine bottles, etc. You're supposed to pay for disposal of these items via an approved facility, and not simply throw them in the dustbin.

Section Nine
Community Initiatives

Community Initiatives

"I do think that groupings of people living near each other, each with his own holding and dwelling place, co-operating in some things and living under some sort of organisation, would work very well indeed." John Seymour

Community living

Unless you're an out-and-out hermit, the chances are that you live in some kind of community. This may be a small village, a street or district within a town, or simply a block of flats. However, what we're talking about here are 'intentional' communities, i.e. those formed when a group of like-minded individuals decide to get together and share a certain lifestyle. The reasons why people choose to do this are many and varied, but may include ethics, religion, or personal circumstances. Ecological issues, and a desire to tread more lightly on our planet, are a common theme, although I have been surprised to learn that relatively few communes

aim to be self-sufficient in food. However, a number do at least produce a proportion of what they require, and some, such as Old Hall, in Suffolk, attain very high levels of self-sufficiency. On the whole though, there seems to be a greater interest in independence from mainstream services such as electricity and water, with 'off grid' living being the target for some groups.

Quite a few community living ventures (some of which are still in existence) were established in the early 1970s, when it was still possible to buy a rambling country house and a few acres of good land for not much money. One aspiring group purchased a 43-acre farm (with cottage and outbuildings) in Wales for £10,000 in 1972, and spent another £12,000 building a house suitable for 16 people, so a total investment of around £1,400 per person. A similar property might set you back more than half-a-million pounds now. Understandably, with property prices as they are, similar groups

wanting to make a start today are lucky if they can get hold of enough land, let alone a house to live in. The result of this has been a move towards the development of 'eco-settlements', with clusters of small, low-impact dwellings being built using sustainable materials by the people who'll live in them, on the land where they hope to grow their crops, tend their animals, and live an altogether 'closer to nature' existence. For a good example of this type of initiative visit landmatters.org.uk. In some cases planning permission for these settlements may be obtained via schemes such as the Welsh Government's 'One Planet Development Policy', but in other instances residents have applied for retrospective permission, or claimed a Certificate of Lawful Use or Development (see pages 34 - 35).

Establishing a new community:
It's noticeable that the type of people who have the necessary drive and ambition to start a community living venture aren't necessarily the ones who'll ultimately make good communards. Often a new project doesn't really find its feet until most of the original members have become disillusioned and moved on, and a significant number fail before they really get going. The example I quoted above, of the 43-acre farm in Wales, lasted only a couple of years despite making a really good start, and the demise was all down to personalities. The survival of the community spirit relies, among other things, on tolerance and sharing, which are things that human beings, on the whole, aren't very good at. If you can overcome these negatives (and probably a few more besides), there's nothing – in principle – stopping from you

One Planet Development Policy

This policy permits the building of sustainable 'eco-dwellings' in the Welsh countryside, provided that certain criteria are met. For example, all structures must be carbon neutral, both during the building process and when in use, and all households have to demonstrate an extremely low ecological footprint. Within five years of establishing the settlement residents are expected to be generating their basic requirements (equivalent to £3,000 per adult per year) from land-based activities, and any additional employment off the holding should be 'low-impact' in nature.

Furthermore, should the project fail, (and it will be reviewed at five yearly intervals,) it must be possible to return the land to its original state, or better.

joining forces with a few other people and establishing your own intentional community.

Funding the new community: Finding a suitable property is one thing, but purchasing it is quite another. If you were to pool your capital resources and buy a property outright, you would at least not have to worry about servicing a large debt (which would probably necessitate seeking employment off the holding, thus reducing your chances of attaining self-sufficiency), but what would you do if a few members wanted to pull out after a year or two? Could the rest of you afford to buy them out? Remember, the value of the property (and hence the value of

Permaculture design excercise at Landmatters Community.

their share) might have increased in that time. Or would they sell their share on the open market – in which case how much control would you be able to exercise over who joins your community? If you aren't able to raise sufficient capital from your own reserves then you'll need a mortgage or loan. Many banks are reluctant to provide funds for ventures of this type because their unfamiliarity with the ethos of community living results in prejudice against it, but there are some financial institutions that specialise in supporting eco projects (e.g. the Ecological Building Society). In most cases it'll be necessary to set up a co-operative, a limited company, a charitable trust, or a housing association, thus giving a legal basis to the community's financial constitution in order to secure the necessary backing, and you will need a sound business plan.

In many ways I think it would be better for one person (or couple) to own the property, with others paying rent (or working) to join

in. However, this could result in a feeling of hierarchy, with uncomfortable landlord / tenant issues developing. Perhaps an absentee landlord would be preferable?

Joining an existing community: Community living won't suit everyone, and the presence of one ill-suited individual in a commune could unsettle the stability of the whole establishment. Therefore, anyone who's hoping to join an existing group will probably have to work a fairly long apprenticeship in order to gain acceptance. This trial period is as important to the individual as it is to the folk already in residence.

Firstly, you'll need to locate a number of communities which have an ethos that matches your perceived ideals of sustainability, culture, social demographics, religion, or whatever. The website diggersanddreamers.org.uk has a very useful directory that'll help you with this. The choice can then be narrowed down to those that have vacancies, or are trying to

Many hands make light work at the Landmatters Community.

attract new members in order to grow. Having made contact with such a group, and expressed an interest in becoming involved, you'll then be expected to visit a few times before graduating to doing longer stints of voluntary work at the community. During this period you'll get to know the other residents (and they'll get to know you), and become accustomed to the routine. This probationary period may last for as long as six months (or even more, in some cases), and then it's up to the rest of the community to decide whether they want you to stay. Once you've been accepted you'll probably have to buy your way in, either by purchasing an appropriate share from the person / family who's leaving (or from the umbrella organisation), or by paying rent. This depends entirely on the type of business structure under which the property is managed. In certain situations, such as where communes are owned and run by charities, it may be sufficient that you simply work in return for your accommodation. In addition there could be charges

Sharpenning shared tools.

for services such as electricity and water.

What to expect: Being part of a community that's striving for a degree of self-sufficiency will entail you putting in a specified number of hours work per week on the land. In some cases each family group tends its own plot, but in others the fields, gardens and livestock enterprises are all communally managed. You'll also be expected to contribute to the domestic workload, but again this will vary – some groups utilise a lot of shared space and eat their meals together, whereas in others the residents lead more private

TIP
It would be worth trying to find out why your prospective community has vacancies – has there been some recent dissent within the group that's caused other residents to move on? What appears at first glance to be a calm and settled environment may actually be an emotional battlefield, with rifts that'll take time to heal – now might not be the best time to join.

lives in their own apartments. A regular financial contribution may also be required to cover the costs of basic household sundries and purchased foodstuffs. The obligatory work commitment may preclude you from seeking full-time employment outside the community, but you'll need some income to cover the costs of living; therefore, many communards have part-time jobs, or work from home. Skilled craftsmen may be able to establish a workshop within the community, and thus run a small business from there. In some communities you're expected to pool a proportion of your earnings.

Regardless of the set-up, the decision-making process within a community is by consensus, with regular discussion meetings held to facilitate this. Anyone who's used to doing things their own way may find this process frustrating in the extreme. Conflicts inevitably arise from time to time, with disagreements being settled by mediation, if possible. Despite the close proximity of other people, when things do go wrong a tight-knit community can feel like a very lonely place to be, and you can't hide beneath the cloak of anonymity.

The benefits:

• An affordable route into a more sustainable lifestyle.

• Being part of a like-minded group of people, with shared beliefs and aspirations.

• Working as a team you can undertake projects that would be too daunting for an individual.

• A safe environment for your family.

• Mutual support.

Co-operative ventures

A lone smallholder doesn't carry much weight when it comes to bargaining power. How could you possibly negotiate a better deal on straw, for example, if you only use a couple of bales a year? But if you could buy a lorry load and share it among a group of you, then real savings would be made. The same applies to many other inputs, and contractors charges too.

Produce marketing is another area where small-scale operators tend to stumble, because consumers require continuity of supply. A group of smallholders working together would be able to address this issue, while sharing some of the inevitable overheads that may render the sale of home-grown produce a non-viable business for the sole trader (e.g. the cost of a market stall).

Co-operation between producers also enables the provision of facilities which might otherwise not be justifiable, such as dairy, butchery or food preparation areas (in order to add value to products), and the collective ownership of equipment.

Underlying all of this is the whole issue of land availability, with property values soaring beyond the reach of many aspiring smallholders. Larger blocks of bare agricultural land are proportionately more affordable (on a £ per acre basis), but the overall price may be too high on account of the total area involved. Co-operative land ownership offers a potential solution to this problem.

Machinery rings: Machinery rings were established by groups of farmers to facilitate the hiring out of machinery that would otherwise be standing idle at certain times of year, to other members of the group. Skills and labour could also be offered through the same network, and I joined just such a ring when we first moved to Ty'n-y-Mynydd, as a provider of contract shepherding services. Almost all of our off-farm employment during the first five years or so was obtained in this way. Machinery rings have evolved somewhat since then, and now it's quite common for the organisation to arrange bulk purchase deals on behalf of members for inputs such as animal feed, diesel and fertilisers, coordinate training courses, give assistance with statutory record keeping, and negotiate better contracts for services such as electricity and broadband.

Co-operative marketing: A good example of a small-scale co-operative marketing venture can be seen in the Peasant Evolution (peasantevolution.co.uk). This West Country-based co-op is a registered company, limited by guarantee, with around 20 producer members. In addition to internet advertising and mail-order sales, the group runs a weekly market stall selling a range of products, including organic vegetables, meat, arts and crafts, and charcoal. They also have a fully-equipped, collectively-owned processing barn, built as a community project, which members make use of when preparing produce for sale. Anyone wanting to establish something similar in their own part of the country would do well to take a look at their informative website.

Co-operative land ownership: The Ecological Land Co-operative (ecologicalland.coop) was established to address precisely the issue I mentioned earlier, by buying up blocks of agricultural land, and then subdividing them into clusters of smaller family-sized holdings. These are to be leased or rented to deserving tenants, who may also be provided with practical support in order to help get their fledgling businesses off the ground.

The co-operative, a relatively young organisation with one successful development in Devon, used its own experienced staff to negotiate the necessary planning consents, with a far greater chance of success than if similar applications had been submitted by individual smallholders. They also arranged for the installation of a certain amount of infrastructure, with the result that each of their current holdings came complete with road access, water supply and a renewable source of electricity, together with planning permission for a sustainable home.

Leasehold purchase (150 year tenure) gives families the stability and confidence required to invest in their homes and their small-scale farming enterprises, while the co-operative retains the freehold of the site to ensure adherence to

Barn raising at the Ecological Land Co-op's Greenham Reach site.

an ecological management plan. Community share offers, together with the capital revenue generated by the leasehold transactions, enable the company to purchase additional parcels of land and to replicate their proven model in new areas, with, theoretically, increasing affordability for potential leaseholders.

Land share

The fundamental principle of land share is that it matches up people who have spare land with those who'd like to use it, on the basis of mutual benefit rather than rental value. In the wider agricultural industry 'share farming' arrangements are recognised as an ideal starting point for new entrants with limited capital. A typical (but somewhat simplified) example might consist of a partnership between an aging farmer who wants to take a step back from the day-to-day side of the business, and a young person trying to get a foot on the farming ladder: One provides the land and buildings, the other provides the livestock and labour. Input costs are shared, as are the profits.

A parallel situation exists within the smallholding world, where perhaps someone purchased a property with a bit of land as a retirement project, but after a number of years find increasing age and infirmity mean they are no longer keeping on top of the workload. This provides an opportunity for a younger person to take over some of the day-to-day routine, and benefit from a share in the produce, while the owners of the land are still able to enjoy some involvement. At the other end of the age scale, we often see smallholdings being bought as a lifestyle choice (or an investment) by early middle-aged couples, who, due to the continuing commitment of regular employment, aren't yet able to make use of the land. Under these circumstances they might rather enter into an agreement with someone who has a similar 'small-scale ethos' to themselves,

than let the grazing to a local farmer, particularly if they can get involved at the weekends and learn the skills they'll need for when they actually start to keep livestock and grow crops of their own.

We have, at one time or another, grazed sheep and cattle, and made hay and silage, over seven different smallholdings, under a wide range of agreements, some of which were straightforward tenancies, but others have involved a degree of sharing. The only caveat I would offer, based on our own experience, is that you get everything in writing so that all parties are aware of precisely what they're committing to. I know it sounds a bit formal, but it can save an awful lot of bother later.

Other opportunities sometimes crop up in arable areas where farmers have reverted fields to grassland in order to claim environmental subsidies, and now need that land grazed, and also on nature reserves where the presence of livestock may be required for habitat management purposes, but the organisation itself has neither the skills nor the desire to own their own flocks and herds. If all of this sounds rather ambitious, you could just see if there's anyone in your village with a rather overgrown back garden; I expect they'd gladly let you grow some vegetables in one corner, if you'll cut the lawn and trim the hedges in return.

Volunteering

Although perhaps not technically a community initiative, the presence of a transient population of active volunteers can make even the most run-of-the-mill smallholding resemble a commune at times. We haven't used volunteers ourselves (although of course anyone who comes to stay is expected to do their bit), but are considering doing so in the future. We know plenty of small-scale producers who have, and the feedback is mixed: on the one hand there are people who swear by it as a rewarding way to keep on top of the workload, and equally there are others who say "never again". I think a lot of this disparity is down to the mentality of the host – some smallholders want to get on and do their own thing with a degree of privacy, and would probably view volunteers as an intrusion, yet others love to share what they're doing with a wide circle of part-time helpers and friends.

If you do decide to welcome volunteers onto your holding then you can either publicise this through your own website or via organisations such as WWOOF, HelpX and Workaway. As a host you'll be expected to provide your volunteers with appropriate accommodation (which needn't be in your home – it could be a way of utilising a camping barn, yurt or pod at a time of year when it would otherwise be standing empty) and food, in return for 4–6 hours of work per day. Volunteers should also help with some of the domestic chores such as washing up after meals and generally keeping the living space clean and tidy. You must be reasonable in the demands that you make upon your volunteers, and at no time should you ask them to carry out potentially dangerous tasks such as operating farm machinery. You also need to ensure that you have an appropriate insurance policy that covers employer's liability.

From the point of view of a potential volunteer, these opportunities enable you to acquire a practical knowledge of working on small-scale subsistence farms, which will stand you in good stead when the time comes for you to take on a smallholding of your own. Often life-long friendships are forged as a result, and your one-time host may ultimately become your mentor.

On the other hand, you do need to be realistic about the potential value of some of the experience gained; many hosts are little more than beginners themselves, so unless you personally are bringing new skills onto the holding (which may, of course, be why you're there) the work might progress with very little guidance or direction, and without you really knowing whether what you're doing is correct. From among our own contacts it's noticeable that the better established (and hence more experienced) small-scale producers are the ones least likely to host volunteers, which is a pity.

Allotment gardening

There's a long history of allotment gardening in the UK, but until the mid 19th century nothing was written in law to protect ordinary peoples' rights to be given access to small plots of ground for food production purposes. The long history of enclosures in England, formalised by the Enclosures Acts of the 1830s and 40s, had resulted in large areas of common land being fenced off, and the average peasant was denied use of the ground that had previously been available for subsistence farming. However, a later act (in 1845) ensured that parcels of land (up to ¼ acre in extent) were set aside for 'the landless poor', partly to assuage fear of public disorder and civil unrest. How successful it was is debatable, as records seem to suggest that less than 0.4 % of the designated area was actually made available to the people.

Since then various pieces of legislation have consolidated the position of allotments in the UK, most notably the 1908 Smallholding and Allotments Act, which placed an obligation on regional governments to provide suitable plots, and today many allotments are still owned and administered by local authorities. In addition there are sites provided by parish councils and private landowners, although privately-owned plots can be particularly susceptible to development pressures. Our nearest allotments were lost a few years ago for this very reason, but to balance that an area was set aside near one of the local secondary schools to provide space for families to grow their own vegetables, and another allotment site has recently been established by the community on the outskirts of the town.

Traditionally the area allowed for one allotment plot is 10 square rods, with a rod being based on the distance measured between the tip of an oxen's nose to the back end of the plough that he's pulling (approximately 5 metres). Therefore each plot would be roughly 250m², which is about the size of a tennis court. However, there's no statutory basis for this, so in actual fact a plot could be any size. The amount of rent paid varies from virtually nothing up to about £125 a year, but there's no legal framework for this either. The fee is intended to cover the landlord's costs with regard to water supply and maintenance.

Each plot holder signs a lease or tenancy agreement which specifies what is or isn't allowed on the allotment, covering issues such as the building of sheds,

A well run allotment site can be a vibrant, socially stimulating place, providing a focal point for the local community.

holders will also be able to provide information on soil types, growing conditions, and the history of what's been planted on your plot in the past. This knowledge will be invaluable to you in planning your crop rotation, and may also give an indication of what pests and diseases are likely to be present. In addition, there may be the opportunity to share tools and equipment, and to benefit from bulk seed orders.

Although some people remain tenants of the same plot for many years, you should perhaps be a little wary of planting long term crops, such as top fruit, on an allotment. If you do want to grow fruit trees you might consider pot varieties, which you could take with you if you decide to move on. Soft fruit bushes shouldn't be a problem, as they can be dug up and transplanted, if absolutely necessary.

greenhouses and polytunnels, subletting, and the keeping of various types of livestock. Before taking on an allotment, ensure that you're absolutely clear about any restrictions in place, because if you ignore or overlook them you'll soon find yourself asked to leave. In addition, there'll be terms relating to the period of notice you're required to give should you wish to vacate your plot, and the landlord will be bound by similar obligations to you.

Over the past 20 years or so the demand for space has increased considerably, and waiting lists are now very long – more than 10 years in some areas. If you can't find an allotment or establish a local land share agreement then guerrilla gardening (i.e. making unofficial use of areas of wasteland and such like) would be an exciting alternative, although it's fraught with difficulty, and legally

rather dubious.

Allotment sites were previously seen as the exclusive preserve of old men and prize marrows, but now there are far more young people and families taking on plots in response to concerns about the provenance of their food. These days a well-run allotment site can be a vibrant, socially stimulating place, providing a real focal point for the local community, particularly in urban areas, where opportunities to engage more closely with land and the food we eat are inevitably limited.

For anyone new to vegetable growing, an allotment gives an obvious advantage in that there'll be lots of other experienced gardeners on site to give you advice, guidance and practical assistance, making this an ideal first step on the road to self-sufficiency. Established plot

Sadly theft and vandalism can be a big problem for allotment holders, often, but not exclusively, in urban areas. A certain amount of crop theft is inevitable, as not many people will be able to resist helping themselves to a ripe strawberry from time to time, but vandalism is a real issue. Beyond the obvious solutions such as keeping your shed locked (and not storing anything of significant value in it anyway), there are a couple of courses of action that may be successful in reducing criminal activity: first and foremost, keep the site busy, thus reducing the amount of time that no-one's around to keep an eye on things. Secondly, involve local young people in the allotments as much as possible. Most vandalism is carried out by children, but they're far less likely to trash something that they feel they're a valued part of.

Appendices

Statutory Requirements

"Laws… like cobwebs, which may catch small flies but let wasps and hornets break through."
Jonathon Swift.

HOLDING NUMBER

Whether you keep a commercial herd / flock or just one animal (of a farmed species) as a pet, you need to be registered with the appropriate authorities. Apply to the Rural Payments Agency / Welsh Assembly / DARD for a County Parish Holding (CPH) number for the land where your livestock will be kept. You must register your holding within one month of the time you first keep animals there.

Flock / herd numbers

Contact your regional Animal Health and Plant Agency office (AHPA) to obtain a unique flock or herd number. For sheep and cattle this will be a seven digit number preceded by the letters 'UK'. Pig herd numbers follow a different format, being 1 or 2 letters followed by 4 numbers.

New cattle keepers should also be sent a supply of barcode labels, printed with your name, address and holding number.

Poultry flocks numbering more than 50 birds must be registered within a month of your acquiring them. They do not all have to be of the same species, nor do they have to be on your holding all year round. In addition, DEFRA encourages smaller flocks to register voluntarily in order to assist with the control of any potential disease outbreaks. The following species all count towards the total: chickens (including bantams), turkeys, ducks, geese, partridges, quail, pheasants, pigeons (reared for meat), guinea fowl, ostriches, emus, rheas and cassowaries

LIVESTOCK IDENTIFICATION

sheep and goats

You must identify your sheep and goats:

- Within 6 months of birth if they're housed overnight
- Within 9 months of birth if they're not housed overnight
- Before you move them off their holding of birth, if this is sooner

• Sheep and goats over twelve months of age are required to have two identification markers, usually ear tags, both of which carry that animal's unique identification number, made up of the seven digit UK number and a five figure individual number. In most cases one will be a yellow EID ear tag which carries an electronic chip. In Scotland it's a recommendation rather than a legal requirement for it to be yellow, and in Northern Ireland the EID tag can be any colour. The other tag will be a visual identifier carrying the same number.

• Lambs intended for slaughter before they are one year old may be identified with a single electronic tag, which shows only your flock number. Goat kids that fall into this category aren't required by law to have an EID tag (although you may use one if you wish), but must have a visual tag which clearly displays the herd number. Lambs and kids intended for breeding purposes should be tagged in the same way as older animals.

• Lost or damaged ear tags must be replaced within 28 days of you discovering the loss (or damage).

• Lost tags can be replaced by identical tags. Alternatively, a different pair of tags can be inserted, but where this is done the new number must be cross referenced to the old ID in your flock register. Where inserting identical tags

isn't an option, and the animal is not on its holding of birth, red replacement tags must be used.

Cattle

• All cattle must be identified with a pair of matching ear tags within 20 days of birth. In addition, dairy calves must have at least one tag applied before they are 36 hours old.

• The primary 'distance readable' tag (the big yellow one) must carry the crown logo, country code, herdmark, individual number and check digit. Secondary tags can be any shape or size. They're also yellow, unless metal tags are used.

• Lost ear tags must be replaced (with an identically numbered tag) within 28 days of the loss being discovered. Some tag companies will provide free replacement tags for the lifetime of the animal, provided that you have the original purchase receipt for the tags. This isn't much help in the case of bought in cattle.

• In addition to tags, all cattle must have a passport. Animals born between 28th September 1998 and 1st August 2011 will have a cheque-book style document, and younger stock will have been issued with single page documents.

• You must apply for a calf's passport within 27 days of that animal's birth. Failure to meet this deadline will probably result in the application being refused, and you will be left with a completely worthless animal. Unregistered cattle are not permitted to be moved alive from your holding except under license from the BCMS to enable them to travel direct to a knacker's yard or hunt kennel. Such animals are not permitted to enter the human food chain under any circumstances (although in theory could be slaughtered on farm, by the farmer himself, for his own personal consumption).

• You can apply for the passport online, on paper (although this method is being discouraged), or over the phone. The passport will be a single page document, with the animal's details on the front and a movement summary on the back. The front page must be signed by you on receipt, and have one of your barcode labels affixed. The passport must be kept with the animal (i.e. on the same holding, or in the vehicle during transport).

Pigs

• All pigs over 12 months of age must be identified with your herd mark before they leave their holding of birth. This can be an ear tag, a tattoo in one ear or a slap mark on each shoulder (like a tattoo) made using permanent ink.

• Pigs under one year of age moving from one farm to another are not required to be permanently identified. They can be sprayed with a paint mark which need only last until they have completed their journey. However, if young pigs are moved to any other premises (e.g. a livestock market), they must be identified in the same manner as adult pigs.

ANIMAL MOVEMENTS

Sheep and goats

Movements onto your holding need to be reported to the relevant authority, and it's the responsibility of the destination holding to submit the details. Paper forms may be obtained from markets, downloaded and printed, or from your local Trading Standards officer. Details of the general licence (including current standstill rules) are obtainable from your AHDO. All animals being moved must be accompanied by a relevant movement document. One copy (the white one) of the completed form must be sent to the relevant authorities within three days of the move, the yellow copy remains on the premises of departure, and the pink one is kept at the destination. Sometimes there's also a blue copy, which is for the haulier. Movements can also be notified electronically in England (ARAMS – arams.co.uk), Wales (EID Cymru – eidcymru.org) and Scotland (Scot EID – scoteid.com). Movements of sheep onto your holding will trigger a six day standstill on all

sheep, cattle and goats, and a standstill of 20 days for pigs.

All movements must be recorded in the flock register.

Cattle

Movements are recorded through the British Cattle Movement Service (BCMS) which must be informed of herd changes within three days of the event. Movements can no longer be reported on paper. Most are now reported online at www.bcms.gov.uk, although there is an option to notify by telephone. You must inform BCMS of animals arriving on your holding, and also animals that leave the holding or die. Movements must be noted in the relevant section of the animal's passport.

Pigs

Pig movements differ from the above in that you must notify the appropriate authorities of the movement before it takes place. This can be done by telephoning the Meat and Livestock Commercial Services Ltd. (MLCSL) bureau of the British Pig Executive (in which case you need to tell them at least 5 days before the planned move), or electronically via the eAML2 system (www.eaml2.org.uk). The receiver of the pigs then needs to confirm the arrival of the animals, and again this can be done by phone or by logging in to eAML2. Pigs arriving on your holding will be subject to a 20 day standstill (as will any already in your possession), while sheep, cattle and goats will have to stay put for 6 days.

Animal transport regulations

• The regulations do not apply to the transport of animals not in connection with an economic activity, or transport to or from veterinary practices or clinics.

• Farmers transporting their own animals in their own transport up to 50km from their holding have limited exemption from parts of the regulation, but must still comply with the general

requirements.

• Anyone transporting sheep on journeys over 65km (but under 8 hours) will need to hold a Type 1 Transporter's Authorisation.

• Journeys over 8 hours require a Type 2 Transporter's Authorisation. The vehicle will need to be inspected and approved.

• Heavily pregnant females in the last 10% of gestation cannot be transported unless it is for the purposes of improving the conditions of birth.

• Females that have given birth within the last 7 days cannot be transported or presented for sale.

• If animals 'in milk' are transported without their offspring, they must be milked at intervals not exceeding 12 hours.

• The maximum permitted loading ramp angle for sheep and cattle is 50% (e.g. a rise of 1 metre over a distance of 2 metres). The angle is reduced to 36.4% for calves and pigs.

• There is no maximum legal journey time for poultry. However, food and water must be offered to adult birds after 12 hours, or 24 hours for chicks if the trip is completed within 72 hours of hatching.

• Different species must be transported separately from others.

It is also necessary to separate:

- Animals of significantly different ages or sizes;*
- Sexually mature males from females;
- Animals with horns from those without;*
- Animals that are hostile to one another;
- Tied stock from untied (e.g. sheep haltered and tied for transporting to a show).
(* Except where separation would cause distress, for example sheep with dependent lambs, or where animals have been raised in compatible groups, and are accustomed to one another.)

Minimum space allowances within vehicles are as follows:

Category	Approximate weight (kg)	Area (m² /animal)
Shorn sheep and lambs 26kg and over	<55	0.20-0.30
	>55	>0.30
Unshorn sheep	<55	0.30-0.40
	>55	>0.40
Heavily pregnant ewes	<55	0.40-0.50
	>55	>0.50
Small calves	50	0.30-0.40
Medium-sized calves	110	0.40-0.70
Heavy calves	200	0.70-0.95
Medium-sized cattle	325	0.95-1.30
Heavy cattle	550	1.30-1.60
Very heavy cattle	>700	>1.60
Goats	<35	0.20-0.30
Goats	35-55	0.30-0.40
Goats	>55	0.40-0.75
Heavily pregnant goats	<55	0.40-0.50
Heavily pregnant goats	>55	>0.50
Pigs	There must be sufficient space for all pigs to lie down and stand up naturally. It is recommended that the loading density should not exceed 235kg per m² where the animals being transported are in the region of 100kg.	
		Area (m² / kg bodyweight)
Day-old chicks	N/A	0.0021-0.0025
Other poultry	<1.6	0.018-0.020
Other poultry	1.6-3.0	0.0160
Other poultry	3.0-5.0	0.0115
Other poultry	>5.0	0.0105
Source DEFRA		

• During journeys of more than 8 hours the temperature within the vehicle must not fall below 0°C. Where young pigs are not accompanied by their mother, they must be provided with suitable bedding in cold weather.

• Very young animals (i.e. lambs and kids under 7 days old, calves less than ten days of age, and piglets under three weeks), must not be transported unless it is within farm and for the purpose of improving their general health and welfare. Any newborn whose navel is not yet fully dried is not fit to travel.

• Lambs weighing less than 20kg and piglets under 10kg must be provided with warm, comfortable bedding material.

Cleansing and disinfection

Vehicles used to transport livestock should be cleansed and disinfected at the destination premises, unless the vehicle is returning directly to the place of departure, in which case it must be washed out within 24 hours or before it's next used to carry livestock, whichever is the sooner. At markets and abattoirs you may be required to sign a declaration undertaking to carry out cleansing and disinfection within the required timescale.

Notifiable diseases

You must report to your nearest AHPA office if you even suspect that one of your animals may be suffering from any notifiable disease. The following notifiable diseases relate to farmed livestock :

African swine fever, anthrax, Aujeszky's disease, avian influenza, BSE, bluetongue, bovine TB, brucellosis, classical swine fever, contagious agalactia, contagious bovine pleuro-pneumonia, contagious epididymitis, enzootic bovine leukosis, epizootic haemorrhagic disease, foot and mouth disease, goat plague, lumpy skin disease, Newcastle disease, porcine epidemic diarrhoea, rabies, Rift Valley fever, rinderpest, scrapie, sheep and goat pox, sheep scab, swine influenza, swine vesicular disease, Teschen disease, vesicular stomatitis and warble fly.

Fallen stock disposal

Fallen stock – livestock that dies on farm due to natural causes, or is killed on farm other than for human consumption – is classified as an animal by-product (ABP). Carcasses must not be buried or burnt in the open, other than in exceptional circumstances, such as during an outbreak of a notifiable disease. Fallen stock must be taken to, or collected by, an approved knacker, hunt kennel, incinerator or renderer, either by private arrangement or under the National Fallen Stock Scheme.

Deaths of cattle must be reported to BCMS within seven days of the event, and the animal's passport must be returned to them within the same time window. The carcasses of cattle older than 48 months must be sent for BSE testing.

TB testing

All cattle herds will be subject to regular tests for Bovine Tuberculosis. The test interval will vary depending on whether or not you live in a high risk area. In regions where there is little threat of the disease, compulsory testing may only be carried out every four years, but in other areas animals will be tested annually. There is no charge for the compulsory tests. In areas where herds are tested on an annual basis, cattle must also be TB tested before they can be moved off farm. Pre-movement tests are arranged by the owner of the animals, and must be paid for. A clear result is valid for a period of sixty days. Cattle less than 42 days of age are not required to be tested. Cattle going directly to an abattoir or slaughter market are also exempt.

Medicine storage

Medicines (and other products such as sheep dips and pour-ons) must be kept in accordance with the label instructions, in a secure lockable store. This could be a container, cupboard, room or separate building. A cupboard within a locked building would be acceptable. Drains must be protected from pollution in the event of leakage. Vaccines that need to be refrigerated should not be stored in fridges used for food.

Veterinary treatments

All treatments (including routine preventative medicines) need to be recorded, whether administered by yourself or by your vet. As a minimum requirement, your record should at least include the following information:

• Name of the product, batch number, and the total quantity in the pack.

• Date purchased, and from where.

• ID of the animal (or group of animals) treated.

• Dates that treatment started and ended.

• Total quantity of medicine used.

• Withdrawal periods for meat, milk or eggs.

• The name of the person who administered the medicine.

TIP

In cattle, intramuscular injections are usually given in the rump, or fairly high up on the side of the neck. The site for subcutaneous injection is lower on the neck, under the loose skin just in front of the shoulder.

In sheep, intramuscular injections are usually given in the back of the thigh (although be aware that an injection site abscess here, in animals intended for slaughter, would damage a prime joint, which could result in the carcass being downgraded or condemned), or in the side of the neck, just in front of the shoulder. Subcutaneous injections can be given high up on the side of the neck (just behind the angle of the jaw), or over the ribcage. Alternatively, if you are vaccinating non-pregnant sheep (e.g. barren yearlings), you can do it at the same time as hoof trimming, using the area of clean skin on the groin.

Pigs are generally injected intramuscularly in the side of the neck, not far behind the ear.

(For any readers not familiar with the terminology, I'll just clarify that subcutaneous means under the skin, and an intramuscular injection is given straight into the muscle).

Feed storage

Feed must be stored separately from any chemicals and other substances prohibited for use in animal feeds. Storage areas and containers must be kept clean and dry, and appropriate pest control measures implemented where necessary. Regular cleansing of feed bins etc. should be carried out in order to prevent cross contamination. Medicated and non-medicated feed

must be stored correctly to reduce the risk of feeding to non-target animals. Ruminant (sheep, cattle, goats) and non-ruminant (pigs, poultry, etc.) feeds must be stored separately, preferably in different buildings, but, failing that, in different bays or bins. Pet foods should not be stored with other feeds.

Waste plastic disposal

It is no longer permissible to burn waste plastic, including feed sacks, silage wrap, baler twine and pesticide containers. Nor is it permissible to place agricultural waste in the bin with domestic rubbish. Waste plastics may only be stored on farm for a limited period before being taken to an approved recycling site, or being collected by an approved contractor.

Registration with the British Wool Marketing Board (BWMB)

If you keep more than 4 adult sheep then you will have to register with the BWMB, and, in most cases, you'll have to sell your wool to them. Certain rare breeds are exempt from this requirement. At the time of writing the list of exempt breeds is as follows: Balwen, Boreray, Castlemilk Moorit, Hebridean, Leicester Longwool, Lincoln Longwool, Llanwenog, Manx Loaghtan, Norfolk Horn, North Ronaldsay, Portland, Soay and Teeswater. This list is revised and updated periodically, and registered wool producers will be advised of the current ruling each season. A producer can also request an exemption for the purpose of retaining their home-produced fleeces for artisan craft purposes, up to a limit of 3,000kg annually, or up to 15,000kg annually for non-textile uses such as insulation. Applications for exemption are considered on a case by case basis.

Useful Tables

Table 1 Conversion factors

Length

inches – cm	x 2.54	cm – inches	x 0.394
inches – mm	x 25.4	mm – inches	x 0.0394
feet – metres	x 0.305	metres – feet	x 3.29
yards – metres	x 0.914	metres – yards	x 1.09
chain – metres	x 20.12	metres – chains	x 0.0497
miles – kilometres	x 1.61	kilometres – miles	x 0.621

Area

sq feet – m²	x 0.093	m² – sq feet	x 10.8
sq yards – m²	x 0.836	m² – sq yards	x 1.20
acres – hectares	x 0.405	hectares – acres	x 2.47

Volume

cubic feet – m³	x 0.0283	m³ – cubic feet	x 35.31
cubic yard – m³	x 0.7646	m³ – cubic yard	x 1.308
pints – litres	x 0.568	litres – pints	x 1.76
gallons – litres	x 4.55	litres – gallons	x 0.22
gallon – m³	x 0.0045	m³ – gallons	x 219.97
fluid ounces – ml	x 28.41	ml – fluid ounces	x 0.0352

Weight

ounces – grams	x 28.3	grams – ounces	x 0.0353
pounds – grams	x 454	grams – pounds	x 0.0022
pounds – kilograms	x 0.454	kilograms – pounds	x 2.2
cwt – kilograms	x 50.8	kilograms – cwt	x 0.020
cwt – tonnes	x 0.0508		
tons – kilograms	x 1016		
tons – tonnes	x 1.016	tons – tonnes	x 0.984

cwt = hundredweight (112lbs)

Temperature

Fahrenheit – Celsius	(°F-32) x 0.556	Celsius – Fehrenheit	(°C x 1.8) + 32

Rate of use

pounds/acre – kg/hectare	x 1.121	kg/hectare – pounds/acre	x 0.8922
cwt/acre – kg/hectare	x 125.5	kg/hectare – cwt/acre	x 0.007966
ton/acre – kg/hectare	x 2511	kg/hectare– ton/acre	x 0.000398
pounds/gallon – gallon/litre	x 99.78	gallon/litre – pounds/gallon	x 0.01
gallons/acre – litres/hectare	x 11.23	litres/hectare – gallons/acre	x 0.08902
fert.units/acre – kg/hectare	x 1.25	kg/hectare – fert.units/acre	x 0.8

Table 2 Potential stock carrying capacity of grassland

Pasture type (predominant species)	Growing season	Yield	Stock carrying capacity
Perennial ryegrass and white clover	6 – 9 months	8 – 11 tonnes DM / ha / year	0.8 – 1.2 LSU / ha (0.32 – 0.48 LSU / acre)
Cocksfoot, timothy and Yorkshire fog	5 – 7 months	5 – 7 tonnes DM / ha / year	0.48 – 0.64 LSU / ha (0.2 – 0.26 LSU / acre)
Bents, fescues and molinia	3 – 4 months	2.5 – 5 tonnes DM / ha / year	0.16 – 0.32 LSU / ha (0.065 – 0.13 LSU / acre)

Table 3 Relative nutritional values of hay and silage

		Metabolisable energy (MJ/kg DM)	Metabolisable protein (g/kg DM)
Hay	High quality	10.3	77
Hay	Medium quality	8.7	70
Silage	High quality	11.8	125
Silage	Medium quality	10.6	105

Source: ADAS

Table 4 Rootstocks

	Apple	Pear	Plum	Cherry	Peach/Nectarine
Dwarfing	M27	Quince C		Gisela 5	
Semi-dwarfing	M26	Quince A	Pixy	Gisela 6	Pixy
Semi-vigorous	MM106	Pyrodwarf	St Julien A	Colt	St Julien A
Vigorous	M25	Pyrus	Brompton	F12/1	

Table 5 Livestock units allocated to different classes of grazing animal

Species	Category	LSUs
Cattle	Dairy cows	1.00
	Suckler cows (excluding calves)	0.75
	Bulls	0.65
	Calves up to one year	0.34
	Weaned calves and stores, 1 – 2 years old	0.65
	Store and replacement heifers over 2 years	0.80
Sheep	Ewes (excluding suckling lambs) and shearling flock replacements:	
	Light breeds (hill and primitive)	0.06
	Medium (most lowland breeds and commerical crossbreds)	0.08
	Heavy (traditional large down breeds and longwools)	0.11
	Rams	0.08
	Lambs, birth to fat or store	0.04
	Store lambs	0.04
	Lambs, birth to hogget	0.08
	Breeding ewes, including lambs (for general calculations)	0.15
Goats		0.15
Horses	All categories	0.80

445

Table 6 Gestation tables

Species	Gestation length	Sesonal breeder?	Oestrus cycle
Sheep	147 days	Yes	17 days
Cattle	283 days	No	21 days
Pigs	114 days	No	21 days
Goats	150 days	Yes	21 days
Rabbits	31 days	Yes	N/A
Ferrets	42 days	Yes	N/A
Dogs	63 days	No	Approx 6 monthly
Cats	63 days	Yes	N/A

Table 7 Compound feed requirements for ewes in late gestation kg / head / day

	Light breeds <50kg (Shetland, Portland, Hebridean etc.)		Medium 50 – 70kg (Lleyn, Shropshire, Dorset Horn etc.)		Heavy breeds >70kg (Oxford down, Suffolk, Wensleydale etc.)	
	SINGLE	TWIN	SINGLE	TWIN	SINGLE	TWIN
6 weeks before lambing	0.25	0.30	0.35	0.45	0.50	0.75
2 weeks before lambing	0.35	0.45	0.45	0.60	0.75	1.00
Feeding	When increasing the ration, split the total amount into two equal feeds / day					
Forage	Good quality hay or high dry matter silage fed ad-lib throughout					

Table 8 Estimating the weight of growing pigs, from a measurement taken around the girth

Girth (in inches)	Liveweight (in pounds)	Deadweight (in pounds)
36 – 37½	140 – 160	100 – 115
38 – 40	165 – 190	120 – 140
41 – 44	200 – 230	150 – 180
46 – 48	250 – 275	200 – 220

Table 9 Comparative analysis of different milks

	Sheep	Goat	Cow
Water (%)	80.82	85.71	87.08
Fat (%)	6.86	4.78	3.73
Protein (%)	6.52	4.29	3.58
Lactose (%)	4.91	4.46	4.90
Casein (%)	5.00	2.50	3.20
Minerals (%)	0.89	0.76	0.71
B vitamins (mg/l)	22.49	12.67	9.83

Table 10 Incubation guidelines / information

For guidance only. Please check your incubator manufacturer's instructions for more detailed information

Species	Incubation temperature	Humidity 1	Humidity 2	Period of incubation
Chickens	37.5°C	50%	65%	21 days
Bantams	37.5°C	50%	65%	20 days
Ducks	37.5°C	63%	75%	28 days
Muscovy ducks	37.5°C	53%	67%	35 – 37 days
Geese	37.5°C	55%	75%	28 – 34 days
Turkeys	37.5°C	55%	75%	28 days
Quail	37.8°C	60%	75%	16 – 23 days

Table 11 Calorific value of firewood

Species	Calorific values @ 20% moisture (kWh per stacked m³)	
Oak	1890 – 2030	Slow burning, good heat output, but needs to be well seasoned.
Ash	1870	Probably the best all-round firewood; can be used green.
Beech	1850 – 1930	Burns in a similar way to ash, but needs to be well seasoned.
Birch	1700 – 1810	Good heat output, but burns quickly with a bright flame. Sweet smelling.
Larch	1780	Reasonably good heat output and nice scent.
Sycamore	1675 – 1780	Moderate heat with a good flame.
Pine	1350 – 1570	Quick burning with lively flames. Spits, so take care if using an open fireplace.
Willow	1440	Slow burning with little flame. May spit.
Fir	1360	Small flame and poor heat output.
Alder	1230 – 1400	Quick burning and produces little heat, but improves if well seasoned.
Spruce	1300 – 1320	Low heat, inclined to spit, burns rather quickly.
Poplar	1100	Poor burning. Produces lots of smoke but not much heat.

Table 12 UK Shooting seasons. The species listed may be shot during the following periods.

Red deer	Stag (England, Wales and Northern Ireland)	1st August – 30th April
	Stag (Scotand)	1st July – 20th October
	Hind (England, Wales and Northern Ireland)	1st November – 31st March
	Hind (Scotland)	21st October – 15th February
Fallow deer	Buck	1st August – 30th April
	Doe (England, Wales and Northern Ireland)	1st November – 31st March
	Doe (Scotland)	21st October – 15th February
Roe deer	Buck (England and Wales)	1st April – 31st October
	Buck (Scotland)	1st April – 20th October
	Doe (England and Wales)	1st November – 31st March
	Doe (Scotland)	21st October – 31st March
Sika deer	Stag (England, Wales and Northern Ireland)	1st August – 30th April
	Stag (Scotland)	1st July – 20th October
	Hind (England, Wales and Northern Ireland)	1st November – 31st March
	Hind (Scotland)	21st October – 15th February
Chinese water deer		1st November – 31st March
Muntjac deer		At all times
Wild boar		At all times
Rabbits		At all times (except on unenclosed land where certain restrictions may apply)
Brown hares	England and Wales	At all times (except on unenclosed land where certain restrictions may apply)
	Scotland	1st October – 31st January
	Northern Ireland	12th August – 31st January
Grey squirrels		At all times
Woodpigeons		At all times
Pheasants	England, Scotland and Wales	1st October – 1st February
	Northern Ireland	1st October – 31st January
Partridges		1st September – 1st February
Grouse	England, Scotland and Wales	12th August – 10th December
	Northern Ireland	12th August – 30th November
Ducks and geese	Inland (England, Scotland and Wales)	1st September – 31st January
	Foreshore (England, Scotland and Wales)	1st September – 20th February
	Foreshore (Northern Ireland)	1st September – 31st January

Table 13 Natural Plant Dyes

Common name	Latin name	Parts used	General colour guide	Suggested mordants
Agrimony	*Agrimonia eupatoria*	leaves	gold	alum, chrome
Alder	*Alnus spp.*	bark	yellow / brown / black	alum, iron, copper sulphate
Alkanet	*Anchusa tinctoria*	roots	grey	alum, cream of tartar
Apple	*Malus spp.*	bark	yellow	alum
Barberry	*Berberis spp*	twigs	yellow	alum
Bilberry	*Vaccinium spp.*	berries	purple	alum, tin
Blackberry	*Rubus spp.*	berries, young shoots	pink/purple	alum, tin
Black crottle (lichen)	*Parmelia omphalodes*	whole lichen	reddish brown (when boiled)	oak bark
Blackcurrent	*Ribes spp.*	berries	grey / deep purple	alum, tin
Blackwillow	*Salix nigra*	bark	red/brown	iron, chrome
Bloodroot	*Sanguinaria canandensis*	roots	red	alum, tin
Bluebell	*Hyacinthoides non-scripta*	flowers	ice blue / bright blue	alum, tin
Bracken	*Pteridum aquilinum*	young shoots, old tops	yellow / green	alum, chrome
Broom	*Cytisus spp.*	flowering tops	orange / yellow	chrome, tin
Buckthorn	*Rhamnus cathartica*	twigs, berries	yellow / brown	alum, cream of tartar, chrome, tin, iron
Cherry	*Prunus spp.*	bark	pink / yellow /brown	alum
Coffee	*Coffea arabica*	used grounds	brown / khaki	alum, chrome, none
Coreopsis	*Coreopsis tinctoria*	flower heads	yellow / orange	chrome, tin
Crab's Eye (lichen)	*Ochrolechia parella*	whole lichen	orange / red (when fermented in urine then boiled)	alum
Crottle (lichen)	*Parmelia saxatilis*	whole lichen	yellow / brown (when boiled)	oak bark
Cudbear (lichen)	*Ochrolechia tartarea*	whole lichen	red / purple (when fermented in urine then boiled)	alum
Cypress	*Cypress spp.*	cones	tan	alum, chrome
Daffodil	*Narcissus pseudonarcissus*	flowers	yellow	alum, tin
Dahlia	*Dahlia spp.*	petals	yellow / bronze	alum
Damson	*Prunum damascenum*	fruit skins	dark red / green	alum, ammonia
Day lily	*Hemerocallis spp.*	flowers	yellow	alum, tin, copper sulphate
Dandelion	*Taraxacum officinale*	flower/taproot	yellow / magenta/ brown	none, alum
Dog lichen	*Peltigera canina*	whole lichen	yellow (when boiled)	alum
Dog's mercury	*Mercurialis perennis*	whole plant	yellow	alum
Dyer's chamomile	*Anthemis tinctoria*	flowers	yellow	alum
Elder	*Sambucus nigra*	leaves, berries, bark	yellow / grey	iron, alum
Fennel	*Foeniculum vulgare*	whole plant	brown/green	chrome, iron, copper sulphate
French marigold	*Tegetes patula*	flower heads	yellow / brown / orange	alum, chrome, iron, tin
Golden rod	*Solidago spp.*	flower tops	gold	alum, chrome, iron
Gorse	*Ulex europaeus*	flower petals	yellow / lime	alum
Heather	*Erica spp.*	tips	yellow	alum
Horestail	*Equisetum spp.*	stalks	green	alum, copper sulphate
Horse chestnut	*Aesculus hippocastanum*	conker peels	brown / bronze / grey	alum, tin, iron
Hypogymnia (lichen)	*Hypogymnia psychodes*	whole lichen	gold / brown	
Ivy	*Hedera helix*	berries	yellow / green	alum, iron
Lady's bedstraw	*Gallium boreale*	roots, tops	yellow / red	alum, chrome, iron

Larch	*Larix spp*	needles	brown	alum
Lily of the valley	*Convallaria majalis*	leaves	gold	lime
Lombardy poplar	*Populus nigra italica*	leaves	yellow/gold	alum, chrome
Lungs of oak (lichen)	*Lobaria pulmonaria*	whole plant	orange	none required
Madder	*Rubia tinctoria*	whole plant	orange/red	alum, tin
Maple	*Acer spp.*	bark	tan	chrome, copper sulphate
Mahonia	*Mahonia aquifolium*	roots, berries, whole plant	blue/brown	alum, chrome
Marigold	*Calendula spp.*	whole plant, flower heads	yellow	alum, chrome
Marjoram	*Origanum vulgare*	whole flower heads	violet	alum
Meadowsweet	*Filipendula ulmaria*	roots	yellow/green	alum, iron
Menegussia (lichen)	*Menegussia pertussa*	whole lichen	pink (when boiled)	washing soda
Nettle	*Urtica dioica*	fresh tops	yellow/green/grey	alum, iron
Oak	*Quercus spp.*	inner bark	gold/brown	alum, chrome
Onion	*Allium cepa*	skins	yellow / orange	alum
Orchil (lichen)	*Roccella tinctoria*	whole lichen	purple / blue / red	alum, chrome, ammonia
Pansy	*viola spp*	yellow petals	lemon / cinnamon / olive / gold	alum, chrome, iron, tin
Pokeweed	*Phytolacca americana*	berries	red / tan	alum
Privet	*Ligustrum vulgare*	leaves, berries	yellow / green / red / purple	alum, chrome, tin
Pyracantha	*Pyracantha angustifolium*	bark	pink / brown / grey	alum, chrome
Ragwort	*Senecio*	flowers	deep yellow	alum
Rhododendron	*Rhododendron ponticum*	leaves	yellow / orange / grey	alum, tin, iron
Rhubarb	*Rheum rhabarbarum*	roots	pale yellow	none required
Saffron	*Crocus sativus*	stigmata	yellow	alum, chrome,iron, tin
Silver birch	*Betula pendula*	leaves, bark	yellow / gold	alum
Sloe (Blackthorn)	*Prunus spinosa*	berries, bark	red / pink / brown	alum
Snowberry	*Symphoricarpus albus*	berries	yellow	alum
Spindle-tree	*Euonymus europaeus*	seed pods	red	alum
St. John's wort	*Hypericum spp.*	flower tops	yellow / green / maroon / black	alum, chrome
Sumach	*Rhus spp*	berry tops, leaves	tan / brown	alum, chrome
Sunflower	*Helianthus annus*	petals / seed hulls	yellow / purple	alum
Sweet pea (purple)	*Lathyrus odoratus*	petals	deep green / grey	alum, chrome, iron, tin
Sweet woodruff	*Asperula odorata*	whole plants	red / pink	cream of tartar
Tansy	*Tanacetum vulgare*	flowering heads	yellow	alum
Tea	*Camelia sinensis*	leaves (cheap tea bags)	pink / tan / dark tan	alum, chrome, none
Usnea (lichen)	*Usnea barbata*	whole lichen	yellow (when boiled)	
	Usnea Lirta	whole lichen	purple (when fermented in urine)	
Walnut	*Juglans regia*	hulls	brown	none required
Weld (wild mignonette)	*Reseda luteula*	whole plant	olive green	alum, cream of tartar
Woad	*Isatis tinctoria*	whole plant	blue	lime
Yellow flag iris	*Iris pseudaconus*	root	grey / black	chrome, tin, iron
Yellow scales (lichen)	*Xanthoria parietina*	whole lichen	purple / blue	

Resources

This is quite simply a list of some of the titles found on our own shelves that we've referred to from time to time during the creation of this book.

Cottage Economy William Cobbett (first published 1821) (Cosimo, 2007) ISBN 978-1-60206-809-4

Mrs. Beeton's Household Management Isabella Beeton (first published 1861) (Ward, Lock & Co. Ltd. and numerous others)

The Fat of the Land John Seymour (Faber & Faber, 1961; Metanoia Press, 1991) ISBN: 0-951-8381-0-5

Self-Sufficiency John and Sally Seymour (Faber & Faber, 1975) ISBN: 0-571-09954-8

The Complete Book of Self-Sufficiency John Seymour (Faber & Faber, 1976) ISBN: 0-571-11095-9

Blueprint for a Green Planet John Seymour and Herbert Giradet (Dorling Kindersley, 1987) ISBN: 0-86318-364-6

The New Complete Book of Self-Sufficiency John Seymour with Will Sutherland (Dorling Kindersley, 2003) ISBN-13: 978-0-7513-6442-2

The Survival Handbook – Self-sufficiency for everyone Michael Allaby with Marika Hanbury Tenison, John Seymour and Hugh Sharman (Macmillan, 1975; Pan Books, 1977) ISBN: 0-330-24813-8

On Next to Nothing Thomas and Susan Hinde (Sphere books, 1977) ISBN: 0-7221-4558-6

Technological Self-Sufficiency Robin Clarke (Faber & Faber, 1976) ISBN: 0-571-10835-0

How to Live Off-grid Nick Rosen (Transworld Publishers, 2007) ISBN: 978-0-553-81819-2

The Self-Sufficient-ish Bible Andy and Dave Hamilton (Hodder & Stoughton, 2008) ISBN: 978-0-340-95101-9

Five Acres and Independence M. G. Kains (Cassell & Co. Ltd., 1947)
Your Smallholding edited by Alan Thompson. (Penguin, 1947)

The Smallholder Encyclopædia edited by Walter Brett FRHS (C. Arthur Pearson Ltd., 1943)

The Smallholder Encyclopædia edited by S. A. Maycock FRHS and John Hayhurst (C. Arthur Pearson Ltd., 1950)

Natural Dyes for Spinners and Weavers Hetty Wickens (B. T. Batsford, 1983) ISBN: 0-7134-2021-9

Colour from Plants – A Simple Dyer's Notebook Cherry Morton and Annette Mortlock (Abbot Hall Gallery and Museum of Lakeland Life and Industry)

Learn to Spin (Ashford Handicrafts) Your Handspinning Elsie G. Davenport (Select Books, 1964)

The Women's Institute Book of Country Crafts W. I. Books Ltd. (Chancellor Press, 1994 edition) ISBN: 1-85152-544-0

Crafts from the Countryside Patricia de Menezes (Hamlyn Publishing Group Ltd., 1981) ISBN: 600-32199-1

Green Woodwork – Working with wood the natural way Mike Abbott (Guild of Master Craftsmen Publications Ltd., 1989) ISBN: 0-946819-18-1

Home Brewed Beers and Stouts (4th edition) C. J. J. Berry (The Amateur Winemaker, 1970) ISBN: 900841-02-8

Home Made Country Wines compiled by Dorothy Wise (Hamlyn Paperbacks, 1978) ISBN: 0-600-34424-X

Wine Making at Home Francis Pinnegar (Hamlyn Paperbacks, 1979, 1984) ISBN: 0-600-39418-2

First Steps in Winemaking (6th Edition) C. J. J. Berry (Amateur Winemaker Publications, 1981) ISBN: 0-900841-40-0

130 New Winemaking Recipes (3rd Edition) C. J. J. Berry (Argus Books, 1985) ISBN: 0-900841-63-X

Home Wine and Beer Making Ben Turner (Treasure Press, 1983) ISBN: 0-907812-31-7

Boots Home Wine Making and Brewing B. C. A. Turner (Wolfe, 1970) ISBN: 72340426-7

Best kept Secrets of the Women's Institute: Jams, Pickles and chutneys Midge Thomas (Simon & Schuster Ltd., 2002) ISBN: 0-74322-113-3

The Best of Mrs Beeton's Jams, Pickles and Chutneys Mrs. Beeton (Orion Publishing Group Ltd., 2007)

Making Cheeses, Butters, Cream and Yogurt at Home Patricia Cleveland-Peck (Thorsons Publishers Ltd., 1980) ISBN: 0-7225-0597-3

Home Preservation of Fruit and Vegetables Ministry of Agriculture, Fisheries and Food (Crown Copyright, 1971) ISBN: 0-11-241321-8

Farm Management Pocketbook John Nix (Wye College, University of London) updated annually. ISBN: 0-86266-151-X

Farm Management Handbook 1993 / 94 (14th Edition) Editor: Linda Chadwick (The Scottish Agricultural College, 1993)

Compendium of Data Sheets for Veterinary Products 2004 (National Office of Animal Health, 2003) ISBN: 0-9526638-9-9

Energy and Protein Requirements of Ruminants An advisory manual prepared by the AFRC Technical Committee on Responses to Nutrients (CAB International, 1993) ISBN: 0-85198-851-2

*Modern British Farming System*s editor: Frank H. Garner (Paul Elek, 1972) ISBN: 0-236-17730-3

Animal Husbandry (2nd Edition, 3rd Impression) D. G. M Thomas & W. I. J Davies (Cassell & Co. 1977) ISBN: 0-304-93797-5

Agriculture – The Science and Practice of Farming (11th Edition) J. A. S. Watson and J. A. More (first published 1924) (Oliver & Boyd, 1962)

Good Farm Workmanship D. V. Fletcher (Hodder & Stoughton / The English Universities Press Ltd., 1944)

Good Farm Crops A. W. Oldershaw (Hodder and Stoughton / The English Universities Press Ltd., 1944)

Farm Machinery C. Culpin, M.A., Dip. Agric. (Cantab). (Crosby Lockwood & Son, 1945)

The Science and Practice of Conservation: Grass and Forage Crops (Volumes I & II) S. J. Watson (The Fertiliser and Feeding Stuffs Journal, 1939)

Improved Grassland Management (New Edition) John Frame and A. S. Laidlaw (Crowood Press, 2011) ISBN: 978-1-84797-261-3

Good Grassland D. H. Robinson (English Universities Press, 1947)

Improving Soils for Better Returns Beef and Sheep BRP Manual 3, EBLEX Better Returns programme (Agriculture and Horticulture Development Board 2010)

The Complete Book of Raising Livestock and Poultry edited by Katie Thear & Dr. Alistair Fraser (Martin Dunitz Ltd., 1981) ISBN: 0-906348-11-0

Incubation – A Guide to Hatching and Rearing Katie Thear (Broad Leys Publishing, 2005) ISBN: 978-0-9061-3725-3

Starting with Ducks Katie Thear (Broad Leys Publishing, 2002) ISBN: 0-906137-30-6

Chicken Breeds and Care Frances Bassom (Interpret Publishing, 2009) ISBN: 978-1-84286-212-4

Chicken Hatching and Rearing for Beginners Ditchfield's Little Wonder Book No.10 (Ditchfield's British Books Ltd.)

Keeping Pigs Elisabeth Downing (Pelham Books, 1978, 1985) ISBN: 0-7207-1613-6

A Guide to Traditional Pig Keeping Carol Harris (Good Life Press 2007) ISBN: 978-1904871-29-3

The Pigman's Handbook Gerry Brent (Farming Press, 1982) ISBN: 0-85236-126-2

Modern Pig Breeding J. A. Greenslade (Pearson, 1952, 1956)

All about Pigs – 800 Questions and Answers (Pig Publications Ltd., 1955)

Charcuterie and French Pork Cookery Jane Grigson (Penguin Books, 1970) ISBN: 0-14-046792-0

The Sheep Book for Smallholders Tim Tyne (Good Life Press, 2009) ISBN: 978-1-90487-164-4

Profitable Sheep Farming (5th Impression) M. McGregor Cooper and R. J. Thomas (Farming Press, 1965 and 1991) ISBN: 0-85236-117-3

The Modern Shepherd (D. Brown and S. Meadowcroft (Farming Press, 1989) ISBN: 0-85236-188-2

Raising a Calf for Beef Phyllis Hobson (Garden Way, 1976) ISBN: 0-88266-095-0

Goat Husbandry David Mackenzie (first published 1957) (Faber & Faber, 1993) ISBN: 0-571-16595-8

Modern Dairy Goats Mary Douglas Gordon (Nicholson & Watson, 1950)

Keeping Rabbits Elisabeth Downing (Pelham Books, 1977, 1979) ISBN: 0-7207-0938-5

Modern Rabbit Keeping W. King Wilson (HMSO, 1954) Bulletin No.50 of the Ministry of Agriculture & Fisheries

Modern Rabbit Husbandry W. King Wilson (Crosby Lockwood & Son, 1953)

Rabbit Breeds and Care Geoff Russell (Interpet, 2008) ISBN: 978-184286205-6

Care for your Rabbit RSPCA (Collins, 1991) ISBN: 0-00-718270-8

Beekeeping Joseph Tinsley (E. H. Taylor Ltd, 1945)

Common Sense Beekeeping M. M. Hooper (Link House Publications Ltd.)

Backyard Beekeeping William Scott (Prism Press, 1977) ISBN: 0-904-727-44-0

Bee Keeping Reginald Gamble (National Federation of Young Farmers' Clubs, 1946)

Beekeeping Colin G. Butler M.A., Ph.D. (Ministry of Agriculture, Fisheries and Food, 1957)

The English Gardener William Cobbett (First published 1829) (Oxford University Press, 1980) ISBN: 0-19-217708-7

Grow your own Vegetables Joy Larkcom (Frances Lincoln, 2002) ISBN: 0-7112-1963-X

Pocket Guide to the Edible Garden Joe Hashman (Spring Hill / How To Books Ltd., 2010) ISBN: 978-1-905862-46-7

The New Vegetable and Herb Expert Dr. D. G. Hessayon (Expert Books, 1997) ISBN: 0-903505-46-0

1001 Hints and Tips for the Garden editor: John Palmer (Reader's Digest, 1996) ISBN: 0-276-42231-7

The Gourmet Gardener Bob Flowerdew (Kyle Cathie Ltd., 2007) ISBN: 978-1-85626-723-6

The Vegetable Grower's Treasury A. J. McSelf (W. H. & L. Collingridge Ltd.)

Greenhouses, Cloches and Frames Peter McHoy (Blandford Press, 1984) ISBN: 0-7137-1418-2

The ABC of Vegetable Gardening W. E. Shewell-Cooper (Hodder & Staughton Ltd., 1949)

Vegetables – Growing and Cooking the Natural Way W.E Shewell-Cooper (Sphere Books Ltd., 1978)

Fruit and Its Cultivation T. W. Sanders (W. H. & L. Collingridge Ltd.)

The Complete Fruit Grower W. E. Shewell-Cooper (Faber & Faber, 1960)

The Fruit Expert Dr. D. G. Hessayon. (pbi Publications, 1990) ISBN: 0-90505-31-2

Food for Free Richard Mabey (Fontana, 1976)

The Wild Gourmets – Adventures in Food and Freedom Guy Grieve and Thomasina Miers (Bloomsbury, 2007) ISBN: 9780747591573

Modern Ferreting D. B. Plummer (Boydell Press, 1977) ISBN: 0-85115-083-7

Ferrets and Ferreting Iain Brodie (Blandford Press, 1978, 1987) ISBN: 0-7137-1831-5

The Ferret and Ferreting Guide Graham Wellstead (David & Charles, 1981) ISBN: 0-7153-8013-3

The Book of the .22 Richard Arnold (First published by Nicholas Kaye Ltd, 1962) (Kaye & Ward Ltd., 1972) ISBN 0-7182-0911-7

The Instinctive Shot Chris Batha (Quiller, 2012) ISBN: 978-1-84689-111-3

Rough Shooting G. K. Yeates and R. N. Winnall (Adam & Charles Black, 1935)

Sea Fishing for Pleasure and Profit R. C. O'Farrell. (Fishing News (Books) Ltd)

Complete Guide to Sea Fishing Hugh Stoker (Allen & Unwin, 1961)

Simply Fish – A Guide to Identifying, Buying and Eating Fish Jenny Baker (Faber & Faber, 1988) ISBN: 0-571-14966-9

Complete British Wildlife Paul Sterry (Harper Collins, 1997) ISBN: 0-583-33638-8

Building with Straw Bales – A Practical Guide for the UK and Ireland Barbara Jones (Green Books 2002) ISBN: 978-1-903998-13-7

A Woodwork Bench Notebook F. S. Haywood (Cassell and Company Ltd.)

The Complete Handyman (Odhams Press Ltd.)

Reader's Digest Repair Manual – The Complete Guide to Home Maintenance (Reader's Digest, 1972)

What on Earth Happened? Christopher Lloyd (Bloomsbury Publishing Plc, 2008) ISBN: 978-0-7475-9459-8

There is a very useful booklet called *A Farmer's Guide to the Planning System* produced by the Office of the Deputy Prime Minister, which will steer you through the planning maze. It is available free as a download from: http://www.planning.odpm.gov.uk/advice.htm or from the DEFRA website at http://www.defra.gov.uk/farm/planning-guide/index.htm

For information relating to permitted development for purposes incidental to the enjoyment of the dwelling house visit: http://www.planningportal.gov.uk/permission/commonprojects/outbuildings/miniguide